Tailing Disposal Today

Proceedings of the First International Tailing Symposium,
Tucson, Arizona; October 31, November 1, 2 and 3, 1972.

Edited by C. L. Aplin and George O. Argall, Jr.

Library of Congress Catalog Card Number 73-78129
International Standard Book Number 0-87930-020-5
© Copyright 1973 by Miller Freeman Publications, Inc.

A World Mining Book

Published by MILLER FREEMAN PUBLICATIONS, INC., 500 Howard Street, San Francisco, California 94105. Printed in the United States of America.

FOREWORD

The International Tailing Symposium was convened to discuss and explore four basic themes:

1. Stability of existing dams and how to improve stability.
2. How best to build at lowest cost the big new dams now being required by today's high tonnage mining and milling operations.
3. Remining of tailing ponds.
4. Stabilization and vegetation of dams and ponds to minimize air and water pollution.

There were many auxiliary themes discussed at the Symposium and incorporated in the pages of this volume, including underwater tailing disposal, abandonment of tailing facilities, transportation of tailings, and a preview of state and federal laws regarding tailings.

So important are the design, operation, and management of tailing disposal systems on a global scale that registrants attended from 21 countries—Australia, Canada, Chile, Dominican Republic, England, France, Honduras, Mexico, Netherlands, New Zealand, Peru, Philippines, South Africa, Spain, Rhodesia, Romania, Sweden, Switzerland, United States, Venezuela, and Zambia.

Recent failures of dams during earthquakes and the inflow of tailing into underground mines as a result of underground mining below the tailing deposits have focused attention on safety problems. They were discussed at the Symposium. The failure of the Buffalo Creek coal reject dam in West Virginia in early 1972 has focused United States government attention to dam safety.

3

TAILING DISPOSAL TODAY

The cost of tailing disposal, from a few cents to as high as 50 or 60 cents per ton, is now a major operating cost for many mining operations. Ecological and safety awareness and safety regulations will tend to increase costs. Methods to minimize these costs were presented at the Symposium.

There is growing interest in underwater disposal of tailing and two of the most important papers at the Symposium described operation and environmental monitoring of the world's largest underwater disposal systems. A special contribution to the mining industry is the procedure to be followed in making Sea Water Trace Analyses before and during tailing disposal. Methods were perfected by the Independent Monitoring Team of 12 members from the faculties of two universities in British Columbia and were publicly released at the Symposium.

Tours, technical papers, and a special chapter on desert vegetation in this book illustrate how vegetation of tailing can be achieved.

Special thanks are extended to the following for their contributions, advice, and assistance in making the Symposium possible and for the opportunity for the delegates to visit the desert plant study facilities and to visit and inspect tailing dams at five mining companies.

American Smelting and Refining Company
Anaconda Company
Arizona Mining Association
Clarkson Company
College of Mines, University of Arizona
Kennecott Copper Corporation
Magma Copper Company
Mining Club of the Southwest
Pima Mining Company
United States Department of Agriculture Soil
   Conservation Service Plant Material Center
Tucson Chamber of Commerce

The following members of the Advisory Committee are thanked for their enthusiastic support and cooperation in planning the technical program and tours.

Lee Aplin
  Clarkson Company
George O. Argall, Jr.
  WORLD MINING
Dan Kealy
  U.S. Bureau of Mines
Milton Lagergren
  Kennecott Copper Corporation
K. L. Ludeke
  Pima Mining Company
Dean Lynch
  Duval Corporation
John Miscovich
  Marcona Corporation
George Roseveare
  Arizona Bureau of Mines
E. S. Smith
  International Engineering Company
W. A. Wahler
  W. A. Wahler & Associates
Jack G. Wulff
  W. A. Wahler & Associates

Our greatest thanks are extended to the authors who took the time to prepare and present their papers and to share their experiences with the delegates. The worldwide milling industry will use this Proceedings Volume as a lasting reference on the entire problem of tailing disposal.

LEE APLIN

GEORGE O. ARGALL, JR.

TABLE OF CONTENTS

6

Chapter		Page

YES

LIST OF ILLUSTRATIONS

LIST OF TABLES

LIST OF PUBLIC BODIES

American Public Health Association, 524
Arizona Plant Materials Center, 379
Arizona State Highway Department, 379, 819
Arizona Water Commission, 822, 823
California Department of Highways, 379
Idaho Bureau of Mines and Geology, 637
New Mexico State Game and Fish Commission, 230
Philippine Atomic Energy Commission, 503
Pima County, Arizona, Soil Conservation District, 379
South Dakota State Health Department, 702
U.S. Atomic Energy Commission, 602
U.S. Bureau of Mines, 450, 451, 456, 468, 602, 637, 827
U.S. Bureau of Reclamation, 818, 819
U.S. Corps of Engineers, 602, 818
U.S. Environmental Protection Agency (EPA), 58
U.S. Federal Power Commission, 602
U.S. Health, Education, and Welfare Department, 602
Utah Highway Department, 609

Tailing Disposal Today

AUTHORS & ABSTRACTS

THE USE OF DRIP IRRIGATION FOR VEGETATING MINE WASTE AREAS

By Dan A. Bach, Dan Bach & Associates, Tucson, Arizona.

Dan A. Bach has a M.S. in Horticulture from the University of Arizona, and has completed one year of post graduate work in Plant Physiology and Chemistry. He has had approximately three years' experience with design and operation of drip systems. Two years ago, Dan Bach & Associates, an agricultural irrigation consulting organization, was formed to make available technical services and materials, including drip irrigation equipment and native vegetation for beautification of mine waste areas. Mr. Bach is Irrigation Consultant with Dan Bach & Associates and is also employed full time by Bud Antle, Inc. as Pecan Orchard Supervisor and Research Director.

Until three years ago, few people in the United States had heard of drip irrigation. Today there are approximately 30,000 acres of orchards and vineyards in the southwestern United States under drip irrigation, and not even the experts will predict the eventual acreage. The rapid success of drip irrigation is due to the many unique features unequalled in any other method of irrigation. The ability to conserve large quantities of water, leach effectively, and irrigate steep terrain without runoff make it a valuable tool for vegetating mine and mill waste areas.

TAILING AS AN ORE BODY

J. J. Bean

By James J. Bean, Consulting Engineer, Miami, Arizona.

James J. Bean graduated from the University of Utah in 1924. His first metallurgical experience was in 1922 when he worked as a flotation operator in the Magna and Arthur mills of what is now the Kennecott Copper Corporation. He was Mill Metallurgist and Assistant Superintendent at the Tooele, Utah, mills of International Smelting Company from 1926 to 1933. He worked for the American Cyanamid Company in the research laboratory, in field sales, and in field service. From 1956 until his retirement in 1971, he was employed by the Miami Copper Company in Miami, Arizona, as chief metallurgist where he worked on L-P-F, copper flotation, leaching in place and heap leaching, and developed a molybdenite recovery method. He is the author of the "Tale of Tails" articles in *World Mining*.

Tailings, past, present, and future are discussed in a general fashion with emphasis on their being assets, realizable in the future, if the expected increase in knowledge provides new means of extracting their possibly unsuspected values as well as the known ones.

A. Blinde   **J. Brauns**

EARTH AND WATER PRESSURES ON RECTANGULAR CONDUIT EMBEDDED IN SETTLING POND DAM

By A. Blinde, Josef Brauns, and Ludwig Zangl, University of Karlsruhe, Karsruhe, West Germany.

A. Blinde is a graduate engineer from the Staatsbauschule Hildescheim in West Germany and a Diploma Engineer and Doctor Engineer from Technische Hochschule Hannover (Technical University). Since 1959 he has been Research Assistant at the Institute for Soil and Rock Mechanics, Technische Hochschule Karlsruhe. He has also been a Research Engineer, a Professor, and from 1968 until 1970 the Assistant Director and Leader for the Branch of Earth Dams at the same institute. In 1970 he was appointed director of the Institute.

L. Zangl

Josef Brauns is a Diploma Engineer in Civil Engineering from Technische Hochschule Karlsruhe (1963) and a Doctor Engineer in 1968 from the Institute. Since 1963 he has been a Research Engineer at the Institute for Soil and Rock Mechanics at the University of Karlsruhe.

Ludwig W. Zangl studied Civil Engineering from 1960 until 1967 at the Technische Hochschule Aachen. He graduated as a Diploma Engineer. Since 1968 he has been a Research Engineer at the Institute for Soil and Rock Mechanics at the University of Karlsruhe.

This paper covers the problem of designing concrete conduits in dam fill and slimes in tailing settling ponds. Experiences are described for such a conduit during its construction and the operation of a settling pond for tailing from a limekiln in West Germany. The dam was designed with an 82-foot-high starter dike with 14 subsequent dikes (each 8.0 feet high). These dikes are designed to be raised using the centerline method. The tailing is discharged along the dam crest. The clear water is reclaimed by means of decant towers and a connecting discharge line entering the concrete conduit (total length 675 feet) at a distance of 395 feet from the axis of the dam.

The design of this conduit (outer dimensions: width=10.5 feet, height= 11.5 feet) was based on pressure assumptions which did not agree with the "state of the art." Considering the fact that the pressures develop progressively over a long period of time and beyond this that there are no reliable theories on magnitude and distribution of pressure on embedded structures, we decided to defer any operation of reinforcement. During this time measurements of the actually developing earth and slime pressures took place.

Up to now, the measurements have been performed over seven years, the depth of burial of the conduit being 40 feet today. This is 30 percent of the final height. The results of these measurements revealed that reinforcement was unavoidable and in fact necessary in the near future. Comparison of the measured pressures to the results of different analytical predictions is carried out.

At the end of the paper, some remarks are made on details of the reinforcement of the structure.

PROBABILITY OF EARTHQUAKE AND RESULTANT GROUND MOTION

By John A. Blume, John A. Blume & Associates, Engineers, San Francisco, California.

J. A. Blume

John A. Blume, president of John A. Blume & Associates, is an internationally recognized authority on earthquake engineering and structural dynamics. Dr. Blume founded his engineering firm in 1945, and it was incorporated into the present firms in 1957. Prior to 1945, he had been in the employ of Stanford University, The U.S. Coast & Geodetic Survey, Seismological Division, and the State of California Division of Highways on construction of the San Francisco-Oakland Bay Bridge. He received the Leon S. Moisseiff annual award for important advances in structural design in 1953 for the paper "Lateral Forces of Earthquake and Wind," in 1961 for the paper "Structural Dynamics in Earthquake-Resistant Design," and in 1969 for "Dynamic Characteristics of Multistory Buildings." Dr. Blume was honored with the Building Industry Conference Board "Man-of-the-Year" Achievement Award in 1961, and in 1962 he became the seventh recipient of the ASCE Ernest E. Howard annual award for a definite contribution to the advancement of structural engineering. Dr. Blume received his A. B. in Engineering in 1932, his C. E. in 1934, and his Ph. D. in 1966, all from Stanford University.

The intensity and frequency of earthquakes are considered together with terms used to define earthquake energy levels and effects. Magnitude, various intensity scales, peak acceleration, depth, duration, the effects of soil conditions on motion, spectral response amplitudes, and attenuation with epicentral distance are described and examples are provided. The relationships between spectral response acceleration, velocity, and displacement are given as well as typical spectral response data and amplification factors for various damping values and other conditions. Comparisons are made between seismic design coefficient, spectral response, and time history procedures of dynamic analysis. In addition, the probability of occurrence at various levels is considered together with statistical data.

THE TAILING STRUCTURE AND ITS CHARACTERISTICS—A SOILS ENGINEER'S VIEWPOINT

By C. O. Brawner, and D. B. Campbell, Golder, Brawner & Associates Ltd., Vancouver, British Columbia.

C. O. Brawner

C. O. Brawner graduated from the University of Manitoba in Civil Engineering and took post graduate studies at the Nova Scotia Technical College in soil mechanics, foundations and geology. He spent 10 years with the British Columbia Department of Highways and joined Golder Associates, consulting engineers, in 1963, becoming a Principal in Golder, Brawner & Associates in 1965. Mr. Brawner has been associated with stability studies on over 100 mining projects throughout the world. These studies have included foundation investigations, design of tailings dams, control of groundwater, and assessment of stability and design of open pit slopes and underground development. He is the author of over 50 technical papers on geotechnical engineering. He is a member of the National Research Council of Canada, Associate Committee on Geotechnical Research, and is vice chairman of the Canadian Advisory Committee on Rock Mechanics.

D. B. Campbell is a Project Engineer and an Associate in Golder, Brawner & Associates Ltd., Vancouver, British Columbia.

The continued development in the scale of open pit mining operations is requiring tailings dams with greatly increased heights and storage capacity. As a result, more consideration must be given to stability. The bearing capacity, settlement, and seepage potential must be assessed. The engineering characteristics of the dam materials must be evaluated to determine safe, economical slope angles to control seepage and surface erosion.

The requirements for tailings dams design and construction are outlined and practical examples of these requirements are described.

H. H. Burke

STRUCTURAL CHARACTERISTICS RE-SULTING FROM CONSTRUCTION METHODS

By Harris H. Burke, Bechtel, Incorporated, San Francisco, California.

Harris H. Burke is Manager of Soils Engineering in the Hydro & Community Facilities Division of Bechtel Incorporated in San Francisco, California. After 18 years with the Army Corps of Engineers, he joined Bechtel in 1956 as assistant resident engineer at the Swift hydro-electric project in Washington. Based in San Francisco since 1959, he was a supervising engineer and senior supervising engineer before assuming his present title. He received his Civil Engineering degree from the University of New Mexico in 1937. His professional memberships include the American Society of Civil Engineers and the U.S. Committee on Large Dams. He has authored several technical papers on soils engineering.

This paper emphasizes that separation of tailing into the coarse and fine fractions and then compaction of the coarse fraction are the two operations that can best be utilized during construction to enhance the structural properties of tailing used for building retention dams.

With growing concern, world-wide, for the preservation of environmental conditions and mounting control over any operations which may affect the safety of the public, there is presently a transition from the tailing dams of the past, which in some cases were merely waste heaps or dumps, to more sophisticated, well-engineered, and safe retaining structures utilizing local available materials.

H. R. Dahlberg

R. C. Laird

BUILDING TAILINGS DAMS IN ARROYOS

By Harry R. Dahlberg and Richard C. Laird, Christmas Division, Inspiration Consolidated Copper Co., Winkelman, Arizona.

Harry R. Dahlberg, Concentrator Superintendent, Christmas Division, Inspiration Consolidated Copper Company, was previously associated with the Andes Copper Mining

Company at El Salvador, Chile. Prior to that he was employed in the iron and steel industry in various technical capacities in the United States, Venezuela, and Chile.

Richard C. Laird, Assistant Concentrator Superintendent of the Christmas Division, is a 1969 graduate of Michigan Technological University with a B.S. in Metallurgical Engineering. Prior to going to the Christmas Division in the fall of 1971, he served for two years as Metallurgist at the Sanchez Project for Inspiration Consolidated Copper Company.

When no level land is available to impound tailing, sloping hillsides, canyons, or arroyos must be utilized. The three original tailing disposal areas at Christmas have, or are approaching, designed capacity and two recently developed dams are described. A drag line was used at the beginning of the development of these two dams. However, due to the drying time required for this system of berm building, cyclones have since been successfully employed to build berm and maintain safe freeboard for operations. Relationship of berm length to pond area is discussed. Another dam is being constructed in an adjacent arroyo to give flexibility to present operations and additional years of tailing storage capacity. A system of diversion dams to carry surface water from the higher hillsides away from the arroyos presently used for tailing storage is also discussed.

E. D'Appolonia   **R. D. Ellison**

ABANDONMENT OF TAILING FACILITIES

By Elio D'Appolonia, Richard D. Ellison, and John T. Gormley, E. D'Appolonia Consulting Engineers, Inc., Pittsburgh, Pennsylvania.

J. T. Gormley

Elio D'Appolonia, President of E. D'Appolonia Consulting Engineers, graduated with a M.S.C.E. from the University of Alberta and a Ph. D. C. E. from the University of Illinois. In the early 1940s, he was a consultant to the U.S. Army Corps of Engineers in Alaska and Northern Canada, developing techniques for construction in regions of permafrost. He joined Carnegie-Mellon University in 1948, teaching and doing research in civil engineering. In 1956 he formed his own consulting firm, devoting his time wholly to the practice of civil engineering and specializing on matters relating to soil and rock mechanics, dynamics, foundations, and earthworks. He is a consultant to government and is active in committee work of national and international profes-

25

sional and technical societies. He received honors for his publications from the Engineering Institute of Canada and the American Society of Civil Engineers.

Dr. Richard D. Ellison received his formal education at Carnegie-Mellon University in Civil Engineering, majoring in soils and foundations and water resources engineering. During the past five years, he has been instrumental in the development of EDCE's professional involvement on projects dealing with water resources and environmental engineering. During this period, the more than 150 projects he managed included earth and rock fill dams, sanitary landfills, flyash and mine gob disposal embankments, and all related structural, hydraulic, and treatment facilities. He is Vice President of EDCE.

Dr. John T. Gormley received his formal education at Carnegie-Mellon University where he majored in water pollution, hydraulics, water resources, and water resources engineering. Since joining EDCE in 1970, Dr. Gormley has acted as special consultant on projects dealing with ground and surface water development, industrial and domestic solid waste disposal, leachate and sewage effluent attentuation through soils, and lagoon construction for water treatment. As a result of his prior background in systems, environmental and thermal hydraulic engineering, Dr. Gormley has effectively managed numerous interdisciplinary environmental problems.

Tailing disposal facilities have generally been planned only for temporary use, even though they remain as permanent structures on abandonment. Present concern for safety and environment has shown that many facilities are not adequately designed for long-term safety and environmental protection and can be a continuing financial burden to the owner or the public.

Abandonment is a primary concept to be considered during the initial design of a tailing facility. Considerations of capital investment, maintenance, and abandonment costs in relation to the life and future use of a facility are needed to optimize its operation and to plan its staged construction.

Key environmental factors are associated with short and long-term protection of the surface and groundwater; particularly when the water or solid portion of the tailings is acidic, toxic, or contains other similar characteristics. In cases where such tailings are soluble in water, the prudent abandonment plan minimizes the volume of water reaching and leaching through the tailings. Other environmental considerations include reclamation, long-term land use and, in some instances, aesthetics.

The principal technical considerations are staged construction so that abandonment is readily achieved at any time in the life of the facility, the use of available materials to provide economical safe retaining embankments, and the control of normal and storm water runoff to reduce embankment pore pressures and to safeguard against overtopping or excessive erosion of the embankment. With certain solid waste materials, economical staged construction for safe abandonment at any time in the life of the facility can be provided with prudent planning. When on-site borrow is required, detailed planning during the initial stage of construction becomes important.

To assure a safe and economic abandonment, surveillance of the behavior of the facility and its environment is necessary. In certain cases, surveillance is mandatory to modify properly the operation of the facility and to avoid building detrimental conditions which could be costly to the owner and/or the public on abandonment of the tailing facility.

K. C. Dean   **R. Havens**

COMPARATIVE COSTS AND METHODS FOR STABILIZATION OF TAILINGS

By Karl C. Dean, and Richard Havens, Salt Lake City Metallurgy Research Center, U. S. Bureau of Mines, Salt Lake City, Utah.

Karl C. Dean is a graduate of the University of Utah, with a B. S. degree. He is a member of Phi Beta Kappa and Phi Kappa Phi. He joined the staff of U. S. Bureau of Mines at Salt Lake City, Utah, in 1941 and carried out manganese, copper, lead, zinc, nickel, and iron mineral beneficiation and pyrometallurgical research until 1945. He was with the Army, Counter Intelligence Corps, European Theater, until 1948 and conducted research on manganese, tungsten, and other metal extraction projects at Salt Lake City until 1951. He served as technical advisor on Point IV minerals projects in Mexico until 1953 and from 1953 to 1965 directed research on cesium, rubidium, magnesium, salt water bitterns, and other metal extraction systems. He is currently directing research on the stabilization and/or utilization of solid mineral wastes in the U. S. Bureau of Mines, Salt Lake City Metallurgy Research Center. He is author or co-author of 85 publications and five patents.

Richard Havens is a graduate of South Dakota State School of Mines and Technology, with a B. S. in Metallurgical Engineering. He joined the staff of the U. S. Bureau of Mines at Salt Lake City, Utah, in 1940. He conducted beneficiation studies related to manganese, copper, cobalt, lead, zinc, iron, beryllium, silver, and various nonmetallic minerals and is currently project leader of the stabilization studies of solid mineral wastes. He is author or co-author of 18 publications and two patents.

Methods using physical, chemical, vegetative, and combined stabilization procedures have been developed and applied in many areas of the country to prevent air and water pollution arising from accumulations of fine-sized mineral wastes. Several milling companies, either independently or in cooperation with the U. S. Bureau of Mines, have applied various stabilization techniques to differing types of wastes in different environments. The principal aim of the work has been to achieve effective low-cost stabilization requiring minimal maintenance. Research has indicated that, with the exception of highly acidic, basic, or saline tailings, satisfactory stabilization can be obtained by many methods at costs of less than $400 per acre. Effective vegetative stabilization of many fine-sized wastes is attainable at a cost of from $100 to $250 per acre using the Bureau's chemical-vegetative technique. Research on initiating growth of Indian rice grass, a nitrogen fixing plant, offers promise for lowering the cost of maintenance on vegetatively stabilized tailings sites. Bureau research on the use of buried layers of sewage sludge also offers promise for reclaiming major problem mineral waste accumulations.

G. W. Dopson

MAGMA COPPER COMPANY'S SAN MANUEL NO. 10 TAILING DAM: DESIGN, CONSTRUCTION AND OPERATION

By G. W. Dopson and D. McGregor, Magma Copper Company, San Manuel, Arizona.

Gaylord W. Dopson is Concentrator Superintendent at the San Manuel, Arizona, Division of Magma Copper Company. He joined Magma in 1956 as a shift boss and subsequently served as general mill foreman and assistant mill superintendent. He was appointed concentrator superintendent in 1969. His responsibilities include surface ore haulage, ore crushing, the copper and molybdenum concentrator operations, tailings disposal, water pumping and reclamation, and repair and maintenance. Prior to joining Magma, he was chemist and metallurgist in several assignments including Silverbell, Arizona, Christmas, Arizona, Amarillo, Texas, Ouray, Colorado, and Vanadium, New Mexico. A native of New Mexico, Mr. Dopson attended the New Mexico School of Mines and studied chemical engineering and industrial metallurgy. He is active in the Tucson section of AIME.

D. McGregor is Supervisor Trainee at Magma Copper Company's San Manuel operation.

Tailing disposal represents an operational expense rather than a profit-making entity and, for this reason, in many instances too little thought and money are allocated for tailing disposal. The overall cost of a poorly planned system could far outrun the initial cost of design and construction of a sound, stable disposal area that could be used for many years. This paper describes in detail a simple and structurally sound tailing disposal system developed by Magma Copper Company.

J. B. Evans **D. V. Ellis**

THE ESTABLISHMENT AND IMPLEMENTATION OF A MONITORING PROGRAM FOR UNDERWATER TAILING DISPOSAL IN RUPERT INLET, VANCOUVER ISLAND, BRITISH COLUMBIA

By John B. Evans, Department of Mineral Engineering, University of British Columbia, Vancouver, D. V. Ellis, University of Victoria, and C. A. Pelletier, Island Copper Mine, Utah Mines Ltd., Port Hardy.

C. A. Pelletier

John B. Evans graduated from the University of Melbourne, Australia in 1951 with B. Sc. and B. M. E. degrees. He has had 20 years of varied industrial experience relating to metal mine development and production in Canada, Australia, and the United States as company engineer, mine manager, and independent consulting engineer. His Canadian experience was with Canadian Exploration Limited as Junior Mining Engineer; Howe Sound Mining Company, Stoping Engineer; Canadian Exploration Ltd., Exploration and Evaluation Engineer; and Craigmont Mines Ltd., Chief Engineer. In the United States he was Vice President Mining and General Manager for the Molybdenum Corporation of America, Questa, New Mexico. In Australia he was Principal and Managing Director, Mineral Engineers Pty. Ltd.; Managing Director, Austminex Pty. Ltd.; and Managing Director, Mount Gunson Mines Pty. Ltd. He was appointed Head of the Department of Mineral Engineering, University of British Columbia, Vancouver, in 1969.

Derek Ellis is a marine ecologist who trained in Scotland, Canada and Denmark, graduating with B. Sc. (Edinburgh) in 1952 and Ph. D. (McGill) in 1957. He has researched primarily on animals of the seabed and shoreline, developing identification and quantification techniques for comparison of populations in different areas. The significance of these techniques has recently expanded from their previous use in academic biological studies to monitoring programs designed to demonstrate the extent of effects of discharging effluents to the sea. As a result, since 1970 Dr. Ellis has participated in marine monitoring programs for three mines, a pulp mill and at three trunk domestic sewers for his home area of Victoria in British Columbia. He is presently Associate Professor in the Biology Department of the University of Victoria, researching in the coastal waters of British Columbia, and teaching in the fields of marine ecology and animal behavior. Prior professional experience includes six years as Associate Scientist at the

Federal Government Fisheries Laboratory in Nanaimo, B. C. researching in salmon migratory behavior leading to better understanding of the biological implications of fishway design. As a graduate student Dr. Ellis was concerned with arctic marine research, and his northern field experience was utilized in 1972 with on-site pre-discharge studies at a proposed mine site in Greenland.

C. A. Pelletier graduated from the University of Saskatchewan with a B. S. degree in chemistry. In 1967 he started employment with the International Nickel Company of Canada Ltd. as a junior chemist in quality control. In September 1968 he joined Allan Potash Mines in Saskatoon, Saskatchewan, and worked with both quality control and pollution control. In October 1970 Mr. Pelletier joined Utah Mines Ltd. as an environmental chemist. Here he is responsible for the field, laboratory, and the reporting of environmental data pertinent to the Environmental Monitoring Program.

The Pollution Control Act, 1967, of the Province of British Columbia states that after January 1, 1970, no waste products can be discharged onto any lands or into any water under provincial jurisdiction without the prior approval of the Director of Pollution Control. A Pollution Control Permit issued to Utah Construction and Mining Company (Utah) on January 20, 1971, specifies the conditions under which permission is granted for the discharge of a mineral processing effluent into a coastal inlet. The particular effluent discharge, being the mill tailing generated by a base metal sulphide open pit mine and its integrated 30,000 ton per day capacity, on site, flotation milling facility located adjacent to Rupert Inlet, Vancouver Island, which commenced commercial production in the fourth quarter of 1971.

The Permit, in addition to stating the physical and chemical limitations of the proposed mill tailing discharge into Rupert Inlet, directs Utah to retain an independent agent to ascertain the influence of mill tailing discharge in the receiving waters, and specifies that an environmental control field program must be approved and initiated prior to March 1, 1971. In February 1971 the University of British Columbia agreed to fulfill the duties required of the independent agent, and assembled an interdisciplinary team composed of earth sciences and biological scientist and engineer faculty members to carry out the task.

The paper describes the program of environmental control undertaken during the eight-month period immediately preceding production, March-October, 1971, and relates the measurements made during that period with the corresponding measurements for the initial eight months of production, November 1971 to June 1972.

NEW TAILING DAM CONSTRUCTION AT WHITE PINE

F. E. Girucky

By Frank E. Girucky, White Pine Copper Company, White Pine, Michigan.

Frank E. Girucky has been employed by White Pine Copper Company, White Pine, Michigan, since 1966 and is currently the Project Engineer responsible for tailing dam construction, and related administrative tasks. Prior to his present employment he was an engineering officer in the embankment and foundation branch of the Soils Division for the Waterways Experimental Station at Vicksburg, Mississippi, from 1963 to 1966 and had earlier spent a year as a consulting engineer retained by the Wisconsin Conservation Department and other interests. From 1951 to 1961 he was employed by Oglebay Norton Company of Cleveland, Ohio at its Montreal mine as an engineering geologist responsible for exploration, mine development, and intermittent evaluation work on potential mineral properties. Mr. Girucky is a registered professional engineer, graduate of the University of Wisconsin with B. S. and M. S. degrees. He is a member of the AIME, ASCE, and NSPE.

The White Pine Copper Company's mine's physiography, ore deposit, mining method, and design of original tailing dam are described briefly.

Changes in local tailing dam design resulting from technological advances are exemplified by comparing current tailing dam design with the tailing dam built 18 years earlier.

Design theory, elements of the new tailing dam, savings possible through a borrow exploration and conservation program, construction procedures, operation of this sand core dam, and water standards for the state of Michigan are described in detail.

Labor and materials used to construct and operate a new tailing dam are summarized. Expenditures to date for three of the 20 years of anticipated construction totals $6,500,000. Anticipated expenditures to complete this project are conservatively estimated at $1,100,000 annually.

CHARACTERISTICS OF TAILINGS FROM A SOILS ENGINEER'S VIEWPOINT

F. Guerra

By Fabian Guerra, Iron Ore Company of Canada, Sept-Iles, Quebec.

Fabian Guerra was born in Ibarra, Ecuador, South America. He was educated in Ecuador and the United States of America. During 15 of his 22 professional years, he has worked for the Iron Ore Company of

Canada and associated companies. His experience includes designing and constructing highways, water systems and hydroelectric projects in the heart of the Andes; making feasibility studies and construction of bridges in the tropics; building railroads and dams in the Canadian Sub-Arctic and in the banded sediments of the lower reaches of the Moisie River.

Some mineralogical and geotechnical characteristics of iron ore tailings obtained from flotation and Humphrey Spiral processing systems derived from the deposits found in the Grenville and Hudsonian Provinces of the Labrador Geosyncline, in the Canadian Shield, are presented. The use of these tailings as a construction material, as soil-cement aggregate, and as a sealant of pervious sand are described. Some of the causes of liquefaction, and the limiting conditions for no liquefaction to occur, are also given.

TAILING DISPOSAL—ITS HIDDEN COSTS

C. E. Johnston

By Charles E. Johnston, Arthur G. McKee & Company, Western Knapp Engineering Division, San Francisco, California.

Charles E. Johnston is a mining engineer with the WKE Division of Arthur G. McKee & Company. He has 25 years of experience in mine engineering, economic evaluations, and construction of mines and surface plant facilities for copper, uranium, potash, gypsum, phosphate, trona, and gold. He received a B. S. degree in Mining Engineering from the University of Nevada, is a member of the AIME and is the author of several papers on technical subjects, including mine transport sytems and earthen dam construction with use of plastic membrane.

The problems of tailing disposal are considered on the basis of operating costs for each part of a typical disposal system. The cost of slurry thickening, slurry transport, tailing containment, seepage control, tailing treatment, effluent transport, and area restoration must all be considered in any economic evaluation of a mining operation. Generalized cost factors for each part of a tailing disposal system are presented as a means of making a preliminary economic evaluation. The requirements of typical tailing disposal systems are discussed and an organized approach to establishing system requirements is suggested.

TAILING DISPOSAL PRACTICE AT THE TYRONE BRANCH OF PHELPS DODGE CORPORATION

By William H. Keener, Phelps Dodge Corporation, Tyrone Branch, Tyrone, New Mexico.

W. H. Keener

William H. Keener was born in Alliance, Ohio. He was graduated from the University of Arizona, and has had experience in production, research and supervision with Phelps Dodge Corporation in Ajo, Arizona, and Tyrone, New Mexico. He is presently Superintendent at Tyrone Concentrator.

The difficulty of conducting tailing disposal operations with Tyrone ore was not revealed during pilot plant testing. Normal spigotting practices had to be replaced by cycloning.

About 45,000 tons of tailing per day at 45 percent solids (5 percent plus-65-mesh, 20 percent minus-5-microns) flows through launder and pipes to the dams. Shop-fabricated cyclones deposit material at the dam perimeter suitable for berm; this material is built to a height of 35 to 40 feet above the header.

The method of water recovery is also discussed.

CONSTRUCTING SOUND TAILINGS DAMS BY CYCLONING AND SPIGOTTING METHODS

By Earle J. Klohn and C. H. Maartman, Ripley, Klohn & Leonoff International Ltd., Vancouver, British Columbia.

E. J. Klohn   C. H. Maartman

Earle J. Klohn, President of Ripley, Klohn & Leonoff International Ltd., is an authority on pile foundations and tailings dams, and has particpated in over 1,500 engineering projects. He is a member of the International Board of Consultants for the Sirikit Dam in Thailand and recently served as a specialist consultant on the proposed Sar Cheshmeh tailing dam in Iran. He is the author of numerous technical papers, one of which won an international award. Mr. Klohn received both his B. Sc. and M. Sc. in Civil Engineering from the University of Alberta.

C. H. Maartman, Executive Engineer of Ripley, Klohn & Leonoff International Ltd., is responsible for geotechnical and civil engineering design, specializing in dams and hydraulic structures. He received a B. ASc. (Honours) from the University of British Columbia, and has had 22 years of experience in the fields of hydrology, hydraulics, geotechnical and general civil engineering. He has been associated with dams, river resource studies, and other projects in Canada, India, Ceylon and Ecuador.

With few exceptions, construction of tailings dams by the old upstream spigotting methods is rapidly being replaced by downstream construction using cycloned sand embankments, blanketed upstream by spigotted slimes. Direct spigotting of tailings is generally used only in those cases where it is economic to build a downstream supporting structure of either borrowed or pit waste materials. The resulting new tailings dams are much safer, under both static and seismic loading, than are the older type dams constructed using upstream spigotting methods.

New and interesting variations of construction techniques have been developed to accomodate the new tailings dam design concepts. Some of these techniques, as used on two large sand dams under construction in British Columbia, are reviewed together with attendant problems, solutions adopted, and success in meeting design objectives.

M. A. Lagergren

DESIGN, CONSTRUCTION AND OPERATION OF OZARK LEAD COMPANY'S TAILINGS DISPOSAL SYSTEM

By Milton A. Lagergren, Kennecott Copper Corporation, Salt Lake City, Utah, and Arthur W. Griffith, Ozark Lead Company, Sweetwater, Missouri.

Milton A. Lagergren is a graduate of the Colorado School of Mines. He has had wide experience in the engineering of minerals projects in the United States, Alaska, and Peru. Currently he is a process engineer at the Kennecott Engineering Center, Metal Mining Division, in Salt Lake City, Utah.

A. W. Griffith graduated from the University of Idaho with a B. S. degree in Mining Engineering. He has had experience in selling mining and milling equipment, construction of mills, uranium, copper, and lead-zinc metallurgy. He joined Ozark Lead staff as Mill Superintendent in October 1966.

Tailing from the 6,000-ton-per-day Ozark Lead concentrator is deposited in a small valley about one mile distant. The tailing dam serves a triple purpose: tailing disposal, water storage, and stream regulation. Tailing is deposited along the crest of the dam, using hydrocyclones. Unusual features of this installation are the use of a 60-inch pipeline through the dam to control storm runoff and an underdrainage system to control phreatic water level together with a shutoff valve to insure water storage. A reservoir and pump station downstream of the tailing dam receives water decanted from the lake upstream of the tailing to furnish the entire mill water supply.

In four years of operation, the dam has been raised 21 feet above the starter dam level. Runoff from several storms has been handled with a substantial reduction in peak flows below the dam. The mill has had an adequate supply of water at all times entirely from the storage lake above the tailing. Tailing disposal and water supply operates as a closed system with no release to the stream below, under normal operating conditions.

HOW TO ESTABLISH AND MAINTAIN GROWTH ON TAILINGS IN CANADA—COLD WINTERS AND SHORT GROWING SEASONS

By Jean-Claude Leroy, Erocon Ltd., Toronto, Ontario.

J-C. Leroy

Jean-Claude Leroy graduated as a geologist from Mount Allison University in New Brunswick, Canada. He gained experience in the various aspects of geology, mineral exploration, and mine development in the Bathurst mining camp of New Brunswick, northern Manitoba, and Saskatchewan, Quebec, and Ontario, as well as in Western Europe, Mexico, and the southern United States. In 1969 he became involved in the systematic development of reclamation techniques, together with Herman Keller, President of Erocon Ltd., specializing in tailings disposal areas not amenable to the then few known methods of rehabilitation. He carried out experimentation and research in mining camps in North America and overseas, and has been instrumental in solving problems associated with the reclamation of all types of wastelands resulting from mining operations.

Waste disposal areas to be reclaimed as a result of mining operations in Canada are found under varied climatic conditions from the 43rd to the 55th north parallels. Extremes of temperature, commonly short growing seasons, and long and extensive ground frost constitute severe handicaps when added to the problems inherent to such disposal areas.

Experimentation, persistence, and ingenuity have succeeded in the establishment of continuous, self regenerating, and useful vegetation covers over particularly forbidding tailings areas. The successful, although often arduous adaptation of certain desirable plant species has helped solve previously taxing problems. The resulting abatement of airborne dusts, the elimination of the siltation and the pollution of streams and water supplies through the release of acid and other noxious substances, together with the aesthetically pleasing expanses of new vegetation becoming now part of most mining communities in Canada, are witness to a drastic change in outlook.

Several substantial and typical reclamation schemes carried out by Erocon at Canadian mining operations have been selected to illustrate the flexibility of approach necessary to the successful rehabilitation of mine wastelands.

K. L. Ludeke

VEGETATIVE STABILIZATION OF COPPER MINE TAILING DISPOSAL BERMS OF PIMA MINING COMPANY

By Kenneth L. Ludeke, Pima Mining Company, Tucson, Arizona.

Kenneth L. Ludeke, a research agronomist, was employed by Shell Oil Company working as a technical representative in its agricultural chemical division for two years before joining Pima Mining Company in 1970. His present responsibilities with Pima Mining Company include research in the field of vegetative stabilization of tailing berms. He has a B. S. degree in agronomy and is presently finishing his M. S. degree, also in agronomy, at the University of Arizona.

A voluntary study was conducted at Pima Mining Company to compare various methods and procedures of vegetative, chemical-vegetative, and physical stabilization of copper mine tailing disposal berms.

In order to maintain the natural desert beauty, Pima embarked on a vegetative program of cultivating and experimental planting of various types of plants. With this experimental program, the most promising features were expanded so that some 85 acres now available along the berms have been planted. Additional acreage will be planted to coincide with the vegetative stabilization program and the growing season.

The primary objectives undertaken by this program were to (1) maintain the natural desert beauty; (2) provide vegetative stabilization to minimize wind blown dust; (3) utilize plants that, once established, require little or no supplemental irrigation; and (4) to minimize erosion.

Severe windstorms and excessive rains have passed over the stabilized tailing berm area without raising dust clouds or carving unsightly erosion crevices into the slope. The ultimate objective is, of course, to maintain the natural splendor of low desert environment to the disposal area. The success of the vegetative stabilization has illustrated that such an objective is feasible, at a reasonable cost, and is being accomplished.

F. L. Matthew

PROS AND CONS OF COMBINED TREATMENT OF MINING AND DOMESTIC WASTES

By Floyd L. Matthew, Brady Consultants, Inc., Spearfish, South Dakota, and Dakota Engineering Co., Rapid City, South Dakota.

Floyd Matthew owns and manages Dakota Engineering Company, a firm specializing in water quality management. He is employed by Brady Consultants, Inc., of

Spearfish as project engineer on the Lead-Deadwood Sanitary District wastewater project. He has a B.S.C.E. degree from the South Dakota School of Mines and Technology and an M.S.C.E. (Environmental) from the University of Minnesota. He has worked in general consulting; served as administrator of the South Dakota Water Pollution Control Program; and taught at the South Dakota School of Mines and Technology. Mr. Matthew wrote the water quality standards for South Dakota and has been involved in several research and design projects related to water pollution control. His firm is currently involved in planning, research, operation, and design of water quality control systems.

Homestake Mining Company and the cities of Lead and Deadwood have discharged their untreated wastewaters to Whitewood Creek since 1876 when the gold rush began in the Black Hills of South Dakota. Spent tailings, cyanide and heavy metals in the industrial wastes and bacteria, solids and organic materials in the domestic wastes contributed to severe pollution problems in the receiving stream. In 1965 the Lead-Deadwood Sanitary District was formed to make it possible to solve both the industrial and domestic waste problems through a unified action.

An engineering study completed by Brady Consultants, Inc. in 1970 recommended an 8-mile interceptor sewer and a 290-acre, 90-foot-deep treatment-storage unit to treat the combined industrial and domestic wastes. Laboratory and pilot plant studies indicated that the treatment provided by interrelated chemical and biological processes in the storage-treatment impoundment produced an effluent capable of meeting specified stream standards. The impoundment volume will be adequate to store all tailings from Homestake Mining Company for an estimated 27 years.

Combining the mining and municipal wastes produced several design problems, but the combined treatment facility proved to be the best solution after comparing all alternatives.

TRANSPORTATION OF TAILINGS

R. E. McElvain

By Richard E. McElvain and Ian Cave, Warman Equipment (International) Ltd., Artarmon, New South Wales, Australia.

Richard E. McElvain graduated from the University of Colorado in 1948 as a Mechanical Engineer. Much of his professional career has been in pumping and hydraulic mining. He has worked for the Allis-Chalmers Mfg. Company; was general manager of the Silica Sand Company Corporation in LeSueur, Minnesota, and worked as Mechanical Engineer for the Continental Sales and Equipment Company. In this last position he specialized in solids pumping with development of the first long-distance (four miles) tailing line in

Minnesota and a six-mile-long line in Michigan. From 1964 to 1966 he was director of engineering for the Ottawa Silica Company using hydraulic mining. He is now Vice President and General Manager for Warman Equipment (International) Inc., and is responsible for its North American operation in Madison, Wisconsin.

Ian Cave joined Warman Equipment (International) Ltd., Sydney, Australia, in 1959, and is presently Senior Project Engineer. He has been engaged on design, development, and testing of slurry pumps; supervised the test program and conducted a feasibility study of a 1,000,000-ton-per-year, 27-mile limestone slurry pumping installation. He designed a 1,200-ton-per-hour heavy mineral concentrating plant for Rutile Zircon Mines and supervised a full-scale test program to establish the effects of suspended solids on centrifugal pump performance. He is a graduate of Sydney Technical College in Mechanical Engineering.

The world-wide concepts on ecology and economics hang in a delicate balance. Tailing disposal now involves very large systems to transport the refuse from the operations. The long-distance pumping requirements for safe disposal are outlined.

The energy determination and the equipment necessary to transport the solids in suspension is reviewed. The present trend to a single station, high pressure system is developed.

Relative advantages on the positive displacement and centrifugal pump designs with alternate means of driving and controlling the system are described. Types of pumps, design points, and materials of construction are outlined.

The international trends and developments on transporting tailings are reviewed.

ALCAN'S EXPERIENCE IN DISPOSAL OF RED MUD TAILINGS FROM THE BAYER ORE PROCESS

K. A. Miners

By K. A. Miners, Aluminum Company of Canada, Ltd., Arvida, Quebec.

Ken A. Miners graduated from the University of Saskatchewan in 1941 with a M. S. degree in Chemical Engineering. During World War II he was employed by Defence Industries Ltd., initially in process control and subsequently in project engineering. After three years in the construction industry he joined the Aluminum Company of Canada Ltd.'s organization in 1948. He helped develop a commercial process for beneficiation of coal or coke by chlorination at high temperatures. Since 1954 he has been working on process control or project engineering for the chemical plants in Arvida Works, with particular emphasis on problems associated with the disposal of red mud.

A brief resume is given of 40 years' experience within the Aluminum Company of Canada in designing, operating, and maintaining a closed circuit tailing disposal system for red mud from the Bayer ore plants located at Arvida, Quebec. As Alcan's production increased over the years, the tailing problem multiplied, requiring economic solutions to dispose of more than 2,000 tons per day which would also eliminate the usual dusting or leakage problems associated with ponding operations.

A more detailed expose is given of Alcan's current operation. This includes pumping mud to the local ponds on a year-round basis with a pondwater recovery system which will operate in spite of minus 40°F. temperature. It also includes a dredging operation in the local ponds during the warm weather months to remove the settled mud, separate the coarse fraction, and pump the fines some six miles through a 14-inch-diameter pipeline to a much larger settling basin. A floating pumping station in this distant area returns all water through a duplicate pipeline to the local ponds for use later in the Bayer ore plants.

TECHNOLOGY, REALITY AND AVAILABILITY FOR THE FUTURE

J. B. Rigg

By John B. Rigg, U. S. Department of the Interior, Washington, D.C.

John B. Rigg joined the Department of the Interior on September 1, 1969, as Special Assistant to the Assistant Secretary for Mineral Resources. He is at present the Deputy Assistant Secretary—Mineral Resources. Mr. Rigg was born in Omaha, Nebraska, and considers Grand Junction, Colorado, where he was raised, as his hometown. He is a graduate of the University of Nebraska, where he continued his graduate studies in Economics. He has been engaged in exploration and development of mineral resources since 1949 in numerous other western states, and is a registered professional engineer in Colorado. For two years he was the Manager of the Colorado Mining Association, where he was instrumental in improving the business climate for mineral activity along with strengthening the health and safety laws, mined land reclamation requirements, and mining education programs in Colorado.

THE DISPOSAL OF MICACEOUS CHINA CLAY WASTE IN SOUTH WEST ENGLAND

By Dr. Michael J. Ripley, English Clays Lovering Pochin & Co. Ltd., St. Austell, Cornwall, England.

M. J. Ripley

Dr. Michael J. Ripley was educated at high schools in Liverpool and Bristol, and at Birmingham University, where he obtained the degrees of B. Sc. in Geology in 1961 and Ph. D. in Geology in 1964. After a short period in 1964 with the Robertson Research organization in North Wales as a junior petroleum geologist he joined English Clays in St. Austell, England, as a geologist. He was transferred to Anglo-American Clays Corporation in Sandersville, Georgia, in May 1965, where he worked initially as a geologist, but subsequently as exploration manager. He returned to England in June 1968 to take up his present position as assistant chief geologist in the China Clay Division of English Clays. In his work he has in recent years been concerned with both the exploration for and the production of the various industrial minerals produced by English Clays. This has meant a considerable involvement with the problems posed by the vast tonnages of waste arising as a by-product of China Clay production.

The China Clay industry of Southwest England is at present producing about 20,000,000 tons of waste per year from 30 open pit mines. Approximately 2,000,000 tons of this waste is minus-0.5 millimeter in particle size. It is disposed of in slurry form. For generations this fine micaceous material has either been allowed to flow into the rivers or deposited on land in tailing ponds.

Concern for the environment plus the recent failure of a number of tailing ponds has caused the industry to re-think radically its waste disposal policy. The major result is a completely new disposal system presently being implemented, which initially will utilize 12 miles of pipeline feeding the tailings into six depositional areas. Standby ponds are being made available in case of emergency. Also, additional ponds are having to be built to serve mines which, because of their geographical remoteness, cannot be connected into the major disposal network.

All dams, which will eventually range up to 300 feet in height, are being built to strict engineering standards. In most instances they are being built from the other coarser waste materials also arising as a byproduct of China Clay production.

All disposal schemes have to receive the approval of both the British Government's Inspectorate of Mines and Quarries and the Planning Authorities. The former is concerned with the stability of the various structures while the later is concerned with effect of these structures on the environment.

DESIGN, CONSTRUCTION, AND OPERATION OF THE TAILING PIPELINES AND UNDERWATER TAILINGS DISPOSAL SYSTEM OF ATLAS CONSOLIDATED MINING AND DEVELOPMENT CORPORATION IN THE PHILIPPINES

By Rogelio C. Salazar and Reynaldo I. Gonzales, Atlas Consolidated Mining and Development Corporation, Toledo City, Cebu, Philippines.

Rogelio C. Salazar is a graduate Chemical Engineer from the University of the Philippines and a Metallurgical Engineer from the University of Wisconsin. After returning to the Philippines he worked for the Steel Foundry Division of Engineering Equipment, Inc., where he became General Superintendent. He joined Atlas Consolidated Mining and Development Corporation as Foundry Superintendent in 1966. He is now General Superintendent for Metallurgical Services and is in charge of the ball and liner foundry, assay and metallurgical laboratories, the research laboratory, and the Sangi port and shipping departments.

Reynaldo I. Gonzales is Engineering Division Manager for Atlas Consolidated Mining Corporation.

This paper describes the P30 million ($4.662 million) gravity-flow tailings disposal system of the Atlas Consolidated Mining and Development Corporation, on the island of Cebu in the Philippines.

ACMDC operates two concentrators located near its two major copper deposits, Lutopan and Biga, about six miles apart by road but less than three miles distant as the crow flies. Combined milling rate averages 70,000 tons per day.

Thickened tailings from the concentrators are piped by gravity and discharged at the sea bottom at Ibo Point, on Tañon Strait, a narrow but deep water channel separating the islands of Cebu and Negros. The system at the DAS concentrator consists of two 44,000-foot, one 20-inch and one 12-inch-diameter pipelines installed at an average 1.06 percent slope and handles about 35,000 tons per day of tailings at a pulp velocity controlled at 6.5 to 7.0 feet per second range. The setup at the Biga concentrator consists of two 60,000-foot, one 18-inch and one 16-inch-diameter pipelines at 1.2 percent slope, handling 32,500 tons per day of tailings at about 6.5 feet per second velocity.

All four pipelines discharge tailings to the sea by drop pipes to points near the bottom where the tailings are carried by undercurrent to the deeper region of Tañon Strait. No appreciable buildup of the sea bottom has been observed since the pipelines started operations in early 1971; to-date the pipelines have transported and disposed to the sea a total of 26 million tons of tailings.

This paper discusses the design features of the system as well as the operational problems encountered and practical solutions adopted.

41

G. T. Sazonov

DESIGN, CONSTRUCTION AND OPERATION OF TAILING SYSTEMS

By G. T. Sazonov, Mekhanobr Institute, Leningrad, USSR.

George T. Sazonov graduated in 1960 from the Leningrad Institute in Water Transport Hydraulic Engineering. From 1961 to 1965 he designed tailings disposal systems for a number of concentrators while a member of the Mekhanobr Institute. From 1965 to 1967 he supervised construction of a big tailing disposal area in the region north of the Arctic Circle. In 1967 he was appointed Head of the Hydraulic Engineering Department of Mekhanobr Institute and since then has been active in designing tailing systems and concentrators. He was promoted in 1972 to Deputy Chief Engineer of the Institute's Design Department. He has completed post graduate study and has published a number of articles on the design of concentrator tailing systems.

This paper presents a modern view on design, construction and operation of concentrator tailing disposal systems. Designing should begin with the working out of a detailed and accurate balance of water required for full water reclamation, taking into account the means of hydraulic transportation and selecting the type of system that allows for maximum safety of all structures.

W. N. Sims

REMINING OF TAILINGS BY HYDRAULICKING AND OTHER METHODS

By W. Norman Sims, Marconaflo Division, Marcona Corporation, San Francisco, California.

W. Norman Sims graduated from Pennsylvania State University in 1949 with a B. Sc. degree in fuel technology. He served as a fuel engineer for the Philadelphia and Reading Coal and Iron Company and then spent 10 years with American Cyanamid Company in its general purchasing department. In 1967 he joined Kaiser Aluminum and Chemical Corporation to assist in the forming and development of a chemical division and served as Vice President and General Manager, Industrial Chemicals. In 1971 he joined Marcona Corporation to help in the development and commercialization of Marconaflo technology. He is now Vice President of the Marconaflo Division with the responsibility for the development and sales of the Marconaflo system.

With the vast technological changes and the new environmental concerns that have occurred during the past 50 years, it has become necessary and feasible to remine many of the old tailing deposits. Remining of tailing deposits is being done for several reasons. To recover minerals that were not recoverable at the time the tailing was impounded. Tailing deposits must be removed to mine underlying ore bodies. Safety and ecological reasons may now dictate removing of old tailing piles. Current operating methods and other factors make remining possible. The Marconaflo system for remining of such deposits is described in this paper. A technical description of the system will be given and general economics of remining will be outlined.

TAILINGS DISPOSAL–FAILURES AND LESSONS

E. S. Smith

By Edwin S. Smith, International Engineering Company, Inc., San Francisco, California.

Edwin S. Smith graduated from Queens University, Northern Ireland, in 1951 with a bachelor's degree in Civil Engineering. After brief assignments with consulting engineers in London, England, and Toronto, Canada, he joined International Engineering Company (IECO) in the fall of 1952 to work on the underground powerhouse at Kemano in British Columbia, Canada. Transferred to San Francisco, California, in 1954, Mr. Smith has undertaken both field and office assignments for IECO, with a one-year interruption in 1957 to obtain a master's degree in Soil Mechanics from Harvard University. As Chief Soils Engineer for IECO, Mr. Smith's work has taken him to many parts of the world. His many assignments have included soil mechanics problems related to water resources planning, foundation engineering, and tailings disposal. His work on tailings deposits has included analysis of failures, study of the safety of existing dikes, and design of new disposal systems.

Mining engineers have repeatedly improved tailings disposal techniques by applying the lessons learned from the investigation of deposit failures. But often, the same type of failure has to occur several times before the message is generally heeded.

The paper discusses different types of failures common to hydraulically placed fill structures. Examples of these are presented, and data are given on specific geotechnical properties.

Fundamental soil mechanics principles that are pertinent to tailings disposal operations are briefly enumerated. The observational approach of design, construct, monitor and, where necessary, modify the design is outlined, and exemplified by details of specific examples. In addition, common distress signals in deposits are described.

W. E. Steiner

ARIZONA'S DAM SAFETY PROGRAM AND ITS IMPLICATIONS FOR TAILING DAMS

By Wesley E. Steiner, Arizona Water Commission, Phoenix, Arizona.

Wesley E. Steiner is a graduate in Civil Engineering from the University of California. From 1950 until February 1969 he was a Water Resource Development Planner for the California State Department of Water Resources. He served as the department expert on Colorado River matters. He was Chief Planning Officer of the California Department of Water Resources from August 1964 to February 1, 1969. He was then appointed State Water Engineer by the Arizona Interstate Stream Commission. On March 1, 1969, he assumed the additional duties of Executive Director. In April, 1971 he assumed the responsibility for Arizona's Safety of Dams Program, which completed the first full year of staffed operations in June 1972.

Arizona's Dam Safety legislation was enacted in 1929. Statutes, essentially unchanged since then, include in jurisdiction all dams 15 feet or more in height, or dams which impound more than 10 acre feet. Federally owned and stock watering dams are excepted. Until recently the Highway Department was responsible for the program. Revenues from fees based on a percentage of the cost of dam construction financed the entire operation.

In 1971 this function was transferred to the Arizona Water Commission under direction of the State Water Engineer. A staff of professional engineers, funded irrespective of fee revenue, operates the program. During its first year the staff reviewed and approved 12 applications for new construction and supervised construction for safety of six projects. Additionally, a special inspection to determine the number and condition of dams under state jurisdiction revealed that Arizona has about 200 jurisdictional dams.

The statutes, virtually unchanged since 1929, need clarification and modernization in fee structure, authority to act against violators, and jurisdiction of off-stream dams, stock tanks, and tailing dams.

Tailings dams, potentially hazardous because of materials and methods of construction, qualify under the state's program as dams on the basis of height and storage capacity. A number of these dams have been excluded from state jurisdiction by opinions of the Attorney General and confusion exists as to authority on all others. As a result, design, construction and operation of tailing dams in Arizona have not been subjected to safety regulation. The Water Commission is studying tailing dams to determine whether regulations are needed and whether the recommendation should be made to the legislature in 1973 to include or exclude tailing dams from the Safety of Dams program.

THE CONTROL OF WATER IN TAILINGS STRUCTURES

By James R. Swaisgood and George C. Toland, Dames & Moore, Salt Lake City, Utah.

J. R. Swaisgood

James R. Swaisgood is a Partner of Dames & Moore and manager of the firm's Denver office. He graduated from the Colorado School of Mines in 1959 with a degree in Geological Engineering. He completed graduate studies in rock mechanics and mining at this school from 1965 to 1967. Since then, he has returned to the School of Mines each summer to teach field courses in engineering geology. Prior to joining Dames & Moore, Mr. Swaisgood worked for a small California consulting engineering firm. With them, he accepted the responsibility for all hydrology, hydraulics, soils and structural design studies for a large flood-control dam. With Dames & Moore, Mr. Swaisgood has been responsible for projects in Australia, Spain, Okinawa, the Pacific Islands, and in almost every state in the United States. These projects involved civil engineering, geology, and rock mechanics studies. A major protion of Mr. Swaisgood's experience has been gained in the investigation and design of earth dams and tailings structures.

George C. Toland is a Partner of Dames & Moore. He joined the firm in 1955 and has served as an Engineering Analyst, Senior Engineer, and Chief Engineer prior to receiving his present assignment of Manager of the Salt Lake City office. He has specialized in the investigation and design of earth dams and tailings disposal systems. Complete studies for new disposal systems were provided for the J. R. Simplot Company; Cominco, Ltd.; Earth Resources; Humble Oil; and Hecla Mining Company. He graduated from the University of Wyoming in 1951 with a B. S. in Civil Engineering.

The costs of controlling water in a tailing structure represent a major portion of the total costs in the disposal of tailings. Furthermore, the water-control measures finally adopted greatly influence the relative stability of the tailing embankment and the potential pollution of existing surface water and groundwater.

The free or standing water produced in normal operations is removed from the tailings pond by one of three decant systems: (1) through decant towers and buried decant lines using gravity flow; (2) by pumps on floating barges on the pond or on inclined tracks at the edge of the pond; (3) through syphons from the top of the ponds.

Excess free water produced by rain storms and/or snow melt can be controlled by diverting the surface runoff waters around the tailing pond, by allowing the excess water to pass through a spillway, or by retaining the excess water behind the tailing dam and returning it slowly through the decant system.

The subsurface or seepage water flows can be controlled with the use of zoned embankments, boundary or toe-drain systems, or downstream drainage systems.

The factors which affect the selection of the optimum water-control systems include relative construction costs, the topography, climate, and geology existing at the tailing embankment site; the physical and chemical characteristics of the tailings liquids and solids; and the pollution prevention requirements in the area.

With these factors in mind, each of the components of the various water-control systems have certain advantages and disadvantages when compared to the others.

Several types of instruments and methods are available to monitor water flows in and nearby tailings structures. Some of these may be used to establish "baseline" water-flow quantity and quality.

J. D. Vincent

THE TAILING STRUCTURE AND ITS CHARACTERISTICS FROM THE METALLURGIST'S VIEWPOINT

By J. D. Vincent, Climax Molybdenum Company, Division of AMAX, Incorporated, Golden, Colorado.

J. Dixon Vincent received his E. M. in Mining Engineering from the Colorado School of Mines and his M. Sc. in Mineral Dressing from the Montana College of Mineral Science and Technology in 1938. From 1935 to 1937 he was Assistant to the Construction Superintendent for the Cerro De Pasco Company in Peru and from 1938 to 1941 he was Mill Metallurgist for the Howe Sound Company. In 1941 he joined the U. S. Bureau of Mines as a metallurgist, and from 1942 to 1946 he was Assistant Director of Research for the Dow Chemical Company. In 1951 he joined the American Smelting and Refining Company as Assistant Milling Engineer, and from 1960 to 1967 was Mill Superintendent of the Mission Unit. He joined Climax Molybdenum Company in 1967 and was Director of Research and Development until his recent appointment as Chief Metallurgical Engineer for Mine Evaluation, Exploration and Mine Evaluation Division, American Metal Climax, Incorporated.

The paper covers the reasons why the tailing disposal facility is a necessary part of any modern mining venture, the question of its location in respect to the concentrator, the question of size that will take care of known and potential needs, the method of constructing the original tailing dam and method used for advancing the structure, and the economic reasons for the type of structure commonly employed. A review of various types of construction commonly employed will be covered with a discussion of the reasons that decide the choice for particular problems due to geography, the character of the waste, ecological considerations, and structural strength of the resulting dam.

W.A. Wahler

AVAILABILITY OF ENGINEERING TECH-NOLOGY FOR DESIGN AND CONSTRUC-TION OF TAILINGS STRUCTURES

By W. A. Wahler, W. A. Wahler & Associates, Palo Alto, California.

William A. Wahler is founder and has been President of W. A. Wahler & Associates since its founding in 1960. Formerly Senior Soil Engineer with Bechtel Corporation, partner in a soil and foundation engineering firm in Denver, Colorado, and soil engineer with U. S. Bureau of Reclamation. He has a B. S. and M. S. in Civil Engineering with a minor in Engineering Geology from the University of Colorado and has done post-graduate work at Harvard, Massachusetts Institute of Technology, and George Washington University. He is a registered Civil Engineer in Alabama, Alaska, Arizona, California, Colorado, Illinois, Kentucky, Nevada, New Mexico, Ohio, Oregon, Pennsylvania, Utah, Virginia, Washington, and West Virginia. Mr. Wahler is a member of the American Society of Civil Engineers, Consulting Engineers Association of California, National Society of Professional Engineers, United States Committee on Large Dams, and International Commission on Large Dams.

The design of tailings disposal structures demands the best in available technology and the development of improved new technology if existing and planned structures are to meet safety, environmental, and economic constraints imposed by recent and proposed legislation. Several disciplines and specialized fields of engineering contain technology and procedures that can help the mining profession meet these new requirements. An interdisciplinary approach is essential because of the wide range and complexity of the problems that are involved in disposing of waste products. Effecting an interdisciplinary approach, however, will involve adapting potentially applicable technologies and procedures so that they can play economic and productive roles in the solution of tailings disposal problems. Much of the research needed to develop improved new technology will be in materials characteristics, analytical procedures, and construction techniques.

R. E. Williams

MODERNIZATION OF COEUR D'ALENE TAILING DISPOSAL PRACTICES

By Dr. Roy E. Williams, Office of University Relations, U. S. Bureau of Mines, Department of the Interior, Washington, D.C.

Dr. Roy E. Williams was born in Tennessee and educated in Indiana and Illinois. He received the B. S. degree in 1961 and the M. S. degree in 1962, both from Indiana University. He completed the Ph. D. degree at the University of Illinois in 1966. His training has consisted of a combination of geology, mathematics, and civil engineering. He has been employed by the Standard of Texas Oil Company, by the California Oil Company, and the Illinois State Geological Survey. Dr. Williams currently is employed by the University of Idaho and the Idaho Bureau of Mines and Geology, but he is on leave to the U. S. Bureau of Mines in Washington, D. C. until August 1, 1973. During the past several years he has conducted and directed the work of graduate students in research on various aspects of wastes and waste waters, including mine wastes.

The Coeur d'Alene mining district in north Idaho (primarily lead, zinc, silver, antimony, copper) has served as a field laboratory for evaluating several methods of disposing of mine wastes. This paper deals with investigations of the effect of different practices on ground water and surface water. In all cases the water table is within a few feet of the ground surface, and most of the waste disposal sites are situated above zones of predominately lateral ground water motion.

The disposal practices evaluated consist of (1) spreading tailings over a valley floor; (2) disposal of mill wastes alone in a tailing pond; (3) disposal of mill wastes plus acid mine drainage and process effluents in a tailing pond; (4) disposal of tailing into a pond using a point inflow system; (5) disposal in a pond using a peripheral discharge system; and (6) disposal in more than one tailings pond connected in series, using a peripheral discharge sytem.

The results of the study indicate that (1) old tailing which has been spread on a valley floor can be expected to be leached and have a detrimental effect on ground water and surface water quality, particularly in the tailing resulting from early day milling with low mineral recoveries; (2) properly designed and managed tailing ponds can be expected to treat mill wastes adequately; (3) tailing ponds cannot alone be expected to treat other than mill wastes. Additional treatment in the tailing pond or of the pond effluent is required if most process effluents and some types of mine drainage are mixed with mill wastes; (4) point discharge systems frequently result in the discharge of poor quality water to the water table, and perhaps more importantly the practice facilitates the formation of a continually dissipating, poor quality ground water mound within the tailing pile after abandonment, particularly if the metals recovery process is inefficient; and (6) the use of a peripheral discharge system eliminates several problems with respect to ground water quality and abandonment, even if the water held in the pond during operation is of poor quality. Ponds in series, using the peripheral discharge system, can be expected to produce the highest quality effluent and to minimize lixiviation and the recharge of poor quality water to underlying ground water, both during operation and after abandonment.

OPERATION OF THE TAILING SYSTEM AND CHARACTERISTICS OF THE TAILING STRUCTURE

By Frank Windolph, Climax Molybdenum Co., Empire, Colorado.

F. J. Windolph

Frank Windolph graduated from the University of Colorado with a B. S. in Chemical Engineering. He was employed by the Climax Molybdenum Company in 1937 and has been associated with this company for his entire career. The first 22 years of his employment were in the mill department at the Climax mine where he became Mill Superintendent. Since 1959, he has held general management positions and was Resident Manager of the Climax mine. He is presently Resident Manager of the Urad Henderson mines near Empire, Colorado.

This paper describes the deposition of tailing in the high mountain valleys of Colorado. The tailing is deposited by the upstream method and has good drainage characteristics because it is relatively coarse and is deposited at low pulp density. The paper stresses the importance of managing the deposition of tailing to control the piezometric level within the structure.

SYMPOSIUM ADVISORY COMMITTEE

George O. Argall, Jr.
World Mining

Lee Aplin
Clarkson Company

Dan Kealy
U.S. Bureau of Mines

Milton Lagergren
Kennecott Copper Corporation

K.L. Ludeke
Pima Mining Company

Dean Lynch
Duval Corporation

John Miscovich
Marcona Corporation

George Roseveare
Arizona Bureau of Mines

E.S. Smith
International Engineering
Company

W.A. Wahler
W.A. Wahler Associates

Jack G. Wulff
W.A. Wahler Associates

AVAILABILITY OF ENGINEERING TECHNOLOGY FOR

DESIGN AND CONSTRUCTION OF TAILINGS STRUCTURES

W. A. WAHLER

W. A. WAHLER & ASSOCIATES

PALO ALTO, CALIFORNIA

INTRODUCTION

The mining industry is becoming more and more regulated. As a result of these regulations, and
the combined effect of more complex mining problems
in order to mine lower-grade ores, there is a great
new demand for engineering technology to solve the
problems that are brought to the fore by the regulations
and the complexity of mining operations. Perhaps
we are wrong to think that the regulations really in-
vent the problems; they don't. The problem is there;
the regulations are a result of society's finding out
about the mining industry through a few unfortunate
disasters. The regulations then are society's way of
trying to protect itself, and the government's role
is the very difficult one of trying to figure out
what to control and how to do it. Now the poor
industry has the tough problem of finding out how to
live within those constraints. So what we are

talking about when we discuss mine waste disposals is emerging technology, and we are only in the very earliest stages of the development of the regulations under which we will live in the future.

When we talk about the availability of technology, we must speak about it from two divergent viewpoints. One is the hopeful and the good news: that there are some elements of the needed technology available within the industry, based primarily, of course, on experience. But this technology - although theoretically available because it exists - must be distributed before it will be effectively available. So it will be necessary for this experienced technology to be passed on in meetings such as this one and in various other ways that the industry can use to communicate within itself.

Additionally, there is technology available from some of the other fields that can be adopted in order to help solve the mining industry problems. We are focusing mainly on tailings, but the same problems exist with all mine wastes. Foremost among these other fields are earth dam engineering and, in a broader sense, any earth work engineering, whether it is highway engineering or experience in the building and structural fields.

Therefore, it is good news that available technology can be used to help evaluate industry problems and develop solutions. On the other hand, however, this technology is not available in a nice neat package. There are no handbooks, and it will take a good many years to write definitive manuals covering an industry as divergent as the mining industry and the types of wastes involved.

Therefore, it is necessary for everyone to know and understand that our emergent technology is a combined operation--between highly specialized people and interdisciplinary use of specialized people-- in order to achieve the needs of the industry, any solution must take into account safety, environmental

suitability, and economy; without all three it cannot
work. The people in the industry feel that they have
given due concern to all three elements in the past
and, from their own standpoint, that is pretty much
true. Unfortunately, society does not believe that
it is true, and so it is beginning to develop requirements that the mining industry will have to meet
and the government will have to regulate. Probably
before a year has elapsed, there will be a complex set
of regulations to live with--regulations that will
deal not only with existing structures, but also with
new structures.

Therefore, it is with this in mind that we must
look to the available technology to determine how we
shall be able to utilize it and to obtain some balance.
The first experiences, I am afraid, will be a bit
disconcerting to everyone involved. The people who
have regulatory responsibilities have a problem to
determine how to use them and how to fulfill their
requirements. It is the same with the regulated.
And so there will be a struggle between the regulators
and those regulated. The disciplines available will
be used from both standpoints and, hopefully, on a
balanced, well-tempered basis that will end up with
the desired combination of safety, environment, and
economy. Available technology is a subject that
you will hear a lot about.

THE TAILING STRUCTURE AND ITS CHARACTERISTICS

FROM THE METALLURGIST'S VIEWPOINT

J. D. VINCENT

DIRECTOR OF RESEARCH AND DEVELOPMENT

CLIMAX MOLYBDENUM COMPANY

GOLDEN, COLORADO

INTRODUCTION

The metallurgist must necessarily define the problems that will be encountered in tailing dam storage, such as the suitability of the tailings for constructing a solid and essentially safe tailing dam from a structural point of view, the necessity for reclaiming or discharging effluent from the dam, toxicity or chemic problems involved in recirculation and reuse of the effluent or the neutralization and purification of the effluent, if it is discharged into natural waterways. All metallurgical operations have varying chances of polluting the atmosphere, land or water resources of the nearby countryside.

All of this can be summed up by saying that mining companies must solve the problem of storing tailing in a safe, ecologically acceptable and economic manner, without endangering health or property. The

metallurgist or mill design engineer is faced with
the fact that a mine is not a mine unless the tailing
disposal scheme fulfills the basic truths mentioned
above.

Actual design of the tailing dam must necessarily
be dependent on the topographical and geologic nature
of the available sites. It goes without saying that
a tailing damsite close to the concentrator will
lend itself to more economical operation and supervision; however, this is not possible in all cases,
and different decisions in engineering development
will be required when the dam is located at a distance.

Normally, the optimum case, of course, is that where
there is a sufficient gradient for the tailing to
flow by gravity to the waste disposal site, but not
too high a gradient to cause unusual design problems
or make impractical the placement of a tailing dam
on the available ground. Ideally, the ground upon
which the tailing dam will be placed will have suf-
ficent area to take care of the foreseeable ore reserve; the soil under the area of improvement will
not be porous; and the tailing material received
from the concentrator will be of the correct size
range to make a structurally sound berm with the minimum of effort and classify itself naturally so
that the fines will not rest against the face of the dam.
In addition, the ideal situation is that where the
metallurgist does not have to concern himself with
polluting stream waterways or aquafirs by seepage of
contaminated solutions from the concentrator operation.

Unfortunately, these optimum cases are seldom encountered and it becomes necessary for the metallurgist
to consider purification of the water, reuse of the
water, sealing of the dam, neutralization of acidic
or heavy metal containing solutions, or treatment
of the water to make it nontoxic for stock, mem, or
the environment.

It is common practice throughout the world, today, to reuse as much of the tailing dam water as is possible, since water costs money and it is not desirable in most instances to discharge the tailing waters into existing stream channels or into the aquafirs below the ground.

In many operations, the tailing water may contain excessive amounts of calcium, sulphate ion, magnesium, iron, or other heavy metals which render it unfit for domestic consumption. Therefore, it must be collected as completely as possible and reused. Certainly, this has been well demonstrated in the Southwest among the copper operations where it is not unusual for 80 to 85 per cent of the water used in the metallurgical milling operation to be reclaimed. Likewise, this has become necessary at such operations as Climax, where the water is recycled from the tailing dam for the mill operation. The balance is lost to seepage and evaporation.

In certain specific instances, the problem becomes more acute, due to the presence of such chemical compounds as cyanide, ferric sulphate, aluminum sulphate, chlorides, or other such elements in the tailing waters. In the case of cyanide, there is always a particular danger to human beings, or animal life, unless the area is well fenced off and the cyanide neutralized or oxidized by chlorine before it is permitted to leave the mill.

The plating mills in the steel industry are an example of where it is necessary to neutralize the oxide of spent solutions which are high in heavy metal salts as well as acid.

We are faced with a revolution in mineral processing, where hydrometallurgy will play a more important role in the recycle of leach solutions or their neutralization will become a must, under the present pressure of ecological control. It is getting more difficult every day to consider putting this

type of waste solution into our rivers, lakes or
oceans without neutralization or precipitation of
the contaminated elements in the solution. This is
true in North America and also is receiving more
attention all over the world.

The metallurgist or mineral processing engineer
is faced with alternatives as to the type of tailing
dam structure that should be used under the geological
and typographical conditions that are available at any
particular location. It has been a general, although
not a universal, practice to construct tailing dams
on an uphill berm. The fines are continually pushed
to the back of the area and, as the dam is raised, sands
are deposited on a mixture of sands and fines. This
has proven practical under average conditions where
the dam does not have to be built to extreme heights
or where it is not enclosed in a narrow and steep mountain valley. Another practice where the gradient is
steeper than normal, and where the tailing dam is
surrounded by rather precipitous canyon walls, is to
build the dam downhill so that the dam face is continuously being reinforced by the coarse materials
classified out of the tailing stream.

Another approach is that which has been employed
by the Utah Copper Division of Kennecott Copper Corporation, the Butte and Twin Buttes tailing disposal
systems of Anaconda Company and others, where the
entire berm is built from the rock or alluvial material
that are available in the adjacent area, and the tailings are stored and distributed behind this berm using
them only as necessary at the base of the dam structure. There are, of course, many examples where tailings have been discharged near sea coasts and allowed
to run to the ocean and this, of course, is a debatable
matter at this moment, although there is scarce
evidence to prove that such tailing disposal schemes
have hurt the environment or that this is an unsatisfactory method when such an opportunity is available.

In conclusion, I think the metallurgist has to look

at each project as a separate problem; no one way or no
single problem is common to the mining or concentrating
industry. It is also necessary to take a closer look
at the Environmental Protection Agency regulations,
the proposed regulations, and the methods of combating
the problems that develop.

THE TAILING STRUCTURE AND ITS CHARACTERISTICS --

A SOILS ENGINEER'S VIEWPOINT

C.O. Brawner, P. Eng.
Principal

and

D.B. Campbell, P. Eng.
Associate

Golder, Brawner & Associates Ltd.
Vancouver, Canada

INTRODUCTION

The steady increase in cost in developing and operating mines throughout the world has led to a continued increase in the scale of operation. Many modern mills are treating tens of thousands of tons of low grade ore daily.

In order to liberate the metal the ore must be finely crushed. For low grade ore bodies, virtually one hundred per cent of the finely ground crushed rock is waste. This waste is pumped in slurry form (tailings) for disposal. Where the mill is near a large body of water the tailings have in some instances been piped and deposited in deep water. In the majority of instances however the tailings are impounded behind man-made retaining structures. On many projects the total volume of tailings will range from one hundred million cubic yards to more than one billion cubic yards. This will require retention dams several hundreds of feet in height, some in excess of 500 feet. These are massive structures.

With the reminder of the loss of life caused by the El Cobre tailings dam failures in Chile in 1965 (1) and the Aberfan waste dump failure in Britain in 1966 (2), the need for a high standard of engineering design is evident. This design must recognize that stability is required not only during the operating life of the mine but also for generations after mining is complete.

A further challenge is the recognition that the disposal of tailings returns no profit benefit to the mining company. This makes it necessary for the tailings disposal system to be constructed at minimum cost commensurate with stability and ecological requirements.

The knowledge and experience available in the field of soil mechanics and earth dam technology is considerable. By using this experience it is possible to avoid failures and at the same time to avoid excessively high factors of safety which represent excessive capital expenditure and reduced profitability of the mine.

This paper outlines the basic planning and design requirements from a soil engineer's stand-point that are necessary to develop a stable and economical tailings retention structure.

GENERAL PLANNING AND DESIGN REQUIREMENTS

The tailings dam must be designed to remain stable during construction and for many generations thereafter. It must provide the required storage at any given time and it must provide sufficient control of seepage so that pollution of adjacent land and water ways does not develop.

To minimize the cost of the retention structures the most economical design must be employed. This frequently requires consideration of the use of the tailings to construct the dam wholly or in conjunction with natural soils adjacent to the site.

Stage construction is frequently considered, with the height of the structure maintained minimally above the storage level required. This procedure minimizes initial capital investment and spreads the cost of construction over many years.

Initial considerations require detailed knowledge of the physical and mechanical properties of the tailings. Since they may be used as an integral part of the dam, the shear strength, consolidation, permeability, sedimentation and construction characteristics must be determined. The chemical qualities of the tailings and slurry fluid must be assessed to evaluate potential pollution.

Detailed consideration of site conditions including climate, geology, hydrology, topography, soil profile must be assessed and evaluated. The foundation conditions must be determined to assess the adequacy of subsurface materials to support the dam without failure and without excessive total or differential settlement. The permeability of foundation soil and rock must be ascertained to estimate the amount of seepage, potential of piping and, if necessary, the methods of control.

The method and sequence of construction must be developed and the availability of construction materials to meet the construction schedule must be assessed.

The design must be analyzed for stability. This analysis must include earthquake considerations. The influence of unusual weather conditions on construction must be assessed. A positive method of tailings water control must be developed to ensure there is no possibility that the dam will ever be overtopped.

Special problems which may be created by the type of tailings to be stored must be assessed, i.e. pyrites and acid potential, radioactivity, burning, freezing and thawing, wind erosion, etc.

The requirements and methods of reclamation for land reuse after cessation of mining is becoming a common design consideration.

In view of the failure of many tailings dams in the past and the increasing height of planned tailings dams, the design of the new structures must be based on sound engineering principles rather than obsolete empirical rules.

CONSTRUCTION METHODS

Prior to the planning and design of any tailings impoundment structure it is necessary that the designer be familiar with the concepts and variations of construction methods.

The materials used and the construction method should be selected to optimize lowest cost and required stability. Where the tailings dam is near the open pit, overburden or waste rock may be employed economically for dam construction. Alternatively, it may be necessary to use borrow materials located near the dam site. If possible these should be obtained from the reservoir area since this will increase the reservoir storage capacity.

Where natural borrow material or overburden and waste rock are used for dam construction, standard procedures for earth and earth-rock dam construction can be used provided two departures from normal earth dam design requirements are taken into account in the design. The unit weight of saturated tailings is considerably greater than the unit weight of water and the placement of spigotted slimes on the upstream face produces a moderately impervious upstream seal. Sherard et al (3), outline standard design and construction procedures for earth and earth-rock dams.

Frequently it will be economical to use the tailings for some of the structure. The liberation grind required to extract the metal from most ores produces particle sizes that range from medium sized sand to fine silt. The finer fraction is unsuitable for dam construction due to low shear strength and high compressibility. Separation of particle sizes is therefore necessary to yield a coarse fraction for construction.

Tailings slurries are usually transported from the mill to the disposal area by pipeline or flume. Two methods of size separation are in common use. One method is to spigot the slurry onto the surface of the disposal area. This forms a gently sloping beach where the coarsest fraction settles near the point of discharge and the fine fraction or slimes is deposited progressively toward the centre of the disposal area. As a result of this variable gradation, the density, shear strength and permeability of the settled solids decrease with increasing distance from the point of deposition. Since the slimes have low permeability and inhibit seepage through the dam, it is common to spigot tailings over the upstream face of the dam.

The second common method of separation is to use cyclones. The resulting gradation usually provides a sand with from 10 to 20 per cent particle sizes passing the No. 200 sieve. This will vary depending on the initial grind gradation, size of cyclones and rate of cycloning. If a coarser gradation is required for special purposes, double cycloning will further reduce the fines content.

If tailings are employed for construction, three methods are in common use. They are the upstream method, downstream method and centreline method (Figure No. 1).

With the upstream method, an initial starter dam is constructed at the downstream toe. It is most important that this initial dam be sufficiently pervious to pass seepage water and that the downstream portion of the dam be designed to resist piping. Tailings are then discharged from the top of the

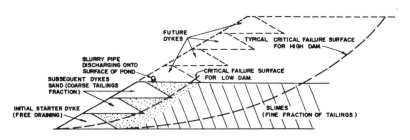

(a) UPSTREAM METHOD

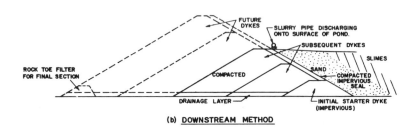

(b) DOWNSTREAM METHOD

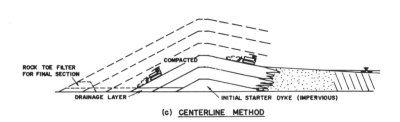

(c) CENTERLINE METHOD

Standard methods of tailing dam construction.

Figure No. 1

starter dam using spigots or cyclones to develop a dyke composed of the coarser fraction. The centreline of the top of the embankment is shifted towards the pond area as the height of the dam increases. The downstream toe of each subsequent dyke is supported on the top of the previous dyke with the upstream portion of the dyke placed over finer tailings. These tailings, normally placed hydraulically, have a relatively low shear strength. Investigation of stability for a tailings dam in the

Philippine Islands revealed a relative density averaging only 30 per cent for hydraulically deposited coarse tailings (4). As the height of the dam increases, the potential failure surface is located at an increasingly greater distance from the downstream face and through the slimes. As a result, the outside shell contributes less to stability as the height increases. This may result in the factor of safety reducing to unity at which time the dam will fail.

Where the upstream method is used, the dam and retained slimes may be in a sufficiently loose condition that the structure could fail by liquefaction if subjected to seismic shock. Vibration tends to cause the weight of the dam to be carried by the pore water which reduces the shear strength of the sand. The shear strength can be reduced to near zero such that the dam collapses and flows. Liquefied tailings from one of the El Cobre failures flowed seven miles. Vibration can be caused by earthquakes, blasting, trains, heavy trucks, etc.

Flat downstream slopes will not ensure stability with respect to liquefaction. One of the El Cobre dams which failed had a downstream slope of only 15 degrees (approximately 4:1).

In the downstream method of construction, the centreline of the top of the dam shifts downstream as the dam is raised (Figure No. 1b). A starter dam is required. This should be impervious to minimize seepage through the dam. This requires that the starter dam will usually be constructed of compacted borrow material which contains significant silt and clay sizes. Each subsequent stage of dyke construction is supported on the top of the downstream slope of the previous section. If tailings are to be used during construction, only the coarse fraction must be employed. Prior to each downstream extension a pervious underdrain layer at least 3 feet thick or alternative drainage system must be placed to minimize the chance for buildup of pore water which reduces shear strength.

If the dam will be located in a potential earthquake zone and/or will exceed a height of about 50 feet the downstream extensions must be compacted. The consensus of engineering experience indicates that not less than 60 per cent relative density be obtained to minimize the risk of liquefaction (5). This is approximately equivalent to 95 per cent Standard Proctor density.

Some recent dam designs have recommended the use of uncompacted cycloned sands for downstream slopes placed at flat angles of 4:1 to 5:1 by hydraulic methods. This is not good practice. Firstly, only thin layers within the dam require saturation or near saturation to become liquefied. With continued hydraulicking, zones of saturation exist. After completion of mining only a modest rainfall is necessary to develop a saturated zone. Studies following the Anchorage earthquake suggested several major slides developed by failure along a saturated granular zone which liquefied (6). Secondly, the cycloned fraction usually contains 10 to 20 per cent silt size particles which migrate down through the sand and tend to plug filters and reduce the permeability of the toe area of the dam. Thirdly, Goodman and Seed (7) have shown that loose dry sand slopes can also liquefy and flow. In this case the depth of flowage is shallower than normally occurs for water saturated flows. However, the failure could be deep enough for the crest to drop sufficiently for the impounded water to overflow leading to rapid failure of the embankment.

The coarse tailings can be piped onto the dam section and spread in thin layers or they can be hauled from a central cycloned stockpile, spread and compacted. The cost of compaction is not as great as may be expected because steeper downstream slopes can be used and the volume of the dam is reduced considerably (8).

If the volume of coarse tailings is not sufficient to construct the dam, local borrow materials can be incorporated for part of the structure. At the tailings dam in the Philippines referred to previously, which will be about 300 feet high, zones of well compacted local laterite are being incorporated in the dam section. On a project in Canada the tailings dam is very near the open pit such that the waste rock can be used to build up the downstream sections (Figure No. 2). Because of the porosity of the coarse rock, a filter or impervious upstream membrane is required to prevent piping of the tailings through the rock.

To minimize seepage through dams that are constructed with tailings it is normally recommended that the upstream face be sealed. The most economical procedure will frequently be to place a layer of impervious soil. To further minimize seepage it is usual to spigot at least some of the slimes off the crest of the dam over the upstream slope. With this method a road can be carried on the crest of the dam for continued access.

In the centreline method, the crest of the dam is maintained at the same horizontal position as the height of the dam is increased. The dam is raised by spreading and compacting additional coarse tailings on the top, on the upstream shoulder and on the downstream slope. Coarse gradation of the tailings is necessary to afford rapid drainage to provide support for construction equipment.

Except for small dams, the tailings placed on the downstream slope must always be compacted. One of the most important criteria for the stability of earth dams is to develop maximum stability in the toe and downstream slope areas. If this zone is loose, lateral pressure which increases due to additional placement of fill may result in sufficient lateral strain for support of the main body of the dam to be reduced. The upstream slope

Tailing dam being constructed with the downstream
method, using waste rock from the adjacent open pits.
Figure No. 2

should also be compacted for some distance since
the slimes placed against this slope can liquefy
and result in failure of the slope toward the pond.
This could drop sufficiently to allow overtopping.

If the pond is large or if ice will develop in
the winter, special precautions may be required to

resist upslope erosion.

PLANNING AND DESIGN

Prior to actual commencement of the design of any tailings impoundment structure, other studies must be developed. They include a preliminary decision regarding the volume of ore to be treated daily and yearly, the general order of the size of the ore body to estimate the total volume of tailings, metallurgical studies to assess the probable tailings gradation and recovery process and potential plant layout.

A preliminary study of topographic maps and air photographs will indicate potential areas for storage of tailings. Information should be obtained on climatic conditions at the site. This should include precipitation (rain and snow), temperature, stream flow and rates of evaporation. Gauging stations should be installed early in the program. Any general soil or geological maps should be reviewed.

With this general information, preliminary layouts should be developed. Air photo interpretation, to provide a preliminary assessment of soil, rock and groundwater conditions, should be made at this time. General comparisons of the required dam height vs. storage capacity (yearly and total) should be made and a preliminary operational, economic, ecological and reclamation comparison of sites should be developed. This assessment should allow the most suitable site to be selected.

The next stage should comprise a preliminary site investigation. For small dams hand test holes or test pits may suffice to assess foundation conditions. For large dams a more comprehensive subsurface investigation is required. Several exploratory boreholes should be drilled to generally define the subsurface conditions, obtain samples to determine soil and rock properties, determine groundwater conditions, etc. Based on an evaluation of this information a detailed site investigation should be performed. The location, thickness, areal extent of each soil and rock type should be determined. It may be prudent to drill one or two holes deep enough to ensure that no economically recoverable ore underlies the potential dam site or pond area.

The field investigation should include representative sampling of soil and rock conditions beneath the dam and in the abutments. If the soils are fine grained, undisturbed samples must be obtained. The best methods of drilling and sampling are outlined in numerous soil engineering texts, for example Terzaghi and Peck (9). Continuous core of the bedrock must be obtained to determine rock type and properties and the presence, location and orientation of discontinuities and the existence of cavities. Triple tube core barrels in minimum NX size should be used. During drilling of the hole in soil, falling head permeability tests should be performed to assess permeability characteristics and seepage potential. In rock, water packer permeability tests are recommended. In a number of the boreholes, piezometers should be installed to determine the water pressure at depth. If care is taken, up to three piezometers can usually be placed in each hole. A typical installation is shown in Figure No. 3. Boreholes in which piezometers are not installed should be filled completely with a sand cement grout.

Field investigations must be performed to locate and prove the quantity and quality of potential borrow materials including drainage or filter materials that may be required, particularly for the starter dam.

Laboratory testing of the soil and rock samples is required to determine the shear strength, stress strain relationships, compressibility, grain size

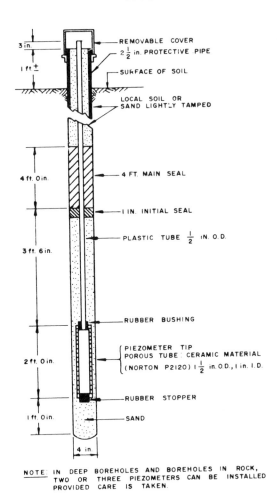

Typical piezometer installation to measure pore water pressure.   Figure No. 3

and permeability of the foundation soils and the shear strength of the rock.

Tests are required to determine the permeability and shear strength of the tailings that will be used in the dam. These tests must be performed at various moisture and density conditions. If the dam will be very large it is recommended that the shear strength be determined under dynamic load conditions (10).

Based on the test data available from the above investigation the stability, settlement and seepage potential through the dam and its foundation can be assessed.

The most favourable location for the dam will be dictated by site conditions, materials availability and the storage volume to fill placement ratio.

Stability

The stability of the dam foundation and the dam proper must be evaluated. Soil and rock will fail in shear if the applied shear stress on any plane exceeds the shear strength. In the embankment and its foundations the shear stresses are governed by the height of the embankment, the unit weight of the fill, the gradient of the dam slope and by the water pressures. The steepest permissible embankment slope depends on the shear strength of the fill and/or the foundation soil or rock, the unit weight of the material, the height of the embankment and the distribution of the water pressures. When the dam is constructed on a sound foundation, the gradient of the downstream slope for any height of dam will be dependent on the shear strength of the dam material. Where the foundation soil is weak, the shear strength of the foundation will usually govern.

Compaction and drainage have considerable influence on stability and hence on the gradient of the downstream slope (8). For example, if a slope in loose saturated sand having a friction angle of 30 degrees has a minimum safety factor of 1.3 the computed downstream slope is 13 degrees (4.2:1). If the sand is compacted so the friction angle increases to 38 degrees the corresponding slope angle is 18.5 degrees (3:1). If the slope is drained so the phreatic water surface is lowered to the level of the toe, the slope angle for a safety factor of 1.3 becomes 31 degrees (1.7:1). These calculations do not include allowance for seismic forces.

Once the dam section, construction method and properties of the fill and foundation materials are known, an analysis to quantitatively assess stability is performed. A trial failure surface is selected and the shearing forces and available shearing resistance along the trial surface are computed. The ratio of the sum of forces available to resist movement divided by the sum of the shearing forces is the factor of safety. Numerous trial surfaces are analyzed. Figure No. 4 shows a typical resolution of forces to compute the safety factor. The trial surface which gives the lowest factor of safety represents the safety factor of the slope or combined slope and foundation.

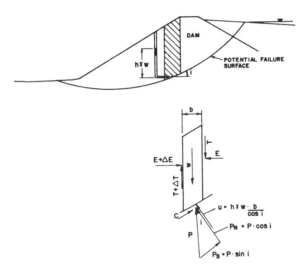

EFFECTIVE NORMAL FORCE ON BASE OF SLICE = $P_N' = P_N - u$

SHEARING FORCE = P_S

AVAILABLE SHEARING RESISTANCE = $P_N' \tan \phi + C$

$$F.S. = \frac{\Sigma\, P_N' \tan \phi + C}{\Sigma\, P_S}$$

Stability analysis by method of slices. Figure No. 4

Numerous methods of stability analyses are available (11, 12, 13). Computer programs are available for all methods and allow stability computations to be made rapidly. An important factor to recognize is that a potential failure surface will follow the zone or zones of lowest shear strength so that the surface may have an irregular shape.

In areas where earthquakes have occurred in the past an allowance for the related seismic acceleration forces on stability must be made. Procedures to assess these effects have been developed by Newmark (14) and Goodman and Seed (7). Seismic vibrations can cause liquefaction of saturated or near saturated loose uniformly graded granular soils for considerable distance from the epicenter of an earthquake. Dams failed more than 100 miles from the epicenter of the El Cobre earthquake in Chile and the foreshore slope failures at Anchorage were located about 80 miles from the epicenter of the Alaska 'Good Friday' earthquake in 1964.

Performance records to date of earth dams that have been subjected to earthquake forces reveal that well compacted unsaturated fills do not liquefy and do not tend to suffer appreciable damage during earthquakes. In areas where past seismic activity has occurred dams constructed using the downstream method and incorporating compaction are unquestionably safer than dams constructed using the previously more common upstream method.

The alignment of tailings dams should be straight or curved upstream wherever possible. Sharp curves should be avoided since differential lateral pressures develop which may cause cracks to develop in the dam.

One of the major decisions for the tailings dam planner is the selection of the safety factor to use. The following minimum safety factors have been suggested in a Tentative Design Guide for Mine Waste Embankments in Canada (15). It is assumed that the stability analysis has located the critical failure surface and that the parameters used in the analysis are known with reasonable certainty to be representative of the actual conditions that will exist in the embankment.

Table No. I

Suggested Minimum Design Safety Factors

	Case 1*	Case 2**
- Design based on peak shear strength parameters	1.5	1.3
- Design based on residual shear strength parameters	1.3	1.2
- Analysis that include the predicted return period accelerations applied to the potential failure mass	1.2	1.1
- For horizontal sliding on the base of embankments retaining tailings in seismic areas assuming shear strength of the tailings reduced to zero	1.3	1.3

*Case 1 - Where it is anticipated that persons or property would be endangered by a failure.

**Case 2 - Where it is anticipated that persons or property would not be endangered by a failure.

Settlement

Where the tailings dam is constructed across a

valley, the vertical load at the centre of the valley will be higher than the load near the ends of the dam. Frequently compressible soils exist under the dam and frequently the subsurface bedrock profile may be irregular. Either condition can lead to differential settlement as a result of the unequal loading or variable thickness of compressible soil. These differential settlements may result in transverse cracks developing in the dam, (see Figure No. 5). The cracks may be produced either by differential settlement of the foundation or settlement within the fill. Dams built using the upstream method are particularly prone to the development of longitudinal cracks. The magnitude of the settlements will depend upon the height of the embankment, the depth and thickness of the compressible strata and the compression indices of the fill and foundation soil. The rate at which the foundation settlements will occur will depend upon the magnitude of the rate of change in vertical stress (rate of dam construction), the permeability of the strata and the drainage characteristics of the foundation.

The amount of the expected settlement can be estimated from laboratory consolidation tests. The rate of consolidation can also be estimated. However, the potential error of estimates of the time for settlement to occur is appreciable since settlement is influenced by soil drainage which is controlled by minute geological details which may not be detected during the foundation investigation.

All predictions of the rate and magnitude of settlement and change in pore water pressures should be checked by field instrumentation installed below and within the dam. The predictions based on laboratory data can be modified by the actual measurements to provide reasonably accurate long term estimates.

Cracks which may develop from differential settlement may lead to subsurface erosion and

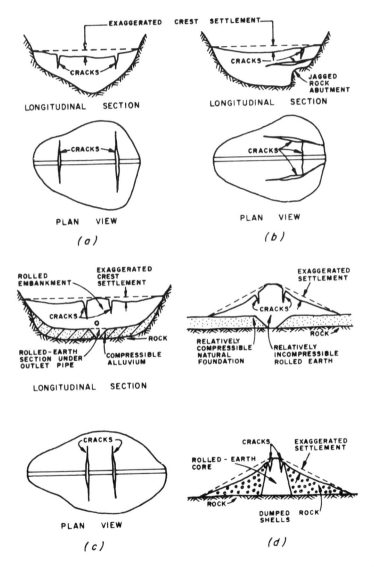

Courtesy of John Wiley & Sons, Inc.

Crack patterns that may develop in earth dams due to differential settlement (3).   Figure No. 5

failure by piping. Differential settlement may also cause damage to pipe drains and decant lines located within or beneath the dam. Therefore the installation of pipes should be avoided at locations where settlement of the foundation is expected.

Settlements which originate within the dam can be reduced by adequate compaction. Where settlements are expected within the foundation the compressible soils can be removed if they are shallow. All organic soils must be excavated. If compressible soils are thick it may be necessary to design the dam to absorb the anticipated differential strains. One method of dealing with this situation is to incorporate a zone of plastic soil at a high moisture content in the zone of anticipated differential settlement to absorb the strain without cracking. This method was used successfully at the Duncan Lake Dam in Canada where differential settlement in excess of 10 feet was expected (16). Another technique is to place transition zones of lightly compacted specially graded cohesionless material within the section to seal cracks that may develop (3, 9).

If considerable settlement is expected the dam must be built higher to allow for the settlement.

Seepage Control

An assessment of seepage through the dam and the dam foundations and abutments is an essential step in the planning and design of any tailings dam. If the seepage is allowed to pass through the body of the dam the shear strength of dam materials is reduced and a flatter downstream slope must be used. If seepage exits from the dam face or downstream of the face and the hydrostatic pressures exceed the weight of the soil there is a danger that piping may develop. This can lead to external erosion and progressive tunnelling and subsequent collapse. Figure No. 6 illustrates a typical pipe

Piping developing in an earth dam (17).

Figure No. 6

developing. This mechanism is potentially very dangerous and has been the greatest single factor contributing to the failure of earth dams. Particular care must be taken to prevent seepage and piping along any culvert which may be located through or under the dam.

If the seepage water contains contaminant constituents, the volume of seepage must be determined to evaluate the influence on adjacent land and water sources. If potential contamination is above allowable limits the design must incorporate procedures to prevent leakage, to maintain it within tolerable limits or remove the contaminants.

The flow of water and piezometric pressures in a

porous media may be evaluated using the Laplace equations. These equations may be represented graphically by a flow net. This is a grid which is formed by the intersection of two sets of orthogonal lines. One set of lines, defined as flow lines, represent the loci of seepage flow through the soil. The other set, defined as equipotential lines represent the loci of points having the same pressure head. These represent the piezometric contours. Typical flow nets are shown in Figure No. 7.

Flow nets may be developed using graphical procedures (18), electric analogs, models, or finite element or finite difference methods (19).

If the studies indicate that seepage pressures through the dam must be minimized it is usual to provide drains beneath the downstream slope. The drainage system may consist of granular blankets, strip drains or drainage pipes. The type of drains will depend on the availability of suitable drainage materials, potential seepage volume, foundation conditions and earthquake potential. The drains will control piping and seepage from the slope and will allow steeper slopes and less embankment fill, negate the possibility of freezing of the slope impeding seepage and minimize the development of ice lenses and subsequent surface sloughing during the spring thaw.

If perforated pipe drains are used they must be designed to withstand the total vertical load. The perforations should be placed down and the perforation diameter should not exceed 0.5 of the 85 per cent size (D_{85}) of the surrounding drainage layer. Since pipe drains cannot be repaired they should not be used in areas of seismic activity or where moderate to high settlement is expected.

Blanket drains or strip drains are placed prior to placement of the dam embankment. If the volume of seepage is expected to be moderate to heavy,

(c) NO DRAINAGE FACILITIES PROVIDED. PERVIOUS
EMBANKMENT OVER LESS PERVIOUS FOUNDATION.

(d) NO DRAINAGE FACILITIES PROVIDED. IMPERVIOUS
EMBANKMENT OVER PERVIOUS FOUNDATION.

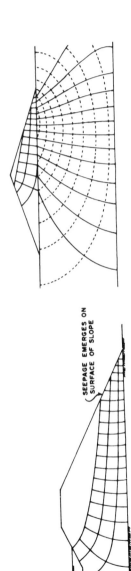

(SEEPAGE EMERGES ON
SURFACE OF SLOPE)

(a) NO DRAINAGE FACILITIES PROVIDED. HOMOGENEOUS
EMBANKMENT ON IMPERVIOUS FOUNDATION.

DRAINAGE BLANKET
DRAIN

(b) BLANKET DRAIN BENEATH DOWNSTREAM SHOULDER.
HOMOGENEOUS EMBANKMENT ON IMPERVIOUS FOUNDATION.

Typical seepage flow nets.   Figure No. 7

blanket drains are preferred. If the potential seepage is small, strip drains comprising pervious drain material may be sufficient. If the foundation is a source of seepage due to artesion conditions or consolidation drainage due to increasing the height and weight of the dam the drainage layers must be designed to carry this volume. The drains must be carried up the abutment slopes of the dam site to control seepage which could lead to abutment failures.

The thickness of the drains will be a function of the seepage volume and soil gradation in the embankment and the foundation. They should never be less than 12 inches thick and should preferably be at least 36 inches thick. The final dam slope should incorporate a coarse toe drain to ensure free drainage and control of piping.

Chemical tests should be performed on the embankment and drain materials and the seepage water to ensure compatibility. For example, the drains should not comprise carbonate rocks if the seepage water is acidic.

The drainage layers must be carefully designed if they are to function satisfactorily on a long term basis. Their capacity should be overdesigned in the event that leakage develops. Where the embankment contains zones of material having significantly different gradation or where the gradation of the foundation and embankment materials differ markedly the zones of markedly different gradation must be separated by filter zones to prevent piping and subsequent subsurface erosion. The filter must meet two requirements; it must be more permeable than the adjacent finer soil so that it will drain freely and it must have a gradation to prevent passage of the soil particles into the drainage layer. Particular care must be taken that segregation does not occur during construction. The recommended filter design criteria is as follows:

(a) $\dfrac{\text{The 15 per cent size of the filter}}{\text{The 85 per cent size of the protected soil}} \leq 5$

(b) $\dfrac{\text{The 50 per cent size of the filter}}{\text{The 50 per cent size of the protected soil}} \leq 25$

(c) The filter material should be well graded (no excess or shortage of one size of material)

(d) $\dfrac{\text{The 15 per cent size of the filter}}{\text{The 15 per cent size of the protected soil}} \geq 5$

(e) The filter should not contain more than 5 per cent particles by weight finer than the No.200 sieve. The fines should be cohesionless.

(f) The coefficient of uniformity of the filter should be less than 20.

Where the gradation differences are great, two or more filter layers may be required to meet the above criteria.

The rate of seepage through the embankment or foundation can be estimated from the equation:

$$q = k \frac{n_f}{n_d} h$$

where q = the rate of seepage per unit length of embankment

n_f = number of flow paths

n_d = number of equipotential drops

h = difference in piezometric elevation between the water in the pond and the location of seepage exit.

The values of n_f and n_d are obtained from the flow net. If zones of variable permeability occur they must be taken into account in the development of the flow net.

Where the dam is constructed using the downstream method it is recommended that the upstream slope be sealed with an impervious membrane to reduce seepage from the pond through the dam. It is also desirable to deposit the slimes on the upstream slope rather than to deposit them in the upstream area of the pond so that the pond water is directly against the upstream face. In this case a flatter upstream slope is required to allow for the potential of suddenly drawing down the pond water level.

If artesian pressures develop in the foundation or below the toe of the dam there is a danger of piping and instability developing. This problem can usually be controlled by the installation of pressure relief wells. The spacing, depth and design of the wells is dictated by the soil stratification, permeability and water pressures. Experience documented by the U.S. Corps of Engineers (20) for hydro and storage dams is invaluable in determining design and construction requirements. Monitoring of pressure relief wells is essential to ensure proper functioning and to provide any necessary maintenance.

If the seepage through the foundation or abutments exceeds the amount allowable it must be reduced or if deleterious substances such as radioactive materials or poisonous chemicals are involved, total control of seepage is necessary. With the present knowledge and experience available in soil mechanics, this is feasible.

The amount of seepage through the foundation can be reduced by placing an impervious blanket upstream of the dam. This may consist of slimes or fine grained overburden. If the pervious soils in

the foundation are shallow, a core trench backfilled with impervious soil may be used to control
foundation seepage. Where the dam is located on an
impervious foundation or an impervious geologic
barrier outcrops downstream a small collection dam
may be constructed downstream and the seepage water
returned to the tailings pond by pumping.

Where the dam is located over thick pervious
deposits, positive pollution control can be accomplished by developing a system of injection and
pumping wells downstream of the dam. The injection
wells are located downstream of the pumping wells.
Uncontaminated water is supplied in the injection
wells and the groundwater is extracted from the
pumping wells. By maintaining the piezometric
elevations at the injection wells moderately above
that at the pumping wells a hydraulic barrier will
develop which will cut off the escape of tailings
pond seepage.

Grout curtains have been used to intercept seepage on numerous earth dams around the world.
Because of the variable success and usually high
cost this method of seepage control is usually not
recommended for tailings dams. Other potential
methods that may warrant consideration for special
conditions include sheet pile cut offs or slurry
trenches.

Surface Erosion

Surface materials may be removed from the downstream slope by wind, rain or spring runoff. If
the surface is dry, winds can cause a dust nuisance
and carry silt and sand particles for considerable
distances. Figure No. 8 shows an abandoned tailings dam that is a source of considerable dirt in a
town two miles away. Heavy rains such as those occurring in typhoon areas may cause severe gullies
to develop. Figure No. 9 shows a severely eroded
slope.

An abandoned tailing dam subject to wind erosion.
Figure No. 8

Slope severely eroded by rainfall.   Figure No. 9

Wind and rain cannot be controlled. Therefore, if surface erosion is a problem, special control or construction methods may be required.

Occasionally tailings contain iron ᵖyrites. Experience has shown that if they exceed 0.7 per cent by weight a relatively hard surface crust will develop which resists erosion. Resistance to erosion can also be obtained by stabilizing the surface soils by incorporating cement or lime. For dams where the upstream method of construction is used vegetation can be established on the slope or batter boards can be installed.

If erosion is serious, coarse rock or mine waste can be placed on the slope. Figure No. 10 shows several trial erosion control methods that are proposed for a tailings dam in an area of typhoon rainfall.

Special Design Problems

There is a wide variety of metallic and non-metallic mining where tailings storage is required. Some of these present specific problems.

Radioactive uranium tailings and sodium cyanide rich gold tailings and mercury tailings require positive control of seepage. All soils allow some seepage, although for compacted clay it will be small, so that special procedures are required if downstream contamination is a potential problem. For maximum seepage control the upstream slope of the dam may be covered with a plastic or similar type membrane. Such membranes have frequently been used to prevent seepage from water storage reservoirs.

Tailings which have a very high sulphide content can under favourable conditions of air and moisture ignite spontaneously and burn. The fires can be extinguished with wet tailings pulp or sprinkling with water.

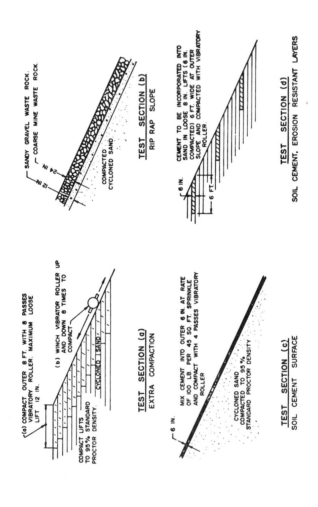

Typical test sections for erosion control (4). Figure No. 10

On coal mining projects special problems exist for tailings storage. Due to the low weight of the coal fines, the rate of sedimentation is very low. Therefore, larger ponds than usual are required. The settled residue when dry is very susceptible to burning. The downstream slopes must never be constructed with coal waste since burning and subsequent cavitation could lead to failure of the dam. Periodic spreading of salt will minimize the danger of fire.

On potash projects care must be taken to ensure the brine does not escape. If any of the dyke is constructed of the settled and hardened brine, care must be taken that solution channels do not develop. Usually the retaining dykes must be constructed of impervious borrow soils. The base of the settling pond should be selected where fine grain soils exist to minimize seepage under the dam. Frequently two ponds are used. In this case much of the brine is decanted from the primary pond to the second pond for sedimentation of the clay fraction.

CONSTRUCTION CONTROL

The engineer who plans and designs any tailings dam must assess the sequence, timing, method of placement and stability control program during construction to ensure that the requirements of practicability, economics, and stability are met.

The cost of compaction will depend on the equipment used. Cohesionless sands, sandy gravels or fine rock are most effectively compacted using vibrating drum or heavy pneumatic rollers. Cohesive clays, silt-clays or glacial tills are most effectively compacted using grid or sheep's-foot rollers. The thickness of layers of cohesive soil should not exceed about 9 inches for effective compaction and for non-cohesive soils, about 12 inches.

The most efficient compaction is developed with the fill soil at the optimum moisture content. If the field moisture content differs from optimum it may be impossible to obtain the required density and shear strength. This may require drying of the soil or the addition of moisture.

Field tests must be made during construction to ensure that the design densities are obtained. It should be noted that the optimum moisture content will vary with the compaction equipment employed. Therefore field test sections with varying lift thickness, moisture content and compaction passes to determine the optimum compaction effect at the least cost are recommended.

If the foundation or embankment soil is cohesive and compressible, it is necessary to determine whether the placement of fill causes a buildup in pore water pressure which will reduce the shear strength and stability. Piezometers should be installed to measure these potential changes. If consolidation is expected settlement gauges should be installed. The measurement of the rate and magnitude of settlement as the dam is constructed will allow comparison with the theoretical estimates and more accurate projection of total construction and long term settlements. Special precautions may be required to protect the instrumentation from theft or damage.

Where drainage layers or filters are required field gradation tests must be carried out to ensure the grain size distribution requirements are met.

Competent engineering supervision should always be specified for construction of the starter dam and periodic inspections by a stability specialist are recommended.

DEVELOPMENT SEQUENCE

A typical tailings dam developed to increase

existing storage capacity which was designed and constructed using recognized soil mechanics and stability principles is shown in Figure No. 11. The step by step planning and design program that was employed is shown in Figure No. 12. For new mines the preliminary stage of ore reserve development, economic analysis, mining rate and tailings volume determination is also required. This step is shown in the hatched area of Figure 12.

It is emphasized that each mine and each site is different. Therefore a standard planning and design program can only serve as a guide. Each project must, to minimize cost and maximize profit within the requirements of stability and ecology, be planned and designed, based on the actual site conditions, the cost and time of construction, the rate of mining and the prevailing and projected market conditions.

Old tailing dam being expanded. The design was based on a detailed site investigation and field construction was supervised. Giant Mascot Mines, Hope, British Columbia.   Figure No. 11

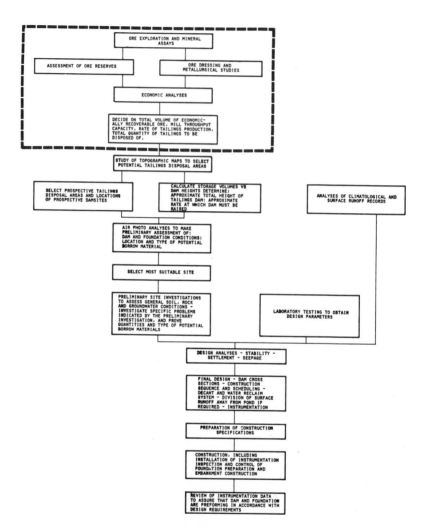

Chart outlining planning and design program for
tailing dam construction.   Figure No. 12

CONCLUSIONS

1. The increasing cost of mining is tending to cause an increase in the scale of mining operations and an increase in the capacity requirements of tailings storage. Many existing and proposed tailings dams rival the major hydro dams in height and volume.

2. Tailings disposal does not generate profit, therefore the cost of tailings control structures must be minimum, consistent with safety and ecological requirements.

3. The most economic tailings dam construction program generally involves the use of the coarse fraction of the tailings for a major portion of the dam.

4. Experience has shown that cycloned coarse sands placed hydraulically, such as by spigotting, have low density, low shear strength and are subject to liquifaction under seismic load conditions if saturated, or if very dry.

5. For dams that are high or are located in areas of earthquake potential, the downstream method or conterline method of construction is recommended. For these conditions, the downstream slopes must be compacted.

6. The planning and design program must include a thorough evaluation of the physical and mechanical properties of the foundation soil and rock, groundwater, borrow materials and tailings fractions proposed for use in the dam. This requires a site investigation and field and laboratory test program.

7. Analysis of stability, settlement, seepage, erosion control, environmental impact and reclamation is a fundamental requirement in the planning of any tailings dam.

8. Construction control using field instrumentation is required to ensure the tailings dam is constructed according to the design specifications, and is functioning as intended.

9. The technical capability and experience available in soils engineering and earth dam engineering provides a sound basis for the design of an economic and stable tailings retention system.

REFERENCES

1. Dobrey, R. and Alvarez, L., "Seismic Failures of Chilean Tailings Dams," Journal, Soil Mechanics and Foundations Division, ASCE, Vol. 93, No. SM6, 1967.

2. "The Report of the Tribunal Appointed to Inquire Into the Disaster at Aberfan on October 21, 1966." H.M.S.O., London.

3. Sherard, J.L., Woodward, R.J., Gizienski, S.F., and Clevenger, W.A., "Earth and Earth Rock Dams," John Wiley and Sons, Inc., New York, 1963.

4. Brawner, C.O., "Redesign and Construction of a Tailings Dam to Resist Earthquakes," Second International Conference on Stability in Open Pit Mining, Vancouver, 1971.

5. Casagrande, L., "Panel Discussion," Stability in Open Pit Mining, Editors, C.O. Brawner and V. Milligan, AIME, New York, 1971.

6. Seed, H.B., "Landslides During Earthquakes Due to Soil Liquefaction," Journal, Soil Mechanics and Foundations Division, ASCE, Vol. 94, No. SM5, 1968.

7. Goodman, R.E., and Seed, H.B., "Earthquake Induced Displacements in Sand Embankments," Journal, Soil Mechanics and Foundations Division, ASCE, Vol. 92, No. SM2, 1966.

8. Campbell, D.B., and Brawner, C.O., "The Tailings Dam - An Engineered Structure," Western Miner, April, 1971.

9. Terzaghi, K., and Peck, R.B., "Soil Mechanics in Engineering Practice," John Wiley and Sons, Inc., New York, 1967.

10. Volpe, R.L., and Wahler, W.A., "Strength of Anisotropically Consolidated Mine Tailing Materials Under Dynamic Loading," Proceedings, Specialty Session on Soil Dynamics, 7th International Conference on Soil Mechanics and Foundation Engineering, Mexico City, 1969.

11. Bishop, A.W., "The Use of the Slip Circle in the Stability Analysis of Slopes," Geotechnique, Vol. V, 1955.

12. Janbu, N., "Stability Analysis of Slopes with Dimensionless Parameters," Harvard Soil Mechanic Series, No. 46, 1954.

13. Morgenstern, N.R., and Price, V.E., "The Analysis of the Stability of General Slip Surfaces," Geotechnique, Vol. 15, 1965.

14. Newmark, N.M., "Effects of Earthquakes on Dams and Embankments," Fifth Rankine Lecture, Geotechnique, Vol. 15, 1965.

15. Dept. of Mines, Energy and Resources, "Tentative Design Guide for Mine Waste Embankments in Canada," Mine Branch Research Centre, Technical Bulletin TB 145, 1972.

16. Gordon, J.L., and Duguid, D.R., "Experiences with Cracking at Duncan Dam," Commission Internationale des Grands Barrages, Dixieme Congres des Grands Barrages, Vol. 1, Montreal, 1970.

17. Casagrande, L., and MacIver, B.N., "Design and Construction of Tailings Dams," Stability in Open Pit Mining, Editors, C. O. Brawner and V. Milligan, AIME, New York, 1971.

18. Casagrande, A., "Seepage Through Dams," Journal of the New England Waterworks Association, Vol. 51, No. 2, 1937.

19. Sharp, J. C., "Fluid Flow Through Fissured Media," University of London, Ph.D. Thesis, 1970.

20. U.S. Army Corps of Engineers, "Design of Finite Relief Well Systems," EM.1110-2-1905, 1963.

DISCUSSION

QUESTION: The availability of the technology for dam construction has been mentioned. My interest is: what is the demand for this technology, or have most companies still a "wait-and-see" and "I can do it myself" attitude?

C. O. BRAWNER: In my experience working on some 100 projects - mining projects around the world - I would say that, in the last three years, I have not encountered a mining company of substance that is interested now in developing tailings dams without some use of the technology which is available. There has been a great change over the past three years, but it has only been very recently and it has been because of the serious failures which have developed and, of course, these failures have developed largely because of the increase in dam size.

W. A. WAHLER (W. A. Wahler & Associates): I
think that the failures have been the impetus for
the demand for the technology. I think you will
see, during the next year, that the regulations
which will be coming out on either federal or state
levels are both for safety and environment and will
cause a reassessment. I think that at this moment,
because of the slow growth in utilization of the
technology (it is certainly there and it has been
relatively slow and on an as-needed basis) there
is some sort of balance between the needed technology
and technologists and the market. With the full
realization of the problems that companies are
going to face when they are thinking of the long-
term demands that the regulations will require, I
think we will find that the technology exists more
in theory than in bodies. There is going to be a
much greater demand than there will be availability
and that is going to make it very difficult for the
supply to fulfill its needs.

E. D'APPOLONIA (E. D'Appolonia Consulting
Engineers, Inc.): I would like to propose a
question to the panel. We recognize that technology
is here for stability, seepage analysis, etc., as
indicated, but there appears to be a tremendous
disparity between the application of this technology
to tailings pond embankments, because many of the
embankments that are standing today, many of the
impoundments that are existing today - disregarding
for the moment water quality - absolutely defy the
technology that Mr. Brawner has suggested that we
now apply. And might it not be that we really
aren't looking at our problems by saying that
technology is here; let's apply it. Maybe we
ought to find out why these embankments and
impoundments - which really defy the technology
which you speak about - stand today.

LEE APLIN (Clarkson Company): I would like
to respond to that if I may. It doesn't seem to
me that there is any disparity between what the
soils engineers are saying and the existence of

tailing structures which seem to defy the rules.
The stability of a structure is a function of all
factors. Comments made here emphasizing either
the advantage or disadvantage of any given structure
or method must be considered together with all other
factors, such as water controls, seismic occurrence,
particle size, deposition methods, climatic conditions, etc. Each of these contributes to the
strength or weakness of any given structure and
each has to be evaluated in relation to the others.
Generalizations tend to emphasize out of context
when applied to a specific example.

C. O. BRAWNER: I just want to add one or two
comments to that. There are two problems which
exist. One is the problem of designing new dams.
I suggest to you that the technology for this does
exist. The second is the analysis of existing dams.
I believe the technology for this also exists, but
it is very difficult to try and define the parameters
which exist in those old tailings dams and this is
the problem. I think one of the best tools that
we have at our disposal is, if failures do occur,
that detailed analysis, back analysis, back studies
to find out why they failed, should be entertained,
because we learn more generally from our mistakes
than we do from our successes.

J. D. VINCENT (Climax Molybdenum Company,
Division of Amax Incorporated): I have been around
this game, I have seen good dams and bad dams. I
think that many years ago it was true that the
mining companies didn't really realize the structural
and engineering problems that they faced.

Today, when a large mining company goes into a
project, a tailing dam is one of the most important
factors that they are looking at for the whole
project. I think most of the leading mining
companies do tend, when there is any doubt about
the problem, to get the services of a soils engineer
involved - to get his advice and suggestions as to
how a particular problem should be controlled.

There are many areas in the world where there is seepage of water from the hillsides of the surrounding ground, which makes the problem of maintaining a stable slope very important. There are various approaches to this; one is the old French drain method in which you make a porous channel underneath the primary berm in order to control the end of the outflow of the seepage. My personal opinion is that the mining companies are waking up to the seriousness of this problem now, and here you are going to have to agree with Mr. Brawner and Mr. Wahler that technology is available and, with these tremendous dams that are being built to handle the tonnages from mills treating 60,000, 80,000 and 100,000 tons a day, this is an absolute necessity.

W. A. WAHLER: The difference between analyzing existing structure and designing a brand new structure has been alluded to here. From a technological standpoint these are totally different. When you are proposing to build a new structure you, at least theoretically, have control over the construction, so you can develop the concepts and the planning specifications; and if you put proper inspection on it, you can get it constructed in accordance with the planned procedure. This gives you a great deal of strength in your analysis because you can evaluate quite readily how applicable your data are. But when you are looking at one of these vast structures which covers even thousands of acres, and literally miles of dike, you are talking about a totally different thing. You are talking about attempting to probe this vast mass to discover what its general characteristics are, and, even more critically, learn what are the weak links in the system. It is a very hard thing to do. We have to develop additional techniques to permit us to get a better grasp, to get more samples, to get a better understanding of what is going on, cheaper, because it is one thing to analyze very thoroughly a given section, but it is another thing to analyze 10 miles of dams.

ROY WILLIAMS (U. S. Bureau of Mines): We have a lot of data which suggests that the use of downstream construction permits coarse materials to be distributed throughout the interior of a tailing pile, which subsequently causes or permits groundwater recharge which forms a groundwater mound which, after abandonment, leaches the tailing deposit continually. Do you have any comments on that?

C. O. BRAWNER: That can be a problem with respect to certain types of tailings and certain types of dam materials. The major problem is, as you say, after the tailing structure has been abandoned. During the process of dam development, during the operation of the mine, there are several techniques that can be used to control this. The degree of control, of course, depends upon the amount of contamination in the water.

A positive method which has been used is called the hydraulic barrier method in which two rows of wells are utilized downstream. The upstream line of wells - and these run parallel to the center line of the dam - are pumping wells and the wells downstream - which may be located 50 to 75 feet away - have water pumped into the well and the elevation of the water in these wells is kept sufficiently higher than the pumping wells so that there is an upstream flow of water. This upstream flow forms a total and complete barrier. This has been very successful.

Of course this is not a technique that you would want to use after the dam is finished, after the mine is finished. This, in my opinion, would be the major type of problem. It could well be that you will have to have a secondary collector system, whether you like it or not, downstream. The other alternative is to attempt in the initial stages to make the dam itself as impervious as is possible. This is necessary anyway in some projects such as uranium where it is essential, gold where you have the cyanide process in which you must make maximum attempts to use an impervious material. If this is the potential problem, then the downstream section of the dam must be designed in such a way that the leaching is not a serious problem. The same applies through the subsoil; if you have the problem that the seepage water may be a contaminated water, then you must design your structure with that in mind. This may preclude the downstream method using the tailing and you may have to go to impervious materials or impervious shelves around the tailing and put them in at a later date, cover the slope, for example, with three to five feet of impervious material, plant the surface, so the water doesn't get into it in the first place.

W. A. WAHLER: Our firm recently worked on a problem, of which this was a very serious part, and the solution was an impervious membrane. Now you can do this either with compacted earth or, as economics indicated in this particular case, with a PVC membrane to shelve the water out above the ground and then put a collective system at the downstream toe. So there are positive methods to handle this. It requires a good deal of money though.

CHARACTERISTICS OF TAILINGS

FROM A SOILS ENGINEER'S VIEWPOINT

Fabian Guerra

Soils Engineer

Iron Ore Company of Canada

Sept-Iles, Quebec, Canada

The characteristics of iron ore tailings from a soils engineer's viewpoint may best be explained by defining the terms soil, soil engineering and soil classification. This is dealt with in detail in Appendix A.

The purpose of this paper is to present some Mineralogical and Geotechnical data of tailings derived from the extensive deposits of iron ore located in the Labrador Peninsula of the Canadian Shield.

LOCATION

There are currently four sources of iron ore tailings in the Labrador Peninsula. The mining centers are located at Knob Lake in the vicinity of Schefferville, at Carol Lake in the vicinity of Labrador City, at Wabush Mines in the vicinity of Wabush, and at Lac Jeannine proper. The locations

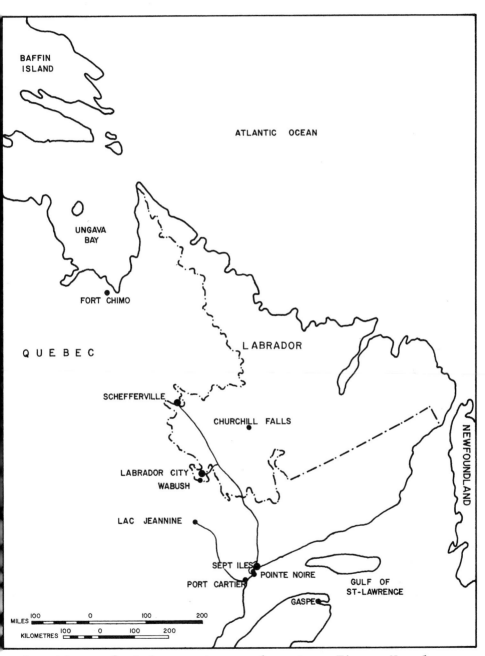

Locations of mining centers and ports. Figure No. 1

of these mining centers are shown in Figure 1.

The data presented herein originates from the tailings disposal area in Carol Lake where the plant has been operating since 1962; and, from the Test Pilot Plant located in Schefferville where extensive research has been carried out for the last ten years.

The Iron Ore Company of Canada operates an iron ore beneficiation plant at Labrador City and late in 1972, will operate another iron ore beneficiation plant in Sept-Iles. The crude ore for the new plant will come from the Schefferville mining center, some 356 miles north of Sept-Iles. Some 150 million tons of natural or "direct" ores have been mined and shipped from the open pit iron mines of the Schefferville area since 1954. No beneficiation except size reduction to 3-1½ inches has taken place during the last 18 years.

GEOLOGY

A notable feature of the Labrador Peninsula is the Labrador Trough, shown in Figure 2, the preserved portion of an Early Proterozoic geosyncline, extending from the Grenville Front at Carol Lake to Payne Bay, over 600 miles further north-northwest. Two lithotectonic units are nearly continuous over the length of the Labrador Trough; a western zone composed mainly of sedimentary rocks, deposited over the Archaean basement gneisses and an eastern zone, where mafic igneous rocks predominate. The rocks of both the zones were deformed during the Hudsonian Orogeny. The folds that resulted, with persistent northwest-trending axes, are reflected in the valley and bridge topography, which is characteristic of this belt. The main northwest regional trend is further emphasized by the faults, which parallel the strike of the major folds.

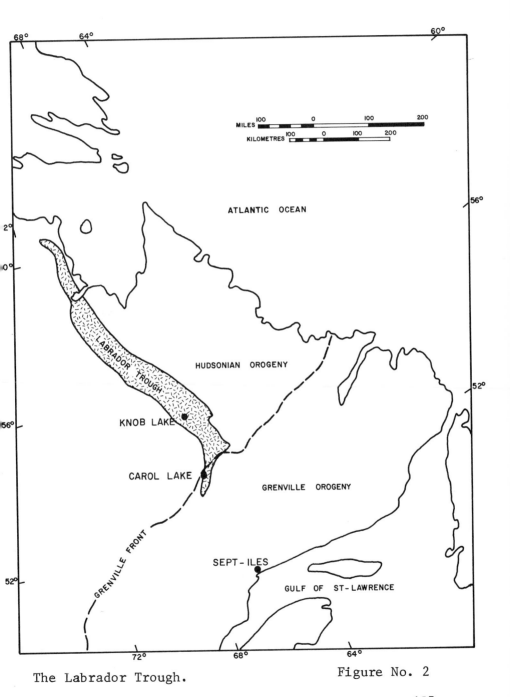

The Labrador Trough.   Figure No. 2

MINERALOGY

In the Knob Lake area, many important deposits of iron ore have been found in the iron-rich Proterozoic sedimentary rocks of the Labrador Geosyncline. The iron ores of the Knob Lake area are of four basic types as determined by their mineralogical characteristics. The four types are: blue ore containing primarily blue hematite and magnetite; red ore containing primarily finely divided, red hematite; yellow ore containing primarily limonite and goethite; and manganese ore. The manganese generally occurs as secondary enrichment in joints and bedding planes in psilomelane or magnetite(1). These ores were formed after the period of major folding and faulting by leaching and enrichment.

The silica in the Knob Lake ore has in general a grain-size of approximately 150 mesh. However, the iron oxide is well liberated at -28 mesh. Because of flotation and the pelletizing processes adopted, the feed ores are ground to 65 mesh and a sufficiently good concentrate grade could be obtained. The tailings are derived from the Flotation process of a blend of Blue to Yellow ores at a ratio of 84:16.

There is basically only one type of ore in the Carol Lake area, although it is broken down to three classes based on its grade: the crude ore that has an iron content of about 38-39 percent by weight; the lean ore with an iron content of about 35-36 percent by weight; and, the treat rock with an iron content of about 33 percent by weight. The iron content is not definitive of ore grade because up to 20 percent iron by weight may be non-recoverable carbonates and hydrated iron oxides. Thus, the iron percentages quoted are only generalizations. These ore bodies formed as a direct result of metamorphism and deformation related to the Grenville Orogeny, (1), Figure 2.

The feed ore is ground to -14 mesh for the Humphrey Spiral and liberation of the silica is obtained at -20 mesh. The tailings are derived from the Humphrey Spiral process.

106

Since the grading is a direct function of concentration and liberation technique, the Flotation tailings are finer than Humphrey Spiral tailings.

Table I shows the Structure and Analysis of these tailings, the Mineralogical Analysis of these two types of tailings are given in Table II, and their physical properties are presented in Table III.

Table No. I
Structure and Analysis of Iron Ore Tailings

Tyler Standard	Mesh Size Microns	KNOB LAKE PERCENT		CAROL LAKE PERCENT	
		Weight Retained	Fe	Weight Retained	Fe
+ 35	417			0.0	0.0
+ 48	295			8.6	12.9
+ 65	208	0.0	0.0	13.5	9.4
+100	147	0.3	6.9	20.1	8.7
+150	104	2.5	1.6	15.0	11.9
+200	74	12.0	1.9	10.4	17.8
+270	53			7.5	26.8
+325	44	22.9	3.3	2.7	38.0
-325	44	62.3	20.2	22.2	32.8

Table II discloses that the predominant mineral present in these tails is quartz, the hardest, very angular and most durable mineral.

It is now clear that the process used to extract a mineral from an ore determines the physical characteristics of the tailings, and this is one of the most important factors to be considered in the planning of disposal facilities.

GEOTECHNICAL

Grain Size Distribution

The grain size distribution of the tailings is

Table No. II
Mineralogic Analysis of Iron Ore Tailings

MINE CENTER	HEMATITE	MAGNETITE	MARTITE	GOETHITE	LIMONITE	MANGANESE MINERALS	QUARTZ	CARBONATE	MIXED GRAINS			
									ORE		SILICA	
									SILICA	ORE	SILICA	ORE
Knob Lake	17.2	-	-	2.1	0.4	-	77.1	0.3	0.2	0.3	2.2	0.2
Carol Lake	14.6	3.3	0.3	1.4	0.1	0.2	70.9	7.2	0.1	0.3	1.3	0.3

The figures for the Knob Lake Tailings represent a volume percentage of the minerals from a Petrographic Point Count of 1281 points performed on one sample from the Test Pilot Plant.

The figures for the Carol Lake Tailings represent a volume percentage of the minerals from a Petrographic Point Count of 1000 points conducted on eight samples. Binocular microscope observations disclosed that the samples are all quite similar in size, grain shape and mineralogic content.

presented in Figure 3, and Table IV summarizes their gradation properties. A single value is shown for the Knob Lake tailings because the sample originates from the Pilot Plant. Because the tailing material from Carol Lake was sampled from the tailings pond, a range is given for the gradation properties, as these tailings varied from the coarse (+297 microns) material of the dyke to the slimy (-20 microns) portions at the beach of the disposal area. The range of the grain-size curves is better represented by the range of the uniformity coefficient which varies from 2.22 to 7.50 with the average of 3.26 represented by Curve B in Figure 3.

The maximum diameter of particles corresponding to the clay-size fraction is about 2 microns, and the clay content of these tailings may be termed as a "non-colloidal" 2-micron clay, Figure 3.

The wide latitude of the gradation curves for the Carol Lake tailings shown in Figure 3 represents the grain-size distribution of several samples taken at the crest and slope of the dyke, at a mid-point between the slope and beach, and at the beach of the tailings disposal area. The coarser tailings were on the crest and slope of the dyke and the finer tailings at the beach. The grain-size Curve B represents the average grading of tails used as foundation material, as backfill, and soil-cement aggregate in the Carol Lake area.

Curve A in Figure 3 is the non-plastic fairly uniform inorganic silt of tailing samples from the Pilot Plant in Knob Lake. Deposition of this tailing will commence in late 1972 in the newly completed Tailings Pond in Sept-Iles.

It should be remembered that tailings, being man-made materials, are much more uniform in their characteristics than are most natural deposits.

These curves may also be used for determinations of the liquefaction potential, and permeability.

Table No. III
Physical Properties of Iron Ore Tailings

MINE CENTRE	Percent Minus 20 microns	Diameter of 60 percent finer in millimeters	Diameter of 10 percent finer in millimeters	Coefficient of Uniformity	Appar Speci Gravi
Knob Lake	43.0	0.032	0.005	6.40	3.0
Carol Lake	3.0	0.196	0.060	3.26	3.0

Table No. IV
Grading of Iron Ore Tailings Based on
Weight in Each Size Class

Size Fraction	Knob Lake	Carol Lake
	Percent by Weight	
SAND	18.0	90.0
Coarse	0.0	2.0
Medium	2.0	36.0
Fine	16.0	52.0
SILT-SIZE	79.0	10.0
Coarse	39.0	7.0
Medium	31.0	2.0
Fine	9.0	1.0
CLAY-SIZE	3.0	
Coarse	3.0	
Medium		
Colloids		

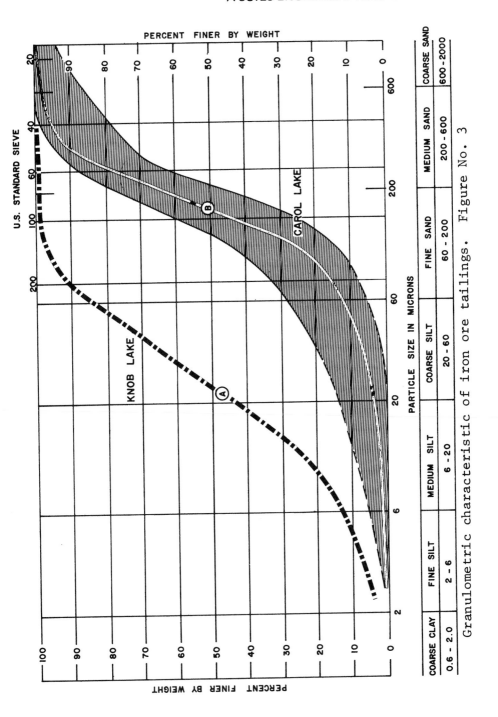

Granulometric characteristic of iron ore tailings. Figure No. 3

Liquefaction

The dictionary defines liquefaction as the "act or process of making or becoming liquid", which is exactly what the word implies. The process of sand liquefaction and related flow slides have been described in technical and non-technical literature for the last two hundred years. These records show that only totally saturated sensitive clays and loose sands or silts are susceptible to liquefaction.

There is ample experimental evidence which proves that liquefaction susceptibility is dependent on the Void Ratio or Relative Density of the material, the confining pressure acting on the material, and the magnitude and number of earthquake induced vibrations to which the material is subjected. More recent studies show that uniformly graded materials are more susceptible to liquefaction than well-graded materials, and that for uniformly graded soils, fine sands tend to liquefy more easily than do coarse sands, gravelly soils, silts, or clays (2).

In general, tailings tend to be uniformly graded materials, and thus are very susceptible to liquefaction.

Seed and Idriss (2) indicate that although the relatively loose sands in Niigata, Japan, have been shaken by 25 earthquakes in the past 370 years, historical records show only three occasions on which liquefaction has been reported in or near Niigata itself. On these occasions the estimated ground accelerations were in excess of 0.13g, culminating in the extensive liquefaction in 1964, when ground accelerations had their probable maximum value of 0.16g. Of special significance, however, is the fact that in 22 other earthquakes producing estimated ground accelerations ranging from 0.005g to 0.12g, there was no indication of any soil liquefaction in the city.

Following the Niigata earthquake of 16 June 1964, where extensive liquefaction occurred in some parts of the city but not in others, Japanese engineers made detailed studies to determine the differences in soil conditions between the heavy damage area where liquefaction occurred and in the light damage area where liquefaction did not develop. It was concluded that the essential difference was a somewhat higher relative density in the light damage area compared to the heavy damage area, as was evidenced by higher values of the standard penetration resistance. The maximum ground acceleration recorded in the city was 0.16g.

Another significant factor in determining liquefaction potential is the duration of ground shaking, because it determines in a general way the number of significant stress or strain cycles to which a soil is subjected. The importance of this is perhaps best illustrated by the landslides which were triggered by liquefaction in Anchorage during the Alaska earthquake in 1964. These slides did not occur until about 90 seconds after the earthquake motions started, indicating the need for development of sufficient stress cycles to induce liquefaction and instability. Clearly, if the duration of ground shaking had been only 45 seconds, no liquefaction or soil instability would have developed.

The "earthquake probability" zoning map of the National Building Code of Canada (1970), places Carol Lake in Zone 1, a minor damage zone. However, Sept-Iles is placed in Zone 3, a major damage zone.

According to a method developed by Milne and Davenport (3), a return period of 100 years is expected for an acceleration of 0.073g at Sept-Iles. According to them, intensity VII corresponds to the 0.073g. Thus, the maximum horizontal ground acceleration for Sept-Iles may be taken as 0.07g.

Records from our Seismic Station near Sept-Iles, indicate that a 5.3 magnitude earthquake took place about 75 miles from Sept-Iles; the closest epicenter to the city was of a magnitude of 5 at about 25 miles away.

In summary, investigations of previous mine tailings failures indicate that among the various causes of liquefaction are the following: (a) vibrations caused by earthquakes, or induced by blasting in the vicinity; (b) loose deposited materials; (c) excess porewater pressures caused by heavy rainfall; and (d) local failure of a retaining dyke causing large strains in the sensitive materials behind it.

The materials most susceptible to loss of strength by dynamic loading are very fine and silty sands. Tailings tend to fall within the category of very fine and silty sands.

Reduction of Liquefaction Susceptibility

The limiting conditions for no liquefaction of tailings to occur would be: (1) by increasing the in-situ densities; and (2) by eliminating excess porewater pressures.

In-situ relative densities of 60 percent or greater are marginally safe against liquefaction.

Lowering the water levels within the tailing deposit would increase the effective weight of the tailings above the phreatic surface, thus increasing the confining pressures acting on the saturated tailings below the phreatic surface, and decreasing their susceptibility to liquefaction.

Consolidation of the slimes can be accelerated significantly by effective underdrainage systems, because consolidation is directly proportional to the dissipation of the porewater pressures.

Liquefaction of tailings behind a well constructed aseismic retaining dyke structure is inconsequential as far as downstream safety is concerned.

Permeability

The coefficients of permeability for various tailings and soils based on the effective size of the

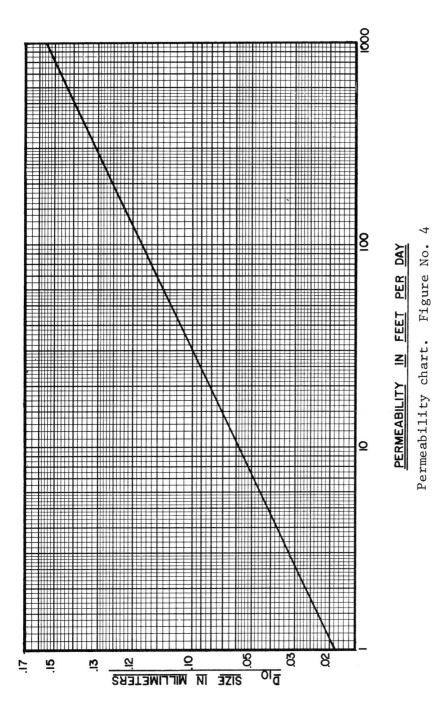

PERMEABILITY IN FEET PER DAY

Permeability chart. Figure No. 4

material may be obtained from Figure 4. The permeability of the Knob Lake tails is 101.4 feet per year, a borderline range between semipervious and pervious soils. The permeability of the Carol Lake tailings is 3,942.0 feet per year and may be described as a pervious soil.

A constant head permeability test carried out on a sample of Knob Lake tailings 4 inches in diameter and 4.6 inches in height at a dry unit weight of 121.0 pounds per cubic foot, gave a coefficient of permeability of 1.3×10^{-4} centimeters per second which corresponds to the coefficient shown in Table V as interpolated from the Permeability Chart shown in Figure 4.

The following permeabilities were computed from the Consolidation tests of Knob Lake tailings:

2×1^{-5} and 1×10^{-7} centimeters per second at densities of 95.0 and 102.5 pounds per cubic foot, respectively;

1×10^{-6} and 2×10^{-8} centimeters per second at 121.4 and 123.7 pounds per cubic foot, respectively;

1.3×10^{-4} centimeters per second at 121.0 pounds per cubic foot as determined in the constant head permeability test.

The permeability derived from Figures 3 and 4 was found to be 1.1×10^{-4} centimeters per second at an effective size of 0.005 millimeters.

The results from the constant head permeability test and Figures 3 and 4 are an excellent correlation. Thus, the permeability of the Knob Lake tailings may very well be the average of these two figures, namely 1.2×10^{-4} centimeters per second.

The permeability for the Carol Lake tailings as derived from Figures 3 and 4 is in the order of 35.3×10^{-4} centimeters per second.

It should be kept in mind that permeability is one of the most important soil properties. It is the facility with which water is able to travel through the pores and is a function of the size and number of the voids between the soil particles. These are dependent on the size and shape of the particles, the gradation of the soil and its density.

Density

Density is conveniently expressed in terms of dry unit weight or the weight of solid particles per unit volume.

An observation of Table V and Figure 5 shows that the tailings have a very wide range between minimum and maximum laboratory densities.

The average in-place density of the Carol Lake tailings is relatively high. It is important to note that this average of densities resulted from the natural deposition; no compactive energy was applied.

In an especially instructive manner, Figure 6 presents the entire picture of the Moisture-Density Relationships. The figure shows that each specific tailing has an optimum moisture content (a very critical one) and a maximum density at this moisture content. The curves have the characteristic shape of moisture-density curves obtained by means of conventional compaction tests.

The optimum moisture content for the Knob Lake tailings is 10.1 percent at a maximum dry density of 132.5 pounds per cubic foot; and for Carol Lake is 10.5 percent at 118.5 pounds per cubic foot. These curves are typical compaction curves. These densities were obtained at a compaction energy of 56,250 foot-pounds per cubic foot of volume known as the Modified Proctor Test. The 100 percent saturation line shown corresponds to the Knob Lake tails only. At the right of the figure the scales of void ratio and porosity are also for the Knob

117

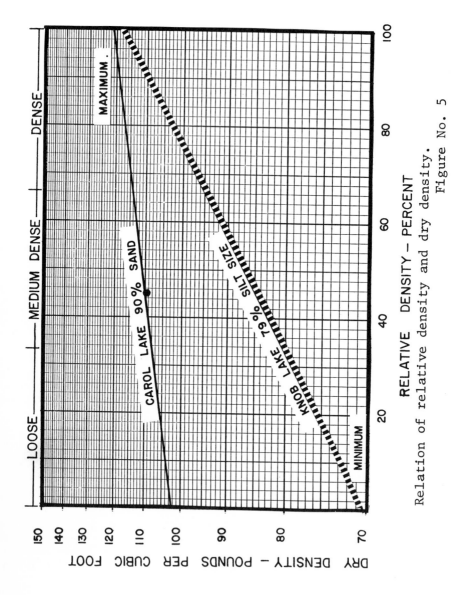

RELATIVE DENSITY – PERCENT

Relation of relative density and dry density.

Figure No. 5

Table No. V
Relative Density Data - Pounds per Cubic Foot

MINE CENTRE	Dry Density Maximum	Dry Density Minimum	Maximum-Minimum Range	Average In-place Density	Moisture In-place Percent	Relative Density Percent	Permeability at D10 in Centimeters/second
Knob Lake	117.5	70.1	47.4	--	--	--	1.1×10^{-4}
Carol Lake	121.0	102.3	18.7	109.9	8.8	44.7	35.3×10^{-4}

Table No. VI
Drained Direct Shear Tests Data

MINE CENTRE	Initial Dry Density Pounds per Cubic Foot	Moisture Content at End of Test Percent	Normal Stress Tons per Square Foot	Shear Stress Tons per Square Foot	Rate of Strain Inches per Minute	Cohesion Pounds per Square Inch
Knob Lake	119.5	Nearly	0.49	0.38	0.0010	0
	112.0	fully	1.60	1.24		0
	118.6	saturated	3.01	2.32		0
Carol Lake	101.3	29.5	0.96	0.56	0.0055	0
	100.9	27.6	1.99	1.26		0
	99.7	28.8	4.04	2.51		0

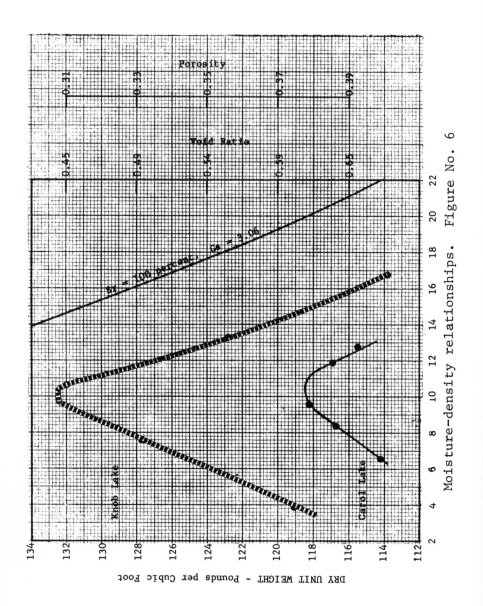

Moisture–density relationships. Figure No. 6

Lake tails only. Lines of saturation at different percentages could also be computed.

It should be noted that a sample that is at the optimum moisture content has nearly as large a degree of saturation as can be reached by compaction, since a limiting degree of saturation is reached when all small individual pockets of air within the pores of the tails become entrapped, or surrounded, by pore-water.

The limiting degree of saturation for the Knob Lake tailings is 70.1 percent and for the Carol Lake tailings is 54.0 percent. No amount of additional compactive energy can cause an appreciably larger degree of saturation.

The degree of saturation is the ratio of the volume of water to the total volume of void space, and provides an indication of the physical condition of the mass of the material.

The following laboratory notes of the minimum and maximum densities of the Carol Lake tailings are of interest.

Minimum Density measured dry, using funnel, filled container, average of 5 tests: 102.3 pounds per cubic foot.

Measured wet, container filled with loose saturated material, one test gave 101.0 pounds per cubic foot and a moisture content of 25.94 percent.

Filled container under water, pouring material slowly through funnel held ½ inch above water; readings taken from Shear Test:

Test 1: 101.26 pounds per cubic foot
Test 2: 100.90 pounds per cubic foot
Test 3: 99.71 pounds per cubic foot

Readings taken from Consolidation Test: 104.3 pounds per cubic foot.

Maximum Density measured dry, large compaction mold 6 inches, filled with dry material and vibrated 2 minutes with concrete vibrator, average of four tests: 120.95 pounds per cubic foot.

Measured wet, saturated material placed in container and tapped with hammer, one test: 115.52 pounds per cubic foot and 18.99 percent moisture content.

Measured wet, compacted in Proctor Mold, 18-inch drop of 10-pound hammer in 5 layers with 25 blows per layer: 117.1 pounds per cubic foot and 14.3 percent moisture content.

These density tests show that the minimum dry density of tailings under water is about 101.0 pounds per cubic foot, which can be increased to about 115.0 pounds per cubic foot by tapping with a hammer, and to about 121.0 pounds per cubic foot by additional vibration.

Plasticity

Atterberg limits were run on these tailings and the results indicate that they are non-plastic.

Moisture Content

The water content of the tailings from Carol Lake based on several samples of in-place densities, ranged from 4.6 to 9.6 percent with an average of 8.8 percent. The in-place density tests using the sand-cone method (ASTM D1556) were taken at one foot below the surface of the tails.

The saturated moisture content at maximum dry density (Modified Proctor - ASTM D1557) is 14.4 percent for the Knob Lake tailings and 20.0 percent for the Carol Lake tailings.

Shear Strength

The values for effective cohesion and shear strength test data are tabulated in Table VI.

The angle of internal friction is illustrated in Figure 7.

The effective cohesion is zero, the angle of internal friction is 37.5° for the Knob Lake tails and 32.0° for the Carol Lake tails.

The angle of internal friction for the Carol Lake tailings seems to correlate well with those of sands.

Uniform fine to medium sands - medium dense, have a range of 30 to 34°, while a uniform sand in a dense state has a range of 34 to 40°.

The Carol Lake tailings were poured slowly through a funnel held ½ inch above the water and the slope obtained was 30°45', however, the slope of the tails poured quickly into the water was almost zero.

The angle of internal friction of loose tails from drained shear tests of 30° agrees rather well with the slope angle of 30°45' obtained in the model slope test. Shock or vibration, however, would reduce this angle to almost zero.

The high content of slimes in the Knob Lake tailings (slimes being defined here as the percent of tails finer than 20 microns) may have the potential to liquefy if subjected to dynamic loads. This potential may well be diminished or completely avoided if the slimes are placed dense enough in the tailings pond.

It should be noted that if the Knob Lake tailings are partially saturated, apparent cohesion would be present. Thus, tailings of this type must be either dry or submerged if they are to be classed as cohesionless materials.

Consolidation

Consolidation tests on tailings samples with a dry unit weight of 93.6 and 121.3 pounds per cubic foot for the Knob Lake tailings, and at an initial

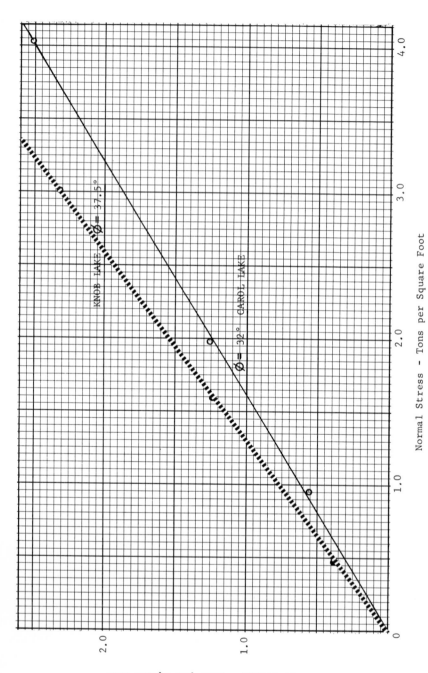

Drained direct shear tests. Figure No. 7

dry density of 104.3 pounds per cubic foot for the Carol Lake tailings, are illustrated in the Void Ratio-Pressure Diagram, Figure 8.

The void ratio-pressure curves give a compression index of 0.075 and 0.012 for the Knob Lake tailings, and 0.035 for the Carol Lake tailings. The average coefficient of consolidation for the Knob Lake tailings is 0.44 and 0.23 square inches per minute, respectively, and 0.002 square centimeters per second for the Carol Lake tailings.

The term consolidation is defined here as the gradual process which involves simultaneously, slow drainage, compression, and stress transfer or gradual pressure adjustment. Consolidation, however, is a relative term, referring to the degree to which the gradual process has advanced, not to the solidity of the material.

These tests show that the density of the tailings does not significantly increase with depth or time.

All the tests described have shown that the sand-type tailings such as are obtained at Carol Lake are excellent engineering construction materials, while the silt-type tailings from Knob Lake have very limited application as a construction material.

TAILINGS AS ENGINEERING MATERIALS

The Carol Lake tailings have been successfully used as bedding for underground conduits such as sewer pipes and water mains; the tailings are tamped on each side and under the conduit as far as practicable in layers not exceeding 6 inches in thickness. Tailings have also been used with success as backfill material under, between and alongside tunnels, as well as fill material under floor slabs. The tailings were placed up to 12 inches in thickness loose measure, and compacted to 95 percent of maximum Modified Proctor at a minimum moisture content of 4 percent.

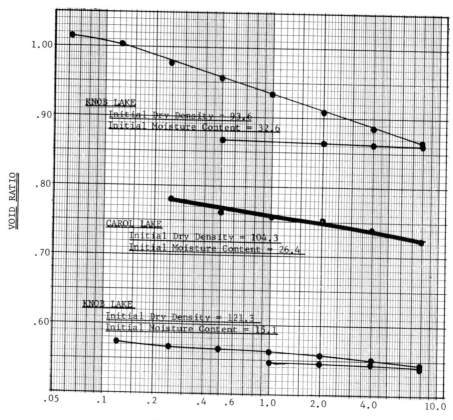

Void ratio-pressure diagram. Figure No. 8

The tailings are fairly easy to compact even with small vibratory rollers.

The following tabulation shows the compressive strengths of soil-cement mixtures using tailings as an aggregate.

Table No. VII
Soil-Cement Test Data

Aggregate	Cement Content Percent Weight of Dry Soil	Compressive Strength - Pounds per Square Inch	
		Age in Days	
		7	28
Tailings	5.0	8	100
Tailings	7.0	50	320
Fine Sand	8.5	16	144
Tailings	10.0	440*	649
Tailings	12.0	790	1100

* At 8 Days

The percent fines (-200 mesh) of the tailings used varied between 8 and 12 percent, and that for the fine sand was 3.2 percent.

The required 7-day compressive strength was 300, thus, the 10 percent cement mixture satisfied this requirement.

The Knob Lake tailings may behave like Silts, may be either cohesive or frictional depending on moisture content and density. These tails would probably be too difficult to compact and are susceptible to severe erosion and frost action; thus, these tailings should not be used for the construction of tailings dams.

Some laboratory tests were performed with these tailings in order to determine the possibility of its usage as a sealant of pervious sand.

TAILING DISPOSAL TODAY

The permeability of a sand compacted to a density of 115 pounds per cubic foot was found to be 15 feet per day. This permeability was decreased to about 0.004 feet per day at a tailings head of 5 feet above the sand interface, with a 50 percent solids slurry. It is expected that the discharged tailings will consist of a slurry which will contain 65.9 percent of solids by total weight. Under these conditions, the sand compacted to a density of 115 pounds per cubic foot will be sealed and be practically impermeable.

CONCLUSIONS

All the parameters required for the design of a tailings dam have been presented, namely: grain-size distribution, relative density, moisture-density relationships, shear strength, consolidation and permeability.

Sand-type tailings have a wide application as an engineering construction material.

Silt-type tailings would probably be too difficult to compact and are susceptible to severe erosion and frost action; thus, these tailings should not be used for the construction of tailings dams. However, silt-type tailings, if dense enough, are an excellent sealant of pervious sand.

Liquefaction can be averted by increasing the in-situ relative density to 60 percent at a limiting degree of saturation.

Consolidation tests disclosed that the density of loose deposited tailings does not significantly increase with depth or time.

APPENDIX A

The Characteristics of Tailings from a Soils Engineer's Viewpoint cannot possibly be complete without the following definitions of Soil, Soil Engineering and Soil Classification.

DEFINITIONS

Soil

The term soil has various meanings and connotations to different professional groups and technologists. For the purposes of this paper, the most appropriate definition is that given by the American Society for Testing and Materials which defines soil as the "sediments or other unconsolidated accumulations of solid particles produced by the physical and chemical disintegration of rocks, and which may or may not contain organic matter" (4).

Soil Engineering

Soil engineering is, in the broadest sense, a phase or subdivision of structural engineering since it deals either with the soil as the foundation material upon which structures rest or with the soil when used as a structural material. It differs from conventional structural engineering, however, in several important respects. For example, in the creation of a steel structure the structural engineer needs to devote only a very minor part of his total effort to a determination of the kind and quality of the material with which he builds. Steel is manufactured material whose physical and chemical properties can be very accurately controlled during the manufacturing process. It is only necessary, therefore, for a designer to specify the kind of steel which he wishes to use. On the contrary, soils are natural materials which occur in infinite variety over the earth and whose engineering properties may vary widely from place to place within the relatively small confines of a single engineering project. Generally speaking, soil must be used in the locality and in the condition in which it is found. Furthermore, steel is a material whose properties remain unchanged during the life of a structure, whereas the properties of soils are continuously changing as the amount of moisture fluctuates and other environmental influences vary.

The fact that properties of soils are not constant throughout the life of a structure or facility requires the soils engineer to employ techniques and methods of approach which differ from those which suffice in conventional structural engineering (5).

Soil Classification

Geological   In a broad sense, soil may be thought of as an incidental material in the vast geological cycle which has been going on continuously and relentlessly throughout the billions of years of geological time. This geological cycle may be considered as consisting of three principal phases; these are: erosion; transportation and deposition; and earth movement.

Exposed rocks are eroded and degraded by many processes of nature, both physical and chemical. The products of these degradation processes are in many cases picked up by some agency of transportation, such as wind, water, or moving ice, and are carried to new locations where they may be deposited as soil material in various land forms. This shifting of the position of material in the surface disturbs the equilibrium of forces in the crustal structure of the earth, and causes earth movements which may expose additional rock formations to erosive forces. Thus, the cycle begins anew. The cycle, of course, is not so straightforward as described; nor does it proceed at the same rate at all points on the earth's surface and at all periods of geological time. However, if several complete or partially complete cycles are imagined as having been superimposed one upon

130

another, some concept of the incidental and heterogeneous nature of soil may be gained.

From a consideration of the geological cycle, it
is obvious that each soil deposit has a definite geological history or background which indicates something of the source of the material and the manner
in which it was brought to its present position. It
seems appropriate, therefore, to classify soil on a
geological basis to facilitate discussion of the
origin of the material. Table I illustrates such a
classification.

In Table I, the tailings are shown as Sedentary
rather than Transported because the ultimate purpose
of geology is to explore the long record contained
in the rocks, and not the man-made deposits of tailings. Furthermore, the tailings are derived from
Sedentary Rocks and not from Transported Soils.

Table No. I
Geological Classification of Soil

Group	Transporting Agent	Geological Class
Sedentary Soils	None	Residual Cumulose TAILINGS
Transported Soils	Water	Alluvial Marine Lacustrine
	Ice	Glacial Drift
	Wind	Loess Dune Sand
	Gravity	Colluvial

A residual soil is located directly above the
parent rock from which it has been derived by
physical and chemical disintegration and decomposi-
tion of the bedrock. Residual soils are more prevalent in older geological areas. Residual soils

are the product of the degradation processes of nature in various stages of cementation, which have not been subjected to the transporting and sorting process phase of the geological cycle.

Cumulose soils are those which have been formed by the accummulation of chemically decomposed residues of aquatic plants in marsh or shallow ponded areas. The tundra soils of the Arctic regions are but an example of cumulose soils.

Tailings are the non-valuable metalliferous man-made waste products of mineral processing from mining operations. Some of these tailings are good, usable engineering materials.

Mineralogical   The general engineering point of view is that it is often interesting to know the mineralogical composition of a soil although the composition is of primary interest only as it affects the physical properties.

The mineralogical content affects to an important degree the characteristics of soils resulting from the breaking down of rock. For this reason a knowledge of geology is helpful in soil mechanics work, although the study of minerals is not considered to be directly within the scope of fundamental soil mechanics.

The mineralogical content often determines the shapes of the individual soil particles. Grains of some minerals such as quartz and feldspar are bulky, whereas those of other materials such as mica and alumina are flat in shape. The presence of only a few flat grains greatly affects the porosity of a soil and has an important effect on its plastic properties.

The shape of the bulky grains has an important bearing upon the part of the shearing strength of a soil which is influenced by the internal friction. The angular grains offer much greater resistance to sliding over each other than do the more rounded grains. Soils containing appreciable quantities of flake-shaped grains have relatively low internal friction because of the relative ease with which the flat grains slide over each other. Flaky grains do not tend to interlock, as do the bulky grains.

For Engineering Purposes   Soils in nature seldom, if ever, exist separately as gravel, sand, silt, clay, or organic matter, but are usually found as mixtures with varying proportions of these components. The American Society for Testing and Materials Classification of Soils for Engineering Purposes (ASTM D2487) is based on recognition of the type and predominance of the constituents, considering grain size, gradation, plasticity, and compressibility. It divides soils into three major divisions: coarse-grained soils, fine-grained soils, and highly organic soils.

Coarse-Grained Soils are those larger than the Number 200 sieve size (74-microns), and they are further divided as follows:

GRAVEL (50 percent or more of the coarse fraction is retained on the No. 4 sieve)

Coarse - 3 inches to 1 inch

Medium - 1 inch to 3/8 inch

Fine   - 3/8 inch to 2 millimeters

SAND   (50 percent or more of the coarse fraction passes the No. 4 sieve)

Millimeter

Coarse   2.0 to 0.6
Medium   0.6 to 0.2
Fine   0.2 to 0.06

Fine Grained Soils are those that 50 percent or more pass the Number 200 sieve and with the following subdivisions:

SILT

	Millimeter
Coarse	0.06 to 0.02
Medium	0.02 to 0.006
Fine	0.006 to 0.002

CLAY

	Microns
Coarse	2.0 to 0.6
Medium	0.6 to 0.2
Colloids	0.2 to 0.0

For particles below a diameter of about 2 microns, an interaction between them and the molecules of the water, known as Brownian movement, is sufficiently strong to overcome the force of gravity. The presence and extent of colloidal material in clays are assessed indirectly by means of the plasticity tests known as the Atterberg Limits.

Clays may be organic or inorganic, the former having generally less bearing capacity than the latter and being a step in the direction of peats.

HIGHLY ORGANIC SOILS are often a component of soil but do not have any specific grain size. These soils are identifiable by their black or dark colour and sometimes by the odor. It may be strongly acid to weakly alkaline.

The sizes of soil particles and the distribution of sizes throughout the soil mass are important factors which influence soil properties and performance. For the convenience in expressing the size characteristics of the various tailings fractions, the grain-size classification in this paper is based on the Massachusetts Institute of Technology scale. The distribution of particle sizes throughout a mass of soil is termed the grading of the soil and is usually represented by means of a particle-size distribution curve. The shape of such a curve shows at a glance the general grading characteristics of the soil. From this curve, one is able to determine the effective size and uniformity coefficient.

Effective size is defined as the maximum diameter of the smallest 10 percent, by weight, of the soil particles. Uniformity coefficient is the quotient obtained by dividing the maximum diameter of the smallest 60 percent, by weight, of the soil particles by the effective size.

A low value of effective size indicates that the soil contains a relatively large amount of fine material, while a higher value indicates a relatively smaller percentage of fines. A low value of uniformity coefficient indicates a soil in which the grains are fairly uniform in size. A high value indicates that the size of the grains is distributed over a wide range. A wind-blown deposit of silt, for example, may have a uniformity coefficient in the neighbourhood of 10 to 20, while a well-graded sand-gravel soil may have a uniformity coefficient in the range of 200 to 300 or more (5).

It is hoped that these definitions provide a language by means of which one person's knowledge of the general characteristics of a soil can be conveyed to another person in a brief and concise manner. However, it is not good practice to rely too heavily upon the classification of a soil for actual design information, because many factors which enter into design are not indicated by the classification of soil alone. Design characteristics should be based upon tests of the individual tailings involved, such as tests for shearing strength, permeability, bearing strength, and shrinkage and swell.

REFERENCES

1.   Glass, D.J., "Field Excursion A55 Iron Ranges of Labrador and Northern Quebec", XXIV International Geological Congress, 1972, Montreal, Quebec.

2.   Seed, H. Bolton, and Idriss, Izzat, M., "Simplifi
     Procedures for Evaluating Soil Liquefaction
     Potential", Journal of the Soil Mechanics and
     Foundations Division, ASCE, SM9, September 1971.

3.   Milne, W.G., and Davenport, A.G., "Distribution
     of Earthquake Risk in Canada" from Bulletin
     Seismological Society of America, April 1969.

4.   American Society for Testing and Materials,
     "Procedures for Testing Soils", Fourth Edition,
     1964, Philadelphia 3, Pennsylvania.

5.   Spangler, M.R., "Soil Engineering", Second
     Edition, July 1960, International Textbook
     Company, Scranton, Pennsylvania.

DISCUSSION

NOEL KIRSHENBAUM (Marcona Corporation):   I'd like
direct this to Fabian Guerra; perhaps Mr. Brawner would
also be able to comment; Mr. Vincent could add some of
his experience. We have had some comments and remarks
regarding the height of tailings dams. I'd appreciate
some additional comments from you elaborating upon the
effect of height and resonance time on the compaction —
or should I say the consolidation — of the settled
material.

FABIAN GUERRA: On the subject of consolidation, we
saw in the graphs that it increased in one particular
case from 94 pounds per cubic foot; when you apply 8.0
weight, that in time you get about 100 pounds per cubic
foot. This means that it has increased 6.0 pounds per
cubic foot when you have a pressure of 8.0 tons per
square foot. You would perhaps need to generate this
pressure; you might need a cone about 200 feet high and
that would be difficult - only the dike is built for tha

AL WALLACH (Kaiser Engineeers): Another question
for the gentleman from Iron Ore Co. of Canada. I think

said that at Carroll Lake you were planning to build a dike out into the lake. Is that correct? How do you plan on doing that?

FABIAN GUERRA: What you saw in the photographs was the tailing deposit area proper, and then you saw the dike we were building with the mobile cyclones. So we are going to go to the toe of the slope under the water; that will be the toe of the slope of the dike. So we will be going around the toe of the slope of the existing tailing pond to build the other dike, with the other coarser cyclone material.

AL WALLACH: Is that not a deep lake?

FABIAN GUERRA: Not at that particular section. Not that deep.

AL WALLACH: But you have been depositing tailings into that lake and you have formed a base which should have the fines on the outside edge because the coarser material should have deposited at the point of entry of your present tailing system. The fines migrate out to the edges and now you will be building with heavy cyclone tailing on top of those fines.

FABIAN GUERRA: No, we are not doing that. What I meant is you have the fines that have been transported by the water and the slimes have settled. That will be the limit of where the toe of the slope of the future dam will come. We are not going to put a dike on the slimes nor on the tailing proper.

AL WALLACH: Are you going to cut the flow from Little Wabush Lake into Big Wabush Lake by doing that?

FABIAN GUERRA: No we are not, because we have ample room.

THE CONTROL OF WATER IN TAILINGS STRUCTURES

James R. Swaisgood
Partner, Dames & Moore
Denver, Colorado

George C. Toland
Partner, Dames & Moore
Salt Lake City, Utah

INTRODUCTION

The old mill superintendent who once said that his tailings pond was made of "nuthin but tailings and water, and mostly water," was quite correct. The control, or lack of control, of this water is a major factor in the relative stability of the tailings embankment and in the quality of water which ultimately leaves the structure. A tailings structure with a properly designed water-control system will make the most economical use of the available water resources. In some cases, such a structure will also provide flood protection to the downstream area which otherwise would not have been present.

The engineer who is responsible for the planning and design of the tailings structure will have certain end results in mind. He may want a "closed" system where seepage and evaporation losses are minimized and all of the water which enters the tailings structure is eventually recycled to the mill. Or, if water is plentiful, and previous water rights have been established, he may design a system that diverts stream waters around the embankment and returns a maximum amount of water from the structure to the stream or underground flows. In all cases, he will want a water-control system that will enhance and maintain the stability of the tailings embankment.

There are a multitude of water-control methods and systems available for the engineer's use. His task is to select the optimum combination of methods -- the ones which will do the intended job at the minimum cost.

To make the proper selection of the optimum system, the designer must understand the ways which water flows into and out of the tailings structure. He must also be aquainted with the details of the various control methods and know the purpose that each one serves. The objectives of this paper are to outline and describe these different factors, and to point out other sources of information which can be used as an aid in designing water-control systems.

WATER FLOW THROUGH A TAILINGS STRUCTURE

Water will flow into a tailings structure as water accompanying the tailings from the mill to the tailings retention area, as water from direct precipitation on the tailings structure, and/or as surface or underground runoff water from the drainage basin upstream and adjacent to the tailings structure. Water will leave a tailings structure by evaporation; by seepage through the tailings embankment and the materials underlying the tailings structure; and/or as free water through decant systems, diversion works, or spillways.

The relative amounts of water flowing into a tailings structure as precipitation, as runoff, or with the tailings, will vary from structure to

structure. These proportions will also vary with
time in an individual structure. In a similar
manner, the proportions of water leaving the structure as free water, as seepage water, or evaporation
will vary. However, for all practical purposes, over
a relatively long time period, there is no increase
or decrease in the total amount of water within a
tailings structure. That is, a water balance exists
and the total inflow volume equals the total outflow volume, as shown in Figure 1.

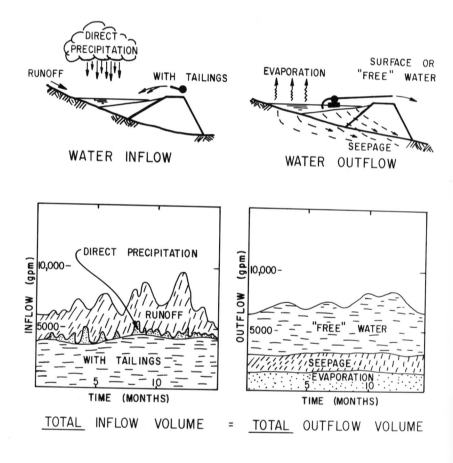

Water flow through a tailings structure.

Figure No. 1

CONTROLLING THE INFLOW AND OUTFLOW

From the standpoint of stability and economics, it may be desirable to control the amount of inflow water and to regulate the manner in which water leaves a tailings structure.

There is not much that can be done to control the inflow of water due to precipitation. The amount of water which enters the tailings structure with the tailings can only be regulated within a narrow range. However, as shown in Figure 2, the inflow due to surface runoff can be controlled indirectly by site selection. A tailings embankment built on flat ground will have no inflow from surface runoff. A side-hill tailings structure will be subject to a moderate runoff inflow volume, derived from the ground surface immediately adjacent to the embankment. The cross-valley tailings structure will develop the greatest volume of runoff inflow which will come from the entire drainage area upstream from the structure.

A great degree of control can be exercised to regulate the manner in which the water leaves a tailings structure. Some of the control methods that can be used are shown in Figure 3. With the proper selection of control methods, the engineer can either maximize or minimize the evaporation, seepage, or free water outflow volumes to suit his needs and to achieve desired end results.

ESTABLISHING THE DESIRED END RESULTS

The establishment of the desired end results is of paramount importance in designing the optimum water-control system. At an early stage in planning the tailings structure, it must be decided whether or not it is desirable to recycle most of the water back to the mill, or to return most of the water to the atmosphere, or to the natural surface or groundwater system. The existence of previous

TAILINGS STRUCTURE BUILT
ON FLAT GROUND
<u>NO</u> RUNOFF INFLOW

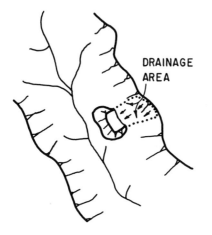

DRAINAGE
AREA

SIDE-HILL TAILINGS
STRUCTURE

<u>MODERATE</u> RUNOFF INFLOW

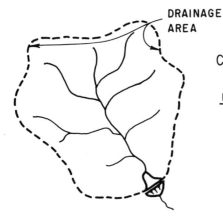

DRAINAGE
AREA

CROSS-VALLEY TAILINGS
STRUCTURE

<u>MAXIMUM</u> RUNOFF INFLOW

Effect of location on potential runoff inflow
volume.

Figure No. 2

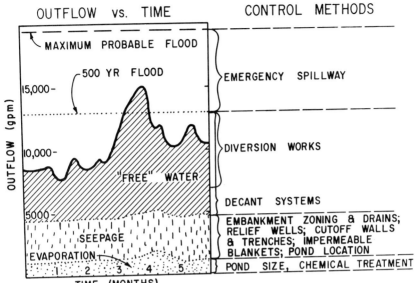

Methods of controlling outflow.   Figure No. 3

water rights, the cost of water, the water quality requirements for mill use and for return to the stream, and the costs of water treatment will be the factors which must be considered in establishing what way to dispose of the outflow water.

With the continued trend of increasingly severe water pollution requirements and the increasing scarcity of water, many mills are completely recycling the water, returning all that is possible to the mill. In these cases, outflow control methods are designed to maximize the amount of water that can be recycled. At Climax Molybdenum Company's Henderson mill in Colorado, control features such as pumping stations below the tailings pond, seepage intercepter ditches, and basin drainage diversion works will be employed to recirculate all water within the tailings structure area (1).

In areas where water is plentiful and inexpensive, and where the water quality requirements for both the mill and the return to the stream are stringent, the

143

outflow control systems may be designed to develop maximum water loss by evaporation. These circumstances existed for a trona mill in Wyoming. In this instance, the tailings retention structure was located on a relatively impervious, natural dry lake or playa deposit which prevented seepage losses. Virtually all of the water leaves the system by evaporation to the atmosphere.

DEFINING THE INALTERABLE FACTORS

Besides establishing the desired end results, certain factors related to the specific milling procedures and site conditions must be defined in order to select the most effective water-control systems. These factors are, for all practical purposes, inalterable. They will extensively affect the flow of water through the tailings structure; and in some cases, will require specific control measures. These unchangable features include the physical and chemical characteristics of the tailings, the local climate, the maximum volume of inflow water which can be expected to enter the tailings structure, and the geology of the tailings structure site.

Physical and Chemical Characteristics of Tailings

Each milling operation will produce a specific type of tailings with unique physical and chemical characteristics. Information regarding these characteristics can be obtained from the designers of the ore-processing operations or from appropriate laboratory testing.

Water Content. The water content of the tailings slurry will vary from operation to operation. Depending on the thickening processes, the tailings slurry may contain anywhere from 50 to 85 percent water by weight. In special cases where the tailings are from oil shale processing or where tailings from electrolytic refining processes have been dried for easier handling, the water content may drop down to as low as 15 percent.

The amount of water which accompanies the tailings into the impoundment area must be considered in determining the optimum sizes for outflow control features.

Gradation and Permeability of Tailings Materials. The gradation of the solid tailings materials will also vary for each ore refining process. Mill tailings particles typically vary in size from medium sand size (1 millimeter in diameter) to clay size (less than 0.002 millimeters in diameter). In some processes such as electrolytic refining, the major portion of the tailings material will be clay size. In contrast, as much as 80 percent of the tailings from other milling operations will be sand size.

The overall permeability of the tailings structure will be directly related to the relative size of the tailings particles. Therefore, a tailings structure composed of fine-grained material can be expected to lose much less water by seepage than a structure composed of coarse tailings. Accordingly, it is necessary to determine the gradations and permeabilities of the tailings materials to accurately estimate seepage flow volumes.

Chemical Properties. The chemical properties of the water and solids making up the tailings slurry will affect certain aspects of the water-control devices. Decant pumps and drain lines must be designed to resist corrosion. Permeable gravels and sands placed in drainage blankets or toe drains should be of a composition which will not react with the seepage waters to clog the drains. Treatment facilities will be required if the outflow waters do not meet water quality standards. For these reasons, a chemical analysis of the tailings slurry should be performed to aid in planning the water-control systems.

TAILING DISPOSAL TODAY

Climate and Weather

The local climatic conditions will have a definite influence on certain design aspects of the water control system, and consequently should be adequately defined. In hot, dry climates, water will be scarse, inflow from direct precipitation and surface runoff will be minimum, and evaporation losses will be high. Methods of minimizing water losses are usually used in these areas. In colder and wet climates, inflow from direct precipitation and surface runoff will be relatively high, and water will be plentiful. In these regions, control systems are designed to efficiently handle large quantities of water, and there is little need in minimizing seepage or evaporation losses. Special precautions may have to be taken in extremely cold areas to prevent freezing ground from forming barriers to seepage flow. Also, high maintenance expenses related to keeping the free water inlet areas clear of ice should be expected in these colder regions.

Information regarding temperature and precipitation and evaporation rates may be obtained from local weather bureaus. If the tailings embankment is to be a major structure, then this information should be obtained from weather monitoring stations set up near the disposal site.

Water Inflow Volumes

Once the site for the tailings structure has been selected and the milling processes have been determined, the maximum, minimum, and average amounts of water which will enter into the tailings structure can be estimated. This information is necessary in establishing the proper sizes for outflow control devices.

The volume of water which will enter the tailings structure along with the tailings can be determined by the methods described earlier in this paper. The expected average and peak volume of water inflow from surface runoff and the frequency with which the peak runoffs will return can be estimated from graphs such as those shown in Figure 4. This type of curve can be developed from historical data from stream gaging stations located nearby the tailings structure. This data may be obtained from federal, state, and/or local water agencies. However, this stream-gaging information is not always available. When the data is not available, the flood frequency curves can be developed by calculations using meteorological data along with information pertaining to the runoff characteristics of the soils in the drainage basin and the physical features of the basin, such as slopes and areal extents of sub-basins. The methods of calculating flood volumes from these data are contained in many reference books on hydrology. A simplified method of flood calculation is contained in the U.S. Bureau of Reclamation's book titled "Design of Small Dams" (2).

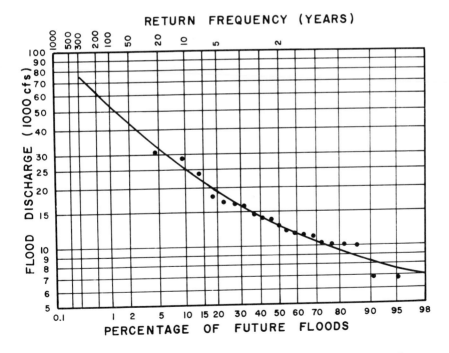

Example of flood frequency curve. Figure No. 4

Geology

The geology of the site of the tailings structure will have an influence on the total amount of water escaping from the tailings structure as seepage water. The geology will also dictate the direction that most of the seepage outflow will take. Where the materials underlying the tailings structure are relatively impermeable, the total amount of seepage water will be minimal and will be forced to exit from the embankment near the outer toe. In contrast, seepage water will generally flow vertically downward where the materials under the tailings structure are permeable. In this latter instance, the total volume of seepage water flow will be great. Additional losses of water by seepage can be expected in areas where the free water pond is placed against permeable slope deposits such as talus.

Information regarding the geology of the tailings structure site can be determined through an appropriate program of exploration drilling, sampling, and testing.

REVIEWING AND COMPARING POSSIBLE CONTROL METHODS

After the desired end results have been established and the unalterable factors have been defined, the various water-control methods and devices can be reviewed and compared. Based on this review, the engineer can select the systems which most adequately achieve the desired end results at the least cost.

The most widely used methods of controlling evaporation, seepage, and free water outflows are in Figure 3, and described in the remainder of this paper.

Methods of Controlling Evaporation

Some control can be exercised to govern the total volume of water lost by evaporation. The evaporation occurs from the pond of free water standing on the surface of the tailings structure. Additional evaporation occurs at the face of an embankment where the top seepage water line emerges or is relatively close to the slope face.

The main method of controlling evaporation losses is to govern the areal size of the free water pond. This can be done by maneuvering the discharge pipes and inlet location until a pond of the desired size is attained. If it is desired to minimize the evaporation losses, the pond size is made small. The pond size is maximized if large evaporation losses are preferable.

Some companies have also been experimenting with the use of a thin chemical film placed on top of water to cut evaporation rates. Most of the major chemical companies have developed these additives and can provide pertinent information to interested parties.

Methods of Controlling Seepage Outflow

Reasons for Control. Besides governing the amount of water leaving a tailings structure as seepage water, the other reason for applying controls to seepage flow is to maintain stability of the outer embankment slopes. The safety factor against sliding for the embankment slope is markedly effected by the relative location of the seepage water line (the phreatic line). The stability of the embankment is enhanced by keeping the seepage water line back away from the embankment face. An example of this relationship, as determined by Kealy and Bush (3), is shown in Figure 5.

Stability is also improved by preventing the water from emerging from the face of the slope.

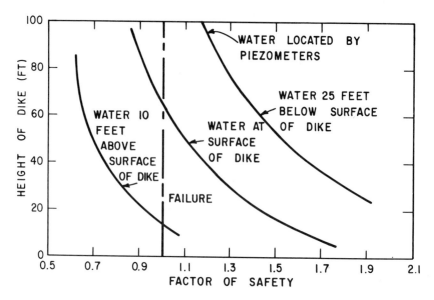

REFERENCE: KEALY & BUSH
USBM RI 7477

Example of relationship of factor of safety to location of seepage water line.   Figure No. 5

Water emerging from the slope face could start progressive deterioration of the embankment by eroding material with a "piping" action. The potential of failure by liquefaction is also reduced if the seepage water line is kept away from the outer portions of the embankment (4).

Dike Construction. The general method of tailings embankment construction will affect the degree of control which can be exercised in maintaining the desired position of the seepage water line. There are three general methods of embankment construction, including upstream construction, downstream construction, and construction with imported materials. These methods are illustrated in Figure 6.

A relatively small amount of control over the placement of material is maintained during the building of an embankment using the upstream construction

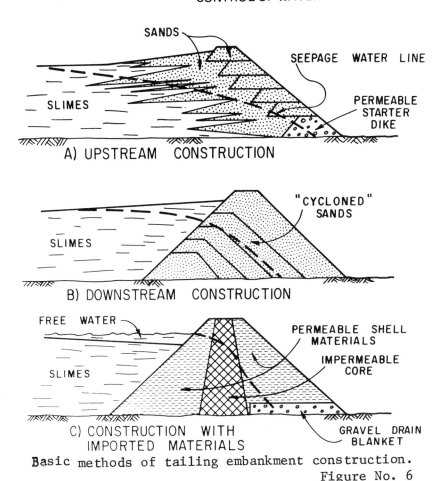

Basic methods of tailing embankment construction.

Figure No. 6

method (Figure 6A). Consequently, there is a good chance that slime layers could be deposited adjacent to the outer slopes. Water percolating down from the surface of the tailings pond would be intercepted by these layers and forced laterally outwards towards the face of the embankment, developing unstable conditions. However, certain precautions can be taken to prevent layers of slimes from accumulating adjacent to the outer embankment. Experience has shown that the most effective method of eliminating the deposition of slime layers in the outer portions of the tailings structure involves the use

of a multiple-spigot, perimeter discharge system.
In addition, if the outer dikes are built with
cycloned sand, a broader outer zone free from slime
layers can be achieved.

An even wider slime-free, highly permeable, outer
embankment zone can be obtained by the downstream
method of construction (Figure 6B). In this method,
the coarse sandy tailings materials are separated
from the slimes by cycloning. The sands are then
continually placed downstream to form the outer dike
which grows wider as the dike height is increased.
The seepage water line remains well behind the outer
dike face in this type of construction.

The most positive seepage-control method in the
outer embankment area is attained when the outer dike
is constructed of imported materials as a water-
retaining earth dam (Figure 6C). In this type of
construction, the entire dike is built with materials
specifically selected to perform certain functions.
These materials are placed under relatively close
inspection. With the use of appropriately-placed
drainage zones and impermeable zones, the water
seepage line can be very closely controlled to
maintain stable conditions.

Embankment Drains. Regardless of the method used
to construct the outer dikes, drains can be installed
in the embankment to effect better control of the
seepage and to repress the seepage water line. The
effects of embankment drains are shown in Figure 7.

In upstream construction, a starter dike composed
of permeable materials can serve as a toe drain.
Sand and gravel drain blankets can be built to control seepage if the embankment is constructed as an
earth dam or if the downstream construction method
is used.

A certain type of embankment drain can be used to
control seepage in cases where the seepage is already
emerging from an existing tailings embankment face.

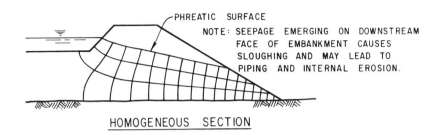

HOMOGENEOUS SECTION

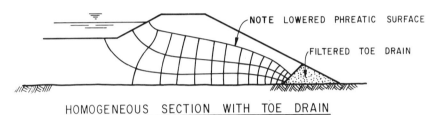

HOMOGENEOUS SECTION WITH TOE DRAIN

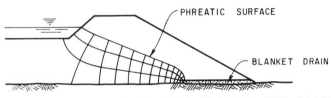

HOMOGENEOUS SECTION WITH BLANKET TOE DRAIN

REFERENCE: "TENATIVE DESIGN GUIDE FOR MINE WASTE EMBANKMENTS IN CANADA"; DEPT. OF ENERGY, MINES & RESOURCES, MINES BRANCH, OTTAWA MAY, 1971

Effects of embankment drains.   Figure No. 7

As shown in Figure 8, a toe dike composed of coarse permeable materials is constructed adjacent to the zone of emerging waters. This will prevent erosion from continuing. This method was used successfully by Idarado Mining Company in Telluride, Colorado, to stabilize an existing tailings embankment, thereby allowing it to be safely raised in height (5).

The sizing of materials placed in drainage structures such as toe drains, drain blankets, or around

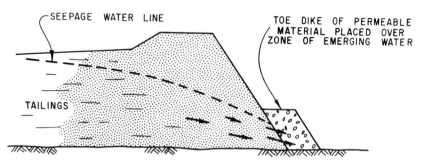

Controlling emerging seepage in an existing tailings embankment.   Figure No. 8

drainage wells, is a critical factor in actual performance of these features. The drain materials should be coarse enough to allow easy passage of the water, and yet fine enough to prevent movement of the adjacent finer materials through the drain. If the drain material is too coarse to prevent passage of the finer materials, then a filter layer should be constructed adjacent to the drain. Commonly used rules for sizing filter and drain materials include (6):

1) $\dfrac{15\% \text{ size of filter}}{85\% \text{ size of protected soil}}$ should be less than 5

2) $\dfrac{50\% \text{ size of filter}}{50\% \text{ size of protected soil}}$ should be less than 25

3) The filter materials should be smoothly graded, gap graded materials should be avoided.

4) $\dfrac{15\% \text{ size of filter}}{15\% \text{ size of protected soil}}$ should be greater than 5

5) The filter should not contain more than 5% of particles, by weight, finer than the No. 200 sieve, and the fines should be cohesionless.

6) The coefficient of uniformity of the filter should be equal to or less than 20.

Drainage Wells. Drainage wells can also be used to aid in controlling seepage outflow. These wells can be installed in the embankment as shown in Figure 9A. This system has been successfully used by Cities Service Company to control seepage in a tailings embankment in Miami, Arizona.

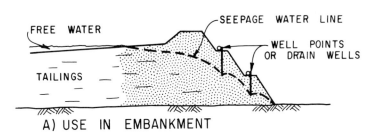

A) USE IN EMBANKMENT

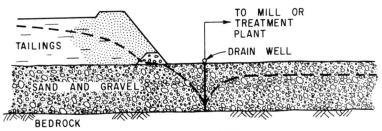

B) USE IN FOUNDATION

Drain well construction.   Figure No. 9

Drain wells can also be used to control water flow in the foundation by intercepting seepage water coming from the tailings structure (Figure 9B). To more effectively control foundation seepage, a line of injection wells could be installed immediately downstream from the line of drain wells to form a hydraulic barrier(6).

Minimizing Seepage Outflow. Many times it is advantageous to reduce the amount of water leaving the structure as seepage. This can be accomplished

155

with the use of impermeable blankets or zones placed in the embankment or foundation as shown in Figure 10. Fine-grained soils such as clays can be used to construct these impermeable zones. Also, plastic or rubber sheeting can be used. Sheet piles, slurry trenches, or grouting can be used to form impermeable barriers in the foundation.

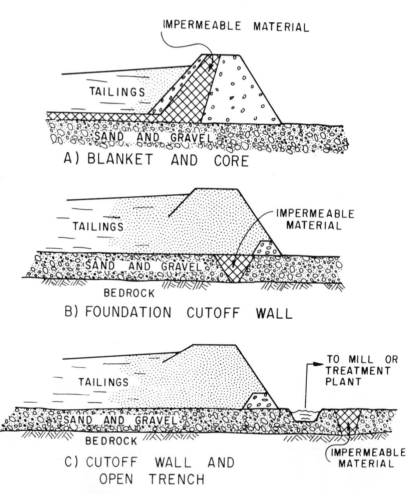

Methods used to minimize seepage outflow.

Figure No. 10

Location of Free Water Pond. The direction of flow and the amount of seepage waters can be controlled by the relative location of the free water pond. The seepage water line will be depressed and the total amount of seepage water will be reduced to a minimum if the free water pond is maintained as far away from the outer embankment area as possible. The stability of the outer embankment will also be maintained if the pond is in this position. Only in cases where positive seepage controls are constructed (e.g., where the outer dike is constructed as an earth fill dam) should the free water pond be allowed to be located near the outer portion of the tailings embankment.

In some instances, the free water pond will be located adjacent to a natural slope composed of highly permeable materials such as talus or coarse alluvium, and relatively high seepage losses will occur. In these cases, if it is desired to minimize seepage losses, impermeable blankets could be constructed over the coarse natural deposits.

Designing Seepage Control Devices. It is necessary to estimate the seepage flow rate in order to properly design the control devices.

The seepage rate is a function of the geometry of the flow path, the hydraulic gradient along the flow path, and the permeability of the materials along the flow path. Using this information as a basis, seepage rates are most commonly estimated by a "flow net" analyses. The flow nets (see Figure 7) can be constructed by hand by an experienced person. However, many common flow net patterns are presented in reference books (6,7). In addition, flow nets can be constructed mathematically by computer. Kealy and Busch (3) have presented a complete computer program documentation and listing for developing flow nets using the finite element method.

Methods of Controlling Free Water Outflow

The main function of the features controlling the surface or free water outflow is to prevent overtopping of the tailings structure. Overtopping of the embankment would cause stability problems and pollution problems, and could result in major disasters.

Controlling Production Free Water. As shown in Figure 3, the most common method of controlling the production free water (the water that enters the tailings structure with the tailings slurry) is the use of decant systems. Decant systems are one of two general types:

1) A buried decant line system in which the water leaves by gravity flow through buried pipelines at the bottom of the tailings embankment; and

2) A surface system in which the water leaves through syphons or pumps leading to surface pipelines over the top of the tailings structure.

Each of these types of decant methods has certain advantages and disadvantages. These are listed in Table I. Detailed discussion of these advantages and disadvantages are included in selected references (6,8).

Controlling Excess Free Water. The excess free water (that water developed primarily from surface runoff or direct precipitation) can be handled by one or all of three methods. These are:

1) Retain the water within the tailings structure and remove through decant systems;

2) Pass the water around the tailings structure through diversion works; and

3) Allow the water to flow through an emergency spillway.

If it is desirable to retain the excess free water on the top of the tailings structure and to

Table No. I
Comparison of Decant Systems

Feature	Floating Pump or Syphon System	Buried Decant Line System
Design and Construction	Pontoon, pump, and return line must be resistant to corrosion. Once barge and pump are installed the only construction requirements are extensions to the return line.	Design and construction is simple. May be carried out in a single operation or in multiple stages.
Operating Requirements	Pump operator required full time in addition to other operators.	Intermittent checking all that is required.
Flexibility	Requires relocation with changing position of free-water pond. Lack of maneuverability would cause problems in early stages when position of pond varies widely. Gives a little more control over quality of return liquor.	No relocation required. Permanent pump installation downstream of embankment.

Table No. I
Comparison of Decant Systems

Feature	Floating Pump or Syphon System	Buried Decant Line System
Maintenance	Pump and barge require considerable maintenance, especially during freezing weather.	Low maintenance requirements for downstream pump.
Potential for Malfunction	Floating pump is more prone to breakdown and damage than fixed pump, due to blockage by flotsam. Power outage or pump breakdown could lead to over-topping.	Requires firm foundation. Settlement of embankment could cause rupture of line. Blockage or rupture of buried line is irreparable. Possibility of "piping" failure along the line in outer portion of embankment.
Flood Control	Removal of floodwaters from storage is limited by the capacity of the pump.	Discharge capacity of pipe increases with corresponding increase in head due to flood conditions.
Drainage of Structure After Abandonment	After termination of discharge operations, new drainage scheme required to handle surface runoff.	Decant system would provide permanent drainage of storage, facilitating reclamation.

eventually decant it through the decant system, the outer embankment or dike must be of sufficient height to prevent overtopping. The additional height of the dike (freeboard) should allow for the total volume of flood water plus wave action. To determine the required freeboard, design floods should be routed through the structure to see what the increase in pond elevation will be. Methods of flood routing may be found in most books on hydrology and in specific references related to the design of dams (2). Such calculations will provide curves similar to those shown in Figure 11, which refers to an actual tailings dam to be constructed in Tasmania. In this example, the drainage basin is relatively small and all excess waters will be retained behind or within the tailings structure and removed through the decant system (9).

Surface runoff waters can be diverted around tailings structures. In cases where there are pre-existing water rights for stream waters, this diversion will be absolutely necessary. Diversion works consist of canals, channels, or pipes which have inlets upstream from the structure and outlet back into the stream somewhere below the tailings embankment. In some instances, a dam is constructed in association with the upstream inlets. The capacity of the dam and the canals and pipes should be sufficient to pass all expected flood volumes. Care should be taken in locating the open canals to prevent blocking or clogging by mud flows or slides.

In almost all instances where excess free water passes through tailings structures, emergency spillways are constructed to handle the maximum peak flood water. The size and dimensions of these spillways are determined by analyzing maximum water inflow rates for design floods. Methods of designing these spillways are presented in many references, including the U.S. Bureau of Reclamation's "Design of Small Dams" (2).

The spillways should be located so that the inlets

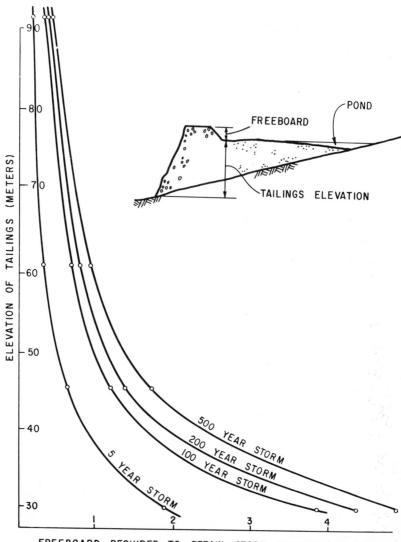

Example of freeboard curves. Figure No. 11

and outlets are at a relatively far distance from
the outer slopes of the tailings embankment to prevent erosion near critical areas which would eventually lead to instability of the structure. In
addition, the floors of the spillway channels should

be lined to prevent erosion. Most spillways are temporary and have to be relocated as the tailings embankment rises in height.

REFERENCES

1) Dahlstrom, Donald A., "Present Trends in Waste Water Treatment in Mine and Milling Operations," AIME Preprint T-III-64, Tokyo Meeting, May 1972.

2) U.S. Bureau of Reclamation, "Design of Small Dams," 1st Edition, 3rd printing, Washington D.C., 1965.

3) Kealy, C. Daniel, and Busch, Richard A., "Determing Seepage Characteristics of Mill-Tailings Dams by The Finite-Element Method," USBM R17477, January 1971, 101 pp.

4) Smith, Edwin S., "Tailings Disposal and Lique-faction," Transactions, Society of Mining Engineers, Vol IX, June 1969, pp 49-52.

5) Dames & Moore, "Tailings Dam Study, Telluride, Colorado, for Idarado Mining Company," unpublished report, September 1971.

6) Canadian Dept. of Energy, Mines, & Resources, Mines Branch, "Tentative Design Guide for Mine Waste Embankments in Canada," Ottawa, May 1971.

7) Cedergren, Harry R., "Seepage, Drainage, and Flow Nets," John Wiley & Sons, Inc, New York, 1967, 467 p.

8) Kealy, C. Daniel and Soderberg, R.L.,""Design of Dams for Mill Tailings," USBM IC 8410, 1969, 49 p.

9) Crooks, Michell, Peacock and Stewart; Dames & Moore; Snowy Mountains Engineering Corp; and Williams Brothers; "Pegara Jarosite Disposal Project Feasibility Study," unpublished report, June 1972.

TRANSPORTATION OF TAILINGS

Richard E. McElvain

General Manager & Vice President

Warman Equipment (International) Inc.

Madison, Wisconsin

I. Cave

Senior Project Engineer

Warman Equipment (International) Ltd.

Artarmon, N.S.W. Australia

1. INTRODUCTION

Pumping of tailings is usually one of the major operations in any mineral treatment plant. Because it is often necessary to transport tailings over considerable distances, the heads required for pumping are often higher than for other operations in a treatment plant.

Introduction of legislation controlling environment and pollution often requires tailings disposal areas to be located at considerable distances from the treatment plant. High friction losses are encountered and tailing pumps to develop higher heads are required.

One installation in the north of Japan collectively pumps tailings from three mines a distance of 44 miles to a disposal area in coastal swamps.

Modern mining methods have allowed exploitation of large low grade mineral deposits. A number of plants throughout the world are milling more than 80,000 tons per day. Most of this material has to be handled as tailings.

The coarser the sizing of the tailings particles the higher the velocity required for transportation and consequently the higher the head and the higher the power requirement. If it is possible to separate the coarser fractions of the tailings and dispose of these close to the plant, considerable savings may be made. (See Fig. 1 for various methods used.) The velocity required for the longer distance haul (of fine solids only) is reduced and consequently less power is required.

In association with underground mining operations, it is often possible to utilize the separated coarser fractions as underground fill material.

For very long pipelines where high pressures are required, positive displacement pumps are employed; for shorter distances and lower pressures, centrifugal pumps are preferable.

2. TO DETERMINE PUMPING REQUIREMENTS

2.1. COMPATABILITY

For a pumping system, the flow rate, pipe size, concentration (density) of solids, pump size and speed should be capable of handling maximum requirements and at the same time provide economically for average conditions.

2.2. CONCENTRATION

It is usually preferred to pump solids at as high a concentration as possible. This reduces water usage (or return water pumping) and, within limits, reduces the size of pumps, pipelines and motors.

(A) In plant segregation

    (1) Primary rejects such as non-magnetic cobber tailings.

    (2) Screen rejects on barren sized pieces.

    (3) Scavenger circuits for process water and mineral value return.

(B) Tailings and segregation systems

    (1) Spiral classifiers

    (2) Cyclones

    (3) Screens

    (4) Hydraulic sizing equipment for process solution return

(C) Thickeners for the entire plant tailings are currently used in most mineral process plants. Flocculating agents are normally used. The water circuit is completely closed with the over flow and tailings pond water recirculated.

Methods of segregating tailing by particle size and water reclamation.   Figure No. 1

Maximum concentration for pumping may be limited by
the operation of the tailings thickeners, or the
plant. In other cases, the maximum concentration
may be limited by the adverse affects of high viscosity on pump performance and pipeline losses.

A concentration of 50% solids by weight is generally
used to meet all requirements.

2.3. VELOCITY

When the quantity and concentration have been determined, the selection of pipe diameter is of
prime importance because this determines the transportation velocity. It is important for economical
operation, that the velocity be as near as possible
to the optimum. If the velocity is too low, solids
will settle out; at the best, money has been wasted
in providing a pipeline larger than necessary; at
the worst, sandups and blockage of the pipeline may
occur. If the velocity is too high, friction losses will be high, power consumption will be excessive,
and wear and tear on pumps and pipeline will be more
severe. The problem then is to determine the minimum safe velocity for transportation. This velocity may be determined from prior experience or by
test. For slurries containing very fine solids
only, pipeline behavior may be predicted closely
from laboratory viscometer tests.

For coarser slurries an approximation of minimum or settling velocity may be calculated using Durand's (1) formula.

$$VL = FL \sqrt{2gD \quad \frac{S-SL}{SL}}$$

where   VL =   limit settling velocity ft/sec.
  FL =   factor dependent on particle size and concentration. See Fig. 3.
  g =   acceleration due to gravity ft/sec/sec
  D =   pipe diameter - ft.
  S =   SG of solids
  SL =   SG of transporting fluid

Fig. 2 shows parameters for FL given by Durand.

Durand's work was reportedly carried out using particles of uniform size. The author's experience has shown that Durand's FL factors are conservative when applied to solids of graded sizing. Fig. 3 gives the author's estimate of FL values for graded solids based on a d50 sizing; d50 being that size for which 50% by weight of the solids are coarser and 50% are finer.

Where very long lines are involved, pipeline tests are warranted, to determine optimum velocity and corresponding head losses. For shorter pipelines, the method given herein will provide a practical installation.

With fine solids (less than 50 microns) the problem of velocity is not related to settlement of solids but to the change in the viscous properties of the slurry. Such slurries usually behave as Bingham type fluids, the behavior of which was investigated and extensively reported by Bingham in 1922 (2).

R. W. Smith (3) gives a method for using a Stormer viscometer to determine the rheological properties

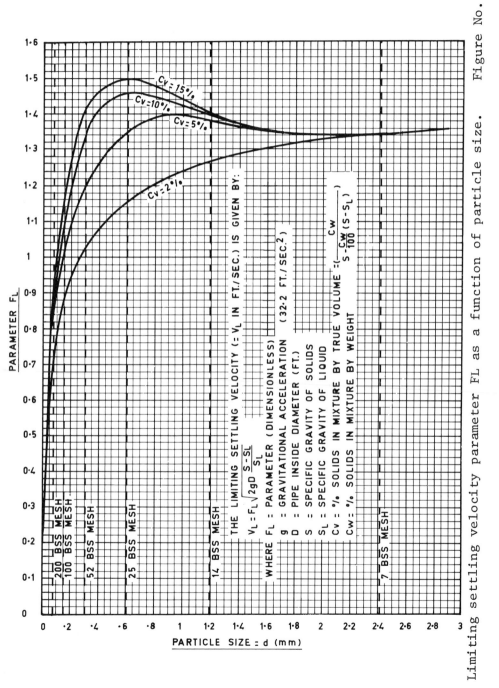

PARAMETER F_L

$Cv = 15\%$

$Cv = 10\%$

$Cv = 5\%$

$Cv = 2\%$

THE LIMITING SETTLING VELOCITY ($= V_L$ IN FT./ SEC.) IS GIVEN BY:

$$V_L = F_L \sqrt{2gD \dfrac{S - S_L}{S_L}}$$

WHERE F_L = PARAMETER (DIMENSIONLESS)

g = GRAVITATIONAL ACCELERATION (32·2 FT./ SEC.^{2})

D = PIPE INSIDE DIAMETER (FT.)

S = SPECIFIC GRAVITY OF SOLIDS

S_L = SPECIFIC GRAVITY OF LIQUID

Cv = % SOLIDS IN MIXTURE BY TRUE VOLUME $= (\dfrac{C_W}{S - \dfrac{C_W}{100}(S - S_L)})$

C_W = % SOLIDS IN MIXTURE BY WEIGHT

200 BSS MESH

100 BSS MESH

52 BSS MESH

25 BSS MESH

14 BSS MESH

7 BSS MESH

PARTICLE SIZE $= d$ (mm)

Limiting settling velocity parameter FL as a function of particle size.   Figure No. 2

169

of slurries and thus predict their pipeline performance. Although his work was for raw cement slurries, it is applicable to many typical tailing slurries.

For short pipelines with fine solids the velocity is not important; for long pipelines, however, it is recommended that the transport velocity should be sufficiently high to ensure that flow is in the fully turbulent range.

2.3.1. SETTLED PIPELINES

The use of partially settled pipelines is "a well practiced art but a poorly documented science".

It is generally agreed that it is not desirable for solid particles to be dragged upon the bottom of the pipe. It must also be acknowledged that some very good operators are successfully transporting solids through settled lines. This condition can be considered one of the operating arts which should be practiced by the most experienced or best students following established operating procedures.

2.4. HEAD LOSS

Having determined pipe size concentration and velocity, it is then necessary to estimate the head loss which will be encountered. Durand (1) sets out a method for determination of head loss for slurry based on head loss for water, concentration of solids and drag coefficient of the particles.

He supports his method with results of tests covering a wide range of pipe sizes, particle sizes, concentrations and particle S.G. This correlation was first published by Durand in 1952 and has been republished many times.

These results were also based on tests conducted with solids of uniform grain size. The authors' experience is that for slurries with solids of graded sizing head losses are lower than those suggested by Durand and for equivalent concentrations.

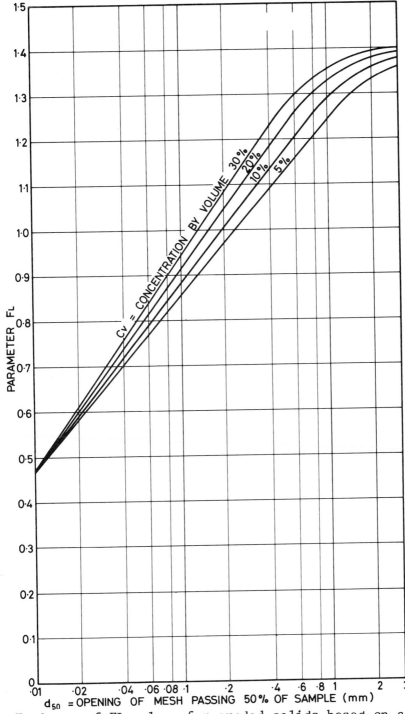

Estimate of FL values for graded solids based on a
d50 sizing.   Figure No. 3

A tailing line profile with the hydraulic gradient is a useful means of plotting the entire system. See Fig. 4.

A method used by the authors for determination of head loss is as follows:

(i) The size of the pipeline is initially estimated based generally on the desired velocity. For the length, type and size of pipe selected, determine the head-quantity characteristic for the pipeline for water, using chart Fig. 5, to obtain f value for the Darcy equation. The curves and formula permit the determination of head loss.

(ii) Plot this head-quantity on a linear plot using a suitable scale for the flow range required. Refer to Fig. 6.

(iii) Draw vertical line on the plot representing the settling velocity derived from Durand's formula and FL factor from Fig. 3.

(iv) Draw a horizontal line on the plot through the intersection of settling velocity value and the H -Q water characteristic from Fig. 5. This will be the minimum slurry head line.

(v) The solids are fully in suspension at velocities of about 30% above the settling velocity. The head loss for slurry expressed in feet of slurry will be approx. 10% higher than the head loss for water.

(vi) An approximate curve representing head loss for slurry may be drawn as shown in Fig. 6. Slurry head curve is assumed to be parallel to the water curve at velocities higher than 30% above the settling velocity, and to be tangential to the minimum slurry head line at approx. 30% below the settling velocity.

The above method is not a precise evaluation, but it has been found to give reasonable results in practice.

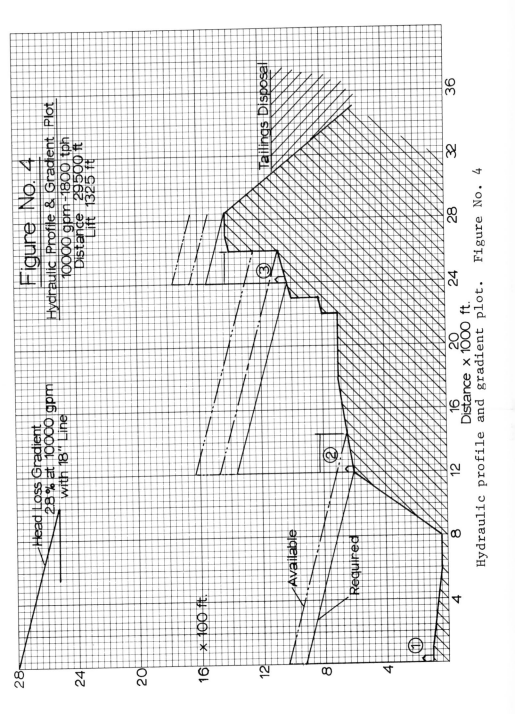

Hydraulic profile and gradient plot. Figure No. 4

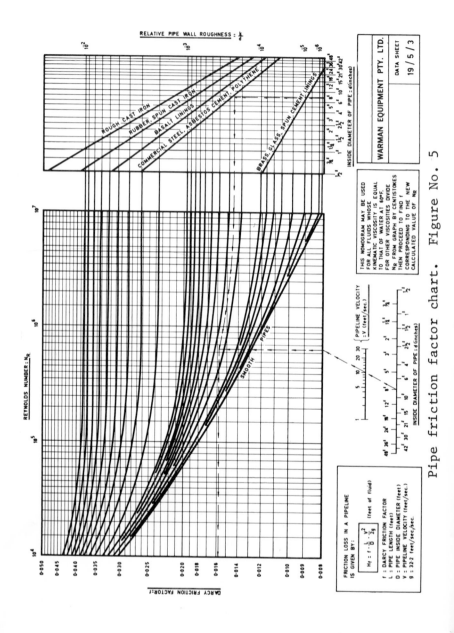

Pipe friction factor chart. Figure No. 5

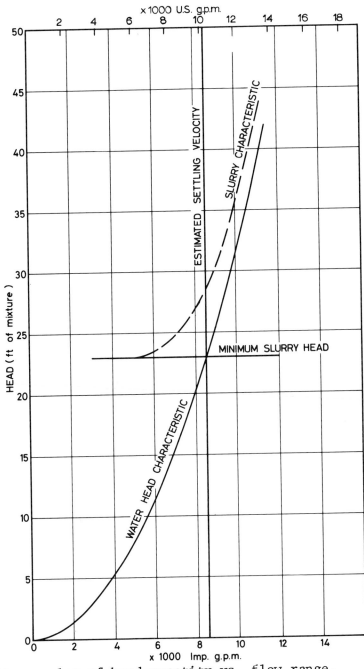

Linear plot of head-quantity vs. flow range.

Figure No. 6

EXAMPLE:

It is required to pump a slurry of 2.65 S.G., solids and d50 sizing of 150 microns (100 mesh) at 50% concentration by weight through 1000 ft., of 18 inch I.D. steel pipe. From Fig. 7 convert to % by volume. CV = 27%

(i) To determine settling velocity from Fig. 2 and 3, say FL = 1.0
     Then VL = $1 \sqrt{2g \times 1.5 \times 1.65}$
     Flow   = 12.6 ft/sec
            = 10,000 USPGM (8250 IGPM)

(ii) To determine pipeline characteristic for water, assume roughness as for commercial steel pipe. Then taking f values from Fig. 5, and tabulating calculation as follows:

USGPM	2400	4800	7200	9600	12000
(IGPM)	2000	4000	6000	8000	10000
V ft/sec	3.02	6.04	9.06	12.08	15.1
f factor	.015	.0143	.0138	.0135	.0133
$H_f = f . \frac{L}{D} . \frac{V^2}{2g}$	1.5	5.5	11.8	20.5	31.5

Head characteristic for water can therefore be plotted, see Fig. 6. Settling velocity and minimum head line have been shown and the estimated slurry characteristic curve drawn in as previously described.

Fig. 14 is given for convenience in identifying and comparing the various mesh standards in common use throughout the world.

3. TYPES OF PUMPS

3.1. SCOPE

Types of pumps suitable for tailings pumping may be separated under the two main classifications of cen-

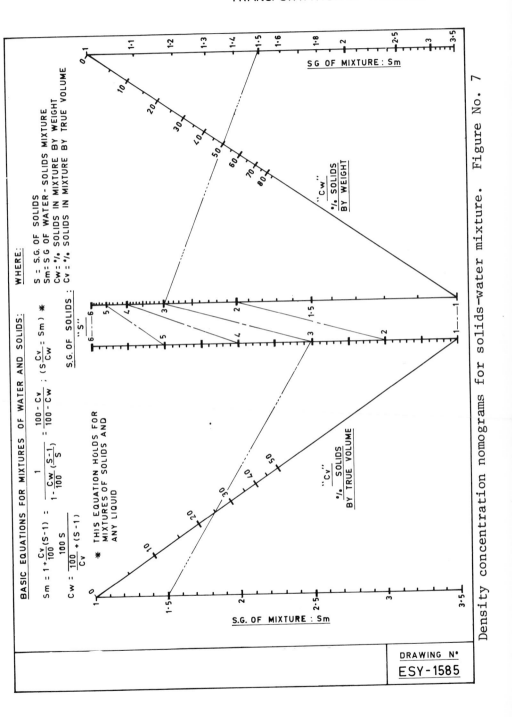

Density concentration nomograms for solids-water mixture.   Figure No. 7

trifugal or positive displacement. Both types have their specific fields of application. Some borderline applications unavoidably occur where careful evaluation of relative merits is necessary in order to make selection.

In general terms positive displacement pumps (P-D-P's) are best suited for very high heads and centrifugal pumps are best to handle relatively low heads and high flow rates.

3.2. POSITIVE DISPLACEMENT PUMPS

Positive displacement pumps should normally be considered on pressures above 500 PSI and for low flow rates at possibly lower pressures. Advantages of P-D-P's are their ability to produce high pressures and their relatively high efficiency.

Disadvantages of most types include high capital costs, high powered low speed drive and speed reducers, and high rate of wear on valves, plungers and glands.

In general capital and maintenance costs will be high, power costs will be minimum.

The principal P-D-P suitable for tailings pumping are of three main types:

(i)   Direct acting plunger type such as the Wison Snyder manufactured by Oilwell Division of United States Steel.

(ii)   Reciprocating oil pressure transfer type such as that manufactured by Mars-Mitsubishi of Japan.

     In this type, the plungers are operating in oil and pressure is transferred from the oil to the slurry in intermediate pressure chambers.

This arrangement is designed to eliminate slurry wear on plungers and glands.

(iii)   Direct pressure transfer type where pressure is supplied from a clear water centrifugal feed pump; pressure is transferred to slurry in sequence to a number of pressure chambers through a series of automatically controlled inlet and exhaust valves.

Clean water enters the chambers at high pressure and is exhausted at low pressure; slurry enters the chambers at low pressure and is exhausted at high pressure.

Clean water is recirculated through the feed pump.

Hitachi of Japan have successfully developed a pump of this type.

This system eliminates plungers operating in slurry and also eliminates the high powered low speed drive and reduction gear necessary for plunger types. All positive displacement pumps have the common requirement of nonreturn valves operating in slurry. These valves usually require considerable maintenance.

3.3. CENTRIFUGAL PUMPS

Well designed centrifugal slurry pumps suitable for heads in excess of 100 PSI per stage, are currently available. By arranging centrifugal pumps in series it is possible to obtain pressures up to 600 or 800 PSI or alternatively to space pumping stations along the length of the line.

In most instances centrifugal pumps will have lower efficiency than P-D-P's; however operation of centrifugals is simple, no valves are necessary and capital and maintenance costs are low.

Where large volumes are to be handled centrifugal pumps will often provide the most economical installation regardless of pressures or the number of booster stations required.

4. TO SELECT A CENTRIFUGAL PUMP

4.1. WATER PERFORMANCE

Published performance curves for centrifugal slurry pumps are usually for clear water only. When assessing the pump requirements for slurry handling duties it is necessary to make certain allowances. These allowances depend upon the nature of the slurry being handled.

Solids in suspension adversely affect both head developed and power consumed. Correction in respect to specific gravity to ascertain power requirements is not sufficient.

The following methods set out corrections to be applied to enable the correct pump speed and horsepower to be estimated.

4.2. EFFECTS OF SOLIDS ON PUMP PERFORMANCE

The adverse effects on centrifugal pump performance caused by solids in a slurry as compared with performance on clear water, are due principally to:

(a) Slip between the fluid and the solid particles during acceleration and deceleration of the slurry while entering and leaving the impeller. (This slip of solids and the attendant energy loss is greatest with particles of greatest settling velocity.)

(b) Viscosity of the slurry.

In this paper, the total head developed by the pump is expressed in feet of actual liquid or mixture being pumped. When pumping water, the head developed is designated Hw in feet of water and when pumping a slurry mixture the head developed in feet of mixture is designated Hm.

The expression, Head Ratio (HR) is the ratio Hm/Hw, where Hm and Hw have the above meanings, at the same flow rate, and the same speed. The Head Ratio is equal to unity for water but decreases as the concentration of solids increases. Head Ratio is affected by the particle sizing and specific gravity of the solids, as well as the concentration.

In addition to lowering the head developed by the pump, solids also reduce the pump efficiency.

In these notes the symbol "ew" is used to indicate the pump efficiency when pumping water, while "em" denotes the pump efficiency when pumping a slurry mixture. The expression, Efficiency Ratio: "ER" is the ratio em/ew at the same flow rate and pump RPM.

4.3 SOME TEST RESULTS ON HEAD DEPRESSION

To illustrate the effects of solids concentration, solids sizing and solids S.G., Figs. 8, 9 and 10 have been included; showing results of some tests which have been conducted by the authors. (Note - the flow rate is given in Imperial GPM)

Tests shown represent one pump at one speed with various concentrations of slurry with two different sizings of silica sand and one sizing of heavy mineral.

Most tests indicate that ER is slightly higher than HR; however results are not conclusive and for practical purposes it may be assumed that HR= ER.

4.4. HR AND ER VALUES

Fig. 11 has been prepared from available data to allow calculation of HR and ER.

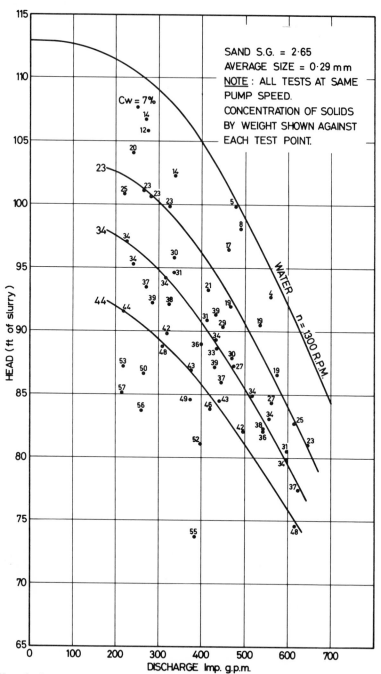

Head depression as a function of concentration of solids by weight; sand 0.29 millimeter.   Figure No. 8

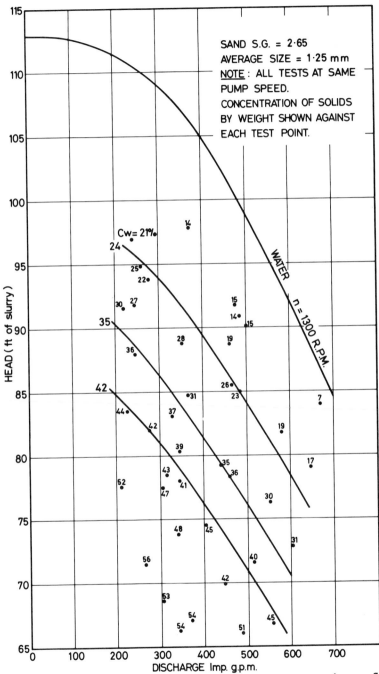

Head depression as a function of concentration of
solids by weight; sand 1.25 millimeters.   Figure No. 9

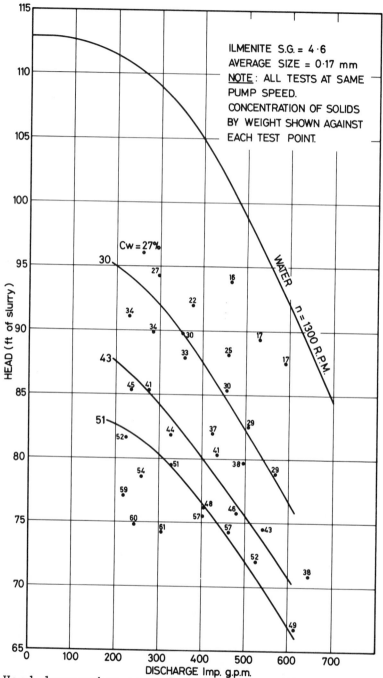

Head depression as a function of concentration of solids by weight; ilmenite 0.17 millimeter.

Figure No. 10

To develop a required head of slurry it is necessary
to run a pump at a higher speed than that which is
required to develop the same head of water. When
Hm has been determined HR is then applied to obtain
Hw. Pump speed for Hw may then be selected from
pump water performance curve.

To calculate pump horsepower, the water efficiency
obtained from the curve must be modified by ER to
obtain efficiency on slurry.

4.5. HEAD AND POWER CALCULATION

The following is an example of the estimation of
pump speed and power consumed when pumping a slurry
mixture.

Duty: A pump is required to handle 1800 (2000#)
tons per hour of tailings having a specific gravity
$S = 2.65$, at a concentration $Cw = 50\%$ solids by
weight against a total dynamic head $Hm = 160$ feet of
slurry. Average particle size of solids $d50 = 150$
microns. (100 mesh)

Solution:

(1) Weight of solids in slurry $= 1800$ TPH

(2) Weight of volume of water equal to
     volume of solids $\dfrac{1800}{2.65}$ $= 680$ TPH

(3) Weight of water in slurry Cw of $50\% = 1800$ TPH

(4) Total weight of slurry add (1) and (3)$=3600$ TPH

(5) Total weight of equal volume of water
     add (2) and (3) $= 2480$ TPH

(6) Quantity of slurry $\dfrac{2480 \times 2000}{60 \times 8.33}$ $= 9924$ GPH

(7) S.G. of slurry (Sm)
     Divide (4) by (5) $\dfrac{3600}{2480}$ $= 1.45$ (Sm)

185

(8)   % solids by volume (Cv)
      divide (2) by (5) x 100 $= \dfrac{680 \times 100}{2480} = 27.4\%$ (Cv)

Values for Sm (7) and Cv (8) can also be read direct from Fig. 7 using S of 2.65 and Cw of 50% solids by weight.

(a)   The head ratio (HR) and efficiency ratio (ER) for this duty may be obtained from Fig. 11 where s = 2.65 and d50 = 150 microns, (100 mesh), the derating factor is:

$$k = 0.075$$

Using the equation in Fig. 11:

$$HR = ER = 1 - \frac{k \times Cv}{20}$$

$$= 1 - \frac{0.075 \times 27.4\%}{20}$$

$$= 0.90$$

(b)   Total head in feet of mixture Hm = 160 feet (given)

Required Head on Water (Hw):

$$\frac{Hm}{HR} = \frac{160}{0.90} = 178 \text{ feet of water}$$

From the Warman Series 'A' pump selection chart, Fig. 12, a Warman 16/14 HAH pump has been selected for this particular duty. The performance curves for the 5 vane closed impeller in this pump are shown on Fig. 13 and will be used for determining pump speed and efficiency as follows:

(c)   Referring to the 5 vane closed impeller performance curve Fig. 13, the speed at which the

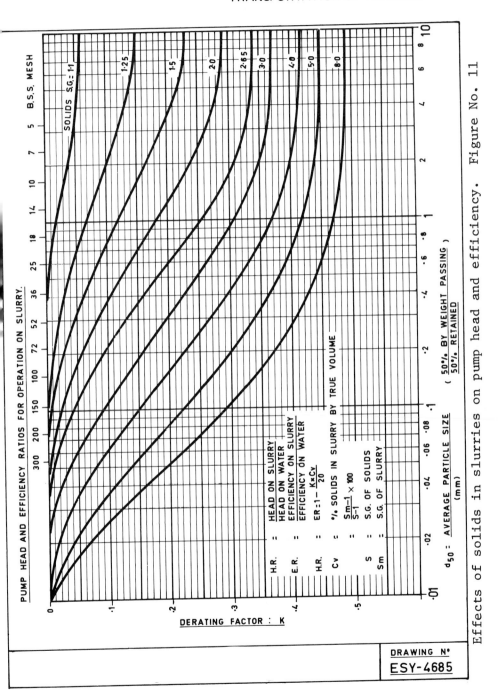

Effects of solids in slurries on pump head and efficiency. Figure No. 11

DRAWING N°
ESY-4685

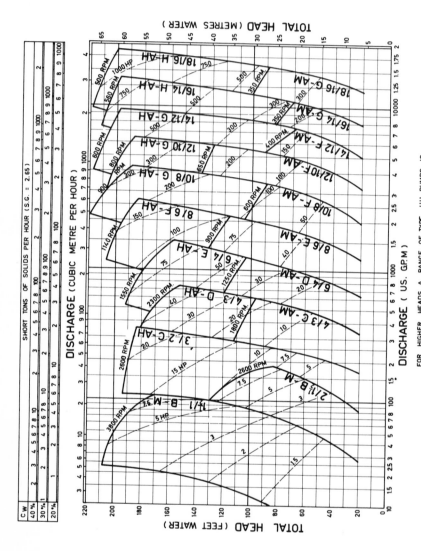

Selection chart for Warman Series A heavy duty slurry pumps Type AM and AH. Figure No. 12

188

WARMAN EQUIPMENT

PERFORMANCE CURVES

PUMP			IMPELLER			SHAFT SEAL CENTRIFUGAL	ESY 5809/3
SIZE	FRAME	TYPE	VANES	TYPE	MAT'L	DIA.	LINER MAT'L RUBBER	EFFECTIVE FROM
16/14	H	AH	5	CLOSED	METAL	42"		14 - 12 - 70

APPROXIMATE PERFORMANCE FOR CLEAR WATER	NORM. MAX. R.P.M.	NORM. MAX. H.P.	MAXIMUM PARTICLE SIZE
CORRECTIONS MUST BE MADE FOR THE SPECIFIC GRAVITY AND VISCOSITY OF THE MIXTURE TOGETHER WITH OTHER EFFECTS OF SOLIDS	550	1200	6" SPHERE

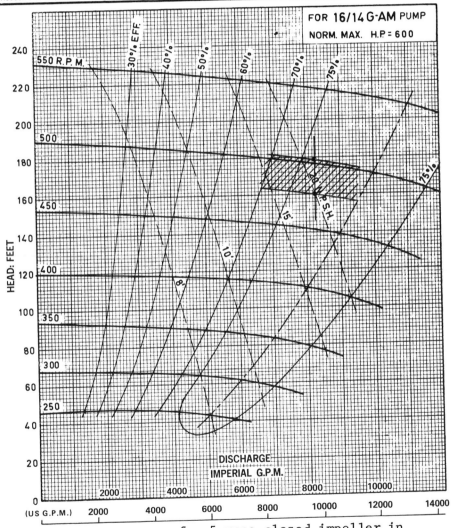

Performance curves for 5-vane closed impeller in pump.

Figure No. 13

pump must operate to develop a head of 178 feet of water when handling 9925 US gallons of water per minute is 505 RPM. Note that this is also the speed required for the pump to develop a head of 160 feet of mixture when handling 9925 gallons of slurry mixture.

(d) The pump efficiency (ew) corresponding to the 178 feet of water is 76% when pumping water.

(e) The efficiency (em) when pumping the sand mixture is then given by:

$$\text{em} = \text{ew x ER}$$
$$= 76 \text{ x } 0.90$$
$$= 68\%$$

(f) Pump Shaft Horsepower consumed

$$= \frac{Q \text{ x Sm x Hm x 10}}{33,000 \text{ x em}}$$
$$= \frac{9925 \text{ x } 1.45 \text{ x } 160 \text{ x } 8.33}{33,000 \text{ x } .68}$$
$$= 855 \text{ HP}$$

5. MATERIALS OF CONSTRUCTION

5.1. REQUIREMENTS

This discussion is limited to materials suitable for resistance to wet abrasive wear as encountered within slurry pumps, and is mainly concerned with application to centrifugal slurry pumps.

Materials to be suitable must fulfill the following requirements:

(i) Provide an economical cost wear performance.

(ii) Be suited to forming to the required shapes and tolerances.

(iii) Have the necessary mechanical strength.

190

Various materials with good abrasion resistant properties are set out below with some discussion on their limitations.

5.2. RUBBER

Rubber has a unique ability to withstand certain types of abrasion. This is apparently due to the rubber rebounding after impact with abrasive particles without damage to the rubber. The size of abrasive particles which can effectively be accommodated by rubber is limited. Where particles are sufficiently large to cut or tear the rubber it will break down quickly. The exact size of particle where rubber ceases to be economical is dependent on many factors, but most materials up to 35 mesh are handled by rubber parts with much coarser (up to 1/2") particles sometimes pumped with combinations of rubber and metal.

Where conditions are best suited to its use, a good abrasive resistant rubber will outlast the hardest alloy iorns by as much as 10 to 1. Mechanical strength of rubber presents limitations of its use and it must be fully supported or reinforced.

The use of rubber in high head centrifugal pumps is limited and special care must be taken in design and construction to avoid breakdown of rubber at points of high energy dissipation. Tailings from most processes are of a sizing ideally suited to handling with rubber components unless rubber is precluded for other reasons.

5.3. HARD CAST IRONS

Early designs of slurry pumps used chilled cast iron components; in more recent times the metallurgy of parts has become more sophisticated, and most of the leading slurry pump manufacturers are using alloy irons with consistently controlled hardnesses of the order of 600 Brinell. These irons, for many applications, provide the most economical compromise between cost and wear performance.

5.4. CERAMICS

Various ceramics are used for some components; however, except for special applications, and considering present manufacturing techniques, ceramics do not appear to be attractive because:

(i)   Cost is high compared to performance.

(ii)   Manufacture to required tolerances is difficult

(iii) Parts are somewhat fragile and require special care in handling.

5.5. SYNTHETIC ELASTOMERS

Various synthetic elastomers including Neoprene, Butyl, Nitrile, polyurethane and others have some application where their special properties give them an advantage.

For general abrasion resistance, however, they have no particular merit, compared to natural rubber.

5.6. CONCLUSIONS ON WEARING MATERIALS

The present trends on metal to elastomers back to metal parts may seem like simple changes in fashion but the established results are very clear when critical pump-circuits (with a pump change out) improve from less than six weeks to over six months continuous operation.

A careful review on the total system is justified but, realistically, the operators are being held accountable for production and total costs. The pump manufacturer must offer a well designed pump which will produce the desired results, preferably including completely interchangeable parts of very hard alloy, rubber and other elastomers.

6. DESIGN FEATURES

Slurry pump designs are a compromise between hydraulic performance and resistance to wear. Large diameter impellers require a lower speed and therefore
reduce wear at the vane inlet; on the other hand,
large impellers result in lower hydraulic efficiency.
Again, a compromise must be made to establish an
economic balance between cost and performance.

Wear is greatest where turbulence is greatest or
where eddies occur. High velocities do not necessarily cause a high wear rate. Severe wear occurs down
stream of any disturbance to flow such as sudden
change of section or projection into the flow.

Where rubber liners are used, it is advantageous if
liners are so constructed that they are self contained components which can be simply attached and
removed from the pump. Linings which require bonding to casings with adhesives have many disadvantages;
there is always the risk of wearing through the casings before a breakthrough in the linings is detected.

Inferior material cannot be economically offset by
increasing thickness of components. As wear occurs
the rate of wear increases and the bad effects are
therefore cumulative. As wear occurs hydraulic performance is also impaired and this can only be partly offset by component design.

7. SERIES OPERATION OF CENTRIFUGAL PUMPS

Installation of centrifugal pumps in series may consist of several pumps close coupled in one pumping
station or single pumps spaced at intervals along a
pipeline.

Advantages of arranging pumps collectively in one
station include the following:

(i)   Simplicity of control, inspection and opera-
        tion.

(ii) Grouping of electrical controls and instrumentation in one center.

(iii) Central maintenance and spare parts handling is simplified.

The main objections to grouping of pumps are associated with the higher pressure to be contained and its effects on pipelines, glands, bearings and pump casings. If steel pipelines are being used then pipeline pressure is not a consideration unless special conditions apply.

Advantages of spacing pumps at intervals along the pipeline include:

(i) Possible use of centrifugal sealing and avoidance of necessity for gland sealing water.

(ii) Reduced pipeline pressure allows use of cheaper pipeline materials such as polythene or asbestos cement.

(iii) Where tailings are corrosive or toxic the danger of high pressure blowouts with risks to personnel are reduced.

Where multistage installations are employed in a single station, thrust loads on pipework between stages can be quite large and special care must be given to layout of pumps and anchorage of pipework to ensure that all loads are satisfactorily accommodated without damage to pumps or pipework.

8. VARIABLE SPEED CONSIDERATIONS

Variable speed drives for tailings pumps can be beneficial for the following reasons:

(i) Quantity of tailings to be handled may vary due to variations in mill conditions or variations in grade of head feed to the mill.

(ii)   It may be required to pump at optimum density in order to conserve water.

(iii) Length of discharge line may vary depending on tailings dam conditions.

(iv)   Static head may increase as height of dam is raised.

(v)   Pump performance varies as pumps become worn. With a fixed speed installation, pumps must be speeded to meet the required maximum conditions when parts are worn. This means that pumps are running faster than necessary when parts are new; parts are therefore being worn out faster than necessary and power consumption is higher than it would be at optimum speed.

Reliable speed variation with suitable control will allow control of density, minimum power consumption, and maximum life of wearing parts.

Although variable speed often looks attractive at first glance, careful assessment of all factors often shows it to be unjustifiable. Inspection of many installations where variable speed units are often being run at top speed either because the variating equipment is unserviceable or because the operator finds it more convenient.

9.   PUMP DRIVES

9.1. RECIPROCATING PUMP DRIVES

Positive displacement reciprocating pumps are normally driven through reduction gear boxes due to the relatively low speeds required.

Small units may have a belt drive between the motor and the gear reducer; larger units would be direct coupled.

9.2. CENTRIFUGAL PUMP DRIVES

Centrifugal slurry pumps may be direct coupled, belt driven or driven through gear reducers with or without some form of variable speed coupling.

For pumps up to 300 HP, V-belt drives usually provide the most convenient form of drive.

With large pumps, rotational speeds are lower and for the higher horsepowers, belt drives are not practical and coupling of pumps through gear reducers becomes necessary.

With such installations some form of speed variation in the drive is usually warranted.

Another possibility for large drives is to direct couple pumps to slow speed motors. This is usually more costly; however, reliability is increased and noise level reduced.

9.3. VARIABLE SPEED DRIVES

9.3.1. D.C. MOTORS

Since the development of heavy duty solid state re tifiers, D.C. motors are finding increasing acceptance for pump drives. Discussion herein, however, is limited to drives suitable for use with A.C. induction motors.

9.3.2. VARIABLE SPEED A.C. MOTORS

The simplest form of speed variation which can be obtained is to use a slip ring induction motor and connect permanently rated resistors into the rotor circuit. This provides the lowest capital cost but is wasteful of power.

A more sophisticated adaptation of the slip ring motor is to provide means to rectify the current taken from the rotor circuit, invert to mains frequency and feed this power back into the stator supply.

This system provides an efficient means of speed variation. The additional electrical hardware, however, introduces more points of possible trouble. One saving of this system is that the control equipment can be arranged so that the motor can be run as a fixed speed machine, if the controls fail.

Special A.C. motors with various commutator arrangements are available to provide speed variation over wide ranges and up to high horsepower ratings. Efficiency of these machines is high and with modern induction regulated types the reliability is high and maintenance is reasonable.

The ultimate for A.C. motor speed variation is probably the use of squirrel cage motors with frequency variation. Such equipment is being developed.

9.3.3. VARIABLE SPEED COUPLINGS

Variable speed couplings allow speed variation by controlling slip within the coupling. Two main types are available being the so called eddy-current coupling and the other the fluid coupling.

These couplings are not highly efficient because the slip which occurs is a direct energy loss. In selecting such couplings the full load slip at maximum speed should be considered because this determines the maximum efficiency which can be obtained.

Efficiency at any reduced speed will be less. The centrifugal pump follows the variable torque characteristic and is easily controlled. The maximum loss is at about 2/3 speed which is at the most desirable operating point.

9.3.4. TWO SPEED MOTORS

Where a number of pumps are arranged in series (or with positive displacement pumps in parallel) it is

197

not normally required to provide variable speed drives for all units. One or two units with variable speed drives operating in conjunction with other fixed speed units will usually provide sufficient control.

One novel means of providing variable output from a multiple pump installation without using sophisticated equipment is to install two speed motors on all or some of the pumps. The installation of 6 pole - 8 pole machines will allow stepping down of output with very simple control equipment. With modern motor winding techniques, two speed motors are only fractionally larger and more costly than single speed machines of the same rating.

10.   GRAVITY FLOW

The ideal plant location provides for gravity flow of the tailings. The same energy concepts apply on the transformation of vertical drop equivalent head for useful transportation on gravity as is used on head generated by centrifugal force. This applies only to closed-full pipe operation.

A review on open flume and drainage concepts is covered by ARMCO (4).

The accepted method of dissipating excess energy is the use of drop boxes. Refer to photo "Fig. 15" of a model by Lee Aplin of the Clarkson Co. This method requires considerable individual design following some of the basic concepts of physics and practical engineering.

The use of orifices and carefully selected pipe sizes is an art when applied to dropping sand fill down several thousand feet into the mine workings (on sand fill operations).

11.   COSTS

Costs of the total system depend so much on the site and operating conditions that estimating the costs

Comparison of testing screens.

British Standard Screens

Mesh	Aperture Inches	Aperture mm	Tolerance on Average Aperture ±%
5	.1320	3.34	3
6	.1107	2.81	3
7	.0949	2.41	3
8	.0810	2.05	3
10	.0660	1.67	3
12	.0553	1.40	3
14	.0474	1.20	3
16	.0395	1.00	3
18	.0336	.85	5
22	.0275	.70	5
25	.0236	.60	5
30	.0197	.50	5
36	.0166	.421	5
44	.0139	.353	5
52	.0116	.295	6
60	.0099	.252	6
72	.0083	.211	6
85	.0070	.177	6
100	.0060	.152	6
120	.0049	.125	6
150	.0041	.105	8
170	.0035	.088	8
200	.0030	.076	8
240	.0026	.065	8
300	.0021	.053	8

I.M.M. Screens

Mesh	Aperture Inches	Aperture mm
5	.100	2.54
8	.062	1.574
10	.050	1.270
12	.0416	1.056
16	.0312	.792
20	.025	.635
25	.020	.508
30	.0166	.421
35	.0142	.361
40	.0125	.317
50	.01	.254
60	.0083	.211
70	.0071	.180
80	.0062	.157
90	.0055	.139
100	.0050	.127
120	.0042	.107
150	.0033	.084
170	.0029	.074
200	.0025	.063

U.S. Bureau of Standards Screens

Mesh	Aperture Inches	Aperture mm	Tolerance on Average Aperture ±%
3	.265	6.73	3
3½	.223	5.66	3
4	.187	4.76	3
5	.157	4.00	3
6	.132	3.36	3
7	.111	2.83	3
8	.0937	2.38	3
10	.0787	2.00	3
12	.0661	1.68	3
14	.0555	1.41	3
16	.0469	1.19	3
18	.0394	1.00	3
20	.0331	.84	5
25	.0280	.71	5
30	.0232	.59	5
35	.0197	.50	5
40	.0165	.42	5
45	.0138	.35	5
50	.0117	.297	6
60	.0098	.250	6
70	.0083	.210	6
80	.0070	.177	6
100	.0059	.149	6
120	.0049	.125	6
140	.0041	.105	8
170	.0035	.088	8
200	.0029	.074	8
230	.0024	.062	8
270	.0021	.053	8
325	.0017	.044	8

Tyler Screens

Mesh	Aperture Inches	Aperture mm	Mesh Double Tyler Series
3	.263	6.680	
	.221	5.613	3½
4	.185	4.699	
	.156	3.962	5
6	.131	3.327	
	.110	2.794	7
8	.093	2.362	
	.078	1.981	9
10	.065	1.651	
	.055	1.397	12
14	.046	1.168	
	.039	.991	16
20	.0328	.833	
	.0276	.701	24
28	.0232	.589	
	.0195	.495	32
35	.0164	.417	
	.0138	.351	42
48	.0116	.295	
	.0097	.246	60
65	.0082	.208	
	.0069	.175	80
100	.0058	.147	
	.0049	.124	115
150	.0041	.104	
	.0035	.088	170
200	.0029	.074	
	.0024	.061	250
270	.0021	.053	
	.0017	.043	325
400	.0015	.037	

NOTES

The ratio between apertures of consecutive British Standard Screens is only approximately equal to the fourth root of 2 because wire diameters are limited to those occuring in the S.W.G. Series.

In I.M.M. screens wire diameter equals aperture and aperture in inches equals one divided by twice the mesh number.

The base of the U.S. Bureau of Standards series is the 18 mesh screen with 1.00 mm. aperture. The ratio between apertures of consecutive screens is the fourth root of 2.

The base of the Tyler Series is the 200 mesh screen with aperture equal to .0029 inches or .074mm. The ratio between apertures of consecutive screens is the square root of 2. For closer sizing, a series of intermediate screens is available, the ratio between apertures of consecutive screens being the Double Tyler Series being the fourth root of 2.
1 micron = 0.001 mm.

Adapted from information Sheet No. 1, C.S.I.R.O. University of Melbourne Ore Dressing Laboratory.

Figure No. 14

Model of drop box for dissipating excess energy. Figure No. 15

by any rule is difficult. Messrs. Wasp, Thompson and Aude (5) illustrated the importance of considering the quantity as a vital factor.

The equivalent distance should be determined. A detailed Hydraulic Profile and Gradient Plot similiar to Fig. 4, but in greater detail, is of value for all phases of route selection in establishing the cost.

The equivalent horizontal length on the system shown on Fig. 4 is approximately 15 miles. The total power is 12000 to 14000 HP with a capital cost of perhaps $2 million exclusive of the pipe and power lines. The cost at 12-16 million TYP (including pipeline) for 15 miles (horizontal distance) should follow Wasp-Thompson-Aude estimated at .35¢ to .45¢ per ton-mile. The six mile haul with 1325 ft. lift results in about 1¢ per ton-mile and 6.6¢ per ton of tailings.

At 12-16 million tons per year, and at 6.6¢ per ton, the total cost is a very significant figure. Considering that some plants are discharging twice this amount and with future total heads in excess of 1000 feet of slurry on a mineral with a small recovery rate, the resultant transportation cost as applied to the final product is very significant.

12.   CONCLUSION

Present developments and costs on tailings disposal prohibit the luxury of major changes once the project is well into the financing and planning stages. There is normally only one opportunity for a full scale or pilot test to prove out the system.

We hope this paper will assist in some of the very basic steps in establishing the essential factors in transporting tailing by hydraulic methods. A review on the estimated cost of 0.35¢ to 0.45¢ per ton-mile as given in this paper and from other sources, will indicate the trend toward moving bulk material whenever possible by hydraulic methods.

REFERENCES

(1)   Durand, R. 1952, Hydraulic Transportation of Coal and Solid Material in Pipes. London Colloquim of the National Coal Board.

(2)   Bingham, E. C. Fluidity and Plasticity. New York, McGraw Hill, 1922.

(3)   Smith, R. W. Slurry Pumping. Portland Cement Association.

(4)   Armco "Handbook of Drainage and Construction Products". Lakeside Press, R. R. Donnelly & Son, Chicago, Ill.

(5)   E. J. Wasp, T. L. Thompson, T. C. Aude, Bechtel Corporation CIM Bul. December 1970.

OPERATION OF THE TAILING SYSTEM AND

CHARACTERISTICS OF THE TAILING STRUCTURE

Frank Windolph

Resident Manager, Climax Molybdenum Company

Empire, Colorado

INTRODUCTION

The tailing from the Climax Mine is deposited in rather steep mountain valleys on foundations that are practically impermeable. This area is at an elevation of about 11,000 feet and long cold winters are experienced. The tailing is relatively coarse and is deposited by the upstream method. Stability investigations of the dams have been carried on for almost 25 years and operating procedures have been developed to achieve a high factor of safety against several modes of failure.

WATER MANAGEMENT AND DRAINAGE

One of the most serious things that could happen to a tailing dam is overtopping in event of a severe flash flood. The Climax tailing areas in Colorado are close to the top of the Continental Divide with relatively small drainage areas above the dams. A complete hydrologic study was made of the area and is reviewed periodically to keep the maximum flood condition in focus. The operators are accustomed to handling the run off from the annual snow melt flood, but must remember that the maximum rainfall flood can be about six times the volume of the snow melt. It was necessary to build a flood control dam upstream from the tailing ponds at the Urad Mine. The spillway of this dam was designed with an ogee section to retain water and even out the release downstream.

From the operating standpoint, all of the flood protection facilities must be maintained so that they will function properly when needed. Good clean-up practices are vital above diversion structures and in retention basins so that trash will not obstruct these structures, spillways, and decanting towers. The water flows are measured continuously so that better information is available for updating the hydrology of the area.

RECLAIM WATER SYSTEM

The water pool of the tailing pond should have enough area so that the solids will settle under all conditions. The slime portion of the Climax tailing has a very slow settling rate which is a distinct advantage in deposition but a disadvantage in that the area of the water pool is larger than normal. The edge of the water pool is kept as far from the crest of the dam as possible to give maximum insurance against overtopping and to reduce the amount of water that has to drain through the tailing dam.

The decanting towers used at Climax are vertical monolithic standpipes with a slotted opening on one side. Concrete flash boards are placed in the slot to maintain the proper water level. The slots in these towers are positioned to face south to give maximum exposure to the sun in the winter. This reduces the tendency of ice to build up at the lip.

The tailing dams are operated with both gravity decanting systems and barge mounted pumps. The gravity systems have ample capacity to handle any water which can fall on or drain into the pond. The barge pumps operate under lower pumping heads to recycle water and offer a saving in power. The pumps also provide an alternative method of controlling water in case the gravity system is inoperative.

It is necessary to have an adequate clear water dam downstream from the tailing dam to catch decanted and seepage water and a pumping plant to return the water to the process reservoir.

In the high mountain valleys in which we operate, separate process water reservoirs are required because of the lack of makeup water during the winter months. The ideal situation, where it is possible, is to have the process water reservoir downstream from the tailing dam. In any case, a clear water pond of generous size is necessary for this service.

BUILDING DAM

Dam building operations are accomplished only in the months of June through October because of the severe weather conditions encountered in the winter. A rubber tired front-end loader is used to build a bank 4 to 5 feet high and the tailing is deposited behind the berm through six inch diameter pipes. When the berm is full the process is repeated. The tailing has good draining characteristics and will be firm enough to support heavy equipment a week after deposition has stopped.

At the end of the summer season, large diameter pipes are laid from the header to a point about 200 feet from the crest of the dam. These lines are laid nearly level and are extended as necessary. The tailing is deposited through this distribution system during the winter months. The whole stream is deposited through one pipe and when this area is full, the flow is moved to another pipe. This causes less freezing and a minimum build up of layers of ice within the tailing. A large amount of coarse sand is deposited far out into the dam with this method, improving the drainage characteristics.

The header pipe which is laid across the dam and feeds the distribution systems is raised to the top of the dam after about 20 feet of dam has been built. The pipe is moved in to achieve the desired slope on the face of the dam. Our dams are now built with a face slope of 4:1 for the bottom 100 feet and a 3:1 slope on the top portion. This produces a terraced surface on the face of the dam which will reduce erosion from heavy rains or minor spills.

A simple sand settlement box in the delivery line has been built to enable us to build the dam at a faster rate. This device will thicken the material being deposited on the crest of the dam from 30 to 45% solids and allow a faster build up of material behind the berm. The fine and dilute material from the top of the settlement box is discharged into the pool of the tailing pond.

CHARACTERISTICS OF DEPOSITED TAILING

The tailing deposit consists essentially of a hydraulically placed pile of finely ground particles of rock resting on a generally strong glacial subsoil. The downstream slope of the pile is 4:1 on the lower portion and 3:1 on the upper. Water is removed with a decanting system and some percolates through the deposit. Most of the water that percolates through the dam originates from saturation of the "beach" when depositing from the crest of the dam.

The Climax tailing is favorable for upstream deposition because it is relatively coarse with a size of 5% + 35 mesh. The material is deposited at high dilution of 30% solids, and the slimes have a slow settling rate. The slime does not settle to any great extent until it reaches the water pool.

In order to determine if loose or low density areas existed in the dam, exploratory drill holes and test pits were made in the tailing to perform standard penetration tests and to obtain samples. The samples from the borings were utilized largely for grain size determinations, and those from the test pits for checking the relative density and permeability. The bore holes were later converted to standpipes for observation of water levels.

One of the important physical properties in connection with looseness or denseness is the relative density which was determined indirectly by the standard penetration tests in the drill holes and directly by the volume and weight determinations on undisturbed samples from the test pits. The standard penetration tests indicated that the materials would be classified as medium to dense, with no very loose zones. The density of the hand-carved samples from the test pits was in agreement with the more extensive standard penetration tests.

There was no indication of loose conditions in any of the borings within considerable distance from the edge of the deposit. Even if loose materials were found near the center of the pile, which appears doubtful, the barrier formed by the relatively dense outer zone would be adequate to restrain the materials in event of a temporary loss of strength.

Information for stability analysis includes the actual contour of the slope of the dam, the shearing resistance of the tailing in the dam, the shearing strength of the soil beneath the tailing and the pore-water pressure conditions in all materials intersected by the surface of sliding. These quantities must be known not only for the present time but also for subsequent stages in the development of the project.

Grain size determinations were made on the samples

from the boreholes and the size with very few exceptions lies within a narrow range. This corresponds to a moderately well graded fine to very fine silty sand with no clay content. Therefore, the material is regarded as cohesionless. From the soils standpoint, there was no discernible trend toward increasing fineness either with depth in a given boring or with increasing distance toward the center of the pond. The exploratory drilling program extended a distance of 700 feet from the toe of the dam. There is no apparent tendency for the upper part of the slope to be underlain by increasingly fine material as the deposit rises.

The porewater pressures are inferred from the piezometric levels in the drill holes, but the future conditions depend to a considerable extent on the drainability of the tailing. Permeability tests were determined on samples from the test pits and compared to the calculated permeability from the results of grain size tests. The results were in close agreement and correspond to the lower limit of good drainability.

The method of constructing the tailing dam and the permeability tests combined with piezometric observations demonstrate the outer parts of the slope are effectively drained. These studies indicated a high factor of safety on failure from sliding.

PIEZOMETRIC LEVEL

The low water level in the outer slopes must be conscientiously maintained by keeping the pool well away from the outer part of the dam and by controlling the deposition from the crest of the dam so that a serious build-up of free water does not occur. Piezometer wells are placed at strategic locations in the dam to monitor the free water level. Variances in the water level can be related to changes in operating conditions. If the water pool is allowed to rise and moves to the sandy beach portion of the

dam, more water will drain through the dam. This
will eventually cause the water level in the wells
to rise. This type of drainage diminishes rapidly
when tailing is deposited and a continuous layer of
impervious material forms under the pool of water.
The water level in the wells also rises when tailing
is deposited from the crest and large areas of the
surface of the beach are saturated. Drainage through
the Climax dam is slow but positive. The piezometric
level will not start to rise until several months
after crest deposition has started, and historical
information had to be accumulated in order to arrive
at the optimum operating methods. Variations in the
water level of twelve feet in the most sensitive wells
can be tolerated without producing wet spots in the
dam. The highest water levels are recorded in the
month of December from the method and timing of depositing the tailing in the summer months, and the
period of time that the tailing is deposited from
the crest is the critical operating factor in controlling the water level in the dam.

Early experience with the water level in tailing
dams induced us to install sub-drains under the new
dams to lower the water table. These drains are usually 12 inch perforated drains laid at 100 foot intervals and extend from 200 to 600 feet upstream as
dictated by the conditions. Each of these is laid
in a six foot trench that is backfilled with properly sized gravel. A blanket of selected tailing is
laid over the entire area to a depth of three to
five feet. These lines have functioned properly
over a period of 12 years.

FUTURE STUDIES

The Climax Molybdenum Company intends to continue
the stability studies and general surveillance of the
deposits. Any marked increase toward dampness, any
signs of erosion or any other unusual developments
are promptly and fully investigated until their implications are understood.

Climax has engaged soil engineers to study conditions of the original ground, to make periodic stability studies and to advise on operating methods. This practice is strongly recommended to other operators.

STRUCTURAL CHARACTERISTICS

RESULTING FROM CONSTRUCTION METHODS

Harris H. Burke

Manager of Soil Engineering, Bechtel Inc.

San Francisco, California

INTRODUCTION

What are the physical properties of tailing?
What can be done to improve their physical characteristics or their suitability for dam building? What
are the factors that affect the strength of tailing,
especially susceptibility to liquefaction or loss of
strength under dynamic stress conditions? Which of
these factors that affect the strength of tailing
are within the control of the operator? What are
the physical things that can be done to tailing to
improve the structural characteristics for dam
building?

In these days of growing world-wide concern for
the preservation of environmental conditions and
mounting control over any operations which affect
the safety of the public, we are in a state of transition from the old tailing dams of the past, which in
some cases were merely waste heaps or dumps, to more
sophisticated, well engineered and safe retaining

211

structures utilizing local available materials. Since the tailing itself constitutes probably the most economical local material, it is highly advantageous to utilize this material for dam building provided it is suitable. This paper emphasizes that separation of tailing into the coarse and fine fractions and then compaction of the coarse fraction are the two operations that can best be utilized during construction to enhance the structural properties of tailing used for building retention dams.

CHARACTERISTICS OF TAILING

The physical properties of tailing are quite variable. Fortunately, the nature of the extractive process, which involves crushing of ore, is such that the resulting plant tailing is often an excellent construction material for building retaining dams. On the other hand, there are some kinds of tailings, such as the black mud residue from cryolite recovery and the clay fines washed out of coal, for example, which may not be suitable for any structural building purpose in a retaining dam. These are some of the materials which must be wasted by storing them behind dams or retaining walls constructed of better materials, perhaps from the mine waste or even borrowed from outside sources for that purpose.

Generally, the tailing resulting from a concentrating process consists of uniform, sand-sized grains with a rather small span of sizes (Figure 1). In addition, the usual hydraulic transporting and deposition processes generally leave the placed or deposited tailing in a loose, saturated mass. Such a deposit, of loose, saturated, uniform grain-sized material, is quite susceptible to liquefaction under dynamic stress conditions such as may be generated during an earthquake. Often mines are located in highly seismic areas where the tailing deposits are thus exposed to potentially damaging earthquake shock. Also, of lesser importance but still a major factor, may be the continued heavy blasting in a nearby open pit mining operation.

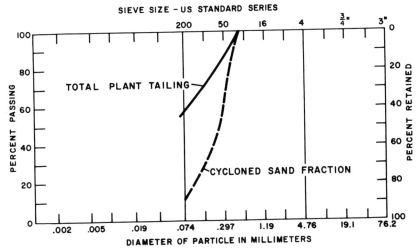

Tailing is general uniformly sized grains with a minimal span of grain sizes.   Figure No. 1

Weather conditions can play an important roll in determining the physical properties, especially the ultimate strength of the deposited tailing. If the tailing is allowed to dry out, as is often the case in the Southwest, the density (or unit weight) of the resulting mass may be increased with an accompanying increase in strength, sometimes a major increase. The method of forming the beach during placement also may have a major effect on the density and strength of the deposited tailing. Some beached deposits are extremely dense and stable much like the raceway at Daytona Beach. On the other hand, some tailing retention dams are called upon to retain and store storm runoff or process water so that the deposit may be wholly or perhaps intermittently saturated, thus preventing the drying or formation of a dense mass and, indeed, creating an interfingering of sand and slime fractions and thus the worst possible conditions in regard to liquefaction potential, that is, a permanently loose, saturated mass of uniform grain-sized material. The rate of production, and thus the rate of deposition, along with the configuration or arrangement of the deposition areas may likewise have a major effect on the ultimate character of the deposited tailing.

213

Generally, a plant tailing of sharp angular rock fragments has the potential for high shear strength, but often is limited by its uniform grain size and deposition in a loose, saturated condition to a mass with a high potential for liquefaction.

FACTORS THAT AFFECT LIQUEFACTION POTENTIAL

The potential for liquefaction of soils during seismic disturbances has been fairly well established (1). The significant factors are:

1. Soil Type
2. Relative density or compactness
3. The initial confining pressure at the time subjected to dynamic stress.
4. The intensity of the ground shaking.
5. The duration of the ground shaking.

In addition to the above factors, the location of the water table is extremely important in regard to liquefaction potential.

The soil type is characterized by the grain size distribution of the tailing. Uniform grain size materials mostly in the fine sand sizes, the typical gradation of a tailing material, are the very materials most susceptible to liquefaction. However, the size constituency of the tailing is at the mercy of the process. Thus, little can be done to change the range of grain sizes of the plant tailing to make it more resistant to liquefaction.

The susceptibility of a given material, such as a uniform grain sized tailing, to liquefaction or flow slide has long been recognized to be dependent to a high degree on its relative density or compactness (2). For a given material, the more compact or dense it is the more resistant it will be to liquefaction. Here, then, is an area where the character of the deposited material can be changed by construction procedures.

The effect of the initial confining pressure is to limit potential liquefaction to the upper, loosest, materials. This offers an opportunity in certain areas to prevent liquefaction by applying overloads to loose deposits to decrease liquefaction potential. However, this has little application to building tailing dams.

Both the intensity and duration of ground shaking are natural occurrences beyond the control of man. The practical significance of these factors is that a particular deposit may not liquefy under a small earthquake but may liquefy under a strong earthquake or even under more prolonged earth movement. Thus, little comfort can be derived from the fact that a particular deposit has been shaken by many small earth movements. This may merely mean that when a really big earthquake comes along the mass will indeed fall apart.

The position of the water table, or in the case of a tailing dam, the seepage line greatly affects the potential for liquefaction. If a tailing deposit, for example, is built on a pervious foundation where it is readily drained, the potential for liquefaction is greatly reduced. On the other hand, a dam with a high seepage line is considerably less safe than if the seepage line is kept low within the structure by providing adequate internal drainage features.

IMPROVING THE STRUCTURAL STRENGTH

Since the extraction or concentrating process and the nature of the ore controls the particle size range and distribution and, in turn, the strength of the tailing and since the forces of nature are the other major controlling factor in seismic stability, what, if anything, can be done to improve the characteristics of tailing materials which may not be adequately stable under the conditions to which they will be exposed?

There are two major ways in which the character of tailing can be improved during construction of the tailing dam.

a. By only utilizing the best part of the tailing for dam construction. This can be accomplished by separating out the best, or coarsest, portion of the tailing for use in the retention structure.

b. By compaction, the density or unit weight of the best or selected coarse fraction can be increased often with a dramatic major increase in strength and resistance to dynamic stress.

In addition, by designing the retaining structure to provide adequate internal drainage and thus ensure a low seepage line, the stability of the dam or tailing deposit can be greatly enhanced.

How then, can the best part of the tailing be separated from the total tailing and how effective will such a separation be? There are two usual means of separating out the better part of such materials.

a. By natural sedimentation on the flat beaches. This method has been successfully used in many tailings dams. Sometimes the natural separation process is aided by varying the distribution of material over the surface by use of spigots or multiple discharge points.

b. By mechanical separation, the most common method being hydro-separation by means of cyclones. Figure 1 illustrates a cyclone separation which shows a dramatic improvement in the character of the material. The total tailing would not be at all suitable for dam building, whereas the sand fraction separated out by a cycloning process has a great potential for use in constructing the retaining wall.

The effectiveness of the separation depends primarily on the nature of the total tailing, and, of course, on the nature of the separation process itself.

Depending on the initial material, even after the best, or coarsest, fraction of the tailing has been separated out, resulting material still may not be suitable for dam building. Should that be the case, the most economic solution could well be to use imported material such as minewaste or local borrow, if available, to build the dam and merely deposit the tailing behind the dam as illustrated in Figure 2.

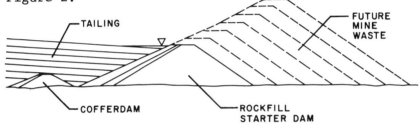

Tailing dam built from imported material such as mine waste.   Figure No. 2

Even with a suitable material and a good separation into sand and slime fractions, the resulting sand material may end up as a loose saturated deposit of uniform fine grained particles which would be extremely susceptible to liquefaction. What, then, can be done to improve the character of this material? The answer is simple and often not costly. You need only to compact it. Generally, the sand fractions of tailing, after being separated from the slimes, are quite easily compacted by modern vibratory compactors which are well adapted to this type of material. By compacting the coarse or sand fraction of the tailing, the end result is a dense mass of strong material which will have greatly increased resistance to liquefaction. Laboratory tests to evaluate the strength of loose or dense materials and the potential for liquefaction are now quite common and the specific gain in strength due to compaction can be easily demonstrated.

SUMMARY

Plant tailing from concentrating operations are quite variable but tend to be of a uniform grain size which, when placed in a loose saturated mass in a retaining structure, is quite susceptible to liquefaction. Increased resistance to liquefaction and thus greatly enhanced stability can be attained by design to reduce the level of the saturation or seepage line through the structure and by the simple construction expedients of hydro-separation to select the coarse fraction of the tailing and compaction of that coarse fraction in the retaining dam or structure. Compaction of the sand fraction into the retaining structure by the downstream building method illustrated in Figure 3 can result in a strong, safe structure and completely eliminate the potential liquefaction resulting from the interfingering of sands and slimes along with the loose saturated sands often generated by the upstream building method illustrated by Figure 4.

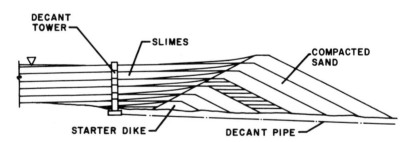

Compaction of sand fraction into retaining structure by downstream method.   Figure No. 3

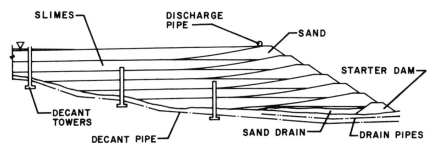

Upstream dam building method can result in
liquefaction.   Figure No. 4

(1) H. Bolton Seed and M. Idriss, Simplified
     Procedure for Evaluating Soil Liquefaction
     Potential, Journal of the Soil Mechanics and
     Foundations Division, Division, ASCE, SM9,
     Proc. Paper 8371, September 1971.

(2) A. Casagrande, Characteristics of Cohesionless
     Soils Affecting the Stability of Slopes and
     Earthfills, Journal, Boston Society of Civil
     Engineers, January 1936.

DISCUSSION

QUESTION: I wonder if the speaker could
elaborate a bit on the relationship between initial
confining pressure or height and the liquefaction

potential. We have heard emphasis on very high
dams being planned now and how crucial they are.
In one of the liquefaction failures in Chile, it
was a very low dam, as I remember, as was the
Sheffield Dam in Santa Barbara, California. I am
wondering if he would comment on that.

HARRIS BURKE: I tried not to comment in
regard to tailings dams. One of the things we do
with nuclear power plants, if we have a potential
for liquefaction, is to load the ground so that it
is under a huge stress which makes it more difficult
to liquefy. Unfortunately, with the dam you can't
do that. The top of the high dam is just like the
whole part of a low dam, so that at the top of the
dam, no matter how you do it, you don't have a
confining load which holds the ground down and thus
increases the stress at which liquefaction occurs.

B. W. RUHFUS (Engelhard Minerals & Chemical
Company): I hear quite often that compactions are
very important and it seems to me that compaction
is quite a big cost factor, especially on the downstream side when the dam is built upstream. Now,
is there any other way to compact the dam except
vibratory rolling; would it be possible to do that
with explosives?

W. A. WAHLER (W. A. Wahler & Associates):
This problem has been brought up many times. We
had an interesting experience in Chile at what was
called the "Second International Symposium on
Tailings," about seven or eight years ago. The
Russians were invited to give some of their
experiences. They sent over some very able men who
were talking about the compaction of sands by
explosive means for the foundation for the Aswan dam.
By the time this was translated into Spanish and
then into English, we found that there was a very
effective method of compaction for tailings dams
using explosives, and the Chilian representative
felt that this was an obvious thing to put into the
regulations: that they had to be compacted by

vibration, and by explosives preferably. This
started a very interesting discussion. The process
of compaction by explosive is a process of going
through the liquefaction cycle. Now if you are on
the horizontal, it is possible to compact by that
method but, if you are on a slope, recognize that
the moment you have liquefaction, if you do not
have confinement, you have had it.

B. W. RUHFUS: But if you do it periodically
that would be different.

W. A. WAHLER: If you were to use retainer
dikes, something of that nature, and to do your
vibratory or explosive compaction strictly in a
confined sense and strictly in a horizontal plane,
the needed strength to liquefy for the moment in a
horizontal sense, confined on all sides, then you
might get away with it. I think that the systematic
approach that you can get by the use of compaction
equipment will give you a uniform stabilized
structure, assuming an explosive procedure would
be economical. I do not believe this would
be possible. With the fact that it would most
probably be a heterogeneous type of application of
density, and frankly because of the different
stress strain characteristics of materials, the
different densities, you would end up with a much,
much worse situation to get progressive failure due
to stream interrelationships. So I think that something needs to be said here, a bit about the
importance of uniformity. Now, it has been
brought out that you start with a uniform construction material, one that has a generally good aspect
from the design standpoint and construction standpoint. But, if you do not use a uniform construction
technique, then you end up with a nonuniform
product, even though you start out with more
uniform material.

HARRIS BURKE: The reason we use rollers to
compact dam materials in this country is because
it is the cheapest way to do it. We have tried the

other ways. and invariably we come back to the use of rollers being the cheapest.

E. D'APPOLONIA (E. D'Appolonia Consulting Engineers, Inc.): I would like to reinforce what Mr. Burke has said, that today with vibratory steel drum rollers, effective compaction of mining materials of the kind being considered here can be carried out to depths as much as 30 feet under water. Where we have a third or more surface above water, the depth of 15 feet has been carried out repeatedly and has proven to be a very effective method. And you are talking pennies per cubic yard. The second thing is that the blasting techniques, though they have been used, are highly variable and you can get poor pockets or loose pockets in the material. Another thing that should be recognized is that the dredging operation normally places sand somewhere between 40 and 50 percent relative density. If you have relative density of an order of 60 to 65 percent, this is usually quite adequate for most of the earthquake loadings that we have to consider with such embankments.

Written comment by Dan Kealy, U. S. Bureau of Mines:

MEETING OVERVIEW--UPSTREAM VS. DOWNSTREAM

There has been much discussion on two types of tailing dam construction (upstream vs. downstream). It must be noted that the construction material of which the dam is physically constructed is the major determinant as to the type of construction. The grain-size distribution of the total tailing product will be a factor in determining if the upstream method can effectively be used. If the ore mined, in combination with the mill circuiting, produces too high a percentage of fines, then and only then should an alternative method be employed. The upstream method is most economical and simple

to use. If cyclones are required to build berm,
then the percentage of fines is too great for
upstream construction. In addition to grain size
tests, a good rule of thumb is: if a tractor
cannot be operated on the first 100 to 200 feet of
beach, the grind is too fine for upstream
construction methods. It is this beach, with
optimum properties and characteristics which can be
developed, that determines at what point in time
the slimes underlay the upper embankment and, consequently, affect the factor of safety.

Also to be noted is the fact that shock or
earthquake-type loading is not the only serious
liquefaction initiator. Another very important
and sometimes overlooked caue of liquefaction
failure is internal movement or strain-induced
liquefaction such as the failure that occurred
at Buffalo Creek. Although the end product is the
same, the strain-induced liquefaction is not as
apparent as the shock or earthquake-induced failure.
Thus the fact that the embankment is not located
in an earthquake-prone area is immaterial as far as
liquefaction failure is concerned. Good compaction
and unsaturated soil are the keys to prevent
liquefaction-type failures. Both upstream and
downstream methods can provide potential liquefaction
failure conditions. Either method, if properly
compacted, can avert failure. Again, the determining factor for upstream vs. downstream construction is grain size distribution of the tails.

TAILING DISPOSAL PRACTICE AT THE

TYRONE BRANCH OF PHELPS DODGE CORPORATION

William H. Keener

Concentrator Superintendent, Phelps Dodge Corporation

Tyrone Branch, Tyrone, New Mexico

Concentrating operations at the Tyrone Branch of Phelps Dodge Corporation commenced in July, 1969. The disposal and reclamation methods in use have evolved since that time.

The research work, including settling tests for thickener design, that was performed on many drill core and underground samples gave no indication that the Tyrone mill tailing would be unsuited to normal spigoting practices. Such procedures at the Arizona properties of Phelps Dodge Corporation involve disposal through 4 to 6-inch disposal lines and berm building by means of dragline.

Almost immediately after the concentrator came on stream it became apparent that routine spillage operations would not deposit suitable material for berm building at the perimeter of the dam and thus the cyclone method was substituted to handle the very viscous tailing.

224

Eight thickeners are used for water reclamation at
Tyrone, New Mexico. Pipe for mill tailing may be
seen in the foreground.   Figure No. 1

Tailing flows through pipeline and drop boxes to
the pond at upper right.   Figure No. 2

About 45,000 tons of tailing at 25% solids and 5% plus 65 mesh are thickened per day in eight tailing thickeners, four of which are torque type and the others traction type. Tailing from these thickeners flows by gravity at about 45% solids through a concrete launder to diversion boxes which route the tailing to 30-inch asbestos-concrete pipe for delivery to the dams through a series of drop boxes.

A by-pass is provided in the system for each dam to allow the introduction of the tailing into the upper areas, thus permitting repairs to pipeline in the sections associated with cycloning.

In the use of cyclones, as the elevation of the cyclone classifiers increases an increase in the head supplied by the 30-inch feeder lines must also be provided. At Tyrone, this is accomplished by fabricating an "S" shaped transition piece that is attached to the entering and departing 30-inch line in each drop box. The drop box is then filled with concrete - encasing the "S" and adding an additional 10-feet of head to the disposal system. This eventually results in a pressure of 45 - 50 p.s.i. on the main line.

The 30-inch pipe is placed on the inner edge of an equipment service road and is equipped with four-inch lubricated plug valves at 52-foot centers. Light weight (Schedule 5) steel pipe connects the valve with the 10-inch cyclone; similar pipe also carries away the overflow. The density of the cyclone underflow is controlled by an adjustable rubber apex.

For the operation of the cyclones, about 12 - 15 p.s.i. are required to effect a satisfactory separation and to produce an underflow of proper consistency.

The positioning of the cyclone is accomplished with a tripod about 15 feet high. The intermediate braces on the tripod are used to locate the cyclone

A view of the Tyrone tailing pond.   Figure No. 3

Cyclone deposits sand to build dam.   Figure No. 4

five, ten or fifteen feet from the ground. The cyclone rests on removable steel pegs placed in pre-drilled holes in the tripod assembly. When the underflow reaches the apex, the cyclone is raised five feet.

The filling to the top limit of the tripod is followed by the placement of a new tripod to maintain the necessary 3 to 1 slope on the outside face of the dam. This slope could, however, be increased or decreased slightly by a different positioning of the tripods and by proper manipulation of the cyclone underflow density.

At the present time, our procedure is to deposit tailing via the cyclone underflow to an elevation 35 - 40 feet above the 30-inch line. Disposal operations are then diverted to another dam while the temporarily abandoned area is leveled by bulldozer for the repositioning of the main line at a higher elevation.

The cyclones themselves are locally fabricated of light gauge sheet metal and equipped with rubber cone liner and apex; a ni-hard vortex finder completes the assembly.

Mechanical couplings are required on the feed pipes to the cyclones, while short lengths of rubber hose are satisfactory for connection of pipe in the overflow line. The light gauge pipe eases the problem of relocation and no wear-out has been experienced in the three years of operation.

To date, parts replacement for the cyclones has been limited to vortex finders.

The ambient temperature at Tyrone, New Mexico, approaches 0° F, in the winter, and foam coating of valves is required to prevent damage from freezing in spite of the use of "freeze proof" valves.

The decant water system associated with the

Decant tower screen prevents trash from flowing
into the underground system.   Figure No. 5

Overflow holes in decant tower are covered by
driving a wedged steel plate into the slot, thus
allowing the pond level to be raised.   Figure No. 6

tailing dams is composed of underlying pipe connected to 20-foot decant towers with vertical risers. The towers are equipped with eight-inch holes on 15-inch vertical centers; as the tailing rises on the towers the holes are banded off by means of a wedge clamping device.

When the tower is abandoned, a steel plate is placed on a shoulder in the bottom, and a concrete plug two feet deep is poured over the plate.

The decanted water flows to ponds adjacent to pump houses and thence is returned to the thickeners in the mill area. Fresh make-up water is also added to the thickeners; this raw water is pumped from the Gila River to the Bill Evans Lake, an off-stream reservoir constructed by Phelps Dodge and now under the supervision of the New Mexico State Game and Fish Commission for public recreational purposes.

Two stages of pumping deliver the water to the Tyrone tanks, 23 miles distant and 1,466 feet above the elevation of the Gila River.

DISCUSSION

QUESTION: I have a question for Mr. Keener on the operation of the spigots. When you have these dozens, or maybe hundreds, of cyclones how do you control the operation of each individual cyclone? The pressure drop changes over the length of the manifold and so how do you control the operation of each cyclone?

WILLIAM H. KEENER: The question was how do we control the operation of the cyclone when we have a number of them stretched along the perimeter of a dam which in some cases would be 6,000 to 7,000 feet long. The only method of control we use is the squeezing down on the adjustable rubber apex of the cyclone. We don't think it is prudent to try

to control the amount of flow to the cyclone by
throttling the plug valves because the valves wear
out there. We have not yet gotten around to the
point of using rubber pinch valves for that kind of
control. So in our case it is all just a question
of the constriction of the rubber apex. Maybe
Harry Dahlberg has a different solution to that.

HARRY R. DAHLBERG (Inspiration Consolidated
Copper Company): Well we control our thickener
underflow to a certain extent, although we have
problems because of ore variations. Sometimes we
have heavy magnetite and we warn the men on the
shift, whenever magnetite is coming, to run the
cyclones at the far end of the line because, otherwise, the line will plug up. We've tried pinching
down, but we haven't had much luck with that. We
have vents on the overflow and it continues to amaze
me, because sometime when the cyclone is not working
well when we open it, and it works well other times,
when it isn't giving a good sand we plug the vent
and it works well. When we get into some of our
limonitic, slimy stuff - that's a different
situation also. Sometimes we'll build four, five,
or six feet of height in eight hours. Other times
we'll build a foot or minus a foot.

Store of tailing cyclone parts.   Figure No. 7

CONSTRUCTION OF SOUND TAILINGS DAMS

BY CYCLONING AND SPIGOTTING

Earle J. Klohn, President
C. H. Maartman, Executive Engineer
Ripley, Klohn & Leonoff International Ltd.
Vancouver, British Columbia, Canada

ABSTRACT

With few exceptions, construction of tailings dams by the old upstream spigotting methods is rapidly being replaced by downstream construction using cycloned sand embankments, blanketed upstream by spigotted slimes. Direct spigotting of tailings is generally used only in those cases where it is economic to build a downstream supporting structure of either borrowed or pit waste materials. The resulting new tailings dams are much safer, under both static and seismic loading, than are the older. type dams constructed using upstream spigotting methods.

New and interesting variations of construction techniques have been developed to accomodate the new tailings dam design concepts. Some of these techniques, as used on two large sand dams under construction in British Columbia, are reviewed together with attendant problems, solutions adopted, and success in meeting design objectives.

INTRODUCTION

Tailings dams are important structures that involve two aspects of public concern. One is the structural stability of the dam and the possible release, if failure occurred, of a very large volume of water and/or semi-fluid tailings. Such an event would not only cause extensive downstream pollution but would also pose a serious threat to life and property. The second aspect of public concern, is the possibility of pollution under normal operation in which polluted effluent might escape through or around a tailings dam and into the streams or groundwater of the area.

In recent years, methods of tailings dam design and construction have come under critical review as both the mining industry and governmental regulatory bodies have become more aware of the need in most areas for better tailings dams to meet basic requirements of safety and pollution control. Fortunately, safe and economical tailings dams can be built by applying the engineering knowledge and experience presently available from conventional water storage dam designs, suitably modified to satisfy the special requirements of the mining industry. However, as might be expected, the introduction of many new concepts to the design and construction of tailings dams has led to some confusion and much controversy. This undoubtedly has been a source of annoyance and frustration to the mining industry, but the situation is now stabilizing and sound tailings dams are presently being achieved at costs that are only slightly greater than those for the older, and in many instances unsafe structures.

This paper briefly describes the basic concepts that are considered to represent the present state of the art of tailings dam design and construction.

To illustrate the application of these current design
and construction concepts, two large tailings dams
presently under construction in British Columbia have
been selected for review and discussion. Both structures use downstream construction methods, involving
mainly cycloned sand. A general description of the
design and construction procedures adopted for each
dam is presented. Emphasis is placed on that work
performed by the mine personnel as opposed to work
done by others under conventional contract methods.
Details of appropriate technical field data and the
indications of the effectiveness of the construction
program in achieving design objectives are provided.

DESIGN AND CONSTRUCTION OF TAILINGS DAMS

Until fairly recent times, most tailings dams
were built by the upstream method of construction,
using spigotting procedures. As such a dam is raised,
each successive retaining dyke is built in the upstream direction, over top of previously deposited
tailings. There is a limiting height to which such
a structure can be raised before a shear failure may
occur, breaching the dam and spilling the contained
tailings. In regions subject to seismic shocks,
failure of this type of dam by liquefaction can occur
at very low heights. Consequently, with few exceptions the once commonly used upstream construction
technique, utilizing previously spigotted tailings
for dam building, is no longer considered satisfactory for major tailings dams and some form of downstream construction is normally adopted. Where the
tailings themselves are used for construction of the
dam, the sand fraction required for dam building is
usually separated from the fines by means of cyclones.

The design requirements for tailings dams constructed by the downstream methods are similar in many
respects to those for conventional water storage dams.
This can be illustrated by the comparison on Figure
No. 1 between a typical water storage dam and two
types of tailings dam; one using upstream construction

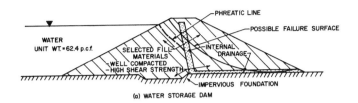

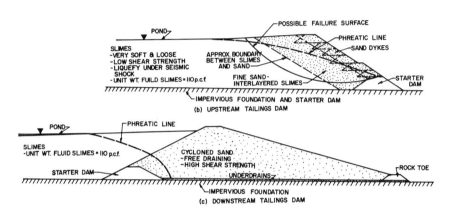

Comparison between typical water storage dam and
tailings dams built using upstream and downstream
methods of construction.   Figure No. 1

and the other using downstream construction.

A critical analysis of the typical upstream dam
on Figure No. 1(b) will show that this type of tailings dam does not meet conventional dam requirements
for slope stability, seepage control (internal
drainage), or resistance to earthquake shocks. As
indicated, a possible failure surface would pass
through a large zone of much weaker materials than
would a similar surface on the water storage dam.
As a consequence, the factor of safety for the upstream tailings dam is very low as compared to that
for the water storage dam, even under normal static

235

conditions of loading only. Any change in conditions that would result in a further rise of phreatic line and complete saturation of the outer sand shell could quickly lead to failure by piping or sliding. Potential causes of such saturation would include: a rise in water levels in the pond, freezing of seepage outlets on the downstream face of the dam, and torrential rainfall. Under earthquake loading of appropriate intensity and magnitude, the slimes in the pond and the saturated portions of the shell would tend to liquefy and lose strength drastically and the fluidized slimes would easily burst through the remaining thin, unsaturated sand-dyke shell.

As indicated by Figure No. 1(c), downstream methods of tailings dam construction present a much more encouraging picture, because dams built in this manner can be designed to closely meet the requirements of conventional water storage dams. Both have substantial cross-sections and extensive internal drainage. The downstream type of tailings dam can be designed to be stable under both static and seismic loadings, including retention of the liquefied slimes.

The major advantages of the downstream method of tailings dam building are that:

1. None of the embankment is built on previously deposited, loose, fine tailings.

2. Placement and compaction control can be exercised, as required.

3. Underdrainage systems can be installed as required, as the dam is built. The underdrainage permits control of the line of saturation through the dam and, hence, increases its stability.

4. The dam can be designed and subsequently constructed to whatever degree of competency that may be required, including resistance to earthquake forces.

The major disadvantage of all methods of down-stream dam building is the large volume of sand required to raise the dam. In the early stages of operation it may not be possible to produce suffi-cient volumes of sand to maintain the crest of the tailings dam above the rising pond levels. If this is the case, then either a higher starter dam is required or the sand supply must be augmented with borrow fill. Both procedures are acceptable but do add to the cost of the initial tailings facility.

Downstream dam building is the only procedure that permits design and construction of tailings dams to conventionally acceptable engineering standards. Details of design and construction can be varied widely to suit the requirements of any given project and produce an acceptable end-product at a minimum cost. All tailings dams located in seismic areas, and all major tailings dams, regardless of their location, should be constructed using some form of the downstream method.

A detailed discussion of the many factors affec-ting the design and construction of tailings dams is beyond the scope of this paper. For a more thorough review of current design and construction practices the reader is referred to Reference No. 9.

CASE HISTORIES

To illustrate the construction procedures currently being used, two major tailings dam projects in British Columbia, Canada, have been selected for dis-cussion. Figure No. 2 indicates the mine locations and the relative seismicity at each site. Both projects involve the construction of very large tailings dams, using cycloned sand and downstream construction methods. At one of these sites (Brenda Mines) a fairly comprehensive field review of dam performance has recently been completed and some of the more pertinent data obtained from that review are presented.

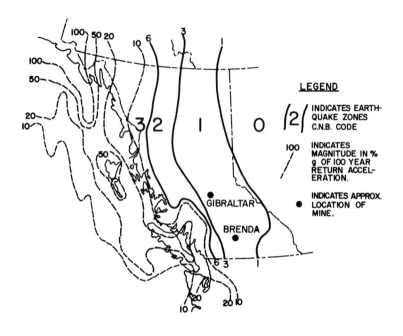

Map of British Columbia showing mine locations and
seismicity zones.   Figure No. 2

Brenda Mines Ltd. - Tailings Dam

General - Brenda Mines is situated on a mountain
plateau west of Okanagan Lake in south central British Columbia, approximately 40 miles from Kelowna,
B. C. The Mine produces copper and molybdenum concentrates from a low-grade, open-pit operation with
a rated capacity of 24,000 tons per day. Originally
planned Mine life was 20 years which, at the rated
capacity, would result in approximately 175 million
tons of tailings for disposal. Recent modifications
are expected to increase the capacity to 30,000 tons
per day.

The Mine is situated at the head-waters of a
stream flowing eastward into Okanagan Lake. Because

the Okanagan Valley is one of the major tourist and recreational areas of Southern B. C., it was made a basic requirement for development of the Mine that the tailings facilities be completely closed circuit.

The valley in which the tailings dam and tailings pond are situated has a steep gradient and is relatively narrow, requiring a high dam to provide the necessary storage volume. The dam was designed originally to rise 400 feet above the stream bed. Recent modifications in design have increased that height to approximately 450 feet above stream bed.

The main dam embankment is being constructed of cycloned sand. A starter dam having a maximum height of 125 feet was constructed of rockfill and impervious blanketing, designated on Figure No. 3 as the Upper Main Dam. The structure indicated on Figure No. 3 as the Lower Main Dam is a free-draining rock toe that provides confinement to the lower portion of the dam and serves to retain the embankment so that it could be sited close to the edge of a steeply dropping section of the valley. Underdrainage is provided by a blanket drain upstream of the rock toe together with finger drains extending up under the body of the sand embankment.

The dam will have an ultimate crest length of approximately 6,500 feet, a maximum base width of approximately 1,800 feet and maximum height above the downstream toe of about 450 feet. The dam is being raised by the centreline method of construction which produces a vertical upstream face of interfingered cycloned sand and slimes. The final downstream sand slope will be approximately 3.5 horizontal to 1 vertical. Total sand requirements will be approximately 32,500,000 cubic yards.

Studies indicated that the Brenda Mines grind would be relatively coarse. Approximately 50% of the total tailings would be available as cyclone underflow sand for dam construction. The cost of the cycloned sand was very low relative to that for borrow

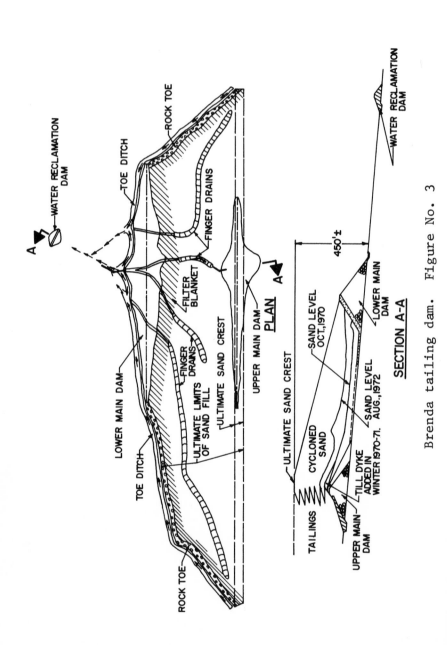

Brenda tailing dam. Figure No. 3

materials. For the initial structures required at mill startup, Upper Main Dam, Lower Main Dam, and the underdrains, it was found economic to use a predominance of pit waste rock materials where these were suitable. Natural borrow was limited to that required for impervious blanketing and for filters on the underdrains.

Water reclaim is by pump barge floating on the tailings pond. Seepage water passing through the Main Dam, and in particular the transportation water used for placement of the sands, is recovered at the Reclamation Dam downstream and returned to the tailings pond. No water from the tailings pond catchment or the tailings pond itself is allowed to pass beyond the Reclamation Dam.

Construction of Sand Dam - Construction of the cycloned sand portion of the dam was commenced on the Brenda site in the spring of 1970. The tailings are transported by gravity in a 30 inch diameter woodstave pipeline, over a distance of approximately 9,000 feet from the mill to a point high on the left abutment above the damsite. At this point, the dam-building sand is obtained by a two-stage cycloning process and is then transported hydraulically through a pipeline for deposition on the dam. Water is added after the second stage cyclones for transportation purposes.

The slimes from the cyclones are transported by pipeline to the dam where they are discharged upstream from the crest of the dam in a conventional spigotting operation, to form a broad, low-permeability beach between the pond and the sand dam. When necessary, slimes can be dumped directly into the pond by means of a channel located on the side of the valley.

Initially, construction was attempted using single stage cycloning, but a suitable product was not achieved owing to a high clay mineral content in the tailings. Consequently, a second stage of cycloning was adopted. At first, temporary second-stage cyclones were situated on the crest of the starter dam and discharged directly to the downstream side. This method of operation was continued for about 1 year, but the arrangement was inconvenient and the quantity of production was considerably below that projected in the design phase. This resulted in insufficient sand being made to ensure raising of the sand dam above the starter dam crest level in time for the spring freshet of 1971. Consequently, in late fall and during the winter of 1970-71, an additional 15 feet was added to the top of the starter dam by placement of glacial till borrow material. This addition was founded partly on the original starter dam and partly on the cycloned sand slope at the back of the starter dam. The section on Figure No. 3 illustrates this measure.

In 1971, a bank of second stage cyclones was completed on the abutment below the first stage cyclone house and operations were commenced with that facility. Because water had to be added at the second stage cyclones to permit transport of the sands through the pipelines to the dam, there was considerable excess water in the sands at the point of discharge and very flat slopes resulted, about 10 horizontal to 1 vertical or flatter. Such flat slopes would not suit the critical dam raising schedule of the early years and construction methods were consequently reviewed. A form of construction similar to that used for conventional hydraulic fill placement was adopted. This involved the construction of cells and the discharge of the diluted sand underflow in a direction parallel to the dam axis rather than transverse to it.

The cell building may be seen on Figures 4, 5 and 6. Sand dykes are pushed up by bulldozer around an area approximately 300 feet long parallel to the dam axis by 100 feet wide. The sand-water mix from the cyclones is discharged into one end of the cell and the sand is deposited at a slope of approximately 25 horizontal on 1 vertical. The excess water accumulates at the low end of the cell and, although some

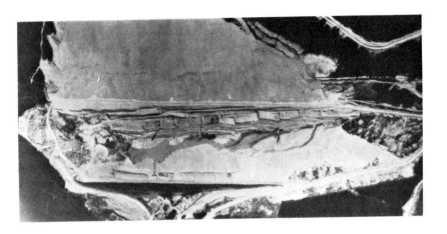

Vertical air photograph of Brenda tailing dam, August 1972. Figure No. 4

of the water percolates downward into the sand and emerges from the base of the dam through the finger drains, most of the water is decanted from the low end of the cells through plastic pipes which extend down the slope of the dam to discharge at a point where the erosive effects will not damage the deposited sand slope.

When a cell is filled, involving some 6 to 8 feet of deposited sand, the spigot lines from the cyclones are transferred to another cell and the bulldozers scrape a foot or two off the top of the deposited material in the completed cell to build a new set of perimeter dykes, following which a new cycle of deposition is started.

Slimes beach construction has continued in the same manner as that planned from the outset, with a slimes line laid along the upstream side of the main crest and discharging to the beach through spigots. The spigot pipes are small diameter plastic lines

243

Brenda: building dyke in cell. Figure No. 5

Brenda: cell filling. Note cyclone house on left
abutment.   Figure No. 6

extending down the steep part of the dam slope and
discharging onto the relatively flat areas of the
beach. It has been possible to maintain an adequate
beach throughout the entire two-year life of this
project, even though a considerable excess of water
has accumulated due to two years of extremely high
inflow from the natural catchment. The phenomenon
that has been most advantageous in permitting maintenance of a safe and adequate beach between the pond
and the pervious sand dam is related to the slopes
at which the slimes tend to deposit above and below
pond water level. Generally, it is found that the
slimes beach has a slope of between 1% and 2% when
deposited above pond level as compared with between
10% and 20% when deposited under water. Thus, when
the pond is low the beach becomes very broad with
any increment of volume being spread thinly over a
large area. When the water rises and overruns the
dry season beach, the steeper underwater deposition
slopes aid in limiting spread of the beach so the
same increment of volume is deposited in a thicker

245

layer over a lesser but still adequate width of beach.

The relatively limited storage capacity of the tailings pond at the bottom of the reservoir has necessitated planning from the outset for winter dam construction over the first two to three years of the project life, and construction was continued throughout the 1970-71 and the 1971-72 winters. This involved extensive snow removal work and considerable care to avoid inclusion of large banks of snow or layers of ice within the sand dam. Observations and follow-up investigations confirm that there have been no extensive inclusions of ice or snow to-date. A few localized zones of frozen sand and minor pockets of snow and ice are known to exist within the structure. However, these are not harmful structurally, provided that they do not interfere with drainage of the dam, and field observations confirm that there are no such zones sufficiently extensive to affect the seepage patterns.

Concerning construction problems, the initial difficulties with poor quality sand were solved by double cycloning. The temporary arrangement involving portable cyclones on the crest of the dam produced high quality sands and deposited these at relatively steep slopes, approximately 4 horizontal to 1 vertical. However, the high heads and velocities required to transport the first stage underflow to these temporary on-dam cyclones created extensive pipe wear problems. Also, maintenance of satisfactory pressures on these second stage cyclones was difficult. Generally, the mechanics of the operation improved considerably with the completion of the second stage cycloning on the hillside above the dam. Sand production at present averages about 40 percent of the total tailings.

Continued difficulties were experienced with abrasion of steel pipes, particularly on the sand lines. Recently, almost all of the sand lines have been of plastic pipe which not only has greatly reduced wear problems but has also proved extremely versatile.

The lightweight pipe has reduced handling costs for moving of pipelines and it is quite common to see two men carrying a forty foot section of 6 inch pipe on their shoulders, a feat that would have been impossible with the steel pipes formerly used. The plastic pipes are joined in some cases by victaulic couplings and in other cases by field-welding procedures. The plastic pipe can also be laid in snake-like bends such that expansion and contraction can be readily provided for.

Difficulties were experienced in the early cell construction work due to failures of the dykes that retain the cells, with consequent washouts of the completed work on the slopes below. The cause of dyke failure was found to be saturation, after prolonged operation, of the relatively loose sand dykes. This problem was solved by limiting the period of cell operation. The water is now shut off well before the perimeter dykes attain full saturation, with the cell filling period limited to six or eight hours.

Design - While there are numerous minor and detailed considerations involved in the design of a sand tailings dam the most critical items are related to stability of the structure under both static and dynamic loading. In areas where earthquake loading is likely, failure by liquefaction poses the most serious potential problem.

For liquefaction to occur under seismic loading, sands of the gradation common to tailings dams normally must be saturated and in a relatively loose state. Therefore, the main protections against liquefaction are drainage and densification. In the extreme, these two provisions tend to be mutually exclusive, such that:

1. When the sand is completely drained, liquefaction is unlikely regardless of the density, provided the slope is well below the angle of internal friction of the sand, and

2. When the sand is dense, liquefaction is unlikely even though the material may be completely saturated.

In tailings dam designs for areas rated as low seismic risks it is usually more economic to strive for complete drainage rather than for high densities. For areas of high seismicity, such as the West Coast of North America, it is deemed prudent at this stage of our knowledge to require both high densities and good drainage.

The Brenda tailings dam is located in an area of low seismicity with a predicted 100 year return acceleration of only 2 percent of gravity. The original design, which includes a large stabilizing rock toe fill, extensive underdrainage, flat downstream slopes, and which utilizes free-draining cycloned sand as a construction material, is considered conservative. In effect, the ultimate tailings pond will be retained by a large mass of relatively loose, dry sand, and the lower portion of this sand mass will be buttressed by the large rockfill toe dam. For this design, density of the cycloned sand is not considered critical, provided it is kept drained. The design includes an allowance in the freeboard requirement for any settlement that might occur owing to seismic shocks.

Recent Field Investigations - The recent field studies made at the Brenda site have been directed mainly at determining the effectiveness of the under-drainage system in maintaining a drained sand dam. Some work was also done on evaluating the in-situ densities achieved by the construction procedures used.

Piezometric observations representative of internal water conditions in the Brenda dam, are shown by the section on Figure No. 7. An examination of these data shows that the saturation level within the Brenda dam is low despite the excess quantities of water being applied in the hydraulic fill operations. Indications are that "through-seepage" is very low and

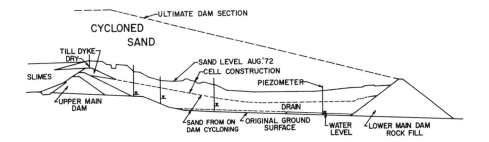

Brenda: typical section with internal water levels.
Figure No. 7

that most of the water observed comes from the construction operation.

Observations made over a period of several days
on two piezometers situated within the cell construction areas showed that these piezometric levels
remained essentially low even during hydraulic filling.
Although the sands beneath the cell undoubtedly have
relatively high water contents, the water percolating
from the cells does not expell all air from the pores
of the material and, as a consequence, these sands are
not saturated.

The internal piezometric observations obtained
to-date from the Brenda dam confirm the original expectations that the ultimate phreatic line will be
very low and that practically all seepage will be
intercepted by the finger drains, well upstream from
the toe of the embankment. Moreover, even the large
quantities of water involved in the hydraulic placement of the cycloned sands are not sufficient to
appreciably raise the line of saturation within the
dam.

Seepage through the ultimate dam is expected to be minimal, and seepage estimates based on flow net construction are in the order of 100 U.S.G.P.M. The present flow of water collected in the Reclamation Dam pond is mainly the result of the hydraulic fill operation and is about 1,000 U.S.G.P.M.

In-situ density determinations, using conventional testing equipment, were made at ground surface and in the bottom of test pits. In an effort to assess the densities at depth, indirect methods of testing have been used, involving the use of both dynamic and static penetration tests.

At this point a brief discussion on penetration tests is in order.

The energy required to drive or press a penetration device into the soil has long been used by Soils Engineers to assess the density of soils, although considerable controversy exists in the profession concerning the accuracy of the various correlations in use. There is however little doubt that such tests do provide a qualitative, if not a quantitative, assessment of in-situ density. Until quite recently the most widely used procedure in North America was the "so-called Standard Penetration Test" (SPT), a dynamic test which involves driving a 2 inch diameter heavy-wall split-spoon sampler, using a 140 pound hammer dropping freely a distance of 30 inches. The number of blows required to drive the sampler 1 foot is called the "N" value for the soil. Various correlations have been developed that relate the "N" value for a cohesionless soil with its density. (6, 7, 8, 17, 22)

Other forms of the dynamic test involve the driving of solid steel cones by drop hammer in the same manner as for the Standard Penetration Test. Blow counts from such pseudo SPT investigations are converted to "N" values by equations that include allowance for such things as dynamic energy, presence or absence of an outer casing, groundwater levels, shape and size of cone, and relative size of the various drill components. (6, 15, 17, 20)

Outside North America, the static type of test has long been in common use. The static test involves the measurement of the force required to press a steel cone through the soil at a constant rate. The rods used for pressing the cone are sheathed in an outer casing so that side friction is eliminated and the measured resistance corresponds only to the actual force applied at the cone tip. Approximate correlations have been developed emperically between the "N" values obtained from the Standard Penetration Test and the q_c values obtained from the static test. The correlations usually take the form:

$$q_c = KN$$

where q_c = the cone point resistance in kilograms per square centimetre; N = Standard Penetration Test value in blows per foot; and K is a correlation coefficient. Values for K range from as low as 2 for very fine silty sands to as high as 20 for sandy gravels. (2, 3, 6, 15, 16, 17, 18, 19, 20)

The static penetration test equipment used in the Brenda evaluation was the Dutch Cone. The Dutch Cone has a 60 degree point and is approximately 3.5 centimetres in diameter. The dynamic penetration test (RKL Penetration Test) used a 1 inch diameter rod and a $1\frac{1}{4}$ inch diameter cone point driven by a 50 pound hammer, dropping 30 inches.

A typical Dutch Cone penetration log from the Brenda dam is presented on Figure No. 8. Also shown on this figure are the results obtained from an RKL dynamic penetration test hole located adjacent to the Dutch Cone test hole. The similarity in the configuration of the two plots is readily apparent. In this particular case the sands were moist but unsaturated throughout and the hole created by the dynamic cone point remained open during driving, so that virtually no wall friction developed on the driving

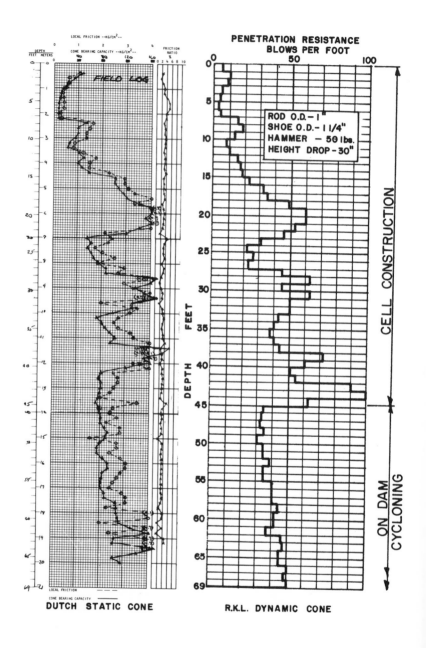

Comparative penetration test data. Figure No. 8

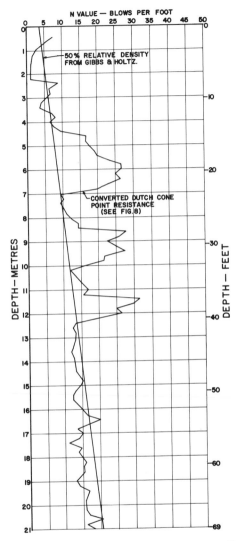

Dutch Cone data from Figure No. 8 vs. "N."

Figure No. 9

rods. Under these conditions the recorded dynamic penetration resistance is considered to be representative of the end-resistance developed while driving the cone point through the sand.

Figure No. 9 presents the log of the Dutch Cone hole of Figure No. 8, with the Dutch Cone values converted to Standard Penetration Test (SPT) "N" values. The relationship $q_c = 6N$ was used for the conversion. Also shown on Figure No. 9 is a line representing 50 percent relative density. This line was established on the basis of the commonly used Gibbs and Holtz relationship (7, 8) between "N" values and relative density. This relative density correlation is considered approximate only and is presented here mainly to provide a means of comparing the Dutch Cone results with the more commonly used Gibbs and Holtz relative density relationship. The latter relationship has had extensive use in recent years by many investigators studying liquefaction problems in granular soils. (e.g. 21)

An examination of Figures No. 8 and 9 reveals that wide variations in density exist within the Brenda dam. Most of these variations are thought to be attributable to the hydraulic fill type construction procedures being used. The highest densities are obtained near the top of each lift within the cells, where the sand is exposed to considerable bulldozer traffic. The very low densities are considered to be indicative of either local slimes pockets or zones of very loose sand, such as might occur in the uncompacted dykes that enclose each cell.

In summary, the penetration tests confirm that the present method of dam construction produces a dam of variable density. The sands placed in the cells and subject to some bulldozer traffic appear to have relative densities in the order of 50 percent or slightly greater. The sands bulldozed into dykes during cell construction are loose and appear to have relative densities of 40 percent or less. The sands that were placed during the early stages of construction, using direct cycloning methods exhibit a more uniform density, but appear to have lower average densities than those presently being obtained in the sand cells. The several direct density measurements that were made, using conventional testing equipment, confirm that the near surface sands range in density from loose to medium dense with the bulk of the material being relatively loose.

Obviously, the cell method of construction could be modified to produce a more uniformly dense fill, by the addition of a minor amount of compaction while the cell is being filled, and by compaction of the retaining dykes as they are constructed. At the Brenda project however, where the seismic risk is relatively low and the design is based on a free-draining, unsaturated, relatively loose sand dam, additional compaction is not considered necessary.

Gibraltar Mines Ltd.

General - Gibraltar Mine is in Central British Colum-bia just east of the Fraser River and about 40 miles north of the town of Williams Lake. The mine is a low-grade copper, open-pit operation and had a rated capacity of 30,000 tons per day. However, the rated production has been exceeded right from the outset and capacity at this time is in the order of 40,000 tons per day. The present tailings facility will provide for storage of approximately 220,000,000 tons of tailings.

The Gibraltar tailings pond and dam are situated in a separate valley approximately 4 miles north of the mill and mine area. In respect of topography for the tailings pond, the Gibraltar site is considerably better than the Brenda site. At Gibraltar a long, flat valley gradient just upstream of the dam site permits much greater volumes of storage with a lower dam than at Brenda.

The dam shown on Figure No. 10 will be approxi-mately 8,000 feet long on completion and will rise approximately 300 feet above original streambed. The main embankment will be of sand with a near ver-tical upstream face involving interfingering of slimes from the pond with the dam-building sands. A small,

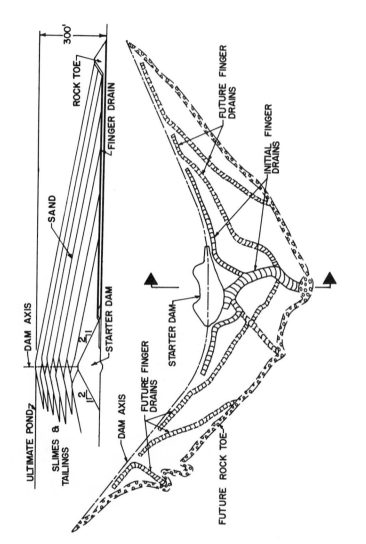

Gibraltar Mines tailing dam. Figure No. 10

100 foot high starter dam was constructed on the line of the ultimate crest. Underdrains in the form of open rock core finger drains are provided as shown on Figure No. 10. Topography, at this site, is such that a large, rock toe-dam similar to that at Brenda is not required to contain the sands at the downstream side. However, provision is made in the design for trimming of the downstream toe of the ultimate dam by means of a low, rock toe-dyke, extending from one abutment to the other.

As at Brenda, the preliminary planning studies demonstrated that there would be adequate sand available from the tailings for construction of this facility and a cycloned sand dam was therefore recommended. The starter dam was constructed almost exclusively of local glacial-till materials which were readily available at the immediate dam site, with a limited amount of local gravel borrow for drainage facilities under the starter dam. The initial finger drains, which are constructed of coarse rock with filters over, were also built from local borrow material, the rock from a local quarry and the gravel from local gravel borrow pits. The choice of a rock quarry for production of the rock in the drains was necessitated by the extremely friable and weathered quality of the pit waste materials in the initial excavation. However, the underdrainage facilities provided initially were kept minimal, only sufficient for the first year or two of operation, and it is intended that subsequent underdrainage facilities will be built with pit waste rock, and filtered by locally borrowed gravel.

Water reclaim for recycling to the mill is by pump barge on the tailings pond. Seepage water and water discharged with the dam-building sands is collected at the Water Recovery Dam downstream and returned to the reclaim water system. At this site a limited amount of water release is permitted under controlled quality conditions.

Gibraltar tailing dam single stage cycloning.
Figure No. 11

Construction of Sand Dam - The Gibraltar Mine commenced operation in March 1972, and the sand dam
building was commenced in May 1972.

The procedure initially adopted for construction
involves cycloning on the dam in a single stage
operation as shown in Figure No. 11. Two rows of
trestles, one on either side of the crest line,
support the cyclones. The sand is discharged directly in zones, alternating from upstream to downstream
lines.

Average sand produced runs at about 25 percent of
the total mill production. The underflow from the
cyclones is a very high density pulp, approximately
70 percent solids. This is a ropy discharge and the
slopes on the cones below the cyclones vary from about
$3\frac{1}{2}$ horizontal to 1 vertical near the crests to about
$4\frac{1}{2}$ horizontal to 1 vertical at the toes of the slopes.

Particular care was taken during start-up to ensure that no mishaps occurred to pour fine, slimy
materials onto the finger drains. The cyclones were
first operated on the upstream line for approximately
two weeks, to ensure that a good quality product was
being obtained. They were then set in operation on
the downstream line and care was taken to prevent any

slime discharge or the erosion of natural, silty
soils by the flow from the cyclones. When the cyclones stationed at the top of the starter dam were
first started, plywood chutes were placed on the
slope of the starter dam, carrying the initial flow
harmlessly down the slope until a fully developed
sand slope was attained.

As work proceeded and areas on the abutments not
covered by finger drains were reached, some partially
saturated conditions developed with water emerging
from the toes of the sand slopes. This water was
collected and guided in special ditches to avoid
erosion of the natural, silty glacial tills and the
deposition of that silt on top of the finger drains.
Occasional mishaps did occur, and these were corrected very quickly by a bulldozer scraping the silt
materials from the filters on the drains, restoring
them to their original porosity.

Some construction is planned for the coming winter,
although cycloning will not be necessary during the
most severe months of January and February. Special
precautions will be taken to ensure against accumulations of water and snow that could cause voids
within the ultimate sand dam.

PHYSICAL PROPERTIES OF TAILINGS

Figure No. 12 presents grain size curves for total
tailings and cycloned tailings at the Brenda and
Gibraltar tailings dams. Figure No. 13 presents the
relationship between density and permeability for
cycloned tailings sands for the two projects. Figure
No. 14 presents the relationship between triaxial
failure envelopes and density for the Brenda tailings
sands. Table No. I presents additional typical data
for cycloned sands from the Brenda and Gibraltar
tailings dams.

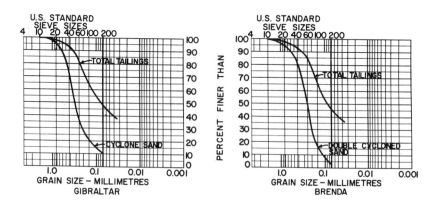

Typical grain size distribution curves.

Figure No. 12

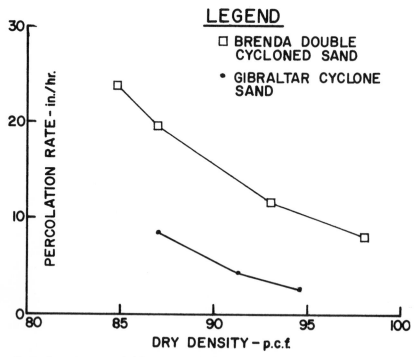

Density-permeability relationships.   Figure No. 13

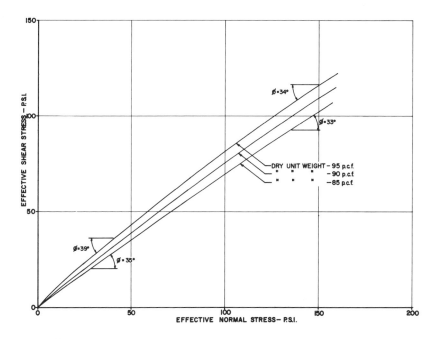

Brenda sand; density-strength relationships.

Figure No. 14

CONCLUSIONS

1. Safe, economical tailings dams, designed to satisfy even the most stringent seismic requirements, can be constructed, using tailings as the major construction material. However, in most areas the design and construction procedures used for such dams must be based on criteria developed for conventional water supply dams, using downstream methods of construction suitably modified to satisfy the special requirements of the mining industry.

2. The Brenda and Gibraltar tailings dams provide two examples of major tailings dams being constructed by downstream dam building techniques. Both structures are located in areas of relatively low seismic activity and consequently the major design consideration has

T A B L E   N O .   I

CYCLONED SANDS

	Specific Gravity	% Passing #200 Sieve	Max. Density pcf	Min. Density pcf	e_{min}	e_{max}	Range in Field Density pcf	Av. Field Density pcf
GIBRALTAR								
Cycloned Sand	2.70	10-12	110	81	0.54	1.08	89 - 94	91.5
BRENDA								
Cycloned Sand	2.71	3- 6	105	81	0.61	1.08	82 - 97	91.3

been to achieve a free-draining sand embankment that will never become saturated. The results of field studies for the Brenda project confirm that the dam does meet these requirements. Similar evaluations have yet to be done for the Gibraltar project, but preliminary observations lead to the expectations of similar satisfactory results.

3. Construction of tailings dams in areas of high seismicity poses more severe problems to the designer than those encountered at the Brenda and Gibraltar sites. Not only must the design resist liquefaction but it must also resist excessive settlement with possible resulting tension cracking under seismic shocks; large tension cracks through the dam could lead to failure by piping or erosion. Consequently, dams constructed in areas of high seismic risk require satisfactory compaction as well as adequate drainage.

REFERENCES

(1) Allen, P. F., "Tailings Disposal at the Morenci Concentrator", Mining Engineering, July 1956, 729-32.

(2) Begemann, H.K.S.P., "The Use of the Static Soil Penetrometer in Holland", NZ Engineering, Feb. 15, 1963.

(3) Begemann, H.K.S.P., "The Friction Jacket Cone as an Aid in Determining the Soil Profile".

(4) Casagrande, L., and MacIver, B. N., "Design and Construction of Tailings Dams", Symposium on Stability for Open Pit Mining, Vancouver, November 1970.

(5)   Debry, R., and Alvarez, L., "Seismic Failures of Chilean Tailings Dams", J. of the Soil Mechanics and Foundations Division, Proc. A.S.C.E., 93, No. SM6, 1967, 237-260.

(6)   DeMello, Victor F. B., "The Standard Penetration Test", Proceedings of Fourth Pan American Conference on Soil Mechanics and Foundation Engineering, Puerto Rico, 1971.

(7)   Gibbs, H. J., and Holtz, W. G., "Research on Determining the Density of Sands by Spoon Penetration Testing", Proceedings of Fourth International Conference on Soil Mechanics and Foundation Engineering, London, 1957.

(8)   Gibbs, H. J., "Standard Penetration Test for Sand Denseness", Proceedings of Fourth Pan American Conference on Soil Mechanics and Foundation Engineering, Puerto Rico, 1971.

(9)   Klohn, Earle J., "Design and Construction of Tailings Dams", CIM Transactions: Vol. LXXV, 1972.

(10)   Klohn, Earle J., "Evaluation of Tailings Disposal Schemes in the Southwestern United States", Internal report, 1968.

(11)   Klohn, Earle J., "Tailings Dams in B. C.", 2nd Symposium Stability of Open Pit Mines, November 1971, Vancouver.

(12)   Klohn, Earle J., and McManus, K. J., "Control of Pollution from Mine Wastes", Australian Mining, November 1971.

(13)   Wright Engineers Ltd., Golder, Brawner and Associates Ltd., Ripley, Klohn & Leonoff International Ltd., "Tentative Design Guide for Mine Waste Embankments in Canada", Prepared for the Dept. of Energy, Mines & Resources, Ottawa, Canada, 1972, Information Canada book shops.

(14)   MacIver, Bruce N., "How the Soil Engineer Can Help the Mill Man in the Construction of Proper Tailings Dams", Engineering and Mining Journal, May 1961.

(15)   Meigh, A. C., and Nixon, I. K., "Comparison of In-Situ Tests for Granular Soils", Proceedings of Fifth International Conference on Soil Mechanics and Foundation Engineering, Paris, 1961.

(16)   Meyerhof, G. G., "Penetration Tests and Bearing Capacity of Cohesionless Soils", ASCE Vol. 82, SMI, January 1956.

(17)   Sanglerat, G., "The Penetrometer and Soil Exploration", Elseveir Publishing Company 1972, pp. 182-184 and 260-268.

(18)   Schmertmann, John H., "Static Cone to Compute Static Settlement over Sand", ASCE Vol. 96, No. SMI 3, May 1970, pp. 1011-1043.

(19)   Schmertmann, John H., "Static Cone Penetrometers for Soil Exploration", Civil Engineering, Vol. 37, No. 6, June 1967.

(20)   Schultze, E., and Melzer, K. J., "The Determination of the Density and Modulus of Compressibility of Non Cohesive Soils by Soundings", Proceedings of Sixth International Conference on Soil Mechanics and Foundation Engineering, Montreal, 1965, pp. 354-358.

(21)   Seed, H. Bolton, and Idriss, Izzat M., "Simplified Procedure for Evaluating Soil Liquefaction Potential", ASCE Vol. 97, SM 9, September 1971, pp. 1249-1273.

(22)   Terzaghi and Peck, "Soil Mechanics in Engineering Practice", John Wiley and Sons, Second Edition, 1968, p. 492.

DISCUSSION

A. M. LAIRD (Placer Development Limited):
Several of the speakers have emphasized the need
for compaction. Since compaction normally would
cost several hundred thousand dollars a year for
a large operation, I think it would be desirable
if Mr. Klohn could elaborate on his opinion of the
need or the lack of need for compaction and methods
by which it can be avoided.

E. J. KLOHN: What we have said - and we hope
we've not been misunderstood in this talk - is
basically this: that if you have a nonseismic
area, your problem is not liquefaction. Your
problem is being able to build a structure that
will remain stable statically for these conditions:
downstream cycloning, any method of depositing sand
in a downstream direction provided you don't have
seepage, concentrated seepage, or a high phreatic
line. That is, if you provide adequate sub-
drainage and internal drainage, this should provide
you with a stable structure at almost any height.
Now, at the extreme other end of the coin, we've
said that in areas that are subject to seismicity -
that is zone three where you're expecting large
earthquakes - you require compaction and drainage.
Between these two extremes is a big gray area.

If you're speaking of Canada, and I presume
you are, zone one (the hundred-year predicted
return period in zone one area is expressed as
percentage G) the boundaries are one to three
percentage G which is 0.01 to 0.03. Zone two is
three to six or 0.03 to 0.06. Those two zones, if
we can believe the people that are predicting
earthquakes, I would suggest are low seismic areas
because, when you move in a zone three, you're
moving from a boundary of six up to a boundary of in
excess of a hundred, if you use the Canadian
National Building Code isotherms or isobars of equal
return periods. What we essentially have said is
that in zero seismic areas and in areas of low

seismicity using cyclone sand - and this is clean free-draining sand - installing proper drainage facilities, and certainly having control of your construction procedures, you should not have to heavily compact the material to have a stable structure. When you move into highly seismic areas, we definitely feel you do.

I didn't have a chance to comment on the value of density. I don't believe that we were looking at one example, but the material being placed in the cells using a hydraulic fill type of procedure ranges in relative density from a little below 50 percent to above 50 and the average is above 50. It is 40 percent in those dikes which don't get much compaction, but it tends to be above 50 percent when the dozer traffic is traveling back and forth over the material being put in the cells. The cyclone sand is about 40 percent relative density.

DESIGN CONSTRUCTION AND OPERATION

OF TAILING SYSTEMS

G. T. SAZONOV

DEPUTY CHIEF ENGINEER

DESIGN DEPARTMENT

MEKHANOBR INSTITUTE

LENINGRAD, USSR

INTRODUCTION

Tailing systems may be definded as a complex of constructions and equipment for hydraulic transport and disposal of Concentrator wastes together with water reclamation and cleaning of effluents.

These four systems are:

- Tailing transport by hydraulic means,

- Tailing disposal by hydraulic means,

- Water reclamation,

- Chemical cleaning of effluents.

The systems are closely interconnected, and each affects considerably the choice of a plan in the design of other systems.

The actuality of the environment protection problem asks for great attention to be paid, while designing, to the effluent purification system. However, as the tailing disposal area is a purification installation in itself, and complete reclamation of water permits, practically, no discharge of clarified water from the tailing pond, attention is to be paid, basically, not to deep purification of effluents up to sanitary and fishery protection standards for water discharge into natural reservoirs but to questions of water preparation for a complete reclamation taking into account the water requirements of the technological process. This trend in design will contribute to a cardinal solution to the problem of protecting natural reservoirs from chemical and mechanical pollution; in a number of cases it will simplify the process and reduce the costs of effluent purification. The experience of the Mekhanobr Institute proves that, practically, all ferrous and non-ferrous ores are treated according to flowsheets including a complete water reclaiming.

Therefore a conclusion may be drawn that the designing of tailing systems must begin with the working out of a detailed and accurate water balance in view of a complete water reclaiming. At this stage the designing is to be carried out in close contact with mineral processing engineers.

When the flowsheet is intended for bulk flotation or magnetic separation, the design of tailing systems is considerably simplified, and operation is cheaper on account of the use of collective systems for hydraulic transport of tailing disposal areas with subsequent water reclamation.

If the flowsheet is for selective flotation, in a number of cases the design must provide for a selective system of hydraulic transport, hydraulic waste disposal and water reclaiming in order to accomplish a water reclaiming per circuit through the tailings

disposal area, thus achieving a complete water reclama
In such cases the tailing system design is more complicated and the costs rise. This must be taken into
consideration by the mineral processing engineers
while choosing a flowsheet for mineral processing.
Then, the aim must be: thickening of the tailings
prioreto hydraulic transportation; this makes possible
a recycling of water per circuit at the concentrator
and considerable reduction in the diameter of water
and pulp pipelines, as well as the size of pumps and
accessories.

Actuality of the environment protection problem
calls for serious concern not only in the protection
of surface reservoirs from pollution but also in the
protection of the underground water basin. That is
why the question of filtration through the body and the
base of tailing disposal areas and technical measures
for avoiding the underground water basin pollution
is of special importance.

The protection of air against dust produced by tailing storage areas has great importance too.

A conclusion may be drawn that the basic requirements to be considered for tailing disposal area design are principles of sanitary engineering, together
with a maximal economic efficiency of technical decisions, coordinated with the mineral processing
technology.

The tailing systems are to meet the following
requirements:

- Air and water basins should not be polluted;

- Threat of potential inundation of townships
  industrial buildings and constructions is to be
  prevented;

- Reliable (continous) hydraulic transport and

waste disposal are to be ensured, as well as the recycling of clarified water, following their special treatment in course of the whole operation time;

- Reuse of waste tailing and plant growth on tailing after the shutting down of the tailing disposal area are to be ensured;

- Maximal economic efficiency.

TAILING SYSTEMS BASIC DESIGN PROBLEMS

- Choice of a collective or selective flowsheet for tailing systems;

- Selection of tailing disposal area type: built by hydraulic means or "filled".

- Location of the tailing disposal area on filtering or impervious-to-waste tailing grounds;

- Selection of a hydraulic transport system: by gravity, combined pressure/gravity-pressure system; with or without preliminary thickening;

- Selection of operation regime and calculation of hydraulic transport system (velocity of pulp flow, size and materials for pulp pipelines, location and conhections between pulp pumping stations etc)

- Section of height and material for tailing dams ("fill" type);

- Choice of method for building tailing disposal area by hydraulic means and filling of the settling pond;

- Selection and calculation of the settling pond volume and the system of flood and clarified waters derivation;

- Selection of effluent chemical purification and water treatment flowsheet.

The value of the tailing system is essentially determined by its economic efficiency, the simplicity of its construction and convenience of operation, reliable equipment and structures, and by the unconditional following of sanitary and fishery standards.

SYSTEM TAILINGS HYDRAULIC TRANSPORT

This system comprises main, distribution and emergency pulp pipelines, pumping stations, equipment and structures for waste pulp thickening, emergency basins and others.

The selection of a system for hydraulic transport of tailing is based on a techno-economic comparison of variants of hydraulic transport systems and pulp thickening constructions, together with a clarified water recycling system.

The formula for the calculation of pressure hydraulic transport of waste is to be chosen from table No. 1.

It is recommended that calculation of a gravity hydraulic transport of tailings be carried out accordir to the method of V.S. Knoroz and P.D. Evdokimov.

Launder flow capacity under critical pulp flow conditions should be assumed as not less than 100 percent of the rated launder capacity.

When a tailing hydraulic transport system is to be reconstructed, use of the practical data obtained on the hydraulic regime of the system is recommended.

The results of hydraulic transport system calculatio should be corrected by data obtained by special experimental investigations.

When determining the rated hydraulic slope of pressure pulp pipelines for hydraulic transport systems, it is recommended to proceed from an analysis of identical systems.

The practice of design at the Mekhanobr Institute proves that pressure/gravity systems for hydraulic transport are to be preferred.

In that case, the life of pulp pipelines is longer when compared to a gravity system, thanks to the possibility of pulp velocity control; power consumption savings are achieved too in comparison with the pressure/gravity transport, as the total of power consumption for hydraulic transport and water reclamation is less.

This is due to the fact that hydraulic resistance in water pipelines is less than in pulp pipelines, and efficiency of centrifugal water pumps is higher than that of centrifugal sand pumps. It is to be added that there is no need for expenses connected with wear of sand pumps.

Steel, pig iron, as well as prestressed reinforced concrete, asbestos-cement plastic and veneer pipes may be used as pressure pulp pipelines.

The operating experience and the practice of design at the Mekhanobr Institute pionts to the fact that in designing main pressure pulp pipelines, steel pipes with weld joints are to be preferred. In operation, steel pipes are well polished by pulp, thus allowing the hydraulic slope to be lowered to 0.005-0.004; and the life of these pipes, while used for the hydraulic transport of copper, iron, apatite and nepheline ores exceeds 10 years.

The diameter and the material of the main pulp and water lines should correspond to the diameter and material of pipelines for reclaimed water.

It is recommended to design main pulp and water

pipelines on one common route providing for their possib interchangeability. Thus the following problems are solved;

- the life of pulp pipelines is increased;

- the number of standby lines of pulp and water pipes is reduced, thus allowing a better economic efficiency, in particular, when a selective flow-sheet is assumed for the tailing systems.

- water pipelines are cleaned of lime build-up by the passing of pulp through them;

- construction and operation are simplified.

The selection of size and material of main pulp pipelines is done after techno-economic comparison of different variants, taking into consideration the points mentioned above.

It is recommended that pulp pumping stations, located inside the concentrator or at the mill site, be designed with sumps, thus providing for a necessary emergency holding capacity. This ensures a better maneuverability, a rapid start and the reliable operation of the pulp pumping station.

It is expedient to locate the pulp pumping stations along the route of the main pulp pipeline without cutting the flow, providing for devices used for hydraulic impact damping (air columns, valve for pressure reduction etc). A flowsheet for location of pulp pumping stations along the main pulp pipe-line route with cutting of the flow (i.e. with sumps) may be recommended only if well grounded from the technical and economic standpoint.

The selection of type and size of sand pumps is done according to the pulp flow and the head pressure, allowing for limitations, determined by the solid component size, the pulp density and conforming to standards for pumping equipment serial production.

While installing sand pumps in pulp pumping stations not less than 100 percent standby pumps are to be provided for. In conditions of considerable and rapid wear of pumps at pulp pumping stations of hydraulic transport systems, a double reserve is to be provided for.

The following conclusion may be drawn: to reduce capital and operation costs and to increase the safety and convenience of operation, preference must be given, while designing, to pressure/gravity tailing hydraulic transportation systems with unification of pulp and water line diameters, and the ensuring of their interchangeability.

SYSTEM OF HYDRAULIC TAILING DISPOSAL
(Tailing Disposal Area)

Tailing disposal areas built by hydraulic means or "filled" are to be chosen depending on the size of tailings.

Tailing disposal areas built by hydraulic means are to be preferred in all cases when tailings contain less than 60 percent of particles - 0.074 mm (22 mesh).

The "filled" type of disposal area is to be used when tailings contain more than 80 percent of particles - 0.074 mm.

For tailing containing from 60 to 80 percent of particles-0.074 mm, both types of disposal area can be used, taking into account the physicomechanical properties of the tailing.

In the USSR the tailing disposal areas are built as a rule by hydraulic means. The filled dams for such areas are to be designed with soils having a filtering capacity greater than that of the tailings.

Moreover, it is necessary to foresee the interception, the organized derivation, and the use of filtering water. The dimensions of the filled dam are to be chosen on condition that water will be clarified in a sedimentation pond and, in winter, tailings are to be stored under ice.

There are two main methods of hydraulic filling of the tailing area: the "trestle" method and the "zenith" method.

The "trestle" method can be used both for the pressure and the gravity hydraulic transport of tailings.

The "zenith" method is to be used only for the pressure hydraulic transport of tailings.

Regardless of the method used, two zones, set up of tails of different granulometric analysis, are to be considered in the cross section of the hydraulically filled dam:

I - Bearing prism, where the coarsest (sand) fractions of tailings are disposed:

II - Tailing pond zone, where the finest (dusty and argillaceous) fractions of tailings are disposed

The distance from the edge of the outer slope of the hydraulically filled dam to the boundary line of the tailing pond (breadth of the bearing prism) can be determined by V. A. Melentiev's formula:

$$X_{bp} = [0.01 \sum_{d=0.1\text{ mm}}^{d=d_{max}} \Phi_i] L, \quad \text{where}$$

$$0.01 \sum_{d=0.1\text{ mm}}^{d=d_{max}} \Phi_i = \text{Content of the fraction} + 0.1 \text{ mm in the initial tailings}$$

L= distance from the edge of the outer slope to the decant tower at the considered stage of the dam construction.

The bearing prism breadth (X_{bp}) should satisfy the condition of the tailing filtration strength

$$X_{bp} \geqslant \quad L \text{ min}$$

$$L \text{ min} \quad = h_i \, (m_1 - m_2),$$

where L_{min} = permissible distance from the edge of the outer slope to the boundary of water in the settling pond

h_i – height from the base of the structure to the surface of the deposited layer under consideration

$$m_1 = \frac{1}{]\,cr}$$

$]\,cp$ – permissible piezometric slope to be assumed from 0.07

to 0.125 (according to the design practice of the Mekhanobr Institute)

m_2 = ratio of the horizontal projection of the structure to its height

The physicomechinical characteristics of tailings (according to the zones), determined as a result of practice in nonferrous ore tailings disposal, are given in table No. 2

At the preliminary determination of the dam horizontal projection it is advised to use information out of the designs of the analogous dams in operation. As a result of experience in designing and exploitation of the tailing dams of nonferrous ore dressing mills in the USSR, it can be said that the stability of the downstream dam slopes is guaranteed at the ratio

height : horizontal projection = 1:4, the height of
tailing deposits being h≤ 100 m.

When designing a tailing disposal area, it is
necessary to take into consideration that in the
tailing pond zone the upper part of the dusty-argilleou
tailing deposits is of flowing consistency (like
a heavy liquid) and, in case of a disastrous breakdown
of the dam, it might flow out of the tailing disposal
area in form of a silt flow.

When disigning and operating tailing disposal areas,
utmost care should be taken of the dependability of the
corresponding structures at differnent process conditio
at the concentrator.

One of the most effective means of providing for an
adequate dependability of all the tailing system struct
is the division of the tailing disposal area into two
sections. Each of these sections has a necessary compl
of structures providing for its autonomy.

For tailing disposal areas at the concentrators
producing tailings 80 to 100 percent - 0.074mm = it is
often necessary to construct a "filled" dam conforming
to the total height of tailing deposits, which calls
for high capital costs.

Therefore, in each separate case, the designers
should strive to combine concentrator tailing and
mine wastes disposal. At that, a part of mine dumps
is used for the tailing dam construction, which would
be built up gradually in the process of the mine
and concentrator operation.

It should be added that, to increase the reliability
and convenience of tailing disposal areas, they should
be divided into two sections. In case of fine tailings
the mine overburden is to be used for the construction
of dams for the tailing disposal area.

CONCLUSIONS

Tailings disposal designing should begin with the working out of a detailed and accurate balance of water required for a full water reclamation. This problem is to be considered, taking into account the means of hydraulic transportation, as well as the type of tailing disposal.

This type of tailing disposal should be selected allowing for maximal safety of all structures, and the utilization of tailing bearing and antifiltering capacity.

Table 1
Calculation of Pressure Hydraulic Transport of Waste

1	2	3	4	5
6	$U_{\kappa p}=\beta\frac{0.157}{\omega}D^2\left(1+3.43\sqrt{CD^{0.73}}\right)$ м/сек; M/sec	—	$d_{cp}\leq 0.07$ av	$\beta=\frac{\gamma-1}{1.70}$
	$U_{\kappa p}=\beta\frac{0.20}{\omega}D^2\left(1+2.48\sqrt[3]{C}\sqrt[4]{D}\right)$ м/сек; M/sec	—	$0.07<d_{cp}\leq 0.15$ av	—"—
7	$U_{\kappa p}=15\sqrt[3]{D}\sqrt[4]{W}\left(\frac{\gamma_n}{\gamma_1}-0.4\right)\sqrt[10]{\frac{3d_{10}}{d_{90}}}$ м/сек, M/sec	—	$d_{cp}\leq 0.5$ av	$\frac{at}{npu}\gamma_\beta<1.25\,t/u^3$ $\frac{at}{npu}\gamma_\beta=1.25\div1.70\,t/u^3$
	$U_{\kappa p}=1.28\sqrt[3]{D}\sqrt[4]{W}\sqrt[3]{F_{cm}}\sqrt[10]{\frac{3d_a}{d_{90}}}$ м/сек; M/sec	—		
8	$U_{\kappa p}=8\sqrt[3]{D}\sqrt[4]{C}\frac{\gamma_1}{\gamma}\cdot\frac{\gamma-\gamma_n}{\gamma-\gamma_1}\cdot\gamma$ м/сек; M/sec	2.65	$0.15<d_{cp}\leq 40$ av	—

279

Notes to Table 1

1 Author of the formula.
2 Formulae for the calculation of critical velocities in a pressure pulp pipeline.
3 Specific gravity of solids in the pulp γ t/m^3.
4 Size range of solids, mm.
5 Correction factors and conditions.
6 V.S. Knoroz and P.D. Evdokimov.
7 Ukranian Scientific Research Institute of Building Industry (NIISP).
8 All-Union Scientific Research Institute of Hydraulic Engineering (VNIIG).
9 Legend.

D - pipeline diameter

$$C = \frac{\gamma(\gamma_p - \gamma_w)}{\gamma_w(\gamma - \gamma_p)} \quad - \text{pulp concentration}$$

W - Hydraulic size, m/sec.

ω - wet cross-section area at critical conditions

γ_p and γ_w - specific gravity of pulp and water, t/m^3
$C_m = 0.35 - 0.40$

d_{10} and d_{90} - particle size, mm, corresponding to 10 percent and 90 percent of solids content

$$\Psi = \frac{\Sigma \Psi_* P_i}{100}, \text{ where P - content (percent) of}$$

i - fraction in solid phase of pulp.

Ψ_* - transportatibility factor.

Table 2
Physicomechanical Characteristics of Tailings

Parameters of disposed tailing	Unity of measure	Parts of Structure		Notes
		Bearing prism	Tailing pond zone	
1	2	3	4	5
Specific gravity	g/cm^3	2.7-3.0	2.7-3.0	
Content of fractions - 0.074 mm	%	0 - 10	90 - 100	
Volumetric weight of the carcass				
a/ On the surface	g/cm^3	1.4-1.5	0.8-1.0	X/ On the surface of
b/ In the base			1.5-1.6	the pond zone the tailings
Humidity:				are in liquid state
a/ On the surface	%	10-20	100	
b/ In the base	%	45-55	40-50	
Filtration factor	cm/sec	10^{-2}-10^{-3}	10^{-6}-10^{-7}	
Shear resistance factors				
φ (on the surface)		25-30$^{\varrho}$	20-25$^{\text{ox/}}$	
φ (in the base)		-	0.00	
C (on the surface)	kg/cm^2	0.10-0.15		
C (in the base)	kg/cm^2		0.05-0.10	

281

Table 2 (con't.)

Parameters of disposed tailings	Unity of measure	Parts of Structure	
		Bearing prism	Tailing pond zone
1	2	3	4
Compressibility factor at:			
P = 0-1 kg/cm^2	cm^2/kg	0.01-0.02	0.15-0.20
P = 0.10 kg/cm^2			0.05-0.07

Table 2 is based on practical data obtained at the tailing systems of the nonferrous ore contractors.

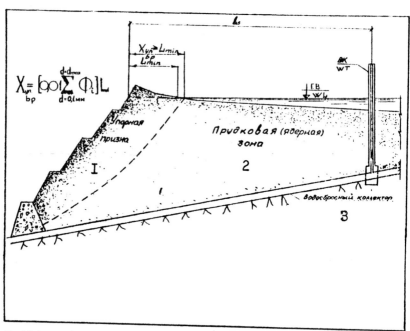

Tailing disposal area cross section with scheme for location of specific tailing disposal zones: (1) bearing prism; (2) pond area; (3) collector.

Figure No. 1

MAGMA COPPER COMPANY'S SAN MANUEL NO. 10 TAILING DAM:

DESIGN, CONSTRUCTION AND OPERATION

G. W. Dopson, Mill Superintendent

D. McGregor, Supervisor Trainee

Magma Copper Company
San Manuel, Arizona

INTRODUCTION

Tailing disposal represents an operational expense rather than a profit-making entity, and many times for this reason too little thought and money are allocated for tailing disposal. The overall cost of a poorly planned system could far outrun the initial cost of design and construction of a sound stable disposal area that could be used for many years.

It will be the purpose of this report to describe in detail a tailing disposal method and system, developed by Magma Copper Company, which is simple and structurally sound.

PLANNING

With an impending increase from a 42,000 to a 65,000 ton per day operation, it became evident that an alternate tailing disposal area would be needed.

TAILING DISPOSAL TODAY

With planning dominated by economics and safety considerations, a new dam was selected for several reasons. Existing dam Nos. 1 and 2 had already grown to a height where pumping of tailing would soon be necessary. Dam Nos. 3 and 4 were also approaching this situation. Dam Nos. 5 and 6 were not considered mature enough to accomodate tailing of the magnitude soon to be produced. Dam Nos. 7, 8 and 9 had been planned out in previous years but would require a considerable amount of development work not deemed necessary at this time. Therefore, No. 10 dam area was conceived. It would be located adjacent to, but not touching dam No. 1. Encompassing a total area of 2 square miles, it would be large enough to receive all the tailing produced by the increased tonnage. Allowed to reach a maximum height of 260 feet, and coupled with the other dams, a total of 26-1/2 years of disposal area would be provided.

Dam No. 10 would be constructed in a manner similar to existing dams. Because of this, much of the preliminary testing and investigations typical for a new dam was avoided.

DESIGN AND CONSTRUCTION

A diversion channel was cut to reroute drainage water from a large desert wash within the dam's perimeter, to one located outside the proposed north wing. It runs in a general northerly direction, for approximately 7,000 feet on a 1-1/2 to 2 percent grade to minimize the effects of washing and erosion. The channel required 114,404 cubic yards of excavation, and 8,318 cubic yards of borrow fill material. (Refer to Figure No. 1.)

The dewater or decant system employed on this dam as on the other dams, is a gravity flow type. Water from the dam is decanted off the top of the existing pool and gravity fed through an underground pipe system and thence to settling sumps. There are two decant lines for No. 10 dam. Two channels were cut

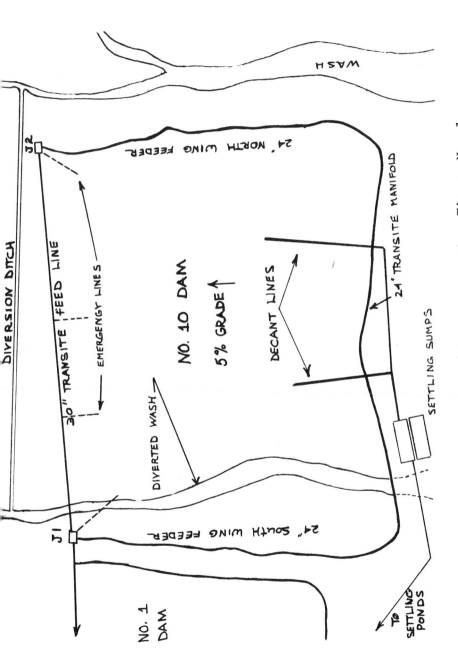

Layout for No. 10 dam (not to scale).   Figure No. 1

through the central portion of the dam area. Class 200, 16-inch-diameter transite lines were laid on a grade corresponding to that of the natural slope, approximately 5 percent. (See Figure No. 2.) These lines were run under and 90° to the dike face. A 24-inch Class 50 transite line connects the two and carries the decanted water into two settling sumps, each 300 by 145 by 10 feet deep.

The dam measures 7,000 feet long with 8,000-foot wings. The sides of the starter embankment have a 1-1/2:1 slope with a 30-foot crown. A total of 377,143 cubic yards of earthwork was involved. Prior to the embankment construction, keyways were dug in selected places of the dikes foundation where seepage might occur. They were cut approximately 14 feet wide, and dug to a depth necessary to reach relatively solid and impervious ground.

These keyways, or trenches, were filled with semi-impervious borrow material consisting of clay and sand obtained from the surrounding area.

When the keyways were completed, appropriate cuts and fills were made to construct the starter embankment. It was almost entirely composed of borrow material native to the location. This dike extended across the entire width of the dam as well as a portion of the wings. The weight of the equipment used in transporting fill was adequate for compaction. The 30-foot level crown served as a service road and also as the foundation for the distribution manifold.

Two concrete junction boxes (NJ1 & NJ2) were located at the ends of the wings and connected by a 30-inch transite line on a 0.5 percent grade. Another 30-inch line was used to join NJ1 box to the feeder line off No. 1 dam. These boxes serve as tailing distribution points for the North and South wings. On the 30-inch transite between junction boxes, four 30-inch valves were tapped in, to be used as emergency dump lines. (See Figure No. 1.) The 24-inch feed lines down the wings are laid on a 0.5 percent slope

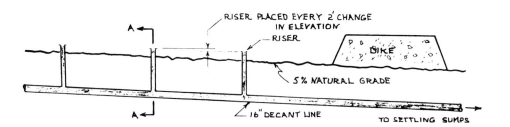

DECANT SYSTEM N.T.S.

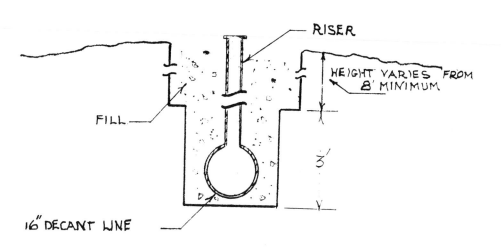

SECTION A-A N.T.S.

Decant system for dam (not to scale).   Figure No. 2

by cut-and-fill down the natural slope of about 5 percent. At intervals, the lines are "stepped" down by means of 6-foot-diameter by 20-foot-high drop boxes. (See Figure No. 3.) The last drop box on both wings was approximately 80 feet above the top of the starter dike. From this last box, the line essentially followed the natural slope of the land.

The final phase of major design and construction was laying out the cyclone distribution manifold. It extends across the inner portion of the service road for the entire length, and curves into the wings until it meets and connects to the feeder lines off the last drop box. Four-inch plug valves for cyclone feed are spaced at 26-foot intervals and strapped on a 24-inch header. Three 24-inch valves are included at various points so that designated areas of the dam could be isolated as required. (Refer to Figure No. 1 for header layout.)

OPERATION AND MAINTENANCE

With the exception of the starter dike, which was built of borrow material, the berm is constructed entirely by sands from cyclone discharge. In preparation for the first run, 5-foot-high stands were placed along the inside of the roadbed adjacent to the distribution manifold. Approximately 366 12-inch cyclones were needed. They were connected to the 4-inch plug valves on the manifold by means of 4-inch steel piping with elbows fashioned from 4-inch rubber tubing. To each cyclone was connected 4-inch discharge piping, approximately 60 feet in length, to allow the slime fraction to be deposited away from the dike.

In many places, the top of the dike was not far off the native ground level, therefore, it was necessary to utilize cyclones every 26 feet. (Figure No. 4 shows the appearance of the dike at the outset of operation.) When the 5-foot stands were nearly covered by cyclone underflow, the feed was shut off, and

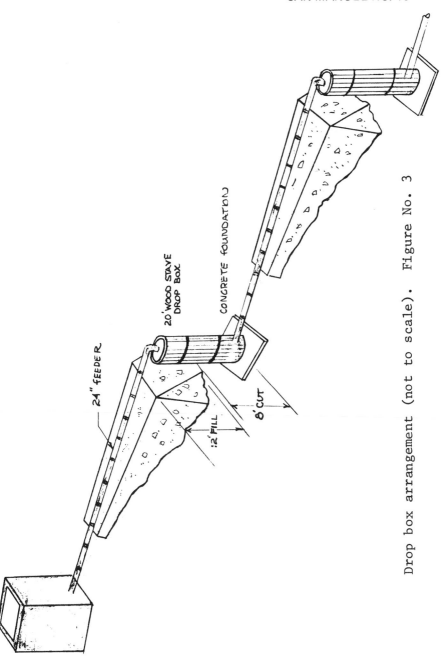

Drop box arrangement (not to scale). Figure No. 3

rerouted to an alternate dam. The area was allowed to rest and set up sufficiently so maintenance could be performed. When this had occurred, a new 3-section, 15-foot-high wooden trestle was placed 30 feet out from the old 5-foot stand emplacement. The cyclones were laid on the lower level of the trestle, the intake and discharge piping was connected, and feed to cyclones resumed. When the cone piles had risen to nearly meeting the cyclones, the feed was stopped, cyclones raised to the next highest level, and the operation continued. Figure No. 5 shows cyclones being lifted and placed on next level of trestle. When the entire 15-foot-high trestle was buried, the area was allowed to set and new 15-foot stands were placed inward from previous placement. With the addition of 20 feet of intake pipes, cyclones were connected, and the entire cycle was restarted. This entire procedure of raising cyclones at 5-foot increments, and locating new stands is repeated as required. (Figure Nos. 6 and 7 respectively show workers resetting cyclones after a new trestle had been placed, and system ready for operation.)

When a total of 140 feet of intake pipe had been added, or 45 vertical feet of berm built, the cyclone distribution manifold was raised to a new level. When a raise is contemplated, feed to the dam is shut off far enough in advance to allow the dam to dry and set up, so heavy equipment may be used.

With this type of operation, the need for alternate disposal areas must be emphasized. Not only for purposes of maintenance, but also to rotate tailing campaigns in various dams, so a high degree of stability can be achieved by the dam being allowed to rest.

At the outset of the raise, all intake and discharge lines were disconnected and placed on the service road. Two bulldozers leveled off the cone piles until a 30-foot-wide roadway was obtained. With the aid of a crane, 13-foot transite sections are raised halfway up the newly built berm. The crane then

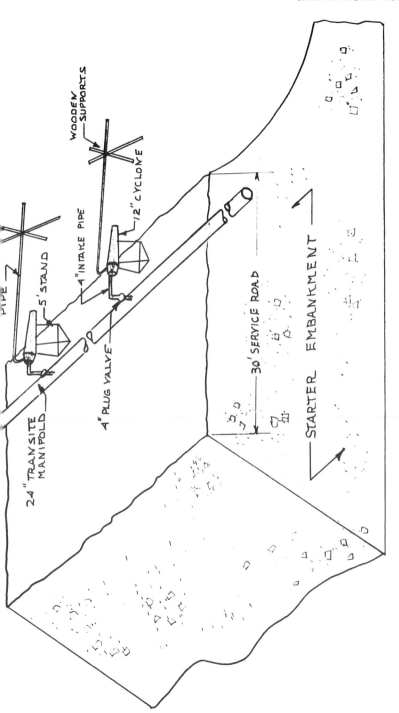

Dike at outset of operation. Figure No. 4

Cyclones being lifted and placed on next level of trestle.
Figure No. 5

Workers reset cyclones after a new trestle has been placed.
Figure No. 6

moves up the roadway to raise the transite up on the new bench. A course is established along the inside of the new service road so the transite can be laid on level. It was during the first transite raise that every other plug valve was removed from the header. It was no longer necessary to have cyclones at 26-foot intervals, because the retaining berm was sufficiently higher than the slime pool. Cyclones placed at 52-foot centers were to be used for the duration of the dam development. After the manifold had been reset, new 15-foot trestles were located 40 feet out from the header. This is where the new berm would begin. Cyclones were placed on the lower trestle level, lines connected and supported, and the operation was ready to continue. The 40 foot distance between the first trestle and the manifold is typical after each transite raise.

Tailing is fed entirely by gravity flow, and to maintain adequate cyclone pressure as the berm height increases, drop boxes are removed from the feed line. Normally, a 40-foot head gives satisfactory pressure (17 pounds per square inch) with minimal pipe wear. With regard to the initial 80-foot head on the No. 10 dam, a calculated risk was taken in hope that the cost of additional drop boxes would exceed any pipe failure costs before the first transite raise was made. As it turned out, the north side line lasted until the first raise was made and only a few sections required replacement in the south side.

The north and south sections of the dam are presently not operated simultaneously. While one end is resting and becoming solid to allow work to be performed on it, the opposite end may be operating. This requirement is temporary until sufficient dam area has been developed. All the necessary maintenance carried out on the dam is performed by a crew of six men and an experienced supervisor. It is their responsibility to transport piping and lumber, set new trestles, relocate and connect cyclones. They keep everything operational not only on No. 10 dam, but all other disposal areas in present use.

System ready for operation.   Figure No. 7

The flow of water to the risers off the two decant lines is accomplished by controlled directional placement of cyclones in operation. In order to start flow of water to the decant area, the feed to the cyclones farthest out on the wings is started, thus causing water to flow down slope. Cyclones along the curve of the wings are then turned on to force water to flow along the face. The cyclones on the dam face are then opened which routes water into the decant line risers. This water flows through the lines by gravity to the settling sumps beneath and outside the starter dike. A floating pump transfers water to the reclaim pump station. Extension collars are added to the dewater line risers as the slime level increases. Two risers on each dewater line are always open. These risers are located on the dewater lines every two vertical feet of change in line elevation. (Refer to Figure 1.) As the water level reaches an open pipe the lower riser is capped off, and its use is discontinued.

SUMMARY

On May 12, 1969, construction on No. 10 dam was started, and on March 10, 1970, it was opened for operation. It goes without saying as witnessed in the previous reading that much time, effort and money are employed in building a dam of this type. In any large operation many problems develop from day to day, and it certainly aids in the peace of mind of management that tailing disposal will never have to be one of them.

EARTH AND WATER PRESSURES ON

RECTANGULAR CONDUIT EMBEDDED

IN SETTLING POND DAM

A. Blinde, Director
J. Brauns and L. W. Zangl, Research Engineers
Institute for Soil Mechanics and Rock Mechanics
University of Karlsruhe, West Germany

Regarding the development in the design and construction of settling pond dams, one - simply speaking - may state: In earlier times, settling pond dams were built, more or less, on the basis of practical experience only, without earth statics calculations or other knowledge in earth dam technology. The final dimensions of the waste deposits were relatively small; due to the low capacity of the mining industry at that time, the rate of raising was low. Today's high capacity of the respective industries now leads to tailings dams and settling ponds, the final dimensions of which are quite comparable to those of water reservoirs, these dimensions being obtained after relatively short periods of operation. This development as well as several disasters in connection with tailings dam failures and the commonly developing consciousness about environmental pollution gradually led to the fact that tailings dams are

now becoming understood as real engineering structures. Today, one tries to design, to construct
and to operate tailings dams with the same care as
is common in connection with water storage dams.
There are several special aspects in building
tailings dams which aggravate these efforts, such
as pointed out for instance in (1) and (2).

Numerous old tailings dams, the condition of
which - from the point of view of today's knowledge - is more or less poor, must be operated
and extended further. Thus, tailings dams practice
partly consists in subsequent improvement and
repair of existing tailings dams or their auxiliary
structures. Comparable work is also to be performed on more recent structures, if they are not·
designed and constructed according to the "state
of the art".

Thus we have reached the subject of this contribution. The paper deals with the loads upon a
conduit embedded in a settling pond dam. The
conduit in mind had been designed for loads lower
than should have been expected and was to be improved on demand of the controlling authority.

For a better understanding of the reported
example and the performed measures, some remarks on the concept and the history of the structure shall be given for a start. Then, the results
of pressure measurements are reported and discussed relative to some analytical predictions.
Finally, the measures to prevent collapse of the
structure are briefly described.

The settling pond in question is the latest and
biggest of 6 ponds of a lime factory in central West
Germany. Some data upon production, tailings and

tailings dam:

Quantity of extracted limestone ~ $4.5 \cdot 10^6$ Mp/year
Quantity of clean limestone   ~ $4.0 \cdot 10^6$ Mp/year
    50 % are used for lime production
    50 % are used for production of classified
        crushed limestone
Percentage of material washed out in washing
plant ~ 6 %
Grain size distribution
of tailings :

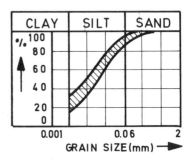

Content of solids in tailings ~ 100 p/liter
Quantity of tailings   ~ 800 m^3/hour
       ~ 12, 000 m^3/day
       ~ $3.2 \cdot 10^6$ m^3/year
Required volume in settling pond
       ~ $0.25 \cdot 10^6$ m^3/year
Volume of tailings dam   (final stage)
       ~ $0.85 \cdot 10^6$ m^3
Storage capacity of settling pond (final stage)
       ~ $6.8 \cdot 10^6$ m^3
Length of tailings line ($\emptyset$ = 400 mm) between
washing plant and tailings dam   ~ 3.5 km

The recycled water is reclaimed by means of
decant towers and a discharge line, and is conducted to a natural rivulet. In the washing plant which
is situated downstream, the water is extracted from
the rivulet. Thus, a cleaning effect of 100 % must be
guaranteed in the settling pond.

The settling pond is built just like a water reservoir closing a natural valley by means of an earth
dam. Figure 1 is a recent view of the dam and the
pond.

View of the tailing
dam and the settling
pond. Figure No. 1

Figure 2 gives the
highest dam cross
section. Details are
not discussed here.
The cross section
in Figure 2 shows
the concrete gallery
under discussion. A
steel pipe (discharge
line) runs through
the conduit which
is situated on the
right-hand slope of
the valley.

by permission of Regierungspräsidium
Nordbaden , No. 0 22 58

The purpose of the conduit is evident from the
operating facilities which can be seen in the ground
plan of Figure 3: From the decant towers, the
cleaned water runs through a concrete pipe, embedded in the subsoil, to the upstream end of the
concrete gallery. From here, a steel pipe
(600 mm $\emptyset$) inside the conduit serves as discharge
line to the downstream slope of the tailings dam. At
the upstream end of the gallery, the spillway structure for flood control (concrete channel, built uphill;
catchment area≈0.55 km^2, calculated amount of water to be discharged = 0.7 m^3/sec) joins the steel
pipe. Upstream of the joint, each of the discharge
lines has a valve.

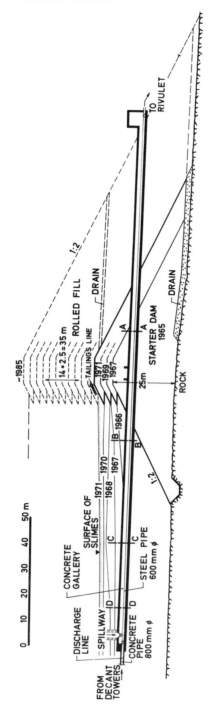

Highest dam cross section and gallery (projected into drawing plane). Figure No. 2

Thus, the purpose of the gallery is to allow - in case of damage at the decant towers or at the embedded concrete pipe - blocking of the discharge line whereas the spillway can be kept in operation.

As is well known, conduits or pipes which cross earth dams are very problematic in several aspects, so that - in general - one should omit such installations. Sometimes, this is not possible or - as in our example - the problems in connection with such structures are recognized too late.

One of the serious problems of such conduits is the static design, involving prediction of the loads later to be expected. Particularly in case of what is known as dam condition (the structure is embedded in compressible material all over its height), a complicated stress-strain field develops in the soil near the structure: Due to its rigidness, the structure attracts loads higher than the net overburden pressure $\sigma_v = \gamma \cdot H$ of the overlying mass (γ = unit weight of the soil, H = height of soil above top of structure). The concentration of stresses on top of the structure causes - beside the conduit - vertical stresses lower than $\sigma_v = \gamma \cdot H$. This effect leads to difficulties in the estimation of the lateral earth pressure.

Even by modern methods of analysis (such as finite-element-method), reliable results cannot be obtained, because the mechanical behaviour of the soils (particularly in the case of settling slimes in a tailings dam) is not sufficiently investigated.

In spite of these difficulties, it is necessary to design and construct such structures so that they are absolutely safe and economical, especially in the case of tailings dams, where conduits may be covered by slimes up to heights of some decameters.

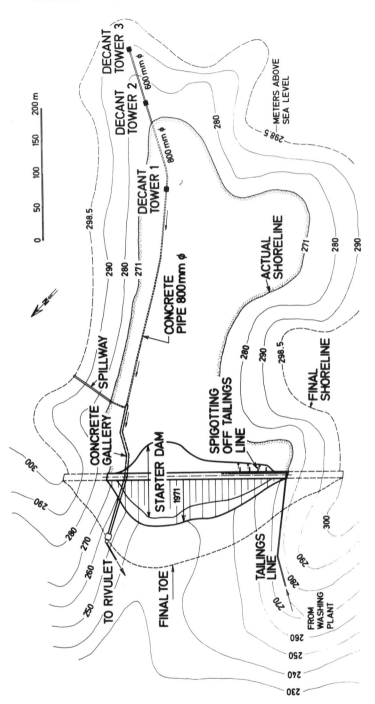

Ground plan of the settling pond with operating facilities. Figure No. 3

In cases such as discussed here, the analytical estimation of the loads is particularly difficult due to the fact that the properties of the slimes change locally and with time.

By means of in-situ measurements which shall not be discussed in detail here, we were able to collect some data concerning density and shear strength of the sands and slimes up to considerable distances from the dam. On the basis of these measurements we can fix $\gamma \approx 1.9$ Mp/m^3 as unit density (saturated condition) and the angle of total shear strength as $\emptyset \approx 33^o$ near the dam and as $\emptyset \approx 17^o$ at some distance from the dam.

But, even the simple analytical methods used in practice for load prediction reveal considerable discrepancies. The results of some calculations for the loads to be expected on top of the conduit (after methods commonly used in Germany) are shown in the diagram of Figure 4. As can be seen, the results differ quantitatively as well as qualitatively. For the final stage of the settling pond, e.g., where the ratio H/h will be ≈ 12, the method of Breth (3) gives $\approx 150\%$, the one of Roske (4) $\approx 200\%$ (for all $\emptyset$-values) and the one of Voellmy (5)$\approx 300\%$ of the net overburden pressure $\gamma \cdot$ H (example $\emptyset = 33^o$). These predictions would hold for sections of the gallery within and near the dam (e.g. cross sections A and B, see Figure 2).

The discrepancies of the results for $\emptyset = 17.5^o$ (thin lines in Figure 4), which may hold for the region of cross sections C and D (see Figure 2), are of the same order of magnitude.

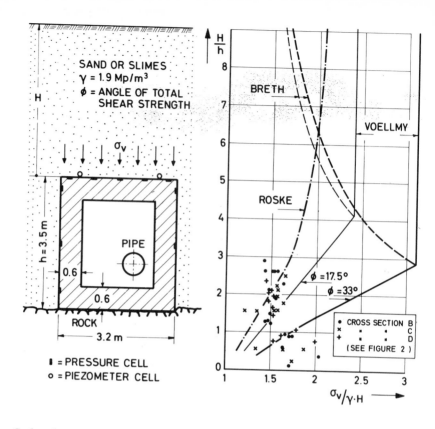

Calculated pressure on top of the gallery as a function of the height of the overlaying mass; results of in situ measurements.   Figure No. 4

As long as there is no method of calculation, the validity of which is proved by means of a sufficient quantity of field measurements, the loads to be expected cannot be predicted with satisfying accuracy.

Not much better are today's possibilities to predict the lateral pressures upon embedded conduits (earth pressure upon the walls of the gallery). Obviously, the state of stresses beside such structures will be of "earth pressure at rest" type. Thus, one may estimate the lateral pressure using

Jaky's (6) formula $\sigma_L = \lambda_o \cdot \sigma_v = (1 - \sin \emptyset) \cdot \sigma_v$
(σ_L = lateral earth pressure; $\lambda_o = 1 - \sin \emptyset$ = coefficient of earth pressure at rest; σ_v = vertical pressure). However, due to the load concentration on top of the structure, the vertical pressure σ_v beside it is unknown.

With the help of simplifying assumptions and using simple earth pressure theories (as commonly applied in practice), we have tried to estimate analytically the lateral earth pressure σ_L, taking into account the different factors of stress concentration as shown in Figure 4 (details of the analysis are not discussed here). The results of these calculations are shown in Figure 5.

Some necessary remarks on the diagram:
For the purpose of direct correlation, the ordinate indicates - as in Figure 4 - the ratio H/h of embedding. σ_L of the abscissa represents the average lateral earth pressure which varies along the height of the side walls. σ_L is related to the fictitious overburden pressure at mean level of the structure:
$\gamma \cdot H' = \gamma (H + \frac{h}{2})$.

As to be expected, the results of those analytical estimations diverge similarly to those for the vertical load upon the conduit. The extreme concentration of overburden pressure after Voellmy (compare Figure 4) leads - especially for high $\emptyset$ -values - to a reduction of vertical stresses beside the structure to such an extent that - beyond H/h $\approx$ 3 - only very low lateral earth pressures result from the calculations.

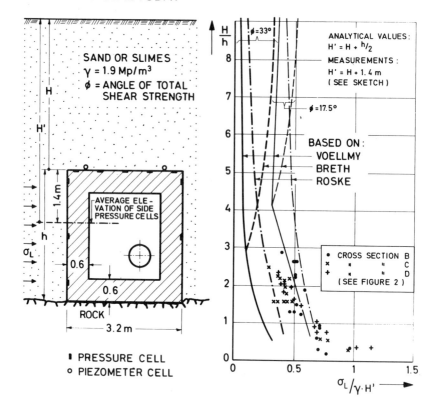

Calculated lateral earth pressure (at rest) as
a function of the height of the overlying mass;
results of in situ measurements.   Figure No. 5

For the static design of structures in question
here, the ratio σ_L/σ_v is of special importance. Ratios
between 0.5 down to nearly zero are possible after
the methods used here.

We come back to the actual example discussed
here: the gallery was designed for the net overburden pressure $\sigma_v = \gamma \cdot H$ (i.e. no pressure
concentration had been taken into account). The
lateral pressure on the walls of the gallery was
assumed to be equal to the active earth pressure.
Thus, even for favourable assumptions in the ana-

lysis, the structure had to be regarded as of unsafe design. A reinforcement measure was necessary.

As can be seen from the diagrams of Figures 4 and 5, there was no reliable basis for the design of a reinforcement. With respect to the fact that - after static calculations - critical loads would occur only after several years of operating the set-- tling pond, it was decided to postpone the reinforcement measures and meanwhile to observe and record the actually developing earth pressures in-situ. The final safety measures should be planned economically on the basis of the results of these measurements.

Instruments for earth and water pressure measurements have been installed at 4 cross sec- tions of the gallery (profiles A to D, compare Figure 2; for the arrangement of the instruments see Figure 4). Earth pressure cells of Glötzl-System, compare (7), and piezometer cells of Maihak-System, compare (8), have been used. Figure 6 gives a view of two of the earth pressure

Two earth pressure cells and a piezometer cell on top of the gallery.

Figure No. 6

earth pressure cells

piezometer cell

cells and of a piezometer cell on top of the gallery (the trench for cables and flexible tubes is not yet filled with mortar).

The results of the piezometer readings can be easily summarised first. The water pressure acting upon the gallery corresponds to a water level of only a few decimeters above the top of the structure, despite the water level in the pond being roughly 10 m above said top. We assume that this is due to the high permeability of the fissured rock foundation and of the material near the structure. The latter is a sand which was placed by spigotting the tailings along the structure for a considerable period of time (temporary beach). This sand is much coarser than the finer slimes deposited at higher elevations.

The results of the earth pressure measurements must be discussed in more detail. Figure 7 gives an example (cross section D, compare Figure 2) for the distribution of the measured vertical and lateral earth pressures. This example can be regarded as representative of all cross sections except A (the conditions in cross section A are so complicated that we must dispense with a presentation here).

The distribution of the stresses on top of the structure is of concave type (concentration of stresses at the edges of the structure, comparable to that observed underneath rigid footings). The stresses increase progressively with increasing height of overburden.

The distribution of the lateral pressures is non-uniform and changes sometimes its tendency in the course of time. Sometimes, a decrease of local stresses with increasing height of overburden is

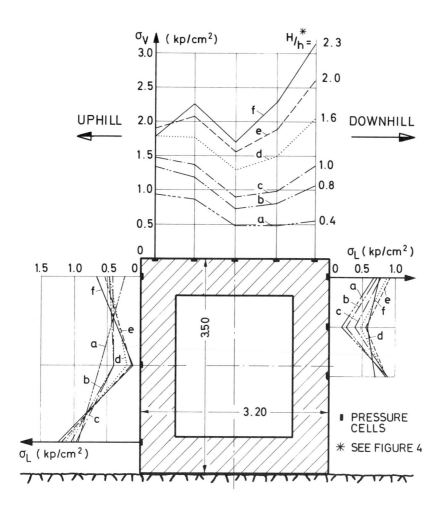

Results of earth pressure measurements at cross
section D (example).   Figure No. 7

observed.

In general, the observed stress distribution is not symmetrical, possibly because of the unsymmetrical embedding conditions due to the position of the structure in a slope.

In presenting this Figure, we want to point out that the pressure distribution in-situ may be highly irregular. Unknown natural effects, which cannot be taken into account analytically, exercise considerable influence. Representative data are to be obtained only by means of an extensive and careful measuring program.

With respect to the irregularities in the stress distributions, the results of the measurements which have been performed over a period of more than 5 years up to now are presented as average values in the following.

The measured vertical pressures of profiles B, C and D are plotted in Figure 4 (each point represents the mean value of the 5 cells on top of the structure in each cross section). Even for these mean values, a considerable scatter is to be observed. For ratios H/h < 1, the measurements are not too reliable, because the pressures occurring are very low here in comparison to the capacity of the pressure cells (the capacity had been fixed high in view of the high pressures possible later on).

For H/h-ratios higher than 1 the results tend to settle around a ratio of $\frac{\sigma_v}{\gamma \cdot H} \approx 1.5$. A variation of this coefficient of load concentration as a function of the distance from the dam (B $\rightarrow$ C $\rightarrow$ D, compare Figure 2) is not evident.

In comparison with the analytical estimations, the measured ratio $\frac{\sigma_v}{\gamma \cdot H}$ is close to the one after the method of Roske. The estimation after Voellmy gives factors of concentration which are much too high in this case, as was also observed in other places, compare (3) for instance. An increase in the coefficient of pressure concentration with increasing height of overburden (this increase is indicated by all analytical calculations used here) cannot be gleaned from the measurements; but the ratio H/h achieved up to now is only ≈ 3. The future readings will show how the factor of load concentration develops for high H/h-ratios, this ratio being nearly 12 in the final stage of the tailings dam (~1985).

The results of the earth pressure measurements along the sides of the structure are plotted in Figure 5, again as mean values of the readings at all 5 or 6 lateral pressure cells. Because of the asymmetrical pattern of these pressure cells the measured values in this particular case are related to the fictitious overburden pressure at the mean level of the cells, i.e.: $\gamma \cdot H' = \gamma \cdot (H + 1.4 \text{ m})$.

As for the scattering and for the poor reliability of the values measured up to ratios H/h$\approx$1, the foregoing statements apply. Beyond H/h $\approx$ 1 the results gather again, the mean value of the ratio $\sigma_L / \gamma \cdot H'$ being ≈ 0.45 here. In order to give a reference value: this ratio corresponds to the coefficient of earth pressure at rest after Jaky for $\emptyset = 33^{\circ}$ ($\lambda_0 = 1 - \sin 33^{\circ} \approx 0.45$). A decrease of the ratio $\sigma_L / \gamma \cdot H'$ with increasing height of overburden is slightly indicated by the field data, such as is indicated by all analytical predictions used above. Furthermore, the results of the measurements correspond to those analytical values which may be predicted on the basis of Roske's method for estimating the vertical pressure concentration. The values concentrate between the curves (based on Roske) for $\emptyset = 17.5^\circ$ and $\emptyset = 33^\circ$ (probable maximum/minimum values in this example).

Roughly summarising, the discussed measurements resulted in a vertical load on top of the structure corresponding to $\sigma_V \approx 1.5 \cdot \gamma \cdot H$ and in a lateral earth pressure upon the side walls corresponding to $\sigma_L \approx 0.45 \cdot \gamma \cdot H'$, the ratio H/h achieved now being ≈ 3.

For this state of external loads, static calculations revealed that measures for reinforcement cannot be postponed without the risk of a collapse.

The main safety measures are:

- installation of a second pipe inside the gallery as an extra discharge line for the spillway. This line is necessary to guarantee flood control in case of damage to the line for water reclamation or at one of the decant towers (in this case the existing steel pipe must be blocked).

- filling up the entire gallery with concrete in order to prevent a collapse of the structure.

Details of the program of safety measures and auxiliary work shall not be discussed here.

Obviously, the necessity of a reinforcement which is almost equal to abandoning the structure was not taken into account when planning the measurement program described above. On the contrary, the measurements were expected to give an appropriate basis for preserving the reliability of the structure in operation. The aforementioned extent of the safety measures is the result of establishing that

even the quality of the materials used for construction did not comply at all with the standards
assumed in the original static design.

Since reliable measurements of stresses upon
embedded structures are rare, particularly for thick
layers of overburden and over long periods of time,
we see an urgent need to continue these measurements, despite the fact that they are of no further
use for the gallery in question. Thus, the instruments for reading the pressures - as far as necessary due to the reinforcement work - have been
removed out of the gallery and into the building at
its downstream end. We shall continue the measurements as long as the instruments work. We hope to
present further data later on.

Even if better analytical methods should be
developed allowing more reliable predictions, this
will be of some interest. Better analytical results
than reported above may be obtained by using the
finite-element-method - compare (9). However,
this requires a more comprehensive knowledge
about the mechanical properties of the soils covering
the structures (in our case: the deposits in settling
ponds). Future investigations should first of all
emphasize this aspect of the problem.

This contribution deals with the problem of
stresses upon a conduit in a tailings dam and a
settling pond. Due to insufficient knowledge about
the mechanical properties of the deposited slimes
and the lack of simple but satisfying analytical
methods for prediction, serious difficulties in
practice often arise from this problem. In particular,
an economic design is not possible today, since
absolute safety of such structures must be guaranteed.

Besides the difficulties in static design, there are a lot of other risks in connection with structures of this type, such as settlements, cracking, erosion (piping) etc. Thus, one usually tries to avoid conduits through dams, if possible. Otherwise, they should be inserted into the subsoil.

In the example presented here, earth pressure measurements became necessary at a poorly designed gallery which will be covered with slimes up to a height of nearly 40 m. The measurements performed until now (height of overburden ≈ 10 m) revealed vertical pressures on top of the structure 1.5 times the net overburden pressure $\gamma \cdot H$. The mean recorded lateral pressures correspond to a coefficient of earth pressure $\lambda \approx 0.45$ (related to the overburden pressure at the level at half height of the structure). A comparison of these field data with the results of some analytical predictions (after methods used in practice) cannot reveal satisfactory agreement, since the analytical values differ considerably. The gallery in question has to be reinforced at high expenditure. Nevertheless, the measurements will be continued.

This seems necessary, since experience is rare and comprehensive knowledge about the properties of soils and slimes (such as is needed in the use of more sophisticated analytical methods) is not yet available.

LEGEND FOR UNITS

mm	millimeter	sec	second
cm	centimeter	p	pond
m	meter	kp	kilopond
km	kilometer	Mp	Megapond

REFERENCES

1. Klohn, Earle J., "Design and Construction of Tailings Dams", The Canadian Mining and Metallurgical Bulletin for April, 1972, pp. 28 - 44

2. Blinde, A. and Brauns, J., "Barrages en terre pour bassins de décantation construits à l'aide de matériaux de remblai hydraulique", Transactions, 10th Int. Congr. on Large Dams, Montreal 1970, Vol. I, pp. 405 - 421

3. Breth, H., "Der Scheiteldruck auf Bauwerke mit hoher Überschüttung", Vorträge der Baugrundtagung 1964 in Berlin, pp. 185 - 196

4. Roske, K., "Betonrohre nach DIN 4032", Bauverlag, Wiesbaden/Berlin, 1962

5. Voellmy, A., "Die Bruchsicherheit eingebetteter Rohre", Dissertation E.T.H. Zürich, 1936

see also:

Kadner, W., "Beitrag zur statischen Berechnung von kreisrunden Kanalisationsrohren", Gas und Wasserfach (Wasser/Abwasser), 111, 1970, pp. 287 - 296

Drescher, G., "Das im Erdreich eingebettete Rohr", Österreichische Ingenieur-Zeitschrift 8, 1965, pp. 89 - 98

6. Jaky, J., "The Coefficient of Earth Pressure at Rest", Journ. Soc. of Hungarian Arch. and Eng., Budapest, 1944

7. Franz, G., "Unmittelbare Spannungsmessung in Beton und Baugrund", Der Bauingenieur, 1958, Heft 5, pp. 190 - 195

8. Altmann, H., "Schwingsaiten-Druckgeber und ihre Anwendung", VDI-Berichte, Band 93, 1966, pp. 75 - 79

9. Brown, C.B., "Forces on Rigid Culverts under High Fills" Proceedings, ASCE. ST 5, 1967, pp. 195 - 215

BUILDING TAILINGS DAMS IN ARROYOS

Harry R. Dahlberg

Concentrator Superintendent

Richard C. Laird

Assistant Concentrator Superintendent

Christmas Division

Inspiration Consolidated Copper Co.

Winkelman, Arizona

In 1962, the Christmas mill started operation
on 4,000 dry tons per day of underground ore.
Three tailings dams were developed to take the
slime fraction of the tailing with the sand portion
being used underground as fill. With the phase out
of the underground operation and the development of
the open pit, mill tonnage has been increased to an
average of 5,200 dry tons per day and four new
tailings areas have been developed.

Of these seven areas, only two dams -- No. 6
and No. 7 -- are in active use and the others have
the following status:
Dam No. 1 is near capacity and is reserved
for emergencies such as pipeline failures.
Dam No. 2 is full.
Dam No. 3 is very small and is held as a
reserve.
Dam No. 4 was abandoned due to starter dam
seepage.

Dam No. 5 was abandoned due to a decant line failure.

No flat land is available for the construction of these dams and one arroyo with off valleys is presently used for four dams, a second arroyo is used for two dams, and a third arroyo is being developed. Before the arroyos could be developed, a series of diversion dams was constructed to carry off surface water from the hills above. This water is directed to carry on to the north and thence into Dripping Springs wash. These diversion dams are earth fill and have only minor seepage.

Since only dams No. 6 and No. 7 are in active use, the discussion will be confined to them. Both dams have starter dams consisting of a concrete core with earth fill compacted to 95 modified Proctor and have decant systems of 36-inch diameter, 9-inch thickwall concrete pipe set in concrete on a bedrock surface.

The decant line on No. 7 is a single pipe through the starter dam, but about 1,600 feet up the canyon the line splits in two, with the west leg going toward No. 6 dam, and thus carries the water coming off of No. 6. The east leg goes toward No. 4 dam and carries the water off of Nos. 1, 3, 4, and 5. No. 6 dam has two decant lines passing through the starter dam. The west line goes up a canyon toward the west diversion dam, while the east line goes up a canyon toward No. 2 dam and the east diversion dam.

Both dams were started with dragline berms. However it was soon apparent that the dam capacity at the start was going to be too small to allow for adequate drying time to have good digging material. As a result, in February of 1971, cycloning was attempted. The Magma system was adapted, using 15-foot-square stands and 6-inch cyclones. The initial cyclone spacing was too great and, due to an adverse pond area to berm length ratio, freeboard

Cross-canyon construction by cycloning at Christmas mill in Arizona.   Figure No. 1

One of the Christmas tailing dams.   Figure No. 2

was hard to develop. After much work and several problems, the cyclone system is in use on both No. 6 and No. 7 dams. Spigotting is still used on No. 1 and No. 3 dams.

The initial dams had large outward curves in them, due in part to the nature of draglining in the canyons. In changing to cyclones, an attempt was made to straighten the berm. The cyclones were set up in a straight line across the pond at the center of the curve. No problems were experienced until about 40 feet of berm had been built and a wet area appeared between the old berm and the new sands. This was of great concern at first, but it has been drying up and it is now concluded that this is the point at which the water draining from the sand pile is forced to escape, since it has hit the impervious slime layer in its downward path.

In a little over a year of cyclone operations, 80 feet of elevation have been gained on No. 6 dam and a freeboard of over 30 feet now exists. This freeboard has allowed the bypassing of tailing into the back of the dam during foul weather, pipeline problems, and the raising of cyclones.

Because of the 225-pound weight of standard 6-inch cyclones, forty lightweight (50-pound) cyclones were made by Christmas personnel. Lightweight 10-inch cyclones are now commercially available and several are now on test at Christmas. Currently a tripod stand and 26-foot centers are used with the 6-inch cyclones. With the 10-inch cyclones, it is planned to move out to a 39- or 52-foot spacing.

The anticipated height of these two dams is 200 feet above the top of the starter dam with No. 6 dam having a capacity of 14 million tons and No. 7 dam having a capacity of 10 million tons.

In the third arroyo north of No. 6 and No. 7

Tailing line to the new dam, which was built below the old dam.　　　　　Figure No. 3

Drop boxes were used on the steep terrain to move the tailing into the pond area.　　　Figure No. 4

dams, No. 8 is being designed. This dam is necessary to give Christmas adequate tailing storage capacity for future development. Cycloning will be used on this dam, and a siphon rather than a decant system will be used.

All decant water flows to a settling pond below No. 7 dam. The water is reclaimed from the pond and is pumped at an 800-foot head to a storage basin above the mill.

When building in these arroyos, the main problem has been a lack of dam capacity as related to the berm length, particularly when the dam is very new. In dragline days, a freshly dug berm would provide only 6 to 10 days running on the new dams, with 3 months required for drying. With the advent of cyclones, it was still necessary to maintain very close spacing and it was difficult to build additional freeboard. Enough sand could not be generated to keep ahead of the pond. By running the cyclones to produce the maximum building rate, and with some luck, this problem was finally overcome and, after 50 feet of dam had been built, the terrain was such that there was a significant increase in pond area and the freeboard started to increase rapidly. A running time of 35 to 50 days now exists between new cyclone stands and, if necessary, the berm could be hosed over for about a year with no new berm building. Pond area is only 29 acres in active use and 35 acres in emergency reserve.

A problem also exists in the transportation of the tailing to the berm. A vertical drop of over 700 feet in a horizontal distance of 5,200 feet exists between the tailing thickener and the berm of No. 7 dam. At Christmas, many dropboxes are employed to get the tailing to the pond area. This is not too great a problem in most cases, but in some areas the dropboxes required seem excessive.

An attempt is made to maintain a grade of 1 1/2

Two tailing ponds built in one canyon are visible
in this picture.   Figure No. 5

Looking down the canyon at one of the dams.
                                         Figure No. 6

to 2 1/2 percent on the pipeline but, to get from
the ultimate dam height at the top of a ridge to
the starter dam, either requires a ridiculous
number of dropboxes, a pipeline zigzaging down the
hillside, or some very steep pipeline that will
wear very rapidly, but that will also be removed
normally in a short time as the berm height increases
At Christmas, the latter route has been taken. It
is felt that the accelerated wear can be tolerated
as long as the pipeline will be taken out of
service anyway. Some typical slopes might be 5
percent for the top 50 feet of berm, 10 percent for
the next 50 feet of berm, 15 percent for the next
50 feet of berm and 20 to 25 percent for the 50
feet of berm next to the starter dam.

Transportation of maintenance material and
manpower around the dams is also difficult with
steep, and sometimes very long, access roads required. This is particularly a problem during wet
weather.

Even with the diversion system, rain is a
problem, not so much in the pond, but on the dam
face itself. The starter dam may be only 200 feet
long, but in a couple of years the berm is over 800
feet long. All the water collected has a tendency
to funnel to one spot and start eroding the lower
portion of the dam. As a result, a system of
diversion ditches is being constructed on the old
roads across the dams to carry the water off the
dam to solid ground, before it flows downward.

A feature possibly unique to Christmas is that
No. 7 dam is eventually going to overcome No. 6 dam
and could overlap the base by 50 to 70 feet. A
reverse dam on one pond leg of No. 7 is being considered to keep the face of No. 6 dam dry. Other
alternatives may be considered, but the problem is
several years in the future and no definite plans
have yet been made.

PROBABILITY OF EARTHQUAKES

AND RESULTANT GROUND MOTION

John A. Blume

President, John A. Blume & Associates, Engineers

San Francisco, California

The world has had earthquakes for millions and
millions of years. There is no reason to expect
them to stop. As we build more structures, including
earth structures, the probability of having damage
or failure increases unless these structures are
carefully designed to withstand the anticipated
earthquake motions. The subject of this paper is
the ground motion or the demand on the structure
and not the structure per se. However, in most
cases the structure and the soil or rock below are
coupled to form a complex vibrational system.

EARTHQUAKE ACTIVITY

The recorded history of earthquakes is extremely
short in geologic time. All we have, except for the
story revealed by geologic evidence, is a few hundred
years of information (as compared to millions of
years) with nothing really set forth objectively
until well into the 19th century.

Measurements of strong, damaging earthquake motion started only four decades ago, and the data are extremely sparse compared to the number of damaging earthquakes since that time.

Figure No. 1 shows worldwide earthquake epicenters for the greatest shocks (1). The entire rim of the Pacific Ocean is quite active, as is a wide belt across the Mediterranean and India to the Pacific rim. Parts of Australia, South America and Africa seem to be relatively free from epicenters. Figure No. 2 shows the world seismicity for 1971 and Figure No. 3 shows the major events in 1971.

Although many think that California has all of the U.S.A. earthquakes, all states have experienced earthquake motion during the short history of the white man in this country. Parts of Florida and Texas were not active in that period. Two of the greatest United States earthquakes had epicenters in Missouri in 1811 and 1812. Figure No. 4 shows epicenters for major U.S. earthquakes as known through 1967 (2). Many of these were felt in several states. In 1971, 361 earthquakes were felt in 21 states. California had 118 of these, Montana had 93, Alaska 90, New Mexico 16, Nevada 9, Colorado 7, Hawaii 5, New York 4, South Carolina and Washington 3 each, Tennessee and Utah 2 each, and 9 other states 1 each. National interest in seismic activity is evidenced by Figure No. 5 which shows the places in the U.S. where we have been asked to conduct seismic investigations. Much, but not all, of this interest springs from the nuclear power plant program.

Arizona has had its own earthquakes as well as feeling the effects of large ones originating in California and Mexico. Although there have been no recorded deaths or injuries in Arizona there has been damage. Figure No. 6 shows the Arizona earthquakes of intensity V and greater (3).

Iran, as an example of a seismically active country, has had major earthquakes and deaths as shown in Figure No. 7 (3). Much of the damage and

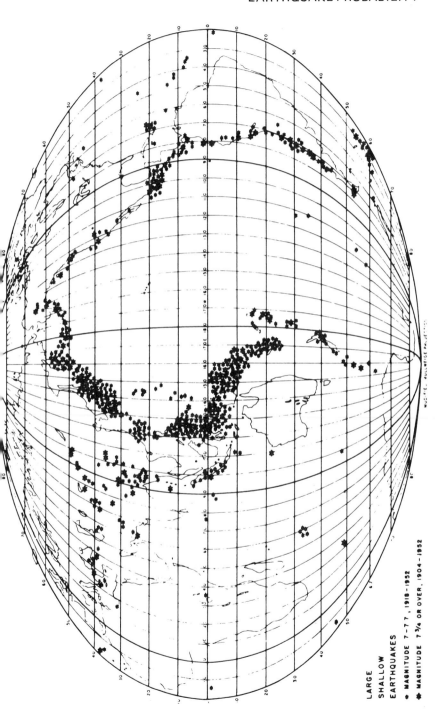

LARGE
SHALLOW
EARTHQUAKES

✦ MAGNITUDE 7 – 7 7 , 1918 – 1952
✹ MAGNITUDE 7 ¾ OR OVER , 1904 – 1952

World map of shallow earthquakes: Class A, 1904–1952; Class B, 1918–1952.   Figure No. 1

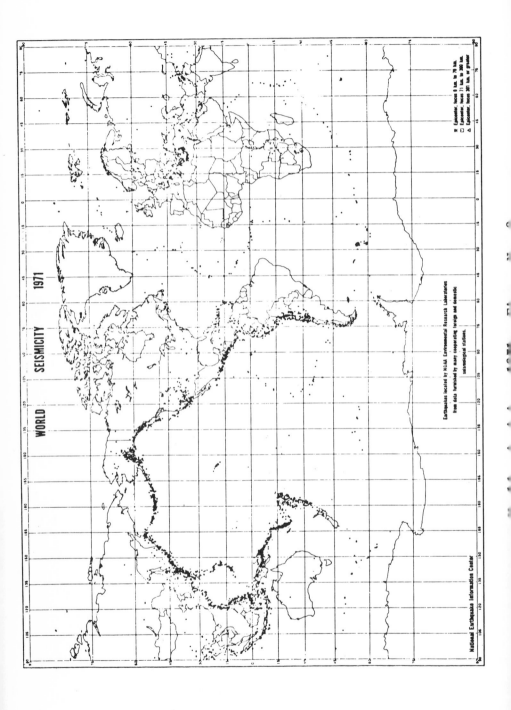

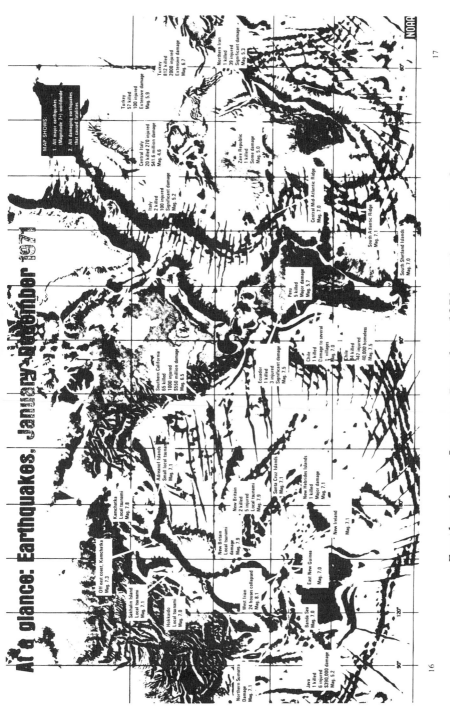

Earthquakes, January–December 1971.   Figure No. 3

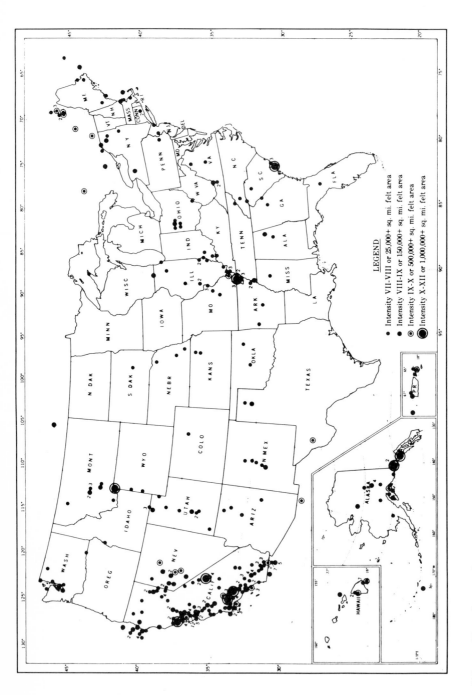

Distribution of earthquakes causing significant damage in the United States through 1967.

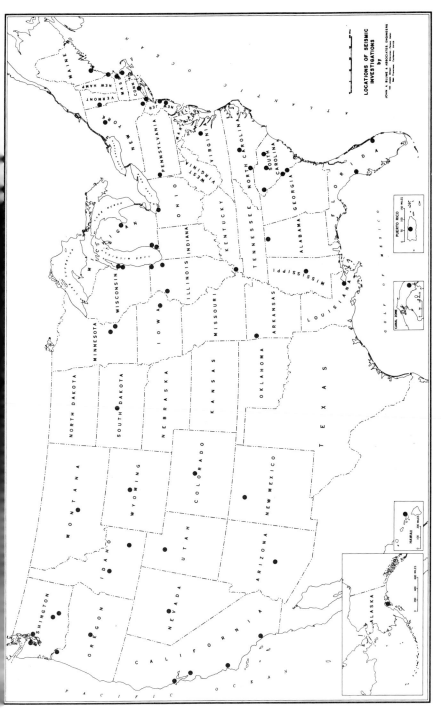

Locations of seismic investigations in the United States. Figure No. 5

Aspect	Permit Limit Value	Average Tailing Value	Intake Water Range
"Dissolved" Cu (ppb)	5	12	1 - 7
"Dissolved" Mo (ppb)	20	200	1 - 7
pH	9.5 - 10.0	10.0 - 11.5	
Flow Rate (gals. per day)	9.3×10^6	10.7×10^6	

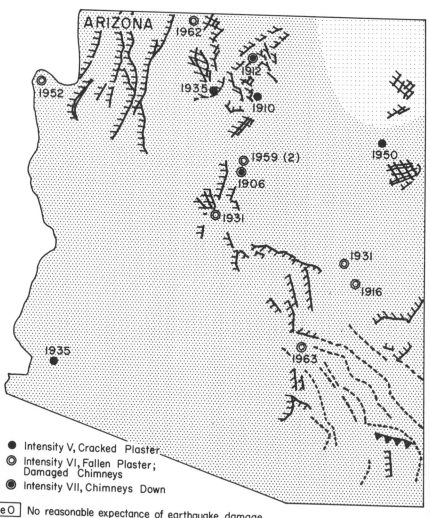

- ● Intensity V, Cracked Plaster
- ◎ Intensity VI, Fallen Plaster; Damaged Chimneys
- ◉ Intensity VII, Chimneys Down

- Zone 0 | No reasonable expectance of earthquake damage
- Zone 1 | Minor earthquake damage can be expected
- Zone 2 | Moderate damage can be expected
- Zone 3 | Major destructive earthquakes may occur

Arizona earthquakes of intensity V and greater.

Figure No. 6

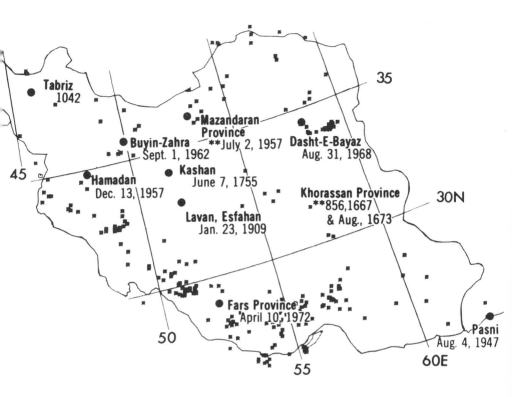

DESTRUCTIVE EARTHQUAKES IN IRAN *

Date	Region	Deaths	Magnitude
**856	Khorassan Province	45,000	
1042	Tabriz	40,000	
**1667	Khorassan Province	13,000	
** August 1673	Khorassan Province	4,000	
June 7, 1755	Kashan	40,000	
January 23, 1909	Lavan, Esfahan		7.4
August 5, 1947	Pasni		7.3
**July 2, 1957	Mazandaran Province	2,000	7.1
December 13, 1957	Hamadan	2,000	7.2
September 1, 1962	Buyin-Zahra	10,000	7.5
August 31, 1968	Dasht-E-Bayaz	11,000	7.3
		estimated	
April 10, 1972	Fars Province	4,000	6.9

*Contributed by the National Geophysical Data Center, NOAA Environmental Data Service.
**Epicenter unknown; widely felt.

Major earthquakes in Iran, with number of deaths.

Figure No. 7

333

death rate could be reduced by improved construction for earthquake resistance.

EARTHQUAKE PROBABILITY

The probability of damaging earthquake occurrence in a given area can be estimated by a study of the history of that area supplemented by a geologic study to reveal any faults or systems that may produce earthquakes not revealed by that short history. Simply using general maps or building code zoning is not an adequate procedure.

Figure No. 8 is a code map used for many years but now replaced by Figure No. 9. Although such maps serve useful purposes, they are not intended for specific use in the design of a critical structure. They do not show detail nor do they evaluate the relative probabilities of events.

Another useful approach in general mapping is shown in Figure No. 10 where the peak accelerations for a 100-year return period are estimated (4). A problem here is that even if such mapping were accurate, there are other return periods to be considered than the arbitrary 100 years. Figure No. 11 shows the estimated return periods for an arbitrary peak acceleration of 10% of gravity (4).

One need only to look at a map like Figure No. 12 to realize that earthquake activity in the Aleutians and Alaska is highly probable. There was a great earthquake on March 28, 1964, magnitude 8.5. Fortunately, the source of energy release was some distance from Anchorage or the results would have been much worse than they were. But there have been many other great earthquakes in that region, and there obviously will be more. There have been 61 earthquakes in the world of magnitude 8 or greater since 1904, with 2 rated at 8.9 (Colombia 1906 and Japan 1933).

California has had 50 earthquakes of epicentral intensity (Modified Mercalli scale) of VIII or greater since 1769, with 49 of these since 1812. One can determine the damaging area for such great

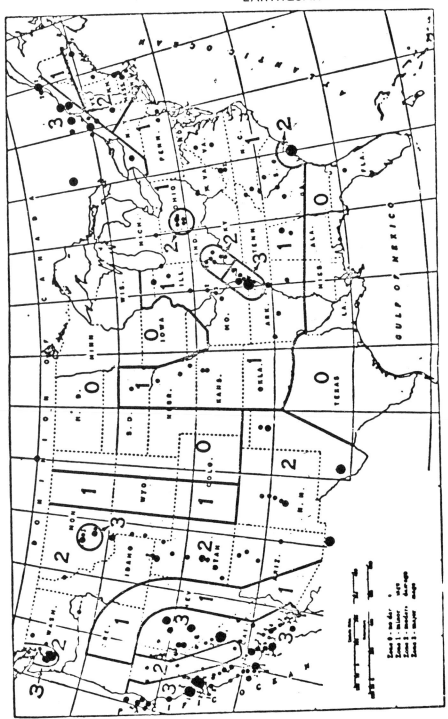

Map of the United States showing epicenters and zones of approximately equal seismic probability.

Figure No. 8

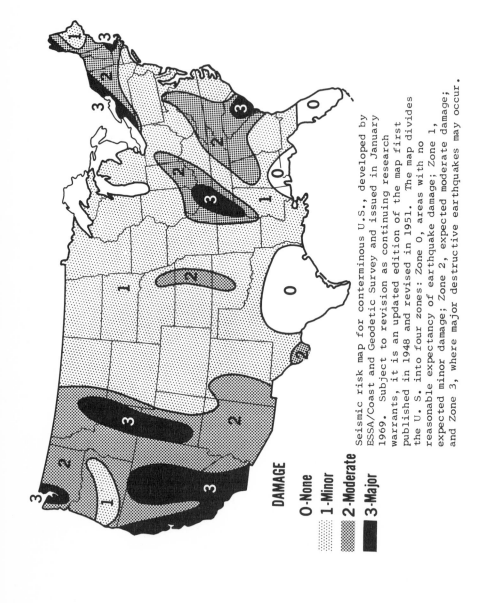

Map of the United States showing probability of earthquake damage. Figure No. 9

Seismic risk map for conterminous U.S., developed by ESSA/Coast and Geodetic Survey and issued in January 1969. Subject to revision as continuing research warrants, it is an updated edition of the map first published in 1948 and revised in 1951. The map divides the U. S. into four zones: Zone 0, areas with no reasonable expectancy of earthquake damage; Zone 1, expected minor damage; Zone 2, expected moderate damage; and Zone 3, where major destructive earthquakes may occur.

DAMAGE
0-None
1-Minor
2-Moderate
3-Major

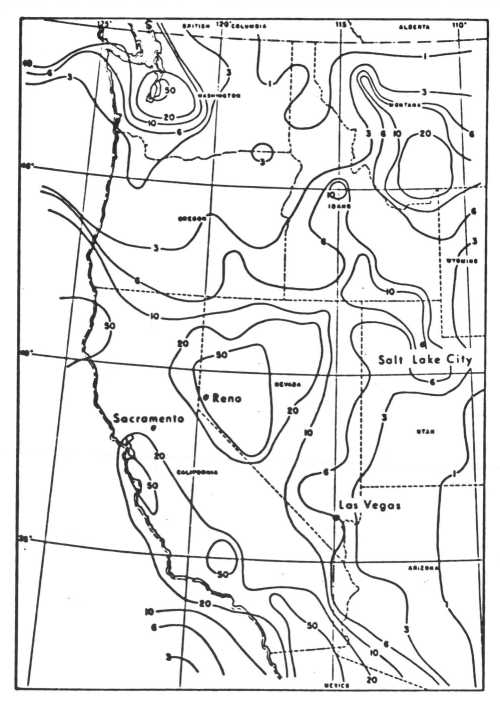

Accelerations as a percent of g with a 100-year
return period for California. (From Milne and
Davenport, 4WCEE, 1969.)   Figure No. 10

337

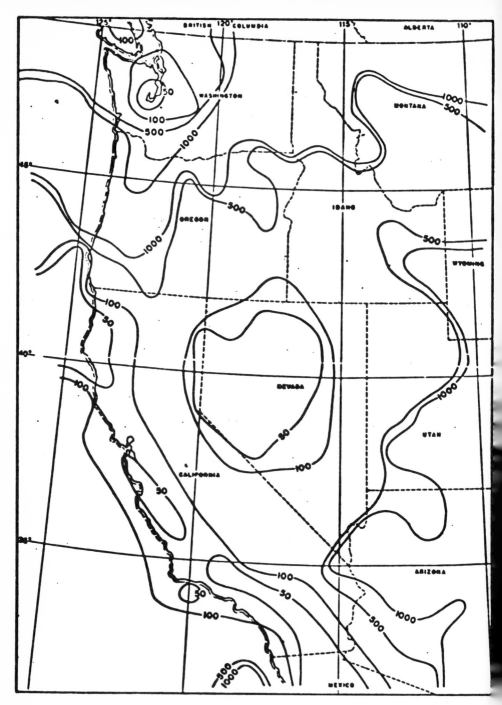

Return periods in years for acceleration of 10 percent gravity for western United States. (From Milne and Davenport, 4WCEE, 1969)   Figure No. 11

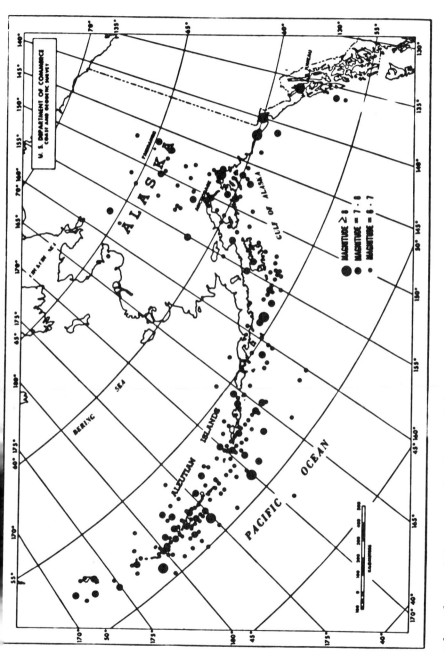

Earthquakes with a magnitude ≥ 6.0 during the period 1899-1964 in Alaska.

Figure No. 12

shocks and, knowing the area of the state, compute the probabilities for a local area. A much better procedure, however, is to make a local study as well and to adjust the probabilities for local history and geologic conditions.

Probabilistic models can be made given enough data points. Poisson modeling is effective. In general, the distribution of magnitude, intensity or peak acceleration is highly skewed, with much more frequent occurrence of the smaller events. The extreme large events are difficult to model because of sparse data.

Table No. I indicates the earthquakes per 100 years per 100,000 square kilometers in 9 areas for 4 Modified Mercalli intensity levels (2). The 9 areas are shown in Figure No. 13 (2). Although area 8 has had as great earthquakes as areas 1 and 2, it obviously has them less frequently. The Modified Mercalli (MM) Intensity Scale is appended (Table AI).

RESULTS OF MAJOR EARTHQUAKES

The loss of life from earthquakes in the United States has been relatively low. This is due in some part to better construction but to a much larger degree to good fortune in the location of the earthquakes, in the time of day, the day of the week, and the time of the year. In other words, the most vulnerable structures were not occupied at the time, such as schools destroyed during vacation period, freeway structures collapsed before the morning traffic, etc. Such luck can not be expected to continue.

Table No. II shows lives lost in the United States through 1965 and Table No. III shows property damage through 1966 (2). San Fernando 1971 would add 65 lives and up to $1 billion of property damage.

Table No. IV shows the record for some recent events and also some great earthquakes of the past. This is by no means a complete listing.

340

TABLE NO. 1

AVERAGE FREQUENCY* OF EARTHQUAKES
WITH MAXIMUM INTENSITIES V THROUGH
VIII FOR THE NUMBERED AREAS SHOWN
IN FIGURE 5

Area	Earthquakes Per 100 Years per 100,000 KM^2			
	V	VI	VII	VIII
1 & 2. California, Nevada	300	84.6	23.8	6.72
4. Montana, Idaho, Utah, Arizona	64.4	17.7	4.89	1.35
3. Puget Sound, Washington	68.0	16.3	3.92	0.94
8. Mississippi Valley, St. Lawrence Valley	24.2	7.65	2.42	0.76
7. Nebraska, Kansas, Oklahoma	13.0	4.20	1.35	0.45
5. Wyoming, Colorado, New Mexico	32.8	6.85	1.42	0.31
6. Oklahoma, North Texas	13.3	3.73	1.07	0.30
9. East Coast	12.8	3.39	0.88	0.23

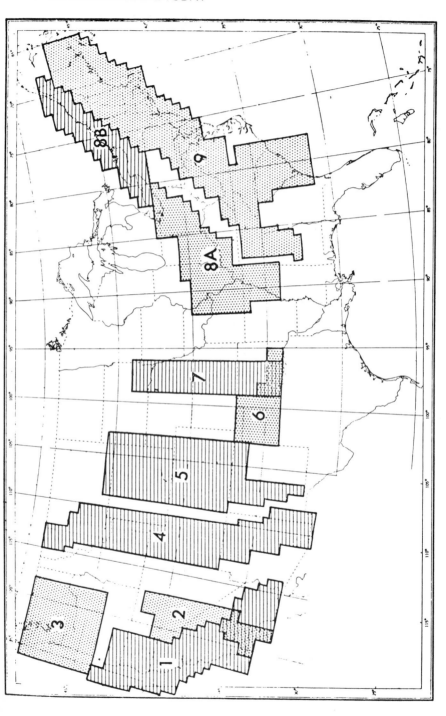

Location map showing areas for which earthquake frequencies were computed

TABLE NO. 2

LIVES LOST
IN UNITED STATES
EARTHQUAKES

YEAR	LOCALITY	LIVES LOST
1811 1812	New Madrid, Mo.	Several
1812	San Juan Capistrano, Calif.	40
1868	Hayward, Calif.	30
1872	Owens Valley, Calif.	27
1886	Charleston, S.C.	60
1899	San Jacinto, Calif.	6
1906	San Francisco, Calif.	700
1915	Imperial Valley, Calif.	6
1918	Puerto Rico (killed by tsunami from earthquake in Mona Passage).	116
1925	Santa Barbara, Calif.	13
1926	. . . . Do	1
1932	Humboldt Co., Calif.	1
1933	Long Beach, Calif.	115
1934	Kosmo, Utah	2
1935	Helena, Mont.	4
1940	Imperial Valley, Calif.	9
1946	Hawaii (killed by tsunami from earthquake in Aleutians)	173
1949	Puget Sound, Wash.	8
1952	Kern Co., Calif.	14
1954	Eureka-Arcata, Calif.	1
1955	Oakland, Calif.	1
1958	Khantaak Island and Lituya Bay, Alaska	5
1959	Hebgen Lake, Mont.	28
1960	Hilo, Hawaii (killed by tsunami from earthquake off the coast of Chile)	61
1964	Prince William Sound, Alaska (tsunami claimed nearly all those killed along Gulf of Alaska and west coast of the United States)	125
1965	Puget Sound, Wash.	7

TABLE NO. 3

LOSSES (IN CONTEMPORARY DOLLARS) FROM SELECTED UNITED STATES EARTHQUAKES

YEAR	LOCALITY	DAMAGE
		Dollars
1865	San Francisco, Calif.	500,000
1868	.... do	350,000
1872	Owens Valley, Calif.	250,000
1886	Charleston, S.C.	23,000,000
1892	Vacaville, Calif.	225,000
1898	Mare Island, Calif.	1,400,000
1906	San Francisco, Calif.	80,000,000
	.... Fire Loss	400,000,000
1915	Imperial Valley, Calif.	900,000
1918	Puerto Rico (tsunami damage from earthquake in Mona Passage).	4,000,000
1918	San Jacinto and Hemet, Calif.	200,000
1925	Santa Barbara, Calif.	8,000,000
1933	Long Beach, Calif.	40,000,000
1935	Helena, Mont.	4,000,000
1940	Imperial Valley, Calif.	6,000,000
1941	Santa Barbara, Calif.	100,000
1941	Torrance–Gardena, Calif.	1,000,000
1944	Cornwall, Canada–Messena, N.Y.	2,000,000
1946	Hawaii (tsunami damage from earthquake in Aleutians)	25,000,000
1949	Puget Sound, Wash.	25,000,000
1949	Terminal Island, Calif. (oil wells only)	9,000,000
1951	....do	3,000,000
1952	Kern County, Calif.	60,000,000
1954	Eureka–Arcata, Calif.	2,100,000
1954	Wilkes–Barre, Pa.	1,000,000
1955	Terminal Island, Calif. (oil wells only)	3,000,000
1955	Oakland–Walnut Creek, Calif.	1,000,000
1957	Hawaii (tsunami damage from earthquake in Aleutians)	3,000,000
1957	San Francisco, Calif.	1,000,000
1959	Hebgen Lake, Mont. (damage to timber and roads)	11,000,000
1960	Hawaii and west coast of United States (tsunami damage from earthquake off the coast of Chile)	25,500,000
1961	Terminal Island, Calif. (oil wells only)	4,500,000
1964	Alaska and west coast of United States (tsunami damage from earthquake near Anchorage, Alaska; includes earthquake damage in Alaska)	500,000,000
1965	Puget Sound, Wash.	12,500,000
1966	Dulce, N. Mex.	200,000

TABLE NO. 4

SOME RECENT AND OTHER EARTHQUAKES OF INTEREST

Date	Place	M	Epicentral distance to main city, miles	Depth, miles	Estimated dead	Estimated property damage $ x 10^6	Houses destroyed
2/1971	SFernando, CA	6.6	10	5-10	65	1000	
5/1970	Peru	7.8	22	27	50,000	250	90% in some areas
3/1970	Turkey	7.1		12	1,086		8,000
9/1968	Iran	6.3		9	11,588		
5/1968	Tokachi-Oki, Japan	7.9		4-5	47	131	95 "ships" to tsunami
7/1967	Caracas	6.5	30		266		5 highrise buildings collapsed
2/1967	Colombia	6.75	185		98	18	
1965	Seattle	5.75	13	35	7	13	
1964	Niigata	7.5	25	24	25	800	1,000
1964	Alaska	8.4	75	12	125	311	
1964	Skopje	5.4	9	8	1,000		37%
1962	Iran	7.5		12	12,000		21,300
1960	Agadir	5.7	5	1-2	12,000		100% at Kasbah
1960	Chile	8.4	80-110		1,000	600	45,000
1957	Mexico City	7.5	220		125	150	Few
1957	SFrancisco	5.3	10	7	0	1	0
1952	Kern Co., CA	7.7	27	15	14	60	
1949	Seattle	7.1	38	45	8	25	
1940	El Centro, CA	7.1	20	15	9	6	
1933	Long Beach, CA	6.3	10	5-6	115	40	
1925	SBarbara, CA	6.3	10		13	8	
1923	Japan	8.3	60		143,000	Vast	600,000
1920	Kansu, China				180,000		
1906	SFrancisco	8.3	30		700	800	Many
1755	Lisbon	8.6	60		60,000		
1737	Calcutta				300,000		
1556	Shensi, China				830,000		

As population increases and more structures of all types are built, the exposure to earthquakes increases. The way this can be counteracted is to build earthquake-resistant structures.

GROUND MOTION AND SPECTRAL RESPONSE

It is convenient, and customary in many disciplines, to consider peak ground motion in terms of acceleration, velocity, or displacement as an index of severity. Figure No. 14 shows at the top acceleration as recorded for the 1940 El Centro earthquake, N-S component. Also shown are the velocity and displacement obtained by integration (5). The lower part of the figure shows the isoseismals or MM intensity contours for the same earthquake.

Two important facts must be kept in mind. First, the magnitude alone is no measure of ground motion intensity at a given point unless the epicentral distance and the focal depth are also considered (see Figure No. 15). A great earthquake may be a thousand miles away and have no effect locally. The second point is that peak particle ground motion is a very poor index of the response of a structure because it eliminates the basic dimension of time in dynamic response phenomena. Thus, for important engineering purposes either the entire time history of motion is used or the convenient response spectrum. The latter represents the peak response to the time history of a whole spectrum of idealized simple oscillators having given damping values and a range of natural periods. Figure No. 16 shows response spectra for pseudo absolute acceleration, relative velocity, and relative displacement.

Another very convenient method of plotting response spectra is on 4-way log paper as shown in Figure No. 17. There is an assumption inherent in such plotting, namely that the peak response motion is harmonic in nature. For most cases of structural response this assumption is acceptable.

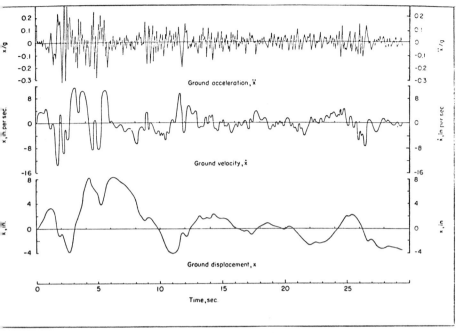

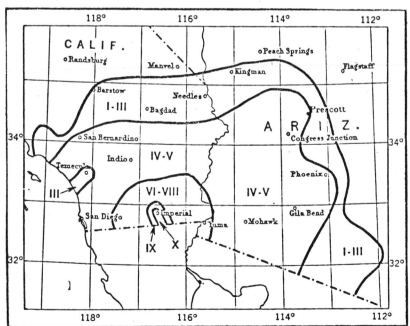

Ground motion and isoseismals of the El Centro
earthquake of May 1940, N/S component.

Figure No. 14

347

Definition of earthquake terms. Figure No. 15

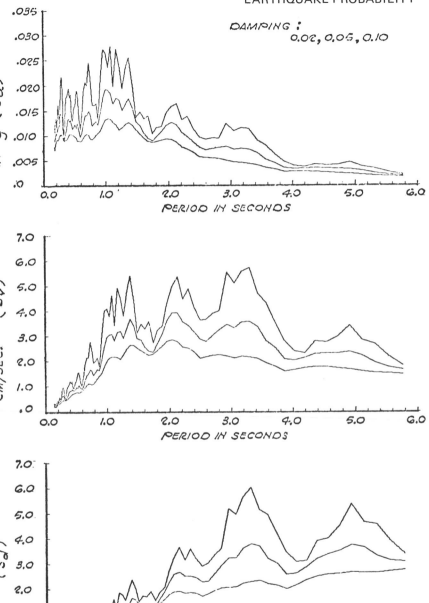

Spectral response to ground motion at Station
SE-6, N/S component, Las Vegas, Event Boxcar
(L-7 instrument).   Figure No. 16

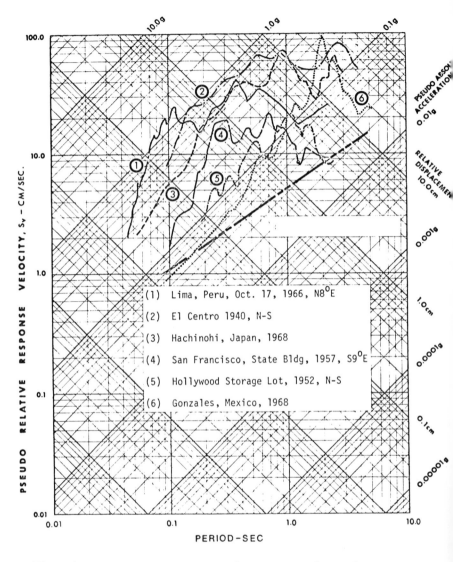

(1) Lima, Peru, Oct. 17, 1966, N8^{o}E

(2) El Centro 1940, N-S

(3) Hachinohi, Japan, 1968

(4) San Francisco, State Bldg, 1957, S9^{o}E

(5) Hollywood Storage Lot, 1952, N-S

(6) Gonzales, Mexico, 1968

Elastic response spectra, 5 percent damped.

Figure No. 17

A new intensity scale has been proposed that eliminates subjective ratings by using the response spectrum. This is called the Engineering Intensity Scale (6). Figure No. 18 shows an example of its use.

The spectral response acceleration, regardless of damping, approaches the peak ground acceleration at zero period. Thus, by normalizing to unit ground acceleration, one can study spectral shape, or dynamic amplification factor (DAF) over the period range of interest. This has been done in a comprehensive study of 33 earthquake records. Figure No. 19 shows results for 5% of critical damping and 4 levels of probability of being exceeded. The heavy lines are "smoothed" versions of the computer output shown by the lighter lines. The 50% exceedance curve is the average value.

The problem involves several random variables which can be condensed into the peak ground acceleration (given magnitude, distance, depth, and soil conditions), DAF (given peak ground acceleration) and finally, the response acceleration obtained as the product of the two. With probabilities for the earthquake in the local area, for the ground acceleration given the earthquake, and for DAF given the ground acceleration, one can arrive at joint probabilities for various levels of spectral acceleration at a given site. Decision making is then needed to reach the optimum design level. There are no simple yes or no answers in the earthquake field because of the wide variation of possible demands and consequences.

MODELING

It is often desirable to model the structure and the soil below as one system. This would be especially true for tailings structures. With the model and the earthquake motion, perhaps taken at the rock level, the response and strains or stresses may be computed. Models used are lumped mass with weightless springs, elastic half space, finite element or combinations. It is important to

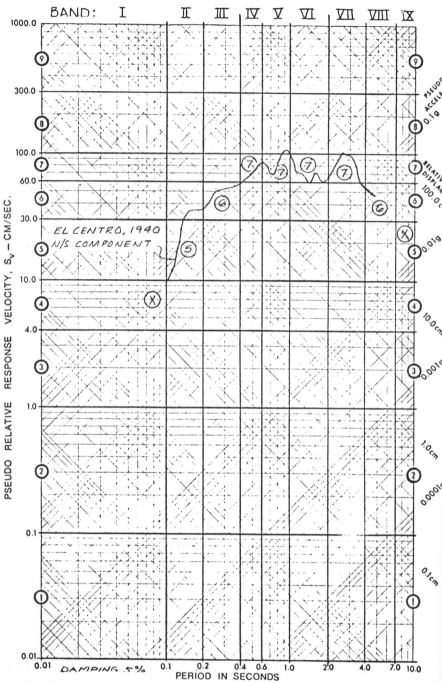

Engineering Intensity Scale matrix with example spectrum.

Figure No. 18

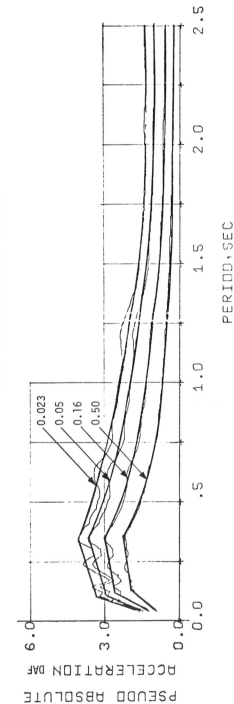

RESPONSE SPECTRA
DAMPING RATIO = 0.050

PROBABILITIES OF EXCEEDANCE
0.50, 0.16, 0.05, 0.023
GROUND MOTION NORMALIZED TO 1.0 G

Results for 5 percent of critical damping and 4 levels of probability of being
exceeded.

Figure No. 19

353

correlate the soil stiffnesses with strain; two or more models or else bi- or tri-linear stiffnesses may be required for different levels of earthquake motion.

REFERENCES

1. Gutenberg, B. and C. F. Richter, "Seismicity of the Earth", Hafner Publishing Co., Inc., New York, 1954, 1965.

2. "Studies in Seismicity and Earthquake Damage Statistics, 1969, Summary and Recommendations", report for Department of Housing and Urban Development, U. S. Department of Commerce, ESSA, C&GS, 1969.

3. Earthquake Information Bulletin, various issues, National Earthquake Information Center, NOAA, National Ocean Survey, Rockville, Maryland.

4. Milne, W. G. and A. G. Davenport, "Earthquake Probability", Proceedings, Fourth World Conference on Earthquake Engineering, Vol. I, Chile, 1969.

5. Blume, John A., N. M. Newmark, and Leo H. Corning, "Design of Multistory Reinforced Concrete Buildings for Earthquake Motions", Portland Cement Association, Chicago, Illinois, 1961.

6. Blume, John A., "An Engineering Intensity Scale for Earthquakes and Other Ground Motion", Bulletin of the Seismological Society of America, 60:217-229, February 1970.

TABLE NO. A1

MODIFIED MERCALLI INTENSITY SCALE OF 1931 (ABRIDGED)

I. Not felt except by a very few under specially favorable circumstances. (I Rossi-Forel Scale.)

II. Felt only by a few persons at rest, especially on upper floors of buildings. Delicately suspended objects may swing. (I to II Rossi-Forel Scale.)

III. Felt quite noticeably indoors, especially on upper floors of buildings, but many people do not recognize it as an earthquake. Standing motorcars may rock slightly. Vibration like passing of truck. Duration estimated. (III Rossi-Forel Scale.)

IV. During the day felt indoors by many, outdoors by few. At night some awakened. Dishes, windows, doors disturbed; walls make creaking sound. Sensation like heavy truck striking building. Standing motorcars rocked noticeably. (IV to V Rossi-Forel Scale.)

V. Felt by nearly everyone, many awakened, some dishes, windows, etc., broken; a few instances of cracked plaster; unstable objects overturned. Disturbances of trees, poles, and other tall objects sometimes noticed. Pendulum clocks may stop. (V to VI Rossi-Forel Scale.)

VI. Felt by all, many frightened and run outdoors. Some heavy furniture moved; a few instances of fallen plaster or damaged chimneys. Damage slight. (VI to VII Rossi-Forel Scale.)

VII. Everybody runs outdoors. Damage negligible in buildings of good design and construction; slight to moderate in well-built ordinary structures; considerable in poorly built or badly designed structures; some chimneys broken. Noticed by persons driving motorcars. (VIII Rossi-Forel Scale.)

VIII. Damage slight in specially designed structures; considerable in ordinary substantial buildings with partial collapse; great in poorly built structures. Panel walls thrown out of frame structures. Fall of chimneys, factory stacks, columns, monuments, walls. Heavy furniture overturned. Sand and mud ejected in small amounts. Changes in well water. Persons driving motorcars disturbed. (VIII+ to IX− Rossi-Forel Scale.)

IX. Damage considerable in specially designed structures; well-designed frame structures thrown out of plumb; great in substantial buildings, with partial collapse. Buildings shifted off foundations. Ground cracked conspicuously. (IX+ Rossi-Forel Scale.)

X. Some well-built wooden structures destroyed; most masonry and frame structures destroyed with foundations; ground badly cracked. Rails bent. Landslides considerable from riverbanks and steep slopes. Shifted sand and mud. Water splashed (slopped) over banks. (X Rossi-Forel Scale.)

XI. Few, if any, (masonry) structures remain standing. Bridges destroyed. Broad fissures in ground. Underground pipelines completely out of service. Earth slumps and land slips in soft ground. Rails bent greatly.

XII. Damage total. Waves seen on ground surfaces. Lines of sight and level distorted. Objects thrown upward into air.

TAILINGS DISPOSAL -- FAILURES AND LESSONS

Edwin S. Smith

Chief Soils Engineer

International Engineering Company, Inc.

San Francisco, California, U. S. A.

INTRODUCTION

Man, by learning from his mistakes, has progressed from the cave to outer space. The technique
of using mistakes to learn is an instinctive one and
is done in numerous small ways many times in every-
day life.

Engineers, in particular, have been methodical-
ly taking lessons from their failures for many years.
Numerous articles on failures of concrete structures
can be found in the technical literature in the early part of this century. Later, as failures, and
the resulting lessons, became more numerous and complex, books were published on the subject.

The American Concrete Institute's first monograph, entitled "Lessons from Failures of Concrete
Structures," (1) was published in 1964. In a most
educational discussion of "ailing and failing" struc-

tures the author, Dr. Jacob Feld, indicates that his monograph was prepared "with hopeful concentration on the ancient admonition of Confucius: 'If you wish to control the future, study the past.'" His reference to the Code of Hammurabi (about 1750 B.C.) makes interesting reading—apparently engineers, under the jurisdiction of these regulations, often did not have the opportunity to apply the lessons learned from failures. The first of five basic rules from the code stipulated the death penalty for the engineer-builder if the owner was killed by a failure of the structure.

In 1920 Lars Torgensen (2) compiled a list of dam failures, giving brief details on the type and, in some instances, the cause of collapse. More recently (1968), Babb and Mermel (3) have published a "Catalog of Dam Disasters, Failures and Accidents", in which "failures" are classified into the following groups:

"● Major disasters. The sudden and complete failure of a dam while in service. Usually with total destruction and loss of the dam and of life and property.

● Failure and washouts of minor dams constructed without benefit of professional skill and having little engineering significance.

● Failures to gates, valves, piers, and appurtenant structures, including cracks, leaks, and erosion where the dam as such did not fail but received publicity associated with its name.

● Accidents and failures during construction and before the dam was ready for service. Usually corrected and not inimical to the satisfactory functioning of the dam after completion.

● Ancient dams about which little is known, and predating any modern era of dam building which might be arbitrarily selected."

Observational Approach

The spiraling production of tailings, resulting from the increased demand for metals, combined with improved extraction methods and lower grade ores, has magnified disposal problems. Application of both soil mechanics principles and past experience from many varied disposal operations has resulted in the development of safe methods of constructing tailings deposits. By taking advantage of the opportunity to make prototype tests during tailings deposition, mining engineers have further improved disposal practices in a most economical manner.

According to mining folklore, no tailings dam has ever been completed without at least one failure occurring during deposition of the particles. Although the term failure is rarely defined in these stories, it can be assumed to include everything from a slight nonconformity with the design to complete collapse. Figure 1 shows a dike failure with liquefaction of slimes in the deposit.

Tailings Deposit Failure   *Figure 1*

In contrast to reinforced concrete and structural steel, one of the advantages in earthwork engineering is the opportunity of using the observational approach, described by Casagrande as "the continuous evaluation of observations and new information for redesigning as needed while construction is still in progress" (4). In this same paper, "Role of the 'Calculated Risk' in Earthwork and Foundation Engineering," Casagrande presents a series of case histories involving calculated risks. His evaluation of the term, "widely if not somewhat loosely used in engineering" suggests two distinct steps:

"● The use of imperfect knowledge, guided by judgment and experience, to estimate the probable ranges for all pertinent quantities that enter into the solution of a problem.

● The decision on an appropriate margin of safety, or degree of risk, taking into consideration economic factors and the magnitude of losses that would result from failure."

Peck, in his discussion of the use of this method in applied soil mechanics, points out its advantages and limitations (5). Because of their applicability to the disposal of tailings, both papers should be required reading for all mill superintendents.

Mining engineers and mill superintendents have been using the observational approach for many years in planning their tailings disposal operations. Indeed, since many tailings deposits were constructed before soil mechanics became a part of the engineering academic curriculum, it was the only method available. The continued existence of many of the old, and often quite large, deposits confirms the success of the techniques used.

Disposal Records

It is not uncommon to find that records of disposal techniques and deposition rates are nonexistent for the older tailings deposits. In most instances, however, it is possible to derive some form of approximate "construction" record. Plant production figures and records of prolonged work stoppages due to strikes,

359

floods, earthquakes or economic depression allow a disposal record to be pieced together with rough verification provided by old photographs.

Until recent years, gradation analyses and in-place density tests have rarely been made at the time of tailings deposition. Few descriptions exist of operation conditions and dike behavior, such as pond freeboard, earthwork equipment operations, local slumping, seeps on downstream face, cracking and excessive settlements. For any subsequent engineering studies of an existing deposit, such records can be invaluable.

Definition

Many definitions of the term failure have been presented in the technical literature. For the purpose of this treatise, any breakdown in a tailings disposal operation or any malfunction of a part of a deposit is considered to be a failure. Although a wet spot on the downstream face of a dike is normally taken to be only a warning of instability, it can also be described as a seepage failure of the dike. Likewise, spreading of the toe of a dike can be considered as a failure of the foundation. In effect, any unexpected dike behavior or deficiency in deposition technique that allows unstable conditions to develop is classified as a failure.

FAILURES

A literature search for information on failures of tailing deposits reveals that until recently the phenomenon was either not known or not regarded as sufficiently important to justify discussion in the technical journals. Because of the conditions known to exist at the time, it is assumed that early experience in tailings disposal operations, while fraught with problems, experienced few cases of total collapse. This is understandable because of the low rates of tailings production and, in most cases, the

smaller size dams required for the retaining structures. As production rates increased and several
catastrophic failures focused attention on the danger
of improperly placed tailings, the problem began to
be studied more closely.

Types of Failure

In his "Notes on the Design of Earth Dams" (6),
Casagrande summarizes the causes of earth dam failures and discusses different types of slides. His
work is applicable to all types of tailings dams.

Among the types of failure most common to tailings deposits are:

- foundation failure
- slope failure
- overtopping by flood waters
- erosion of face
- piping, in either the dike or foundation
- collapse of dewatering conduit
- liquefaction.

Foundation Failure   *Figure 2*

Discussion

Foundation failures. Such failures are not uncommon among earthfill structures. Where a weak layer of soil exists at shallow depth in the foundation,
movement along a failure plane will occur when the
earthfill loading produces stresses in excess of the
shear strength of the soil in the weak layer. In
Figure 2 the slumping of the crest and heaving at the
toe of the slope clearly indicate that shearing has
occurred in the foundation of the dike.

Slope failures. Many variations exist--from
local sloughing of particles at random areas along
the face of an embankment to massive circular arc
slides extending over the entire structure. Slope
instability can result from earthquakes, loss of
shear strength due to an increase of porewater pressures in the soil or excess internal stresses produced by increasing the height of a dike without
flattening its slope. Figure 3 shows a slope failure
that probably resulted from increased porewater pressures behind the frozen impervious face of the dike.

Slope Failure   *Figure 3*

Overtopping failures. One of the most common causes of failure is overtopping by flood waters. Where no provision is made to pass major floods a-round or under a tailings dike, overtopping, breach-ing and total loss of semiliquid slimes can be ex-pected. Generally, the problem is of major concern only for cross-valley deposits, where river diversion can be a critical factor in any economic feasibility study of a tailings disposal operation. However, the danger of flooding and overtopping the dikes of a side-hill deposit should not be overlooked.

Erosion failures. In areas of heavy rainfall, some form of protection against erosion is usually required. Because a single storm, by itself, rarely causes major damage, the problem is generally consid-ered to be one of maintenance. When erosion is se-vere, repairs are made immediately to the slope, with some preventive maintenance at the areas of worst damage.

Decant Conduit Leak

Figure 4

Piping failures. As the phenomenon of piping in embankments has become more fully understood, the in-

363

cidence of this type of failure has decreased. Tailings deposits with the decant pond immediately behind the dike are much more susceptible to piping problems than tailings operations in which the decant pond and chimney are located as far as possible from the retaining structure.

Decant conduit failures. Many tailings deposits have experienced problems with the dewatering conduit, ranging from minor leaks, as shown in Figure 4, to total collapse. The latter can, of course, result in total evacuation of the slimes from a deposit. Most of the serious structural failures of dewatering conduits result from increases to the "final" dike height as the life of the mine is repeatedly extended.

Liquefaction failures. Because of their often catastrophic nature, most of the tailings deposit failures that have received publicity have been those resulting from liquefaction. One spectacular failure, where there was no loss of life, but considerable property damage, is shown in Figure 5.

Liquefaction Failure   *Figure 5*

(Courtesy Courrier-Journal and Louisville Times)

Such failures occur instantaneously with little, if any, warning. They may be triggered by seismic or other vibrations, foundation spreading or some form of dike collapse (7). One of the earliest (1920) and best descriptions of a liquefaction failure is given by Hazen, in his paper on the failure of the Calaveras Dam, during its construction by hydraulic methods (8). Tailings retaining structures placed by hydraulic methods are particularly susceptible to liquefaction, especially if the upstream method of construction is used.

LESSONS

Many lessons have been learned from the study of the behavior of both tailings dams and reservoir embankments. Such lessons can be divided into two categories: general and specific. Lessons in the first category are applicable to all earthfill structures, whereas those in the second category are applicable primarily to the specific conditions existing at a particular deposit.

General Lessons

The foundation of a retaining dike must always be able to resist the forces imposed upon it as the height of the tailings deposit is increased. With the subsurface sampling and testing equipment and soils laboratory facilities now available, there is no longer any necessity for taking calculated risks with respect to the adequacy of the foundation materials. A thorough investigation of the subsurface soils should always be performed.

Mill mangers are obligated to dispose of tailings at a minimum cost, consistent with maintaining acceptable safety standards. One of the simplest methods of reducing costs is to steepen the slopes of retaining dikes. Experience gained over many years from construction of many different types of tailings deposits has shown that it is possible to design and construct retaining dikes using the calculated risk technique in conjunction with the observational approach. The most important lesson learned from such operations is the need for a comprehensive monitoring program and continuous detailed analysis of all data.

All mining engineers responsible for tailings disposal operations estimate the danger of the dike being overtopped by floods. But the selection of a design flood for the "life" of a deposit can vary considerably, depending on the amount and accuracy of the data available, and on the probable consequences of an overtopping failure. Lessons learned from past failures indicate that designers often underestimate the probable maximum rainfall, sometimes overlook the possibility for spillway debris stoppages and, periodically, are inclined to operate the pond with less than the recommended minimum freeboard. Figure 6 shows a side-hill deposit where a calculated risk was taken during the dry season to accommodate an unforeseen temporary operating condition.

Minimum Freeboard

Figure 6

Although they are less common among failure
types, erosion gullies can result in total collapse
of a deposit if proper maintenance is not performed
promptly. Experience has shown that water lines
should not be passed across the dike crest unless
extra special precautions are taken to ensure that
pipeline rupture cannot occur. Figure 7 shows the
high degree of erodability of loose tailings.

Erosion Gulley

Figure 7

Most soil mechanics textbooks have a chapter on
seepage and its control. One author, realizing the
many complexities of the subject, has devoted his
entire book to the subject: "Seepage, Drainage and
Flow Nets"(9). Embankment drainage features for
control of seepage have been developed using empirical rules and theoretical principles of flow through
soils. These engineering features include the installation of both filters and drains in the embankment, with gradation specifications for the materials

used in both features. Piping failures in embankments
have been reduced considerably since the provision of
seepage control features has become standard practice.

The lesson learned most repeatedly from problems
with dewatering conduits is the need for a conservative design. Repairs to, or replacement of, the concrete structure are prohibitively expensive and can
often require shutdown of the plant. Where the deposit is in a seismically active zone, a possible
alternative to a rigid concrete structure is the
boulder drain shown in Figure 8.

Dewatering "Conduit" in Seismic Zone.   *Figure 8*

Although more and more research studies are being
made on the phenomenon of liquefaction, the findings
of such work, while increasing our knowledge on the
subject, also seem to be extending the "zone of igno-
rance" surrounding the problem--generating further
questions rather than providing answers. Very simply, the two basic lessons that have been learned
from several well-publicized failures resulting from
liquefaction are: (i) ensure that the density of the
dike tailings is greater than "critical" and

(ii) provide positive drainage so that all tailings within the retaining structure are not in a saturated condition.

Observations on the behavior of a deposit often produce useful information from which lessons can be learned. An excellent example is the beneficial effects of consolidation by desiccation and by over-burden pressure. Because the buoyant weight of tailings is about half the saturated, or moist, weight, every attempt should be made to lower the phreatic surface in the materials immediately behind the retaining structure. This factor is especially important if the upstream method of construction is used for tailings deposition. The results of laboratory tests on undisturbed samples from two tailings deposits, as discussed by Smith (7), clearly indicate the advantages of encouraging consolidation (with resulting increased shear strength) by maintaining a low water table behind the dike and by permitting desiccation. In Figure 9 the high-slimes mark on the decant chimney indicates the consolidation (about 1 meter) resulting from a few months of desiccation.

Consolidation by Desiccation   *Figure 9*

TAILING DISPOSAL TODAY

Successes, as well as failures, present opportunities for the engineering profession to learn practical lessons and thus contribute to advancement in the field of engineering. The successful performance of a structure when subjected to extreme forces of nature confirms the design criteria and analytical methods used in the engineering.

More unusual, but equally educational, are the successfully completed projects that belie some of the generally accepted engineering hypotheses. Probably one of the best examples of such a project is discussed by Casagrande in his paper, "An Unsolved Problem of Embankment Stability on Soft Ground" (10). The unresolved problems described by Casagrande include: (i) the shear stresses introduced into a very soft, but brittle clay foundation from an embankment built largely of loose sand and (ii) the state of earth pressure within the embankment. For many of the stability analyses made on failures of full-scale test sections, it was found that the driving forces (earth pressures within the embankment) and resisting forces (foundation shear stresses) computed using accepted soil mechanics principles could not be reconciled. (The factor of safety was assumed to be unity for analysis of the failure.) One of Casagrande's conclusions is: "Without resorting to full-scale test sections, but using only conventional soil tests and stability analyses, it is not possible to carry out a satisfactory design of granular embankments on this type of soft clay."

Specific Lessons

These lessons generally pertain to minor detailed items for a tailings disposal operation. Most are learned from a series of trial and error attempts to determine optimum operating conditions for a particular deposit. For this type of lesson, it is important to remember that operations that are optimum at one deposit will not necessarily be optimum at another deposit. Confirming checks must always be performed before applying any operating procedure to a particular deposit.

Where dike deficiencies are found to exist, field tests can be made to determine the acceptability of any special maintenance or repair program. Webb and Smith (11) have described an example of the use of calculated risk in conjunction with the observational method in the repair of a badly leaking dike. Slimes pumped from the bottom of the tailings pond were placed on the upstream face of the dam and allowed to flow down the slope. Where cracks or more pervious zones existed, the seepage and hydrostatic pressures forced the slimes into the voids, thereby reducing leakage.

Monitoring Programs

A continuous, detailed program for monitoring the behavior of a tailings dike during its construction is mandatory to ensure safe and economical operation during the "life" of the deposit. Many types of instrumentation, both simple and sophisticated, are available for such programs. They include survey monuments, "tell-tales," piezometers, pressure gages and inclinometers, all of which can be used to show developing trends in the behavior of the materials in the deposit.

With the exception of liquefaction, all types of failure give some warning signs. Distress signals such as cracking, wet spots on the downstream face, critical settlement and piezometric trends all indicate deficiencies in the structure, but without proper instrumentation it may be difficult to accurately interpret the extent of the problem.

Most of the instrumentation needed for an adequate monitoring program is relatively inexpensive; however, no attempt should be made to save money at the expense of good data-gathering and interpretation.

To properly analyze the observations obtained from an instrumentation program, it is essential to study the disposal operation logs, which show dates and locations of deposition, meteorological conditions, extent of earthmoving operations, etc. Soil test results giving gradation characteristics, in situ densities, moisture contents, shear strengths, etc., should also be available for review. All of these records, when analyzed carefully and together, provide the backup information necessary for making modifications in either the dike design or the disposal method.

SUMMARY

The disposal of tailings is an engineering operation that uniquely lends itself to the use of both calculated risks and the observational approach. Indeed, it can be argued that mill managers are obligated to take calculated risks in the development of safe, economical methods of disposal.

The only method of taking calculated risks with reasonable assurance of success is to study all available information on material properties and to use all applicable design tools to determine the trial dike section or disposal layout. As a particular technique is tried, observations are made on the operational behavior and the results are analyzed so that modified operating procedures can be instituted, if necessary.

Use of the observational approach is effective in modifying the design of a tailings deposit because retaining dikes can normally be raised very slowly. To achieve the best results, a well-planned monitoring program is essential. Using a section of the dike as a test section, with all necessary instruments placed in and adjacent to the test zone, the behavior of the materials and the structure can be monitored for the various loading conditions being studied.

Most tailings disposal and retaining dike failures can be controlled to the extent that damage is minimal and economics or safety is improved by applying the lesson learned. Such failures can be described as "successful failures". This description applies to failures resulting from either faulty disposal technique (construction method) or a problem with some design feature of the deposit (dike, decant chimney and conduit or spillway).

In recent years some embankment designers have included a compaction method specification in contract bid documents, instead of the more common performance specification. Both the lift thickness and number of passes of the available construction equipment are specified, rather than the percentage of maximum density determined in a soils laboratory. By using compaction test strips, engineers can convert laboratory test results into the most economical placement and compaction methods for the construction equipment proposed for use at the site. Figure 10 shows a dike raising project in progress with beneficial effects of bulldozer "vibratory" compaction.

Dike-Raising Project   *Figure 10*

The relatively slow rate of placement at any specific area of an average tailings deposit allows effective control techniques to be developed on test strips located on the retaining dike. Periodic improvement of the disposal method and the subsequent treatment of the materials can be made as indicated by observations and the results of tests.

When studying a failure, it is important, though frequently difficult, to differentiate between causes resulting from design deficiencies and those result- ing from poor construction methods. The best-planned tailings deposit can experience serious difficulties when the specified disposal methods are modified for economic reasons without a thorough reassessment of the technical consequences.

Many of the large tailings deposits constructed during the early part of this century are excellent examples of successful construction without the bene- fit of established design techniques or theoretical analysis. Figure 11 shows such a successful tailings deposit. Over 200 feet high, it was constructed be- tween 1911 and 1932 using perimeter discharge with gravity flow segregation.

The Many Massive "Manhills" that Mark the Mortals' Map
Make Magnificent and Mighty Monuments to
  - the Miners' Muscle,
    - the Metallurgists' Magic and
      - the Meaningful Meditations of the Master
        of Mud Mechanics, the Mill Manager.

Tailings Disposal Success   *Figure 11*

REFERENCES

1. Feld, Jacob, Lessons from Failures of Concrete Structures, Monograph No. 1, American Concrete Institute, 1964.

2. Jorgensen, Lars, "Record of 100 Dam Failures," Journal of Electricity (San Francisco), Vol. 44, 1920, pp. 274-276, 320, 321.

3. Babb, A. O., and Mermel, T. W., Catalog of Dam Disasters, Failures and Accidents, U.S. Dept. of Interior, Bureau of Reclamation, Washington, D.C., 1968.

4. Casagrande, A., "Role of the 'Calculated Risk' in Earthwork and Foundation Engineering," Journal of the Soil Mechanics and Foundation Division, American Society of Civil Engineers, Vol. 91, SM 4, 1965, pp. 1-40.

5. Peck, R. B., "Advantages and Limitations of the Observational Method in Applied Soil Mechanics," Geotechnique, Institution of Civil Engineers, Vol. 19, No. 2, 1969, pp. 171-187.

6. Casagrande, A., "Notes on the Design of Earth Dams," Contributions to Soil Mechanics, Boston Society of Civil Engineers, 1950, pp. 405-429.

7. Smith, E. S., "Tailings Disposal and Liquefaction," Transactions, American Institute of Mining, Metallurgical and Petroleum Engineers, Vol. 244, 1969, pp. 179-187.

8. Hazen, A., "Hydraulic Fill Dams," Transactions, American Society of Civil Engineers, Vol. 83, 1920, pp. 1713-1745.

9. Cedergren, Harry R., Seepage, Drainage and Flow Nets, John Wiley & Sons, Inc., New York, 1967.

10. Casagrande, A., "An Unsolved Problem of Embankment Stability on Soft Ground," Proceedings, First Panamerican Conference on Soil Mechanics and Foundation Engineering, Mexico, D. F., Vol. 2, 1960, pp. 721-746.

11. Webb, S. L., and Smith, E. S., "Tailings Dam Sealed by Slimes Slurry," Mining Engineering, Vol. 23, No. 12, Dec. '71, pp. 59, 60.

VEGETATIVE STABILIZATION OF COPPER MINE

TAILING DISPOSAL BERMS OF PIMA MINING COMPANY

Kenneth L. Ludeke

Agronomist, Pima Mining Company

Tucson, Arizona, United States

PIMA MINING COMPANY

The Pima Mine lies 20 miles southwest of Tucson, Arizona and 45 miles north of the Mexican border. Pima is managed and 50 percent owned by Cyprus Mines Corporation. Union Oil of California and Utah International, Inc. each have a 25 percent interest. Discovered in 1950 by geophysical methods, it was originally conceived to be operated as a small, high grade underground operation. However, Pima started production in January 1957 as a small open pit operation with an expected life of ten years at a concentration rate of 3,000 tons per day. As a result of four expansions, the last being completed early in 1972, the plant capacity has grown to a rate of approximately 54,000 tons per day.

INTRODUCTION

With the greatly increased capacity of the concentrator, tailing disposal ponds have had to become larger and it was required that they be located nearer interstate highway going from Tucson to the border city of Nogales, Arizona.

In order to maintain the natural desert beauty, Pima embarked on a voluntary program of cultivating and experimental planting of various types of plants. With this experimental program the most promising features were expanded so that some 85 acres now available along the berms have been planted. Additional acreage will be planted to coincide with the growing season.

The primary objectives undertaken by this project were to:

1. Maintain the natural desert beauty

2. Provide vegetative stabilization to minimize wind blown dust

3. Utilize plants that once established required little or no supplemental irrigation

4. Minimize erosion.

CONTRACT GROWING PLANTS

With the newness of the expanding planting program, and the necessity of using many native plants, it is most difficult to locate adequate quantities of nursery grown plant material. Except for a few types of plants, transplanting and collecting is uncertain and very costly. Pima Mining Company is now contract growing plants as a temporary means to overcome this handicap until the supply catches up with the demand. To do this, cooperative efforts have been made establishing native plants on the tailing slopes, working with various local nurseries along with the following agencies:

1. The University of Arizona
2. The Plant Materials Center
3. The Arizona Department of Highways
4. The California Department of Highways
5. The Pima County Soil Conservation District.

VEGETATIVE STABILIZATION

As previously cited the vegetative stabilization of the various surfaces was of prime importance. Special treatments and techniques are needed for plant establishment and continued growth on the tailing berms. Tremendous progress has been made producing vegetative growth on sterile and arid soils. To produce growth on such land it has been necessary to add the essential elements. These elements would be humus, nutrients, moisture and bacteria or microorganisms. Tests have been conducted utilizing hay or barley straw as a mulch. This gives the following benefits.

1. The straw mulch insulates the surface from both heat and cold. This stabilizes the temperature of the soil, creating a better environment for the fast germination and root growth of the seed.

2. A uniform coverage of straw mulch over the area to be seeded breaks up the falling raindrops and permits the soil to absorb this moisture. The mulch also creates small dams to slow down the velocity of fallen water which causes erosion.

3. Finally the use of mulch adds to growth of bacteria and the microorganisms.

Salinity is a common problem in arid soils thus leaching must occur before vegetation can be established. In the initial vegetative process it is desirable to utilize plants that can withstand high concentrations of salt.

New planting is carried out throughout the year to utilize both of the Arizona growing seasons. In winter cover crops, such as barley and rye, are planted to be utilized as green manure crops. Other types of winter and summer annuals are also disked back into the ground as a mulch. Ultimately, indigenous vegetation will take over. There are very encouraging signs that this is already taking place.

Major research emphasis has been directed toward developing vegetative, physical and chemical stabilization and combinations thereof. A combined chemical-vegetative stabilization procedure utilizing a resinous adhesive compound (Soil Seal), used in conjunction with selected vegetation appears exceptionally effective for achieving stabilization of mill tailing.

This test was accomplished by the use of hydroseeding, due to ease of handling, mixing and speed involved in the planting operation. Hydroseeding is a rather simple operation in which the seed, wood fiber, Soil Seal, fertilizer, and water are all combined into a 2,000 gallon tank. All the materials are slurried, then pumped through a nozzle and sprayed on the side of the slope.

Two men can conduct a hydroseeding operation. About 5-10 acres of slope can be planted in a single day. This compares to several weeks of hand planting with the aid of 6-8 men. Hydroseeding of a one acre plot requires 1,500 pounds of wood fiber, which acts as the artificial seedbed, 40 pounds of fertilizer, 60 gallons of Soil Seal, which is the adhesive compound holding the slurry to the tailing slope, along with the seed and water.

Fifty acres have been hydroseeded utilizing various seeds such as lovegrass, bermudagrass, African daisy, desert broom, desert marigold, four wing saltbush, three wing saltbush, Australian saltbush, California poppy, lupin, acacia and eucalyptus.

PHYSICAL STABILIZATION

Physical stabilization includes massive coverings of soil, bark plus properly used straw and brush to prevent erosion of tailing berms. The physical stabilization principle using soil coverings was considered impractical due to the high cost basis. Cost estimates obtained for digging, short haulage, and placing a 12 inch soil cover ranges from $0.23 to $0.36 per square yard. This would amount to $1,113 per acre. Therefore, if vegetative or combined chemical-vegetative stabilization can do an equivalent job of preventing or reducing erosion and at the same time produce a more aesthetically appealing berm, then it would be more desirable.

VEGETATION ON PURE TAILING

Initiation and perpetuation of vegetation on fine, dry, sandy tailing presents a number of challenges which require a solution before there is an effective program. These challenges are:

1. Provide sufficient plant nutrients
2. Provide normal microbial populations
3. Remove excessive salts and heavy metal phytotoxicants
4. Consolidate sandy soil to minimize wind blown sand that destroys the young plants by sand blasting or burial.

An area consisting of pure tailing material has been set aside for testing of the persistance of cacti and indigenous plants in this material. Normally, tailing is infertile, tends to compact but with disturbance becomes unconsolidated thus tailing does not have good soil structure. The mesquite, palo verde, and the ironwood all provide the plant material needed to grow on the tailing berm. Some of the native shrubs that have done well at Pima include the desert broom, creosote bush, hopseed bush, lovegrass, bermudagrass, and the atriplex (saltbush) species.

No introduction of native Arizona plants would be complete without the succulents of cacti. In view of the difficulties and considerable time involved to grow them from seed, cacti have been transplanted on the barren tailing slopes. The cacti were obtained from inside the waste ponds before the area was covered with tailing.

The Arizona state flower is found on top of a desert giant, the Saguaro cactus. Several species of this cactus have been saved from the encroaching tailing but, in view of the tremendous weight of this cactus, only the smaller unbranched specimens of this type could be used. Other species transplanted on the barren tailing include the prickly pear, ocotillo, cholla, barrel cactus, yucca, joshua tree and catclaw. Perennial rye and various legumes were seeded to insure that the fine dry tailing sand would not be drifting and thus bury the smaller cacti. Thus, by establishing indigenous plants on the tailing slopes, Pima Mining Company can control wind and water erosion with the minimum amount of irrigation and maintenance.

IMPROVING TAILING FOR PLANTING

The success of Pima Mining Company in initiating and perpetuating vegetation on fine mill wastes involves making tests to characterize chemically and physically the many different soil types as well as to control solar radiation. The tailing berms have tremendous sloping sides which receive varying amounts of solar radiation. Photosynthesis in plants is not a continuous process during full sunlight. Under extremely high temperature conditions, photosynthesis slows down and, in many instances, may almost completely terminate.

The mill tailing material consists of siliceous sands which are extremely light in color and reflect excessive solar radiation to immediate plant surfaces, thus placing a tremendous physiological stress on the plants. Therefore, the plant material that is growing on a northern and eastern exposure may not be suitable for southern exposures.

Considerable effort is being directed towards developing improved methods for achieving better initial germination and more rapid growth than is now common on mill tailing. To obtain these results, sewage effluent has been applied to the tailing slopes at a rate of 1,000 gallons per acre along with five tons of compost manure per acre.

The processed sewage effluent (Activite, soil conditioner) used is produced from normal cattle feed lots and is not to be confused with effluent from municipal sewage plants. The compost manure applied is darker in color than the tailing and provides some protection from heat reflection and offers a favorable environment for a more rapid seed germination and seedling establishment. The Activite and manure compost aid in improving the soil condition of the mill tailing and enhance vegetative growth. These can, when mixed with tailing, furnish soil textures conducive to providing better soil, air and water relationships. The Activite and the compost manure demonstrated much better growth than any of the materials used alone on the tailing slopes.

CHEMICAL-VEGETATIVE STABILIZATION

Tests have been conducted recently utilizing a combination system involving vegetation and chemicals. This system was applied to a ten-acre plot of tailing in mid-August of 1970. Soil Seal was used in a hydroseeding operation to stabilize the surface against sand blowing and to retain moisture in the wood fiber slurry by decreasing evaporation until the plant cover was able to take over that function by itself.

The seed mixture used in this chemical-vegetative hydroseeding test was lehmans lovegrass, weeping lovegrass, bermudagrass, African daisy, desert broom, desert marigold, Australian saltbush, three wing saltbush, four wing saltbush, California poppy, acacia, lupin, eucalyptus and chrysanthemum. A germination observation of the plants was made three weeks after seeding. This observation illustrated that good germination was obtained from the grasses, lupin, desert broom and acacia.

During the month of October, additional germination was observed from atriplex species (saltbush), California poppy, chrysanthemum and the African daisy. The seedlings were vigorous and healthy, and budding was evident on many of the flowering plants. However, in January 1971 a killing frost destroyed most of the flowering plants and frost tender saltbush seedlings.

The chemical-vegetative hydroseeded area was surveyed during the year and this survey indicated that the primary objective had been attained. The tailing berm was stabilized against wind erosion, and existing plant material was persisting in the hydroseeded area.

COST OF CHEMICAL-VEGETATIVE STABILIZATION

A ten-acre tailing berm plot was set up in order to determine chemical-vegetative hydroseeding costs. The following was used per acre in this test plot.

Table No. I
Chemical-Vegetative Hydroseeding Costs

Item	Rate of Usage	Cost
Seeds	75 pounds per acre	$ 287

Table No. I (Continued)
Chemical-Vegetative Hydroseeding Costs

Item	Rate of Usage	Cost
Fertilizer	55 pounds per acre	16
Wood Fiber	1500 pounds per acre	70
Hydroseeder	Seed one acre	150
Soil Seal	80 gallons per acre	387
Labor @		
$4.00 per hour	Three men for three days	288
Water Truck	Supply water for seeder	100
Total		$1,298

The Soil Seal was applied at a minimum rate of 40 gallons and a maximum rate of 80 gallons per acre. During the year observations were recorded, and it was noted that the minimum rate had no appreciable difference from the maximum rate. This would indicate that the preselected quantity of 40 or 50 gallons per acre of Soil Seal could be reduced with a resultant savings in cost. The estimated cost of $1,298 for one acre could probably be reduced if larger acreages were treated, smaller dosages of adhesives used, and proper equipment were available.

DISRUPTIVE INFLUENCES OF WILDLIFE

Cattle, rabbits, pocket gophers, javelina, field mice, deer and other animals have invaded the tailing berm seeded with various succulent grasses and forbs and have been a disruptive influence. However, the tailing berms appear to be completely stable, and excessive damage is not apparent. The rabbits and gophers have chewed off the tops of most of the grasses; however, this produces a tillering effect of the plants and a better plant structure is obtained. In attempting to restore nature's balance, and even improve on it, Pima constructed a small game refuge which is utilized by the animals in the surrounding area. A 750 gallon watering tank has been placed below the tailing berm, and it has been surrounded by desert plants that are a natural habitat for the animals.

CONCLUSION

Severe windstorms and excessive rains have passed over the stabilized tailing berm area without raising dust clouds or carving unsightly erosion crevices into the slopes. The vegetation has satisfactorily maintained the surface of the tailing berms and appears fully resistant to wind erosion. As tailing berms increase in height, successive benches will be planted with material that has proved successful. The ultimate objective is, of course, to maintain the natural splendor of low desert environment to the disposal area. The success of the vegetative stabilization has illustrated that such an objective is feasible, at a reasonable cost, and is being accomplished.

Table No. II
Trees Tested on Tailing Disposal Berms

Name	Objective	Present Performance
Eucalyptus rostrata (Red gum)	Ultimately 80-120 feet. Form varies; typically has curved trunk, spreading crown, gracefully weeping crown.	Long slender lance-shaped leaves, medium green leaves. Good color, strong growing tree.
Eucalyptus microtheca (Tiny capsule)	Bush tree, 35-40 feet, round head, may be single or many trunked.	Strong looking, strong growing tree of character, drought tolerant, no breakage from wind.
Eucalyptus polyanthemos (Silver dollar gum)	Slender, erect tree, single or multistem, 20-60 feet. Used primarily for fast growth.	Excellent cut foliage, very popular for landscaping. Grows almost anywhere. Not good in wet places.
Pinus austrica (Australian pine)	Commonly a large bush tree, 10-25 feet high, some good horizontal branches and very wind firm.	Has well developed tap and lateral root system. Strong growing tree.

Table No. II (Continued)
Trees Tested on Tailing Disposal Berms

Name	Objective	Present Performance
Juglans nigra (Black walnut)	High branched tree, grows to 150 feet high with round crown.	Big hardy shade tree for big places. Not injured by early frost.
Acacia constricta (White thorn acacia)	Plant reaches height of 10-15 feet with spread of 10-15 feet. Very cold tolerant.	Thorniness makes it natural habitat for wildlife.
Prosopis juliflora (Native mesquite)	Native to desert. May reach 30 feet high and 40 feet wide. Extremely deep tap root system. Tolerates alkaline conditions.	Serves as a good windbreak or screen. Very drought tolerant.
Platanus wrightii (Arizona sycamore)	All grow large, native to Arizona.	Can withstand hot, dry summer with proper management.
Prosopis chilensis (Chilean mesquite)	Native to desert, drought tolerant, capable of reaching 30 feet high. Very pronounced tap root system.	Good size hardy tree, frost tolerant, can withstand insect damage to an extent.

Table No. II (Continued)
Trees Tested on Tailing Disposal Berms

Name	Objective	Present Performance
Schinus polygamus (Peruvian pepper)	Evergreen and semi-deciduous. Single or multiple trunk. No serious pest or disease.	Very fast growing, 15-25 feet high and about as wide. Can tolerate alkaline soils. Especially useful in desert.
Cercidium floridum (Blue palo verde)	Native to desert. Will survive much drought, but is denser, more attractive and grows faster with water and fertilizer.	Grows very rapidly and reaches height of 25 feet and almost as wide. Can withstand alkaline soil conditions.
Chilopsis linearis (Desert willow)	Deciduous large shrub or small tree. Native to desert washes and stream beds. Grows very fast (35 feet in a single season).	Capable of propagation by hardwood cuttings. Can withstand cold temperatures as well as drought.
Nicotiana glauca (Desert tobacco)	Tender perennial, grows as annual. May live over in mid-winter areas. Large plant, 15-20 feet high, reseeds profusely.	Grows on alkaline soils, slopes, rocky areas.

Table No. II (Continued)
Trees Tested on Tailing Disposal Berms

Name	Objective	Present Performance
Celtis reticulata (Desert hackberry)	Deciduous tree, related to Elm and similar to them in most details, but smaller. Only pest of note seems to be aphid occasionally.	Deep rooting tree. Can withstand high excessive winds. When established can take desert heat, much drought and alkaline soils.

Table III
Shrubs Tested on Tailing Disposal Berms

Name	Objective	Present Performance
Datura arborea (Datura)	Evergreen shrub, large of leaf and flower. Very impressive flower.	Dominating shrub. They appear in summer and fall, often as late as November or December in warmer areas.
Dodonaea viscosa (Hopseed bush)	Evergreen shrub native to Arizona, very fast growing with many upright stems 12-15 feet high, spreading almost as wide.	Plants grown from seed. Arizona natives appear more cold resistant than the introductions from Australia.

Table No. III
Shrubs Tested on Tailing Disposal Berms

Name	Objective	Present Performance
Dodonaea viscosa (continued)		Willowlike, green leaves to 4" long.
Baccharis sarothroides (Desert broom)	Evergreen shrub, remarkable climate and soil adaptation. Makes a dense, rather billowy mat of bright green 8-24 inches high and spreading to 6 feet or more.	Thriving in almost all ground covers and is dependable bank cover for minimum maintenance areas.
Atriplex canescens (Four wing saltbush)	Evergreen or deciduous shrub. Unusually tolerant of direct highly alkaline desert soils. Dense growth 3-6 feet spreading to 4-8 feet.	Many species are useful as fire-resistant plants on arid hillsides. Plants char but come back.
Atriplex lentiformis (Quail bush)	Native to alkali wastes in California valleys and deserts. Densely branched, sometimes spiny shrub 3-10 feet high, 6-12 feet wide.	Useful as a hedge or windbreak where salt tolerant plants are needed.

Table No. III (Continued)
Shrubs Tested on Tailing Disposal Berms

Name	Objective	Present Performance
Atriplex semibaccata (Australian saltbush)	Evergreen shrub. A drought-resistant plant. Good on alkaline soils and very salt tolerant.	Excellent gray-green ground cover to 12 inches, spreading to 1-6 feet or more. Forms a dense mat, deep rooted.
Convolvulus cneorum (Bush morning glory)	Evergreen shrub. Evergreen perennial, and an annual. A very rapid growing plant to 2-4 feet high, as well as 2-4 feet wide.	Will do well on sandy, light soils with good drainage. Can withstand hot, windy conditions.
Larrea tridentata (Creosote bush)	Evergreen shrub, one of the most common native shrubs in desert Arizona. Grows with many upright branches 4-8 feet high. Small yellow flowers off and on all year. Can be used as a windbreak.	Very tolerant to shallow, dry soils. Attractive, dense, rounded but spreading where water accumulates. With water and fertilizer, grows taller, more dense, with larger shiny dark leaves.

Table No. III (Continued)
Shrubs Tested on Tailing Disposal Berms

Name	Objective	Present Performance
Lavatera assurgentiflora (Mallow)	Annual shrub. To 3-6 feet from spring-sown seed. Can withstand hot, sunny summers.	A very colorful summer hedge if trimmed properly and watered and fertilized accordingly.
Enchylaena tomentosa (Ruby sheepbush)	Evergreen shrub, a very hardy plant on alkaline soils. Can withstand high levels of salt in soils.	Excellent green ground cover to 12 inches, spreading to 1-6 feet or more. Forms a dense mat and deep root system.
Calliandra eriophylla (Fairy duster)	Evergreen shrub. An open growing plant to 3 feet spreading 4-5 feet. Native to warm, dry areas.	A very fast growing plant. With proper fertilizer and irrigation, can provide adequate soil holding capabilities.
Acacia greggii (Catclaw)	A very straggling shrub. May grow to height of 4-6 feet. Very dense growth but very persistent.	A desert plant growing in hot, dry areas. With proper management does well on various soils.

Table No. IV
Cacti and Other Desert Plants Tested on Tailing Disposal Berms

Name	Objective	Present Performance
Carnegiea gigantea (Saguaro)	A desert cactus giant. Native to Arizona. A columnar and branching plant, with prominent ribs that give it a fluted appearance.	Plant grows very slowly to 50 feet. Smaller unbranched specimens are easily transplanted to other locations.
Opuntia bigelovii (Prickly pear)	Cactus. Many kinds of varied appearance. Hardiness is variable. Flowers are generally large and showy.	Plant is easily transplanted. Grows into a large plant with many branched structure. Propagated by vegetative means and from seed.
Fouguieria splendens (Ocotillo)	Cactus. The cholla family. Takes in all of the "cylinder-jointed" varieties, whose segments range in size from links no bigger than a pencil to 15-20 feet.	Plant may reach a height of 15 feet with many branches spreading 6-8 feet. Vegetative propagation is easily accomplished to desired area.

Table No. IV (Continued)
Cacti and Other Desert Plants Tested on Tailing Disposal Berms

Name	Objective	Present Performance
Echinocactus grusonii (Barrel cactus)	Cactus. Many species ranging in size from little "kegs", a few inches high, to high "drums" 10 feet tall.	Easily transplanted. Can withstand extreme dusty blowing conditions. Excellent along ridges as partial windbreaks.
Yucca thornberi (Giant yucca)	Evergreen perennials, shrubs, trees. Some plants are stemless while others reach tree size of 15-30 feet. Best in drained soils.	Plants will take considerable drought when established. Transplants easily to desired location. Many are true desert plants.
Yucca bierifolia (Joshua tree)	Evergreen. A tree or large shrub. Tree of slow growth 15-30 feet with heavy trunk, a few heavy branches.	Plant does well on dry soils, with low moisture conditions. May be transplanted if proper care taken in uprooting plant. Responds well to fertilizer and adequate moisture.

Table No. IV (Continued)
Cacti and Other Desert Plants Tested on Tailing Disposal Berms

Name	Objective	Present Performance
Peniocereus gregii (Night blooming cereus)	Tall branching tree-like cactus eventually branching 30-50 feet.	Desert plant, may be transplanted if properly cared for afterwards. Excellent cover for ridges or slopes.

Table No. V
Grasses, Forbs, and Legumes Tested on Tailing Disposal Berms

Name	Objective	Present Performance
Lespedeza striata (Common lespedeza)	A slender, much branched, leafy, summer annual legume which grows to a height of 4-24 inches.	May be used in midsummer or late summer for soil improvement. Plant will grow on most soils, but poor on acid soils. It responds to lime and fertilizer applications.

Table No. V
Grasses, Forbs, and Legumes Tested on Tailing Disposal Berms

Name	Objective	Present Performance
Boutelova certipendula (Side oats grama)	A warm-season perennial, mid-grass with short scaly underground stems. Seed stalks may reach height of 18-36 inches. Grass grows on well-drained soils, shallow ridges and rocky areas.	Side oats grama is a good producer. Side oats responds to nitrogen fertilizer for seed and forage production.
Lupinus augustifolius (Blue lupine)	An herbaceous, upright, winter-annual legume that branches freely and may reach a height of 2-3½ feet.	Plant used as a soil conditioner and soil cover. Grows well in sandy soils.
Eragrostis currula (Weeping lovegrass)	A warm-season, perennial bunch-grass which grows to a height of 2-4 feet. Makes rapid, early growth and produces a great many basal leaves 10-20 inches long. Seed head is loose and measures 8-12 inches long. May stand erect or droop.	Weeping lovegrass is easily established by seed and spreads by tillering. A single plant may form a dense sod bunch 12-15 inches in diameter within 2-3 years. It does well on most any type of well-drained soils.

Table No. V (Continued)
Grasses, Forbs, and Legumes Tested on Tailing Disposal Berms

Name	Objective	Present Performance
Eragrostis currula (Continued)		This grass responds well to nitrogen and phosphate.
Sorghum halapense (Johnson grass)	A warm-season, persistent perennial grass that grows from 3-6 feet tall and spreads by seeds and extensive underground stems and rhizomes.	Johnson grass is a very persistent grass due to its extensive rhizomes and aggressive spreading habit.
Pennisctum ciliare (Buffel grass)	A deep-rooted, warm-season perennial grass. Easily established and vigorous growing. Grass is capable of spreading by short rhizomes and reproduces by seeds. It has slender, leafy stems up to 4 feet in height.	Good results have been obtained in tests on light and non-productive blow-sand areas. It prefers heavy, clay soils and will grow on relatively poor soils but must be fertilized and managed properly for highest production and growth.

Table No. V (Continued)

Grasses, Forbs, and Legumes Tested on Tailing Disposal Berms

Name	Objective	Present Performance
Digitoria sanguinolis (Crab grass)	A warm-season, shallow-rooted annual that reproduces by seed and the bunches increase in size by rooting where the nodes touch the soil.	Crab grass produces a heavy seed crop on stems 15-24 inches tall during early summer to fall. This annual grass is found growing on a wide variety of soils.
Eragrostis lehmanniana (Lehmans lovegrass)	A warm-season, perennial bunchgrass which grows to a height of 6-15 inches. Makes rapid growth under proper fertilization and adequate moisture.	Lehmans lovegrass is easily established by seed. It does well on most soils and can withstand hot, dry winds.
Hordeum vulgare (Winter barley)	A cool-season, tufted, annual grass which is used primarily as a winter lawn crop for barren soils. Stems are slender, 4-15 inches tall, erect, bent slightly at each node. Plant will germinate in the fall if	Can withstand high salt contents and low moisture requirements. This annual has a shallow refined fiberous root system that feeds mostly in the top 6 inches of soil. Plant is also capable

Table No. V (Continued)
Grasses, Forbs, and Legumes Tested on Tailing Disposal Berms

Name	Objective	Present Performance
Hordeum vulgare (Continued)	adequate moisture is available, and stays green through winter.	of growing on alkaline soils.
Chrysanthemum segetium (Chrysanthemum)	Annuals, perennials. Plant may reach a height of 1-3 feet and about 3 feet wide. A very showy plant, with a lot of color.	Plant will grow in light or heavy soils. Plant will also grow in windblown sand if properly managed with adequate fertilizer and moisture.
Arctotis stoechadifolia (African daisy)	Annual. Plant has very definite color characteristics which add to color of particular area. Plant grows to height of 1-3 feet and grows to about 2 feet wide.	Plant will grow in light soils with low moisture requirements. African daisy is a very hardy plant and reseeds very well for next year.
Eschscholeia segetium (California poppy)	Perennial usually grown as annual. Plant is very capable of covering fields, slopes, roadsides in spring and early	Plant can't be surpassed for naturalizing on summer hills, slopes or roadsides. Plant can do well on many differ-

Table No. V (Continued)
Grasses, Forbs, and Legumes Tested on Tailing Disposal Berms

Name	Objective	Present Performance
Eschscholeia segetium (Continued)	summer. Plant branching from base, stems usually 8-24 inches long.	ent soil types if moisture and fertilizer are adequate.
Lolium perenne (Perennial rye)	A cool-season, perennial, bunch-grass which reproduces by til-lering and by seed. It reaches a height of 2-3 feet. May re-main straight and upright after maturity.	Plant is very capable of do-ing well mixed with warm-season native grasses, or in the early fall for winter ground cover.
Sorghum sudanense (Sudangrass)	A heavy-tufted, warm-season, an-nual grass with fine erect stems and numerous long narrow leaves. With adequate moisture and fer-tility the degree of tillering is increased.	It grows best under warm moist conditions. Plant can reach heights of 18-24 inches tall. Excellent for warm-season cover on slopes.
Voltus corniculatus (Birdsfoot trefoil)	A leafy, fine-stemmed, warm-season, perennial legume. Has very showy flowers of yellow	This legume is a soil con-serving plant. It does well alone or in mixtures with

Table No. V (Continued)
Grasses, Forbs, and Legumes Tested on Tailing Disposal Berms

Name	Objective	Present Performance
Votus corniculatus (Continued)	to orange. Drought resistant and salt tolerant.	other grasses.

Plant material on tailing berm shows the tremendous growth acquired with adequate fertilization.

Figure No. 1

Indigenous plant material adequately provides stabilization of tailing berms.   Figure No. 2

When the grasses have been established, one gallon
size trees and shrubs are transplanted to the slope.
Figure No. 3

Large trees and shrubs also aid in providing vegetation to tailing disposal berms.   Figure No. 4

Once the plant material has been established, irrigation is no longer necessary.   Figure No. 5

A small game reserve has been constructed on Pima property to encourage wildlife to feed in designated areas rather than on the tailing berm.

Figure No. 6

Initial establishment of vegetation requires irrigation and fertilization.
Figure No. 7.

Severe windstorms and excessive rains have passed over the stabilized tailing berm area without raising dust clouds or carving erosion crevices.
Figure No. 8.

No introduction of Arizona plants would be complete without cacti succulents. Because they are hard to grow from seed, cacti were transplanted on to barren slopes.
Figure No. 9.

REFERENCES

1. Baines, S. S., and K. D. Lingh, 1966. "Utilization of Solar Radiation in Desalination of Ridges
   Plantbeds on Saline Soils." Nature. 212:
   (5069). 1391-1392.

2. Barnett, A. P., 1967. "Evaluation of Mulching
   Methods for Erosion Control on Newly Prepared
   and Seeded Highway Backslopes." Agron. J. 59:
   83-85.

3. Berg, William A., 1970. "Nutritional and Physical
   Aspects Plants Establishment on Mine Wastes."
   Society of Mining Engineers of A.I.M.E. Pre-
   print 70-F-11: 1-6.

4. Bridges, J. P., 1968. "Stabilizing Mine Dumps."
   Mining Magazine. 119: 16-17.

5. Dean, Karl C., Richard Havens and Kimball T.
   Harper., 1969. "Chemical and Vegetative Stabil-
   ization of a Nevada Copper Prophyry Mill Tailing."
   Bee Mines Report of Inv. 7261: 14.

6. Eagles, L. P., and O. S. Kickpatrick, 1969.
   "Roadside Beauty and Safety." Soil Conservation.
   4: 111-112.

7. Earley, W. O., 1952. "Native Plant Material for
   Roadside Planting". U. S. Department of Agriculture Circ. 908: 70-73.

8. Gates, David M., 1965. "Radiant Energy, Its
   Reception and Disposal." Meteorological Monograph. 6: 1-26.

9. James, A. L., 1966. "Stabilizing Mine Dumps with
   Vegetation." Endeavor. 96: 154-157.

10. Turelle, J. W., 1969. "Wind Erosion Control
    Guides." Soil Conservation. 10: 107-109.

REFERENCES (Continued)

11. Wesley, D. G., 1970. "Mines and Conservationists Discuss Ecology in the Arid Environment." World Mining. 6: 28-30.

DISCUSSION

QUESTION: Ken, I noticed on the field trips that there is a considerable amount of mine rock, non tailing dams. Have you given any thought to handling those? I noticed one of them was right near your cacti vegetation experiment.

KEN LUDEKE: That is a stockpile and possibility of trying to establish vegetation on it has been suggested to me. It is an earthen body covered with rocks so a simple manipulation of the material would expose the earthen body, and vegetation could be established in that area. In fact it probably would be similar to establishing vegetation on fine tailings material.

I would like to mention just one thing about physical stabilization of a tailing disposal berm or the waste dump. It certainly is one means of stabilization insomuch as plant trash, tires, or demolition debris - or whatever you utilize on the slope - will certainly lend a certain aspect of holding some of the finer material together. But in the Twin Buttes Mining District, where we have the city encroaching in the area as well as resort communities, Green Valley etc., there are many aesthetic objections posed by the public. Therefore, many laws for this purpose are now coming into effect and are in legislation. So vegetation or chemicals in conjunction with each other is a far superior means of stabilizing the tailing berm. In my talk I was simply mentioning the fact that there is an area where physical stabilization can be utilized.

NORMAN WEISS (Consulting Metallurgist, Tucson, Arizona): I have a question for Mr. Ludeke. In view of the frequent talk we hear of downstream dam building, and especially the talk by Harris Burke on the soils engineer's viewpoint, I'd like to know how these viewpoints affect vegetation of slopes.

KEN LUDEKE: If I understand your question adequately, as Karl Dean was mentioning to us, the question was brought up as far as cost comparisons on slopes vs. ponds. The cost is on the amount of acreage and the feasibility of establishing vegetation on a slope regardless of its size, shape, or arrangement is a practical question, because vegetation by nature can grow along the highways, on steep highway cuts, or on flat surfaces as explained. But I think that the engineers have engineered a tailing dam with vegetation stabilization in which the erosion problem due to wind or water is minimized, if not adequately controlled. I hope that answered your question.

NORMAN WEISS: The erosion by wind and water is certainly a serious problem, but how about when you're replenishing the surface of the bank by downstream building constantly. Is there any chance of vegetation stabilization? This point was not brought up Wednesday during the papers that I heard. Nobody raised that question. Still downstream dam building is popular in some places. In other words, the sand is thrown over the bank continuously so you have a continuously fresh surface, and still this question was not brought up.

KEN LUDEKE: If you have a tailing dam where new areas of construction are continuing, there is a continuous buildup. Now, as far as vegetating stabilization, if you have your initial vegetation toward the bottom and then successive growths on up the face, there would be no problem. It would be just simply manipulation of the type of plant material or the type of equipment or irrigation system. But as far as putting we material or fresh material on existing slopes, of course there is going to be problems with burial and so forth.

K. I. HYMAS (Tech Corporation Limited): Mr. Ludeke mentioned this matter of flooding the places to be vegetated with sewage effluent. I'm wondering whether he might like to expand on that a bit, particularly in regard to the absence of potash and phosphate in this sewage effluent.

KEN LUDEKE: That's a good question. Most of the sewage effluent that we have tested at Pima Mining Company was municipal sewage effluent. This is the clear effluent derived from lactating heifers. Now, the sewage effluent from municipal waste is clear, it has a lot of phosphates and so forth in the effluent. The results were far superior by the use of effluent from dairy or from feet lots, due to the high concentrations of vitamins and nutrients that are available to plants that are extracted in the total processing from municipal waste. As far as using this on tailings dams for fertilization, it can really be only characterized as a soil builder or as a mulch and not really as a fertilizer application.

HOW TO ESTABLISH AND MAINTAIN GROWTH

ON TAILINGS IN CANADA --

--COLD WINTERS AND SHORT GROWING SEASONS

Jean-Claude Leroy

Head, Research & Development
Erocon Limited, Toronto, Canada

INTRODUCTION

Effective and economical remedial measures for the reclamation of tailings waste disposal areas have been developed in the heartland of Canadian hardrock mining camps.

We are now in the era of systematic reconversion of mine wastelands into areas of usefulness as a logical sequence to the production of the essential metals and minerals our civilization requires.

This paper is based essentially on the research and reclamation work carried out on a wide spectrum of tailings disposal areas by Erocon, an organization specialized in that field. It has successfully tackled the full range of the problems inherent to the various types of wastelands resulting from mining activity and is recognized as an innovator in that field of endeavour.

The scope of this study has been limited to the northeastern quarter of this continent where the extensive Canadian pre-cambrian shield has proven so rich in base and precious metals among others.

THE CONCEPT OF RECLAIMED LAND

We have come a long way since waste disposal areas were considered the unavoidable evil of any mining operation, and as such only bearable to the extent that most mining operations were remote from larger inhabited areas with of course the exception of the mining community itself which had to suffer from whatever unpleasant effects may have resulted from the operation.

In our work, we consider carefully to what useful purposes the tailings wasteland can be put, and the answers can be remarkably varied when the needs of the mining community itself and its larger surrounding region are studied, and when the potentialities of the tailings material itself are fully understood.

It has therefore become our policy to extend our basic aim which is to bring about the immediate establishment of a permanent, self sustaining, and maintenance free vegetation cover into the planning and actual carrying out of a specific, integrated reconversion scheme.

In this context, an economically viable nursery-cattle farm-sod farm complex is being created from a discarded tailings disposal area in the Timmins area of Ontario, as dealt with in detail further below.

Tailings can all be made green and we know there is a solution available now to all related problems in spite of what some "experts" may say.

From wasteland to cropland at the Dome Gold Mine,
Timmins, Ontario. Top: In 1969, the 80 foot-
high impounding dam's outer slope is smoothed out.
Wooden props were discarded to prevent possible
breaks. Bottom: The same slope completely trans-
formed into a prime cropland thickly covered with
birdsfoot trefoil, thus creating a grazing land
of the highest quality.   Figure No. 1

BACKGROUND

Canada is known worldwide for the magnitude and dynamism of its mining industry. It produces over $5 billion worth of metals and minerals annually and employs over 130,000 people. It also creates jobs for some 800,000 people in related industries.

From 1971 to 1975 some $500 million will be spent by the Canadian mining industry to control water and land pollution.

To produce these metals and minerals, some 400 million tons of ore and waste are mined and processed annually. About 130,000 acres of land are disturbed in the process and this figure is estimated to reach 150,000 acres by the mid seventies.

To gain some perspective on size of area involved, let us say that the total land area of the country is 2,280,000,000 acres, that farmlands cover some 172,000,000 acres and highways alone cover 30,000,000 acres (an average mile of secondary highway disturbs some 40 acres).

To be precise, lands disturbed by mining involve a mere one thousandth of 1% of the country's land, while for every acre disturbed by mining, some $40,000 worth of goods are produced annually.

Of course we now know not only how to rehabilitate practically instantly every single acre of land disturbed by mining quickly and effectively, but also to do so in a lasting manner.

Such reclamation is impressive: a typical tailings area which took over half a century to accumulate, we make green in a matter of weeks, and into a lush, thriving vegetation cover within two or three vegetative cycles. And this applies to particularly forbidding wastes considered long as unreclaimable.

BASIC CRITERIA FOR RECLAMATION

The basic guidelines for successful and acceptable reclamation of tailings are simple and need little elaboration:

Amenity: The overall amenity of the land surrounding the tailings disposal area must be preserved by insuring the general neatness, compatibility and harmonious aspect of the completed reclamation work, the gradient of slopes and the essential architectonic elements of the whole.

Unity: There must be unity in the reclamation scheme, piecemeal attempts being discouraged to avoid partial or total destruction of the reclaimed parts by wind, water and heat acting on the barren unreclaimed portions.

Ingredients: Lessons learnt from experience and the consideration of other factors will permit the selection of plants of specific qualities and proven usefulness. They will be compatible with the environment at large since there appears to be very few that will not grow on a prepared tailings surface.

New species will be introduced where it is justified and profitable.

Economics: Study of the physical, economic, and social framework will help determine the economic aspect of the reclamation scheme. The best use will be made of the tailings with regard to the creation and maintaining of secondary industries and services where applicable.

RECONVERSION TO USEFULNESS

Any or more of the uses listed below are feasible within reasonable economic limits, giving due consideration to the local needs and returns anticipated:

<u>Pastureland</u>   Milk, beef and hog can be produced for returns comparable to common farmland

<u>Cropland</u>   Seed harvesting of legumes, cereals: rye, oats ; crownvetch, trefoils

<u>Nursery</u>   A tree nursery is generally of considerable value to the community and its hinterland. Evergreens, deciduous, shrubs

<u>Sod Farm</u>   Beyond a certain community size, common sod and "Golden Sod"- a leguminous sod-, will sell readily

<u>Urban Development</u>   Reclaimed wasteland commonly finds itself adjacent to the center of the originally smaller community, hence the need for space to expand

<u>Recreation/Golf Course</u>   Tailings lend themselves particularly well to this use as elaborated below

<u>Airfield</u>   In many areas of the Shield where rugged topography puts flat space at a premium

FROM WASTE TO SOIL

In nature, deleterious elements and substances as occur from the presence of a base metal deposit, for example, are not necessarily damaging to the vegetation because their release into the environment generally takes place at a naturally controlled rate.

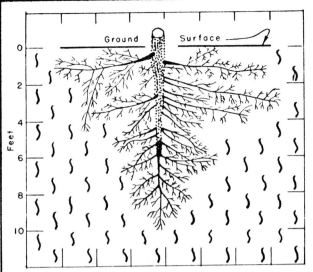

A good loam soil allows moisture penetration and deep, uniform distribution of tree roots.

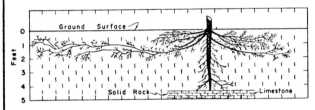

These tree roots could not grow any deeper because of the solid rock.

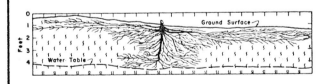

A high water table prevents deep root penetration. These roots stopped at 4 feet. Tree roots must have air to grow.

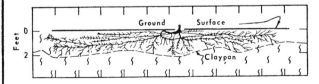

The claypan soil restricted the roots of this tree to 2 feet in depth.

ROOTS & SOIL
Figure No. 2

Here are illustrated typical conditions affecting the development of plant roots. Tailing material properly worked and conditioned will permit the plant to grow essentially in the way of a plant in a well aerated, loose, and moist loam as in the first illustration.

Homogeneity of the growing medium is the key factor together with proper aeration, abundant but not excessive moisture, and absence of fungus and other diseases common in "natural" soils but unknown in reclaimed tailings areas

417

Conversely, the establishment of a vegetation cover on tailings will result in the deleterious substances, if any, being in fact sequestered or neutralized, precipitated, by the developing humus layer and the various natural colloids present. Hence, the vegetation cover becomes a protective, neutralizing, pollution-controlling natural device of unsurpassed effectiveness. A fully vegetated acre will transpire from 5,000 to 10,000 gallons of water daily, and eliminate all previous erosion brought about with every precipitation.

An area of tailings, unprotected and exposed to summer heat, will quickly lose all available moisture in its topmost layer and will readily reach temperatures of 100-120° F. Even a moderate wind, blowing unhindered, will cause sand storm conditions; and at over 15 mph a sand blasting effect will quickly take its toll of any freshly established seedlings if there is an exposed partially reclaimed area

Tailing waste will remain sterile until properly conditioned for plant growth. But since, however, uncontaminated, clean and salt-free sand is the ideal medium for plant growth, we will come very near to achieving optimum conditions provided we have:

1. moisture, of which there is generally no lack in tailings;

2. fertilizing chemical elements, of which 16 are necessary for plant growth, from N, P, K, down to the lesser and the micro-nutrients;

3. an adequate bacterial population to promote germination and continued growth.

Once the specific needs of the particular waste area to be reclaimed are determined, it will be a mere matter of weeks, with proper conditioning before vegetation blankets the prepared area.

The basic combination is one of fast growing grasses to act as nurse crop, and slower, nitrogen-

fixing legumes to provide the long-range permanent
and maintenance free vegetation cover.

A detail of considerable importance, is the
homogeneity of the tailings throughout the mass.
It means that it can be shaped to any desired form
very easily, and the plants established in it will
be able to develop a full, coherent root system,
a factor of prime importance in the growth of healthy
plants. Therefore, in careful hands, this material,
this waste, can be made more versatile than the
common soil, particularly where the poorer podzolic
soils of this part of the continent prevail, with
their thin fertile horizon.

ENVIRONMENTAL CONDITIONS

Location : The area under consideration here
is limited approximately by the 45N and 55N parallels
and the 60W and 100W meridians, thus encompassing the best part of the pre-cambrian Canadian shield
in the northeastern quarter of the continent.

Conditions beyond these limits , particularly for
a considerable distance to the northwest, the sub-
arctic regions, would permit a basically similar
reclamation approach as described here.

Climate: In spite of the fact that Toronto in
southern Ontario lies at the latitude of Rome, the
shape of the continent, the disposition of the mountain ranges etc, make the cold northern influence
reach farther south than anywhere else.

The conditions for most of Ontario and Quebec
are therefore those of high latitude continental -
the Cool, snow-forest region of the Koppen classification. The winters are long, and the land snow
covered from four to eight months of the year.

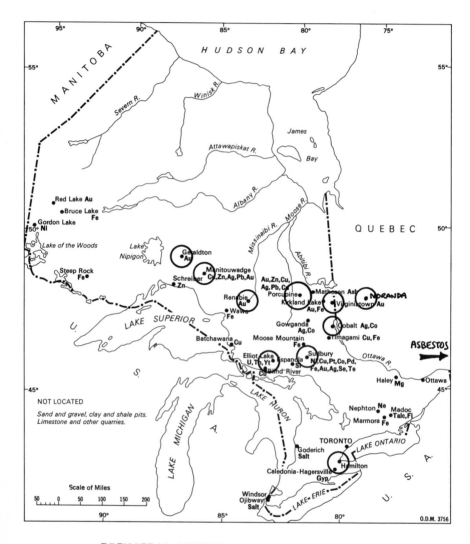

PRINCIPAL MINING AREAS OF ONTARIO

Erocon has carried out reclamation programs
at circled locations. The asbestos mining
camp of Quebec lies about 150 miles east of
the right hand side edge of the map, at about
46° North.   Figure No. 3

420

The summer temperature average of the warmest month is 60°F while the temperature for the coldest month is near 0°F.

Precipitation averages 30" yearly with somewhat of a maxiumum in the summer, and snow making up about one quarter of the total for the year.

The ground is frozen from 6 to 8 months of the year and hence "breakup" in the spring and "freeze up" in the fall set definite limits to cultivation practices.

Vegetation: The dominant climatic conditions together with the particular nature of the available soil left on the old pre-cambrian shield underlying most of the area result in an extensive forested zone of the boreal type, - the Cool Coniferous Forest of Koppen-, most dense wherever the pleistocene glaciation that covered the whole of Canada left extensive surficial deposits.

Soils: The prevalent natural soils in the region consist of thin, acidic, grey podzolic types grading into thinner subarctic soils in the northern parts. The actual land surface is divided in about equal parts of rock outcrops, lakes and rivers, peat bogs and forest. They are therefore soils of limited potential for cultivation except where deeper, more extensive clay belts occasionally occur.

RECLAMATION PROCEDURES

Under the "normal" circumstances and prevailing conditions of the Shield area where tailings are being reclaimed, these typical steps apply:

1. Heavy and fine grading, particularly on impounding dam outer slope. A heavy machine can

Preparatory reclamation work at two sites. Top:
Reclamation of the Hollinger Mine tailings in
1968. Raking and harrowing are the first steps
taken here, where the surface is fairly level, in
order to prepare a seed bed. Bottom: Liming the
acid tailings at the Nordic Mine, Rio Algom,
Elliot Lake, Ontario. Where tailings cannot support
conventional crawler tractors, low pressure equipment is used.   Figure No. 4

cut a 40°slope 200 ' high at the rate of one acre per day.

2. Ripping all areas where iron sulphides have created an armour-like crust (particularly the top of the impounding dam) and all areas of excessive compaction such as haulage roads. Smoothing out of irregularities.

3. Neutralizing the tailings. Two men with a Nodwell type mounted spreader can spread about 100 tons of calcidic/dolomitic crushed limestone, minus 1/4" screenings, per day per machine. Acidifying compound for alkaline tailings.

4. Raking and harrowing, where minor irregularities do not require grading, but where the surface is still too rough for seed bed establishment.

5. Discing neutralizing agent into seedbed, and harrowing.

6. Fertiliser application, mostly by cyclone. A common rate is 1,000 pounds per acre of high analysis fertilizer.

7. Seeding. Mechanical seeding, Brillion-type is preferred wherever possible. The seed is put into the ground at the right depth, in the right amount and is immediately packed in. The normal rate is 20 acres seeded and compacted per day, per machine.

Up and down slope work will allow flash runoff and prevent destruction of seedbed in the event of heavy downpour shortly after seeding.

8. Mulching and artificial membrane spraying. The provision of a protective layer of inert material to assist germination by creating a propitious microclimate may be necessary by means of an appropriate holding and breathing membrane.

The emulsion is physiologically harmless and non-phytotoxic, and compatible with fertilizers. According to the degree of dilution, it will penetrate to a certain depth and within a few hours will provide a netlike, water insoluble layer that will effec-

Hydroseeding versus mechanical seeding. Top:
Result of hydroseeding on a slope. When the
seedbed has not been compacted, precipitation
quickly causes erosion and dispersal, besides
heavy losses to predators, etc. Bottom: Note
the evenness of distribution of plant growth.
Brillion-type mechanical seeding is best for
accuracy and economy of seed and material.

Figure No. 5

tively prevent evaporation from the ground, create the most favourable micro climate and allow germination to take place by breaking through unhindered.

9. Hard Seeding & Dormancy. When introducing new species in a new and harsher environment, the reclaimer can gain enormously be seeding mixtures having a fair percentage of "hard" seeds which will take some time to germinate, generally in the next vegetative cycle.

Desirable plant varieties can thus be introduced in areas removed from their usual habitat by a natural "conditioning" or habituation to more severe conditions. For example, crownvetch, Coronillia varia, which was thought to be able to thrive only in Pennsylvania is now well established on the open pit walls of TGS Kidd's orebody near Timmins, where $50^{\circ}F$ below in winter is not uncommon.

CASE ONE : AN INTEGRATED REHABILITATION SCHEME

The famous Hollinger gold mine, in Timmins, Ontario, which operated from 1910 to 1968 and produced some $566 million worth of gold, also left behind some 56 million tons of tailings waste.

In the past few years it has become a showpiece of Erocon's approach to reclamation: the establishment of a permanent, thriving, maintenance free vegetation cover of high quality. The area reclaimed shows remarkably rich and sturdy growths of grasses and legumes with the latter gradually taking over. A living soil is in fact being created, and at a rate considerably faster than in nature.

Diversification of End Uses : Our understanding of creative reclamation being that rehabilitation of tailings means more than growing grass on top,

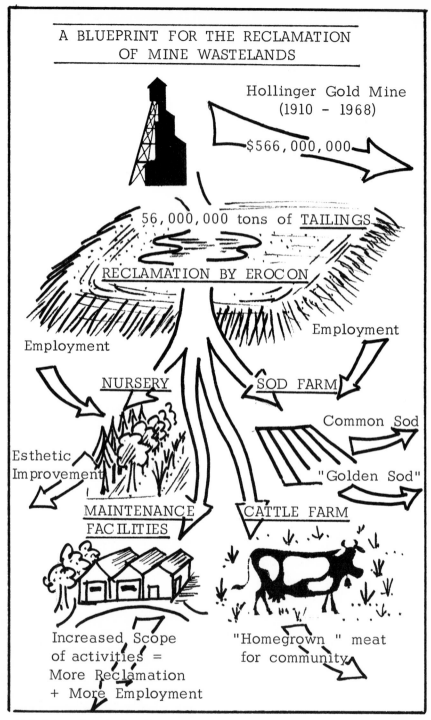

A BLUEPRINT FOR THE RECLAMATION
OF MINE WASTELANDS

Hollinger Gold Mine
(1910 – 1968)

$566,000,000

56,000,000 tons of TAILINGS

RECLAMATION BY EROCON

Employment

Employment

NURSERY

SOD FARM

Common Sod

Esthetic
Improvement

"Golden Sod"

MAINTENANCE
FACILITIES

CATTLE FARM

Increased Scope
of activities =
More Reclamation
+ More Employment

"Homegrown " meat
for community

Reclamation of Mine Wastelands   Figure No. 6

we will detail below specific uses these tailings will be put to. It is estimated this particular scheme will generate a 50% return on investment before taxes and that the initial outlay will have been recovered by the third operating year.

The completely reclaimed tailings will carry a commercially viable complex consisting of a tree nursery, a sod farm and a cattle farm, together with auxiliary service facilities.

Benefits : This complex will serve the community of Timmins and its wider region in providing goods and services not presently readily available.

It will provide needed diversified employment and help retain skilled personnel.

It will fit particularly well within the general framework of the discussed national Mid Canada Region development project, which is concerned with the development at all levels of a secondary belt of economic activity at a higher latitude in order to offset the present unbalance created by heavy population concentration along the Canada- USA border.

It will be a useful adjunct to the diversification of the agriculture and related activities of the region.

It will serve as a showpiece for the mineral industry and possibly as a blueprint for other similar schemes throughout the country.

It will permit continued experimentation in adaptation of desirable species into the northern environment.

The Nursery

The nursery will consist initially of some 30 acres to be planted with selected species particularly suited to the climatic conditions and the local demands. It is known that there is a strong need for an abundant and varied source of nursery stock for the community and its vicinity.

The conditions are such that trees grow more slowly but develop much more fully and harmoniously in comparison with their warmer climate counterparts to the south. Pruning will be reduced, and cultivation of the nursery ground will be considerably easier because of the homogeneity of the growing medium as discussed above. It will also be far less prone to fungus infections and insect pests as compared to long established nurseries on common soils.

Preparation:
.Grading and shaping of the land, condition-ing of the surface
.Application of fertilizers:
2 tons of triple superphosphate / acre
1 ton of 15-15-15 / acre
2 tons of agricultural limestone / acre
.Planting of lining out stock
25,000 evergreens
15,000 deciduous
15,000 shrubs and perennials
. Membrane application whenever required
. Irrigation system

By the very nature of the enterprise, it will take three years of preparatory work to establish a full blown nursery. However sales can be started on a limited scale until large volume is attained by the third year.

A by-product of this work will be the develop-ment of a blueprint for the establishment of nurseries in all suitably located, similar waste disposal areas throughout the Canadian hinterland.

Selected Nursery Stock
The table below describes a selection of proven hardy plants well suited to the environment studied.

TABLE 1
SELECTED NURSERY STOCK FOR NORTHERN CLIMATE

EVERGREENS

Picea alba	white spruce
Picea pungens clauca	Colorado blue spruce
Abies concolor	Colorado fir
Abies balsamea	balsam fir
Thuja occidentalis	white cedar
Larix	tamarack
Taxus canadenses	Canadian yew
Pinus strobus	white pine
Pinus negra austriaca	Austrian pine
Pinus banksiana	jackpine
Pinus montana mughus	mugo pine

DECIDUOUS

Acer saccarinum	sugar maple
Acer nagundo	Manitoba maple
Acer rubrum	red maple
Acer ginnala	shrub maple
Acer campestre	field maple
Betula papyrifera	paper birch

(will be planted to produce multi-stemmed trees as well as single ones)

Populus bolleana	silver poplar
Salix	common willow
Fraxinus americana	American ash

SHRUBS

Amelanchier canadenses	
Caragana arborescens	pea bush
Cotone aster	
Chanonelis japonica	
Lonicera vulgaris	honeysuckle
Potentilla fruticosa	
Riebes alpinum	arctic currant
Salix canadenses atropurpurea	

Selected Nursery Stock (cont'd)

PERENNIALS

Astilbe
Heuchera sanguinea
Parcesandra coccinea
Vinca minor
Lupinus

The Sod Farm

The sod farm will be started on 40 acres initially, and then increased to 100 acres at a rate of speed dictated by the development of the market, keeping in mind that it takes two years to grow a crop of sod.

Sod is presently brought into the Timmins area from as far south as Toronto and there will be little difficulty in establishing a competitive source of supply.

Preparation: After proper grading of the acreage selected, fertilizer will be applied, and after proper cultivation, seeding will take place.

.Application of 80 tons triple superphosphate
.Application of 40 tons 15-15-15
.Seeding
.Herbicide application (In this case only to deal with weeds introduced with the commercial seeds, since none would be present in the growing medium)
.Liming will not be required inasmuch as grass thrives best under slightly acid conditions as prevail here.
.Conventional sod farm equipment
.Irrigation system

The Golden Sod

One of Herman Keller's (Erocon's founder and president) cherished objectives has been to introduce a new concept in sod farming and in systematic "instant reclamation" of erosion prone and severely disturbed or derelict areas.

This can be achieved by combining several desirable factors: the ease of handling, transport, and application of the conventional sod strip together with the priceless regenerative qualities of the commonly available leguminous plant: birdsfoot trefoil.

Birdsfoot trefoil (Lotus corniculatus) is a vigorous herbaceous perennial with well developed branching taproots thriving under particulary difficult climatic and soil conditions. Being an ideally productive legume, it quickly enriches the soil wherever it becomes established.

It is also blessed with a very attractive bloom, is high in protein and an excellent grazing crop, although that aspect may not be of prime importance in all situations where it will be used.

Erocon's Golden Sod, "golden" for several reasons: the colour of the flower, and the soil created from the tailings of past gold producers, - this sod will consist basically of a two and a half inch thick birdsfoot trefoil sod, bearing young and vigorous plants with well established root systems, the latter stronger and more extensive than grass.

This sod can be laid by itself in critical areas prone to erosion and needing immediate attention, and all forms of other unstable ground conditions like steep cuts in urban areas, along highways etc.

It will prove of far greater usefulness than the common sod inasmuch as it will readily achieve the prime aim of establishing a vegetation cover that will hold securely the ground in place and permanently stabilize any slope without the extensive maintenance required of common grass sod.

The Golden Sod being produced from a homogeneous matrix of virtually inexhaustible growing medium of the finest quality, can in fact only be commercially produced under the particular conditions described here: obviously the common sod farms could not possibly afford to lose 2.5" of topsoil with every crop!

The Cattle Farm

The stands of thriving birdsfoot trefoil are ready to be used for grazing. That growth is notably free from fungus and insect infestation, and as pointed out earlier, provides a forage of the highest quality.

The cattle can be brought in early in the spring and disposed of within the season. This should prove particularly advantageous to the community by aiming towards a degree of self sufficiency in the production of foodstuffs.

As a side benefit from exploratory diamond drilling, there is on the property an artesian type well producing excellent potable water, ideal for watering purposes.

CASE TWO : PIONEERING IN LEGUMINOUS COVERS

Stabilization of Clay Slopes With Legumes

To elaborate on the usefulness of legumes generally and crownvetch, Coronillia varia, in particular, in the rehabilitation of northern mine wastelands, here is the case history of the reclamation of the slopes of a large open pit.

One task of the total rehabilitation program at the Texas Gulf Inc.'s Kidd Creek Mine, near Timmins Ontario, involved the largest crownvetch seeding

Stabilizing a clay slope. Top: Texas Gulf Inc.'s
Kidd Creek open pit clay slope in its original
state. Clay contains up to 60 percent moisture.
Bottom: the same slope after crownvetch cover has
been established. This leguminous plant sends
roots down to 8-10 feet and renders the ground
firm and stable. This is another example of
successful acclimatization of a very useful plant.

Figure No. 7

program in Canada to date. Here are some highlights of this successful acclimatization of crownvetch in a harsh environment for a specific purpose. This portion of the work was carried out by Erocon from 1966 to 1970 : it was pioneering work at that time at that latitude.

Reclamation work at this major base metal producer is carried out continuously, being an integral part of the overall mining and processing operations.

The particular pit area to be reclaimed, which concerns us here, consisted of approximately one hundred acres of the highly unstable clay slopes making up the upper part of the open pit where the clay overburden averages from 60 to 80' in thickness.

This sterile clay contained up to 60% moisture and was a potential danger if left unattended. It was also a difficult, gumbo-like material unsuited to conventional methods of rehabilitation. It was devoid of any organic content and bacterial life, and had a pH close to neutral. The magnesium content was high, a factor favourable to legumes.

The first seeding resulted in fast germination, but because of its lateness in the season, the plant were not able to reach the given stage of their development which would permit them to survive the severe winter conditions at that latitude. The following spring, however, the hard seeds germinated and provided adequate coverage for the second year.

A second seeding was carried out in June 1967 with a booster dose of 400 lbs per acre of Blue Chip Nitroform, which resulted in lush growth up to the winter. That winter proved severe and caused the elimination of the weaker plants due to the light snowfall leaving an inadequate insulating cover.

Some of the plants were eliminated in a peculiar way: in the spring thaw, the moisture was heaved out, lifting bodily along with it crownvetch plants several inches out of the ground, although the plants had already established roots one to two feet in depth. The gap created between root and soil and the repeated freezings and thawings had caused the outer skin of the roots to separate from the plants.

The more resistant of the hard seeds left germinated in the spring and provided an adequate coverage thus proving the invaluable inherent ability of plants to adapt themselves selectively to alien environments. Here are plants generally considered, at that time, as able to thrive only in parts of the northeastern United States, now successfully adapted to a severe continental climate and difficult "soil" conditions.

New specialized Erocon equipment was allowed to work the fluid slope area in early May, giving the considerable advantage at that latitude of an extra month and a half of growing time resulting in lush growth within three months.

The areas established in crownvetch are now densely covered and spreading by rhizomes and re-seeding themselves. All soil movements have ceased. The ground is appreciably drier because of the regulating evapotranspiration power of the plants.

Erosion and Dust Control

Areas left unpaved after the construction of the Texas Gulf Inc. concentrator just east of Timmins were sodded or seeded with suitable grasses. Should this not have been done, unprotected areas could have become a source of bothersome dusts and caused a substantial increase in the cost of machinery maintenance through greater wear of moving parts and deterioration of exposed surfaces.

Grassing as done here is a basic and essential remedial measure to provide a healthy turf that can absorb a considerable amount of airborne dusts as well as provide a pleasant working environment.

Vegetating impounding dams at Preston Gold
Mine, Ontario. Top: The initial slope is
reduced, the crest is smoothed out. Note
sedimentation from runoff at the base of the
dam. Bottom: With seeding and compaction on up
and down slope, there was full germination and
growth four weeks after reclamation started. Today
there is a thick, thriving erosion-proof cover.

Figure No. 8

Farther away from the plant, a more varied vegetation cover has been established: birdsfoot trefoil and crownvetch have been seeded and have fully covered sloping and marginal areas to provide a maintenance free cover of great attractiveness in bloom from June to September.

Beautification

Also at the concentrator site, some 3,000 roses were planted, the species selected for their hardiness and brilliant colours: Floribunda and Poly-antha. These have successfully resisted the onslaught of the severe 50°F below zero spells characteristic of the region.

Concrete planters set flush with the turf surface facilitate maintenance of the roses and ease trimming.

Vegetating Impounding Dams

A 9.5 mile perimeter tailings impounding dam contains the waste disposal area at the concentrator site. The walls of the dam are also being vegetated according the proven formula of the grass + legume combination. All erosion of the outside slope is eliminated, the ground is firmed up by the regulating effect of the plant cover on the available moisture and work on and about the structure is rendered easier and safer.

CASE THREE : VEGETATING ACID TAILINGS

Base Metal Mines & Acid Tailings

Numerous base metal deposits of the massive sulphide type occur throughout the Canadian Shield and have resulted in the creation of some of the most important mining camps.

The extractive process to win the base metals from these massive sulphide deposits requires a high degree of comminution of the ore. The tailings then consist of a large portion of finely ground sulphide particles, commonly pyrite and pyrrhotite, making u 30% or more of the tailing mass. Obviously, enormous quantities of acid effluent can be released by such a mass with every substantial precipitation, and particularly in the spring thaw at these latitude

Fortunately, the problem is again being eliminated by the establishment of that insulating, sequestering layer: the vegetation cover with its regulating properties discussed above.

The difficulty here lay initially with carrying out the establishment of that cover quickly enough through its more vulnerable stage where it could be damaged or destroyed by the contained acidic fluid. It results that the neutralization of the topmost laye is in fact what matters most .

The movement of acid effluent through the tail ing mass is critical and must be assessed carefully for, on partial vegetating schemes, it does happen to lose a good growth to a sudden heavy precipitat ion causing a flash flooding of acid waters.

It is therefore simple and mandatory to isolate portions of tailings being reclaimed from the larger area left untouched, otherwise, almost invariably, effluents from the latter will destroy the new vegetation about to establish itself. This is accomplished easily enough by ditching the reclaimed area, and in cases where discharge of tailings is not altogether complete, taking precautions to avoid any uncontrolled spilling.

Neutralizing & Vegetating

The use of limestone as a neutralizing agent is well known where acid waters are concerned, but its proper use appears still rather empirical where tailings are involved, for there are many variables: composition of the limestone, sizing of the crushed stone, method of application, depth of application, interaction if any with fertilizers, as well as the

Establishment of a permanent, maintenance
free, vegetation cover at the Hollinger Mine
tailings, Timmins, Ontario. Top: Typical tailings
disposal area. Bottom: After rehabilitation, the
grass is dominant for the first two vegetative
cycles, but by the third, the legumes (in this case
birdsfoot trefoil) take over. A "soil" is being
created at a rate considerably faster than in
soils made by nature.   Figure No. 9

stone, method of application, depth of application, interaction if any with fertilizers, as well as the physical and chemical make up of the tailings themselves. It must be remembered here that excess acidity blocks the assimilation of certain fertilizing elements rather than destroy the plant tissues themselves.

It has taken some experimentation to arrive at the right proportions to be used in given circumstances.

In the Elliot Lake uranium mining camp the conglomerate host rock carries sulphides and a minimal application of 30 tons of crushed limestone per acre is required: high calcium limestone in 1/4" screenings together with two tons per acre of fertilizer high in P and K bring definitive neutralization and rapid germination of grasses and legumes.

To insure permanent growth on less well located areas of the tailings with respect to drainage, the rate of application has to be raised to 50 tons per acre. Under adequate weather conditions, the plants reach one and one half inch in height in a few weeks after seeding.

In the Noranda area of Quebec, Erocon has done experimental and reclamation work and is now succeeding in its aim to establish permanent, vegetation cover on very acid tailings.

The absence of a good source of supply of limestone in the area has meant resorting to a substitute, in this case asbestos tailings, from an inactive mine near Matheson, not far away.

It was found, that after some experimentation, asbestos is somewhat as effective as limestone in neutralizing acid tailings in this instance, and that a grass and legume vegetation cover becomes established on the prepared tailings material just as readily.

In the case of the Horne Mine tailings at Noranda, good vegetation growth was obtained with

440

application of 90 tons per acre of asbestos tailings in one instance and 60 tons asbestos + 30 tons crushed limestone in another, whereas a rate of 40 tons per acre of asbestos alone proved insufficient to neutralize enough for vegetation growth.

Taking into consideration the various factors difficult to assess quantitatively, as the flow of effluents, etc on such tailings areas, it is considered here that a minimal rate of 80 tons of asbestos tailings or 60 tons of high calcium limestone are required.

CASE FOUR : VEGETATING ALKALINE TAILINGS

Background: Asbestos mining in Canada is concentrated in a 50 mile long belt in the province of Quebec, where 8 operating mines produce 82% of the Canadian asbestos output which in turn represents 44% of the world's production and of course makes Canada the first and major producer of that commodity.

In the process, some 600 million tons of very alkaline tailings have accumulated and the rate is increasing by 15 to 20 million tons annually.

The nature of the ore and the method of recovery of the valuable asbestos fibre result in the disposal of waste material ranging from coarse fist-sized or larger fragments down to a fine fibrous mass compacting quite tightly.

Chemical analyses of the waste material indicate that the serpentine minerals antigorite and chrysotile make up 85%, iron oxide 7-10% of which 70% is magnetite, chromite 0.5% with about 0.25% nickel, and the remainder being made up of varied silicates and carbonates.

Yet vegetation can be made to grow on such material, without topsoil of course, as our experimental work has demonstrated.

Experimentation at Asbestos
The purpose of the work was to establish a permanent, self-sustaining grass and legume vegetation cover on asbestos tailings as they are found, i.e., without the addition of any topsoil.

Prevailing Conditions : The area lies at about $46^\circ N$ latitude, receives close to 50" precipitation yearly, has no dry season, has January temperature average of $10^\circ F$ and July average of $70^\circ F$; severe winters with abundant snowfalls in the foothills of the Appalachians.

The experimental reclamation work was carried out by Erocon on the tailings from Canada's largest open pit mine, the Jeffrey Mine of Johns-Manville at Asbestos, province of Quebec.

The natural vegetation consists of a mixture of conifers and temperate hardwoods on a typical podzolic soil.

Acid Tailings vs Alkaline Tailings : The asbestos tailings, described above, appear to retain considerable amounts of moisture for a long time by virtue of their very physical composition. On flat parts of the tailings disposal areas, sedimentation of the fines causes wet cardboard-like layering whic can be peeled back like wet cloth.

No vegetation of any kind was observed to volunteer on the tailings, even on relatively ancient parts.

Asbestos tailings are highly alkaline, and the first step in their conditioning for vegetation is to lower the pH to near normal values.

In this instance it was decided to provide the necessary acidity by the use of sulphide tailings from a base metal mine on one hand, and with commercial flour sulfur on the other.

The known scales describing the recommended proportions of neutralizing agents to be used as in agricultural practice unfortunately do not apply in the case of tailings, and therefore, these proportions have had to be determined experimentally or empirically as the case may have been. It has been seen, in the case of acid tailings, that the complete lack of buffering effect due to the absence of organic elements in the "soil" necessitate a considerable increase in the rate of application.

Sulphide tailing material consisting of fine mesh particles carrying some 60% sulphides was brought to the site and worked into the ground.

Commercial flour sulphur was also used.

Procedure

The first series of tests was carried out on October 7 & 8, 1970, under warm, humid and sunny conditions.

Eight plots, each approximately 1/100th of an acre, were laid out as shown on the diagram below, on a flat area near the edge of the tailings outer slope.

Each plot was subdivided into four quarters, thus giving 32 permutations; five plots being treated with sulphide tailings and three with commercial sulphur.

The neutralizing agents were applied at the following rates:

Plot A	20 ton/acre	sulphide tailings
Plot B	10 ton/acre	
Plot C	5 ton/acre	
Plot D	2.5 ton/acre	
Plot E	1.25 ton/acre	
Plot F	2.5 ton/acre	sulphur
Plot G	1.25 ton/acre	
Plot H	0.5 ton/acre	

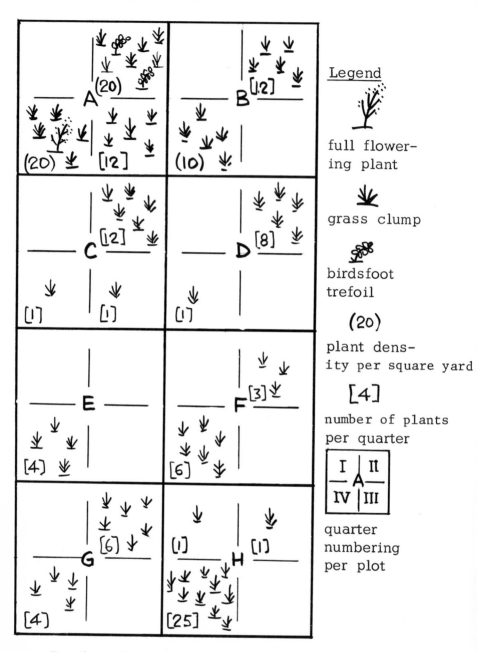

Results of an experiment in establishing a vegetation cover in asbestos tailing.

Figure No. 10

Since the tailings surface was highly compacted
- it could support heavy tyred vehicles -, a roto-
tiller was used to loosen it up and to prepare a
seed bed. In the process countless fist size and
larger fragments came up , and the larger ones were
piled at corners to prop up corner stakes.

After application of the neutralizing material,
the plots were tilled again to ensure some evenness
in the spreading, difficult because of the lumpiness
of the wet sulphide material.

Three fertilizers were used:

1. A 10-10-10 chemical fertilizer

2. A 6-9-6 chemical fertilizer carrying also
some calcium, sulphur and magnesia

3. A composted poultry manure (4-3-2) to
provide bacterial population

These fertilizers were applied in this manner:

1. 10-10-10- applied in Quarters II and III
at rates of 1 and 0.5 ton/acre respectively.

2. 6-9-6- applied in Quarter IV at the rate of
0.5 ton/acre.

3. Manure- applied in Quarters I and IV at
the rate of 0.5 ton/acre.

All plots were seeded by hand with a mixture
of timothy, inoculated birdsfoot trefoil and a forage
mix .

Results 1971: The test area had been left completely unattended, and a little less than a year
later, it was observed as illustrated in the accompanying diagram.

Noteworthy:

Plot A, Quarter II: this quarter exhibited the
best overall growth. It had a density of about 20
plants per square yards, of vigorous growth. 8 individual trefoil plants were in evidence, the largest
about 4-5" high. Some purplish discolouration of

445

the edges of blades of grass due to phosphorus deficiency. No trefoil was found on any other plot.

Plot A, Quarter IV: The density of growth was similar to the above, and one grass plant was some 13" high and had produced a good quantity of seeds. All specimen very healthy.

In the plots neutralized with sulphur, many pea-sized lumps of sulphur remained, and even powdered sulphur under some of the bigger fragments. The rate of degradation thus appears very low, although neutralization is effected as the log of growth indicates.

The sulphide tailing material appear to break down more thoroughly, leaving some crusty, limonitic fragments up to egg size.

The texture of the tailings material suggests that very little movement seems to take place under the top one inch. It might mean that accurate distribution of fertilizer, seeds, neutralizing agent could be achieved with little being lost to percolation and other movements commonly observed in other types of tailings material. Excellent stability is also achieved on slopes.

Organic fertilizer by itself is not sufficient to promote growth.

The best overall growth appears linked to the highest rate of application of sulphide material, hence subsequent experimentation used that rate as a minimum rate.

Follow-through: Experimentation in 1971:

More testing was carried out under similar weather conditions on August 18, 1971. Four plots were treated in this manner:

Plot W :   Overall sulphide application rate of 20 ton/acre

Plot X :   Overall sulphide application rate of 30 ton/acre

Plot Y :   Overall sulphide application
             rate of 40 ton/acre
Plot Z :   Witness plot: only fertilizers
             were applied

Fertilizers were applied:
Chemical (10-10-10) at 2 ton/acre in quarters I & IV;
at 1 ton/acre in quarters II & III.
Organic (poultry manure) at 2 ton/acre in quarters I
and II; 1 ton/acre in quarters III and IV.
A mixture of grasses and trefoil was seeded
by hand at a high rate.
The procedure followed was the same as explained for the 1970 experimentation work.

Results 1972 : Good growth was obtained in
all plots except the witness plot which only received fertilizer and seed. The best growth,-substan-
tially better than the best of the first year-, was
in plot X and Y, with a good distribution of grasses
and legumes. The grasses and legumes grow well
and produce seed, unquestionably going through their
full vegetative cycle.
In the particular case of the asbestos mining
district of Quebec, acid tailings are available from
neighbouring base metal mines and the reclamation
procedure that has been established here is so
straightforward that there is little doubt that large
scale reclamation work can be carried out there and
in similar mining camps where alkaline conditions
prevail.
To sum it up, in our experience there is no
mine wasteland that cannot be reclaimed systematically and effectively. All can be vegetated, and in
most cases much better use can be made of the
reclaimed land than could ever have been possible
before mining took place.

DISCUSSION

ROY WILLIAMS (U. S. Bureau of Mines): Mr. Leroy could you tell us what the status of reclamation legislation is in Canada?

J. C. LEROY: I am afraid I am not quite an authority on that subject. I think it has changed very quickly in the past few years. But I believe that now our provinces have some measures to compel mining companies to do something for either vegetating tailings or something else to prevent any possible damage to the countryside. Of course, the situation is somewhat special in that most mining communities and mining operations in Canada are far removed from populated centers, and the only immediate effect is on the mining community itself. However, there is no outstanding problem, I am afraid that I do not quite answer your question, but there is legislation, I believe, in all provinces. I believe the most severe legislation is in British Columbia, but I am not sure of that.

QUESTION: I'd like to ask Mr. Leroy if he can give us some of the costs of reclamation projects that Erocon has been involved in?

J. C. LEROY: This is getting into a very touchy subject. However, we believe that reclamation can be done reasonably economically and that is why we have developed methods to establish vegetation on tailing material as it is. We have never used soil brought onto the site because this is an extremely expensive proposition, and surely the problem is not to rob one area of top soil to cover up another. However, if you are dealing with tailing which is close to neutral, the cost is quite reasonable. It is difficult to quote a figure because it will depend, for example, on the amount of preparation of the seed bed and whatever amount of grading, for example, has to be done. I think the cost is quite reasonable and within the reach of every mining company, so to speak. Now,

when you have a very acid tailing, it is somewhat
more expensive because the first step is to bring
the tailing closer to neutral. However, it doesn't
have to be neutral. You can have excellent vegetation cover in material having a pH of 3 to 4. It
is also more expensive at the other end when dealing
with highly alkaline tailings. That's all I can say
on this.

COMPARATIVE COSTS AND METHODS

FOR STABILIZATION OF TAILINGS

Karl C. Dean, Research Supervisor

Richard Havens, Metallurgist

Salt Lake City Metallurgy Research Center
Bureau of Mines
U.S. Department of the Interior
Salt Lake City, Utah

ABSTRACT

Methods using physical, chemical, vegetative,
and combined stabilization procedures have been
developed and applied in many areas of the country
to prevent air and water pollution arising from
accumulations of fine-sized mineral wastes.
Several milling companies, either independently or
in cooperation with the Bureau of Mines, have
applied various stabilization techniques to differing types of wastes in different environments. The
principal aim of the work has been to achieve
effective low-cost stabilization requiring minimal
maintenance. Research has indicated that, with the
exception of highly acidic, basic, or saline tailings, satisfactory stabilization can be obtained by
many methods at costs of less than $400 per acre.
Effective vegetative stabilization of many fine-
sized wastes is attainable at a cost of $100 to
$250 per acre using the chemical-vegetative tech-
nique developed by the Bureau of Mines. Research

on initiating growth of Indian ricegrass, a nitrogen-
fixing plant, offers promise for lowering the cost
of maintenance on vegetatively stabilized tailings
sites. Bureau research on the use of buried layers
of sewage sludge also offers promise for reclaiming
mineral waste accumulations not amenable to simpler
treatment.

INTRODUCTION

About 1.7 billion tons of mineral solid wastes
are discarded annually in the United States. Total
accumulated mineral solid wastes amount to about
25 billion tons. These mineral waste piles currently
cover over 2 million acres of land. They are second
only to agricultural wastes in quantity and represent
nearly 40 percent of the total solid wastes produced
in the United States. A part of the mineral discard
is fine-size material requiring some sort of stabilization if air and water pollution are to be minimized.
On active mill tailing ponds, air pollution is controlled by keeping the surfaces of the ponds wet
either by tailings discharge or by sprinkling. On
inactive ponds, a more permanent solution is required,
usually that of physical, chemical, or vegetative
stabilization.

The U.S. Bureau of Mines has been conducting
research on the utilization and stabilization of
mineral wastes for many years. This paper reports
on various methods and approximate   costs of
achieving stabilization of fine-sized milling
wastes. The fine wastes represent the most difficult materials to stabilize of those deriving from
the mining and milling industry. Many mining and
milling companies have worked independently for
many years and during the past few years coopera-
tively with the Bureau in evaluating various
stabilization methods in the field. A free
exchange of information has taken place and a
summation of cost figures for the different methods
is included in this report. Newly completed

research offering promise of achieving stabilization
on exceptional problem areas and for lowering
maintenance costs is also presented.

STABILIZATION PROCEDURES

The principal methods for stabilization of milling wastes include--

1. Physical--the covering of the tailings with
    soil or other restraining materials.

2. Chemical--the use of a material to interact
    with fine-sized minerals to form a crust.

3. Vegetative--the growth of plants in the
    tailings.

The vegetative procedure is preferred in that
esthetics of the area are improved while obtaining
stabilization. Also, if a mineralized waste is to
be conserved for possible later retreatment or if
the area is to be used later for residential construction or recreational purposes, it is beneficial
to stabilize the area with vegetation. Vegetation
does not hinder retreatment procedures as much as
covering the tailings with other foreign materials.

Physical Stabilization

Many materials have been tried for physical
stabilization of fine tailings to prevent air pollution. Other than water for sprinkling, perhaps the
most used material is rock and soil obtained from
nearby areas. The use of soil often has a dual
advantage in that effective cover is obtained and a
habitat is provided for local vegetation to encroach.

Crushed or granulated smelter slag has been used
by many companies to stabilize a variety of fine
wastes, notably inactive tailings ponds. On active
tailings ponds, however, the slag-covered portions

are subject to burial from shifting sands. Slag has
the drawback, unlike soils or country rock, of not
providing a favorable habitat for vegetation.
Furthermore, suitable slag, like soil and rock,
must be locally available.

Other physical methods of stabilization evaluated
include (1) the use of bark covering and (2) the
harrowing of straw into the top few inches of
tailings.

Chemical Stabilization

Chemical stabilization involves reacting a
reagent with mineral wastes to form an air- and
water-resistant crust or layer which will effectively stop dusts from blowing and inhibit water
erosion. Chemicals have the drawback of not being
as permanent a stabilizing means as soil covering or
vegetation. However, chemicals can be used on sites
unsuited to the growth of vegetation because of
harsh climatic conditions or the presence of vege-
table poisons in the tailings, or in areas that
lack access to a soil-covering material. Chemical
stabilization is also applicable for erosion
control on active tailings ponds. Chemicals can
be effectively used on portions of these ponds to
restrict air pollution while other portions continue to be active.

Seventy chemicals have been tested in the laboratory, and selected materials have been tested in
field plots. Optimum conditions and effective rates
of application for all materials tested have not
been determined, and testing is continuing. The
more effective chemicals of those tested are listed
below in order of effectiveness based upon the cost
in cents for the amount of reagent required to
stabilize 1 square yard. An overlapping of costs
resulted because some of the reagents were required
in greater quantities to stabilize different tailings. The general conclusions derived from tests
conducted to date are as follows:

1. Coherex,[1] a resinous adhesive, furnished wind-resistant tailings surfaces when applied in quantities costing as little as $0.01 per square yard, but resistance to water jet testing was not achieved until reagent costing about $0.10 per square yard was applied.

2. Calcium, ammonium, and sodium lignosulfonates, as well as redwood bark extracts, were all effective surface stabilizers at costs of about $0.02 per square yard.

3. Cement and milk of lime additives were effective in stabilizing surfaces when applied in amounts costing $0.03 per square yard.

4. Paracol S 1461 (a blend of wax and resin) and Paracol TC 1842 (a resin emulsion) were effective as stabilizers in quantities ranging in cost from $0.04 to $0.10 per square yard on various tailings samples tested.

5. Potassium silicates having SiO_2-K_2O ratios of 2.5 were effective stabilizers when applied at a rate of $0.07 to $0.15 per square yard.

6. A cationic neoprene emulsion and Rezosol, an organic polymer, effectively stabilized tailings at costs approximating $0.08 per square yard.

7. Sodium silicate applied in quantities of 4.5 pounds per square yard and at a cost of $0.11 per square yard was an effective stabilizer. Calcium chloride was an effective additive to the sodium silicate, whereas ferrous sulfate was not. Addition of 6 percent by weight of $CaCl_2$ permitted reduction of the cost of sodium silicate used from $0.11 to $0.02 per square yard.

[1]Reference to trade names is made for identification only and does not imply endorsement by the Bureau of Mines.

8. Peneprime (a bituminous base product), selected amines, dicalcium silicate, and elastomeric polymers (Compound SP-400, Soil Gard, and DCA-70) produced wind- and water-resistant surfaces at costs of $0.10 per square yard and up.

9. Pyrite treated with sulfuric acid, Aerospray Binder 52 (a synthetic resin), Landscape (solution of combined sulfur in water-soluble oil), and Water Mate (an organic, nonionic product) were all ineffective on the tailings used in the testing.

Vegetative Stabilization

The successful initiation and perpetuation of vegetation on fine wastes involves ameliorating a number of adverse factors. Mill wastes usually (1) are deficient in plant nutrients, (2) contain excessive salts and heavy metal phytotoxicants, (3) consist of unconsolidated sands that, when wind-blown, destroy young plants by sandblasting and/or burial, and (4) lack normal microbial populations. Other less easily defined problems also complicate vegetative procedures. The sloping sides of waste piles receive greatly varying amounts of solar radiation depending on direction of exposure. Studies by Gates (1) have indicated that, contrary to popular belief, photosynthesis of plants is not continuous while the sun is shining; under high-temperature conditions, photosynthesis may almost stop. Furthermore, most accumulations of mill tailings are light in color and may reflect excessive radiation to plant surfaces, thus intensifying physiological stresses. For these reasons, vegetation that may be effective on northern and eastern exposures may not be suitable for southern or western exposures.

Ideally, vegetative stabilization should produce a self-perpetuating plant cover directly, or foster entrapment and germination of native plant seeds which will form a self-regenerating community. In the latter case, an ecological succession would be established leading to a vegetative covering so completely in harmony with the environment that irrigation or special care would be unnecessary. If the area were not cropped or grazed, only an initial fertilization should be required because the essential nutrients would be largely cycled in place.

Research indicates that, other than the excessive acidity, basicity, or salinity, perhaps the greatest problem to be overcome in establishing vegetation is that of windblown sands. Several approaches have been postulated for preventing windblown sands from covering or cutting off the growing plants, including extensive water sprinkling while the plants are growing, covering the tailings with soil or country rock, hydroseeding, using excelsior-filled matting as a cover directly over the tailings, and a combination chemical-vegetative procedure developed by the Bureau of Mines. Sprinkling, soil covering, hydroseeding, and matting have all been proved on various types of wastes, and the chemical-vegetative procedure has proved effective during the past 4 years on six different tailings ponds.

The hydroseeding procedure as normally used encompasses blowing a slurry of wood chips or paper pulp with admixed seeds and fertilizer over the surface to be stabilized. After the seeds germinate, the wood chips or paper pulp serve as protection for the seedlings and inhibit blowing of sands. Matting serves the same purpose as the wood chips for that method. Usually the area is planted with seeds and fertilizer and then 3-foot-wide strips of excelsior-filled matting are staked continuously or at 3-foot intervals over the planted area. Matting is used most commonly on the sloping surface of tailing dikes to inhibit slippage of the sands.

The Bureau-developed chemical-vegetative procedure involves the application of a small amount of chemicals to newly planted tailings to achieve several worthwhile goals. Sandblasting of plants is minimized. Moisture is retained in the tailings. Germination is promoted and wilting minimized by creating a dark, heat-absorbing, nonreflecting surface.

The procedure ultimately developed from laboratory testing involved planting the tailings with a mixture of fertilizer and grass, legume, and grain seeds, watering the plot, and applying a stabilizing chemical in water solution. Early fertilization tests showed that all tailings required nitrogen (N) and phosphorus (P) additions, but that N in quantities of more than 45 pounds per acre seriously hampered legume seed germination. Hence, most tailings were fertilized with 30 and 75 pounds per acre, respectively, of N and P_2O_5. A few tailings required potassium (K), in which case up to 40 pounds of K per acre were added. All seeds used for planting were selected for compatibility with the particular climatic environment in which the tailings are located. A suitable grain was added to the seed mixture to provide early growth for assisting the chemical in stabilizing the surface. The chemical, preferably thus far a resinous adhesive type, was applied to the moistened tailings in amounts costing 1 cent or less per square yard. This stabilization procedure generally is best applied in the fall of the year so as to achieve some growth before the onset of winter, thus allowing the root system to develop under a cover of snow and with good moisture conditions.

The chemical-vegetative procedure has been effectively applied to copper, lead-zinc, uranium, and clay tailings under widely different climatic conditions existing in Colorado, Michigan, Missouri, Nevada, and Washington.

ONGOING RESEARCH

Development of several different vegetative procedures has provided satisfactory stabilization for
many of the mill tailing accumulations scattered
across the country. However, many major problems
still require resolution. High maintenance costs
cause concern on vegetated tailing plots, but the
principal problems occur in establishing vegetation
on tailings of excessive salinity or acidity. Work
is ongoing to reduce maintenance costs by reducing
fertilizer requirements on vegetated plots.
Research also is continuing to aid in the growth of
vegetation on problem tailings by making synthetic
soils from the tailings by adding sewage sludge or
refuse compost.

Reducing Maintenance Costs

Practically all mill tailings are deficient in
fertilizer elements, especially nitrogen. Nitrogen
not only is low in most tailings, but it is also
readily depleted from vegetated wastes containing
heavy metal salts. This lack of nitrogen can be
overcome by planting nitrogen-fixing legumes, but
legume growth on tailings is difficult to perpetu-
ate. Considerable work has been done to promote
the growth of nitrogen-fixing native plant species
that may be compatible with the harsh environment
of tailings. Such a plant is Indian ricegrass, a
desert-type plant that fixes nitrogen in a root
sheath of sand particles invaded by bacteria.
Obtaining growth from such plants, however, is
difficult to achieve in that native plants are
frequently unreliable germinators. Seeds from
this plant have been gathered during the past 2
years and germination studies made in an effort to
break the dormancy. The ricegrass seeds contain a
natural inhibitor that limits germination to 1
percent or less on newly matured or up to 2-year-
old seeds. Treatments by attrition grinding with
quartz to break the seed covering, sulfuric acid
and water soaking and boiling, and cool and below

freezing incubation were all ineffective when treating both newly matured and 2-year-old seeds. When soaking seeds less than a year old in 70-percent-by-volume sulfuric acid for 25 minutes at 25 degrees centigrade, germination was nil; and with a subsequent 24-hour soaking in 10^{-3} molar gibberelic acid or kinetin hormones in a solvent of 9 parts dichloromethane and 1 part ethanol (1 cubic centimeter solution per 100 seeds), the germination was still less than 5 percent. However, when using a combination acid soak followed by a soak in both gibberelic acid and kinetin, the germination after 2-, 4-, and 6-week intervals was respectively, 55, 75, and 90 percent. When treating 2-year-old seeds, treatments with an acid soak plus respective treatments with kinetin, gibberelic acid, or gibberelic acid plus kinetin gave 5-week percentage germination rates respectively of 5, 80, and 80. Thus, it appears that after 2 years of aging the inhibitor effect decreases and kinetin treatment is no longer necessary. Breaking the dormancy of Indian ricegrass seeds offers substantial promise for initiating this type of growth on adverse tailing materials, thus offering the potential of reducing nitrogen fertilizer requirements markedly with an attendant drop in maintenance costs. Tests are underway to determine if properly treated seeds can be germinated and growth sustained in adverse tailing materials.

Vegetating Adverse Tailings

Practically all mill tailings contain deleterious inorganic salts, lack organic components and essential nutrients, and do not have the physical nature required for sustaining vegetative growth. For average tailings these adverse conditions can be overcome in time by fertilization, gradual buildup of organic and microbial populations by encouraging plant growth, and use of chemicals for binding the surface to prevent blowing of loose sands that cut off or bury established vegetation. However, overcoming problems occasioned by excessive salinity or acidity presents a more difficult challenge. Combination problems can exist in which tailings may be excessively saline, because of the recycling of processing waters, and simultaneously contain sulfide materials such as pyrite that upon oxidation will markedly drop the pH of the tailings to a low level in a relatively short time. Such a tailing is Kennecott's Utah Copper Division milling waste. This material with a pH of 7.8 contains salinity equivalent to 2.4 atmospheres osmotic concentration plus approximately 1.3 percent pyrite. The salts in the tailings cause an osmotic gradient that transfers fluid from the plants; thus vegetation deriving from seeds planted in the tailings dies of dehydration. Another problem is that, if vegetation is planted on these tailings and irrigation of the plants leaches away the salts, the pyrite will oxidize and the pH may drop from 7.8 to less than 3.0 within a month's time. Therefore, this material was considered as a typical adverse waste and was used for laboratory testing.

Buried Organic Layers. As noted, one of the major problems with growing plants on tailings is the lack of organic matter and accompanying microbial populations. Efforts were made to offset this problem by combining tailings with sewage sludge or municipal refuse compost. Preliminary, encouraging tests were made by mixing the equivalent of 15 tons per acre of these materials into the surface 2 inches of tailings. Subsequently, tests were made on pelletizing tailings with sewage sludge to form a surface layer and on the effect of buried layers of sewage sludge on the pH and salinity of the tailings being tested.

A series of tests was made in which 2-inch layers of sewage sludge were placed at different depths in barrels containing an 18-inch depth of Kennecott tailings. Sludge was placed at depths of 3, 7, 11, and 15 inches below the surface of the tailings. In another test series, the layering pattern was unchanged but an additional equivalent of 15 tons per acre of sewage sludge was mixed into the top 3 inches of tailings. Crested wheatgrass, ranger alfalfa, and rye grain seeds were planted for both series of tests with barley used as the fourth seed in one test series, and a small transplanted tomato was used as the fourth plant variety in the other series of tests. Table No. I shows the number of plants germinating per 100 seeds 2 weeks after planting and the number surviving at the end of 10 weeks.

Table No. I
Germination and Survival of Four Species
of Plants with 2-Inch Sludge Layers at
Various Depths

Depth of Sludge Layer Below Surface, Inches	Number of Plants							
	Crested Wheatgrass		Ranger Alfalfa		Rye Grain		Barley Grain	
	G^1	S^2	G	S	G	S	G	S
			Series 1					
	No Sludge Admixed Into Top 3 Inches of Tailing							
3	71	4	70	8	83	23	89	0
7	88	37	78	4	92	39	97	21
11	73	42	81	9	89	43	94	14
15	53	28	59	6	83	28	95	2
			Series 1A					
	15 Tons Per Acre Sewage Sludge in Top 3 Inches of Tailing							
3	90	26	36	5	74	64	See	
7	80	24	41	4	71	56	Foot-	
11	78	15	59	1	78	53	note	
15	77	56	67	19	80	60	3.	

1. Germination rate at 2 weeks after planting.
2. Survival of plants after 10 weeks' growth.
3. Tomato plants approximately 2 inches high were planted in the fourth quadrant of the barrels.

The great variability in germination for the various seeds is not readily explained. Differences between series 1 and 1A, however, can be readily compared by assessing the combined results of germination and survival for the three comparable plants in each series. This shows that, of a total of 1,200 wheatgrass, alfalfa, and rye seeds planted in series 1, 920 seeds germinated and 271 survived after 10 weeks to furnish a 77-percent overall germination and 23-percent survival of the total seeds planted. The results in series 1A show that with sludge present in the top 3 inches of tailing the germination rate was 69 percent, but that the survival rate was 32 percent of the total seeds planted. Addition of sludge to the top 3 inches of tailings thus appeared to be beneficial to overall plant survival.

For evaluation of plant-specie response and the effect of sludge-layer depths on germination and survival, the overall combined results from both test series were compared. These show that the combined germination and survival percentages for wheatgrass, alfalfa, and rye grain plant species, respectively, were 76-29, 61-7, and 81-46. The grain and wheatgrass showed major advantages over the legumes. The overall germination and survival of plants with sewage sludge layers at depths of 3, 7, 11, and 15 inches were, respectively, 71-22, 75-27, 76-27, and 70-33. These data indicate that the test with the sludge at a 3-inch depth was the poorest of the group. However, the vegetation appeared healthier in plots with the shallow sludge layers. Once the roots penetrated the sludge layer, the plants took on a much healthier appearance and were much hardier than plants with roots only in the tailings.

Comparison of series 1 and 1A plots was made at 10 weeks, after which the series 1 plots were disassembled for other tests. The 1A plots were permitted to grow until 10 months to determine the effect of longevity on the plants and especially the deep-rooted tomato plant. The plots were systematically disassembled at 10 months to evaluate the plant and root systems of all the tomatoes. Results of this examination are presented in Table No. II.

Table No. II
Plant and Root Growth of Tomatoes

Sludge Position, Inches	Weight of Plant and Recoverable Roots, Grams	Length of Plant and Main Root, Inches		
		Plant	Root	Total
3	411[1]	89[2]	19.5	108.5[2]
7	193	64.5	54.5	119
11	97	67.5	3.25[3]	70.25
15	69	50	32	82

1. Includes 70 grams pruned from plant while growing so as to keep plant in bounds of plot.
2. Does not include length of plant pruned during growing period.
3. The main root system grew only in the surface layer of sewage sludge and tailings.

Inspection of the root systems showed that practically all roots for the sludge at depths of 7, 11, and 15 inches had grown and remained in the upper 3 inches of tailings containing admixed sludge. The main root for the 11-inch buried sludge layer had grown only 3.25 inches downward and had then sent out lateral feeder roots. The main roots in the plots with sludge layers at depths of 7 and 15 inches were much longer but grew in a circular manner, again only in the presence of the organic admixture. Conversely, the main root system for the plot with sludge at 3 inches grew down into and through the sludge layer to within 2 inches of the bottom of the tailings in the barrel. Figure No. 1 depicts this plant and root growth. Table No. II clearly shows the much greater plant growth attained with the sludge layer at shallow levels.

Tomato plant system grown on tailing with sewage sludge layer at three inches.　　　Figure No. 1

Pelletization of Tailings. Preliminary tests indicated a better root environment and soil aeration was obtained by pelletizing the tailings. Pelletized material also appears well suited for use on tailings ponds slopes, because the textured surface provides natural sites for plant growth. Therefore, a test series was made using a 1.5-inch layer of pellets on top of tailings containing sludge layers buried 3 and 15 inches under the normal tailings surface.

The pellets were minus 3/8- plus 1/8-inch size and contained, in percent, 92.4 tailings, 6.6 sewage sludge, and 1 chemical binder (either Coherex or Paracol TC 1842, both resinous compounds). The pellets contained the equivalent of 10.8 tons per acre of sludge in the top 1-1/2-inch layer, somewhat less than the 15 tons per acre used in the top 3 inches of tailings as in previous tests. Approximately 1-1/4 inches of pellets were distributed over the surface of the plots, the seeds were planted, and the final 1/4 inch of pellets was used as a cover for the seeds. Seeds used on each plot included crested wheatgrass, ranger alfalfa, rye grain, and alsike clover. A 2-inch tomato plant was also transplanted into each plot. Two plots had sludge layers 4-1/2 inches under the top of the pellet layer. The other two plots were made up similarly but with the sludge layers at 16-1/2 inches under the surface. Table No. III shows the number of plants germinating per 100 seeds 2 weeks after planting and the number surviving at the end of 10 weeks for each plot.

Table No. III
Germination and Survival of Plants with Buried
Sludge Layers and Pelletized Cover, in Percent

Type of Binder	Coherex				Paracol			
Depth of Sludge Layer, Inches	4-1/2		16-1/2		4-1/2		16-1/2	
Plant	G[1]	S[2]	G	S	G	S	G	S
Crested Wheatgrass	79	75	82	70	72	66	79	69
Ranger Alfalfa...	57	49	67	42	70	55	58	38
Rye Grain..	54	43	72	48	63	43	64	49
Alsike Clover....	29	10	50	7	54	17	49	11
Tomato.....	-	1	-	1	-	1	-	1

1. Germination rate at 2 weeks after planting.
2. Survival of plants after 10 weeks' growth.

As in previous tests the germination of seeds
varied broadly and comparison of results was best
made by comparing survival of plants at the conclusion of 10 weeks. This comparison showed that
the overall germination for all three seeds in the
pelleted tailing test was 68 percent with a survival rate of 54 percent. Germination and survival
rates for the specific seeds, in percent, were
respectively, wheatgrass 78-70, alfalfa 63-46, and
rye 63-46. At the 10-week time interval, few
differences existed in the survival of plants in
the 4-1/2- and 16-1/2-inch-deep buried sludge layer
plots or between the two chemicals used to make the
pellets. However, visual inspection of the surviving plants showed markedly better plant growth
for the shallower layer and for the Coherex binder.

All plots reported on in Tables No. I through III were maintained for at least a 10-week interval, and the results are compared in Table No. IV.

Table No. IV
Comparison of Overall Germination and Survival of Plants on Buried Sludge Layer Plots, in Percent

Plant	No Sludge Added		Sludge Mixed in Top 3 Inches		Sludge Mixed Into Pellets	
	G^1	S^2	G	S	G	S
Crested Wheatgrass	71	28	81	30	78	70
Ranger Alfalfa...	72	7	51	7	63	46
Rye Grain..	87	33	76	58	63	46
Overall....	77	23	69	32	68	54

1. Germination rate at 2 weeks after planting.
2. Survival of plants after 10 weeks' growth.

The comparison clearly shows an advantage for addition of sludge to the tailings, particularly in pelletized form.

Combination of Pelletization and Buried Organic Layers. A series of tests employing a combination of buried organic layers together with pelleted surface materials were established to determine the effects upon vegetative growth and pH values of the component materials. Four plots were established using Kennecott tailings that had a pH of 7.8 when first obtained but which had decreased to a pH of 6.6 after several months' storage. Two replicate plots were established with a 2-inch sewage sludge layer placed under 15 inches of tailings capped by a 1-1/2-inch layer composed of, in percent, tailing 92.4, sludge 6.6, and chemical binder 1.0. The second two replicate plots were the same except

the 2-inch sewage sludge layer was placed under
3 inches of tailings and capped by pellets.

Each plot was planted with a tomato and crested
wheatgrass, alfalfa, and rye grain seeds. The plants
were allowed to grow for 13 months, by which time
most of the wheatgrass, alfalfa, and rye had matured
and died, and then the plots containing living
tomato plants were dismantled and examined. The
examination showed the following: (1) The root
systems of all plants were principally located in
the pelletized portion of the tailings, and (2) placing the sewage sludge layer at 3 inches prevented
to a great extent the oxidation of pyrite in the
tailings as witnessed by an average tailings pH
range of 3.9 to 6.1 and a sludge pH of 6.8 for
the 3-inch-deep layer as compared with a tailings
pH range of 1.7 to 2.0 and a sludge pH range of
3.6 to 4.0 for the sludge layer at 15-inch depth.
A comparison of Figures No. 2 and 3 shows the
difference in pH change and moisture content within
the tailings materials. Proper placement of the
sewage sludge layer to control water and gas movement appears exceptionally promising for controlling
acidification of pyrite-bearing tailings.

COMPARATIVE COSTS

Mining companies alone or in cooperation with
the Bureau of Mines have tested most of the outlined
procedures for stabilizing and reclaiming mineral
wastes with the exception of the pelletization and
buried sewage layer methods. For comparison purposes,
the stabilization costs obtained from the mining
companies have been based on a tailings accumulation
consisting of 80 and 20 percent, respectively, of
pond and dike areas and estimating that stabilization costs for sloping dike areas will be about 25
percent greater than for the flat pond areas. Costs
for the buried sludge layers and pelletization were
estimated by the Bureau of Mines after consultation
with firms having land moving, transportation, and

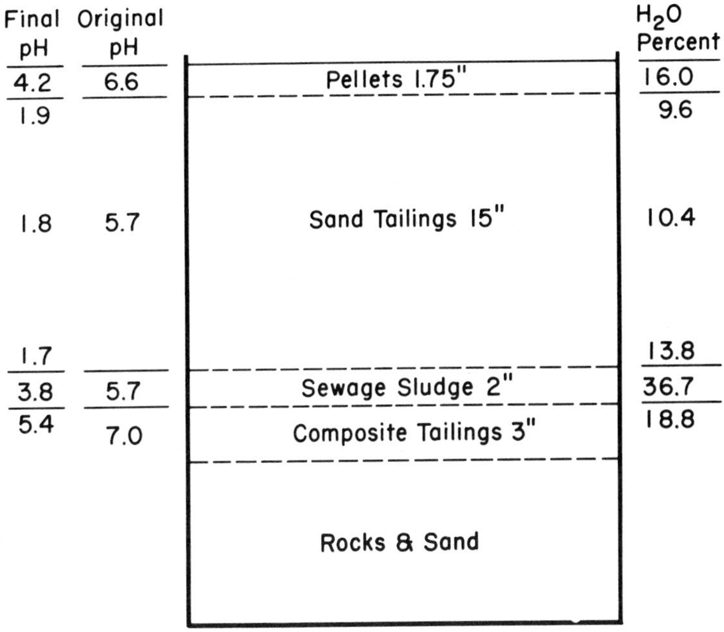

Final pH	Original pH		H_2O Percent
4.2	6.6	Pellets 1.75"	16.0
1.9			9.6
1.8	5.7	Sand Tailings 15"	10.4
1.7			13.8
3.8	5.7	Sewage Sludge 2"	36.7
5.4	7.0	Composite Tailings 3"	18.8
		Rocks & Sand	

Effect of a buried sewage sludge layer 16-3/4 inches deep on the oxidation of tailing sulfides.

Figure No. 2

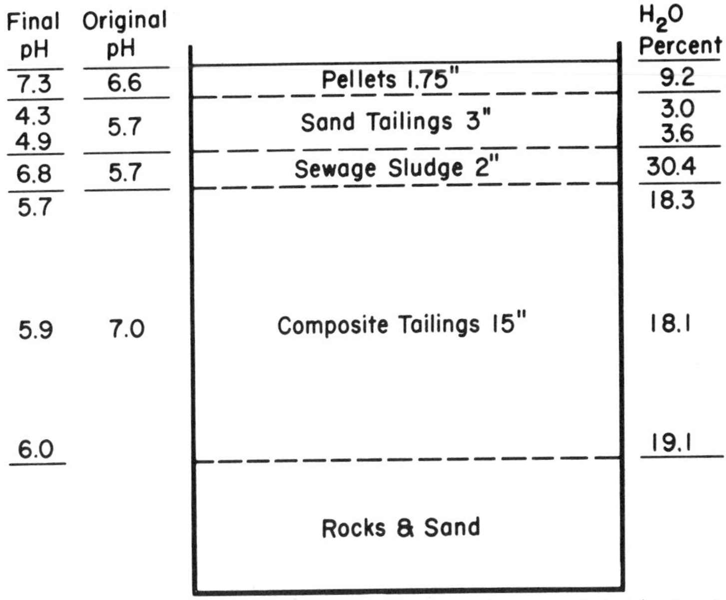

Final pH	Original pH		H_2O Percent
7.3	6.6	Pellets 1.75"	9.2
4.3	5.7	Sand Tailings 3"	3.0
4.9			3.6
6.8	5.7	Sewage Sludge 2"	30.4
5.7			18.3
5.9	7.0	Composite Tailings 15"	18.1
6.0			19.1
		Rocks & Sand	

Effect of a buried sewage sludge layer 4-3/4 inches deep on the oxidation of tailing sulfides.

Figure No. 3

pelletizing capabilities. The following figures
were basic to the Bureau evaluations: cost of
sludge $1 per ton; hauling of sludge $0.42 per
cubic yard, based on a 7-mile haul; amount of
sludge per acre 130 tons for buried layers and
11 tons for pellets; and a cost of seeds, fertilizer, and planting of $50 per acre. Calculations
on laying of the buried sludge were made using
(1) an agriculturally developed method using a
broad flat plow for lifting the soil and a device
for spreading a layer of buried material under the
long plow, and then allowing the lifted soil to
drop back and bury the layered material, and (2) use
of a conventional wheel scraper and spreader method.
The mixture for pelletizing consisted of, in percent,
92.4 tailing, 6.6 sludge, and 1.0 chemical binder.
Pelletizing was calculated as being done in place
on the tailings using a recently designed high-speed
light compaction roll pelletizer which can produce
pellets at an estimated cost of $0.80 per ton. All
sewage layer costs were based on application to flat
pond areas only. These costs, although broadly
generalized, provide comparison for the different
methods and are presented in Table No. V.

Table No. V
Cost Comparison of Stabilization Methods[1]

Type of Stabilization	Effectiveness	Maintenance	Approximate Cost per Acre, Dollars
Physical			
Water Sprinkling	Fair	Continual	-
Slag (9-Inch Depth)			
By Pumping....	Good	Moderate	$350- 450
By Trucking...	do.	do.	950-1,050
Straw Harrowing.	Fair	do.	40- 75
Bark Covering...	Good	do.	900-1,000
Country Gravel and Soil			
4-Inch Depth..	Excellent	Minimal	250- 600
12-Inch Depth..	do.	do.	700-1,700
Chemical			
Elastomeric Polymer........	Good	Moderate	300- 750
Lignosulfonate..	do.	do.	250- 600
Vegetative			
4-Inch Soil Cover and Vegetation[2].	Excellent	Minimal	300- 650
12-Inch Cover and Vegetation......	do.	do.	750-1,750
Hydroseeding.....	do.	do.	200- 450
Matting[3].........	do.	do.	600- 750
Chemical-Vegetative	do.	do.	100- 250
Buried Sludge Layers	do.	do.	405- 810
Pellet Cover (1-1/2 Inches)............	do.	do.	330- 660
Combined Buried Sludge Plus Pellet Cover..	do.	do.	735-1,470

Table No. V Continued - Footnotes

1. Based on average tailings. Costs should be revised upwards for acidic tailings requiring limestone or other neutralizing additives.
2. Generally used on pond area rather than on dikes. Also, not as effective as 12-inch soil cover when tailings are excessively acidic or saline.
3. Based on placing 3-foot-wide matting at 3-foot intervals over the seeded area.

These data indicated that several methods are available for stabilizing mill tailings at costs of less than $400 per acre. The chemical-vegetative procedure appears to be the most economical procedure for establishing vegetation on tailings and wherever applicable should be a preferred method. Where prevention of blowing sands is the major problem in achieving stabilization, both the chemical-vegetative and hydroseeding methods appear to be economically preferable to the matting or soil-covering procedures. The buried sludge layer and pelletized cover methods are still unproven in the field, and the actual costs incurred from application of these procedures to differing sites may range to double the lower calculated figure. However, if the calculated cost range of $735 to $1,470 per acre is approximately correct for the combined buried sludge and pelleted surface method, this procedure is comparable on a cost basis to that using a 12-inch soil cover and vegetation, and tests should be made to evaluate the relative effectiveness of both procedures for obtaining vegetation on adverse sites. If the use of pellets is not mandatory to achieve satisfactory vegetative stabilization, the cost would be for application of buried sludge layers and vegetation only, and the method would be competitive.

REFERENCE

1. Gates, David M., "Radiant Energy, Its Reception and Disposal," Meteorological Monograph 28, v. 6, 1965, pp. 1-26.

DISCUSSION

T. H. PETERS (International Nickel Company of Canada Limited): I'd like to address this question to Karl Dean. From looking at the slides and being in a similar position to Mr. Dean, that is in coming along afterwards and trying to straighten these things up, what would be his recommendations for outside slopes, what angle? And may I also have your comments on finishing off a tailing area, as you abandon it, with a coarser grade of material?

KARL C. DEAN: Tom is an acknowledged expert in this field himself. I think this is a logical way to do it. You must have pre-planning for finishing off any of these tailings ponds, I think. As far as the outer slopes, the one that we would prefer right at the present time, even though it is a little more expensive, is the matting procedure. If you have some kind of organic material that you can put on before you do your seeding of these outer slopes and then use the matting, we think this would be the preferred procedure, because it has worked, as I mentioned, on slopes up to 39°. Most highway cut men wouldn't want a slope one half that steep.

As far as coarsening up your grind, I think this would be perfect. This is the reason that we use the pelletization procedure, because it does give some structure to the tailings and allows far more rapid germination and growth than if one just had loose sands. So what we would visualize on some of these areas that may contain pyrite which may be acidic over a period of time would be, if you could do it: just before you close down the operation, put some kind of an organic in there - whether it be a municipal refuse composte or sewage sludge -- then put coarse ground tailing on top of it, and I think you are right that this would be the better way to approach it.

W. A. WAHLER (W. A. Wahler & Associates): There is quite a little difference, obviously, in the cost of vegetating slopes vs. the vegetation of the top. Could you give us some sort of a rough ratio figure or something along that line? When we think of the slopes, of course, we're generally thinking of a relatively smaller area, even though at higher cost and so, if we could have some sort of indication, it would be helpful.

KARL DEAN: The figure that we used in our calculations was a 25 percent greater cost, overall. And this came not only from consultation with some of the mining companies that have been doing this type of thing, but also with the highway department. They have developed a system that may be used if you can drive along the berm proper. They have a sheepsfoot roller, which can be hung over the side, that will compact the area and give a better germination than by just broadcasting seed wi a cyclone or something similar. But some people have found, if their slope is not too steep, that all they need to do is scarify the surface in some manner and make a broadcasting of seed over this type of an area, and they do it much cheaper. So the 25 percent tends to be a median figure of these two approaches.

QUESTION: Mr. Dean, what is a minimum cost per acre you could expect for vegetation fertilizing on the flat surface of the tailing area?

KARL DEAN: As I noted, our cheapest cost was about $100.00 per acre and this was for the combination chemical-vegetative. But if you were going to use strictly vegetation it should be some-where near $50.00 an acre, just about half of what it is for the chemical-vegetative. I'd like to differentiate, if I may, between chemical-vegetative purposes and strictly chemical purposes. When we go for strictly chemical stabilization, we want a hard crust, firmly resistant to both wind and water; whereas, when we go to chemical-vegetative, we want just a minimum amount of chemical that will help hold the water in and help hold the dust down, yet speed up germination.

QUESTION: Most of the emphasis here has been on vegetative cover. I think the question was asked about the possibility of the use of mine waste other than tailings in a manner similar to riprap for a dam. What would be the various opinions of the speakers here on that alternative — either from the cost standpoint or from the environmental aesthetics?

KARL DEAN: I covered to some extent in my talk the fact that they've used granulated slag for this - but you are talking about the slope. I see no reason why your mine overburdened material can't be used quite readily. For instance, Kennecott Copper Corporation in Utah makes their berms out of mine refuse and they have planted this to trees. I haven't seen any evidences of grasses in this particular area, but the trees seem to be doing quite well. There are several other operations around the country that don't use the tailing for their berm construction, but use some of the mine overburden for this - and, I think, with no objectionable problems. In the main this material should be lower in the heavy metal salts that tend to kill off the vegetation and it should give you some better structure than the loose sands.

QUESTION: In certain delta areas where there are levees, governmental agencies have been removing some of the trees which, it has been stated, can lead to seepage of river water into the area below the river. Mr. Dean mentioned that, at one large tailing pond, trees have been planted. I wonder if he could mention if there is a problem of reconciliation here?

    KARL DEAN: That's a good question. I really don't know. As far as I know, any vegetation, and especially trees, put on the dike area of a pond would tend to lessen the amount of seepage simply by being transpirees themselves and absorbing water from the tailing pond itself and evaporating it. Did you say that by removal of the trees they got more seepage?

    QUESTIONER: Well they removed the trees because the trees were a hazard.

    KARL DEAN: In what way? I can't visualize this, unless you mean that trees put out many roots and when they die these roots may become a seepage tube. This could be possible, I suppose, but other than that I would think that, as with most vegetation, the trees would help dewater the face of the dam, to some extent. Anyone want to contradict?

DESIGN, CONSTRUCTION AND OPERATION OF THE TAILINGS PIPELINES AND UNDERWATER TAILINGS DISPOSAL SYSTEM OF ATLAS CONSOLIDATED MINING AND DEVELOPMENT CORPORATION IN THE PHILIPPINES

by

ROGELIO C. SALAZAR
General Superintendent - Metallurgical Services

and

REYNALDO I. GONZALES
Engineering Division Manager

ATLAS CONSOLIDATED MINING AND
DEVELOPMENT CORPORATION
Toledo City, Cebu, Philippines

ATLAS CONSOLIDATED MINING AND DEVELOPMENT CORPORATION is located in Bo. Don Andres Soriano, Toledo City, in the central part of Cebu island, in the Philippines. It is about 10 miles by road but actually less than 4 miles distant by air from the seashore off Tañon Strait. Tañon Strait is a relatively narrow (approximately 16 miles wide) and very deep (over 200 fathoms about one mile from the shore) channel between the islands of Cebu and Negros.

The company operates two concentrators built near its two major copper deposits, Lutopan and Biga, which are about 6 miles apart by road but less than 3 miles distant as the crow flies. The Lutopan concentrator is situated on a hillside at an elevation of approximately 600 feet above sea level. The Biga concentrator site is on an 800-foot elevation. Present combine milling rate of both plants averages 70,000 tons per day.

The original concentrator at Lutopan (re-named Don Andres Soriano in 1967) has been expanded several times over the years since its initial operations in March 1955, and presently treats 37,000 tons ore per day on the average. Peak daily milling tonnage exceeds 40,000 tons on favorable days. Prior to 1970, the plant tailings, which totalled 75.3 million tons since 1955, were discharged into an adjacent industrial river (Ilag River).

Ilag River is a small (about 120 feet wide), meandering river with fairly steep (as much as 45-degree slope) banks, and seasonal stream flow which ranges from a low 200 gallons per minute in the dry summer months to more than 3,000 gallons per minute during the rainy season. The river flow exceeds this rate several times fold during typhoons. From Abaca until the Tinahas – Bawod boundary, approximately 8,000 feet downstream, the river bed follows a natural slope of 2 per cent and then drops abruptly at a 12 per cent grade at this boundary point. As expected, the river area from Abaca to this point shows no marked signs of accumulated tailings.

The river widens to about 450 feet, approximately 3,000 feet farther downstream. Another 3,000 feet farther Sigpit River joins Ilag, and the river bed at this junction becomes 600 feet wide. At the Magdugo flats, which is 5,000 feet farther downstream, the river bed reaches 1,500 feet width and the river assumes a much lower grade of 0.3 per cent, which is generally maintained up to the river mouth at Talavera Bay on Tañon Strait. Considerable accumulation of tailings sand in this area results and the silting up of the Sapang Daku River valley, which covers more than 300 hectares in land area, caused damage to farms along both sides of the river, adversely affecting in no small degree the social conditions in such a densely populated area like most places in the province of Cebu. It is estimated that about 10 million tons of tailings still remain on the river bed from Abaca to Talavera Bay, a total river length of 39,000 feet.

Another problem is the silting of the bay at the mouth of the river, which is near the Atlas piers from which the company's concentrates are loaded and shipped, and where most mine supplies are received. This situation still necessitates considerable continuous dredging to keep the harbor deep enough for the ocean-going and inter-island vessels which dock with frequent regularity.

The new Biga concentrator, which started operation in the second quarter of 1971, treats approximately 33,000 tons ore per day and currently produces about 400 tons of copper concentrates per day, and eventually about 200 tons magnetite and 300 tons pyrite daily. The plant is located on the upstream side of the river which feeds the water storage dams at Malubog (approximately 3 miles away) and Sigpit (2 miles farther) which are the main sources of water for the plants and mine camp. Tailings disposal through the river, therefore, is out of the question.

Tailings ponds built in the surrounding areas are limited in capacity due to the topography of the area and the threat of yearly typhoons (Cebu island is within the Philippine typhoon belt) and torrential rains which preclude the possibility of constructing larger ponds. The present ponds at Bigacon can keep the concentrator in operation for only a few months. There are no possible sites for tailings ponds near the DAS concentrator. With the present ore reserves of over 700 million tons, which is expected to reach 1.0 billion tons eventually and which will take more than 30 years of mining, tailings disposal ponds are beyond consideration.

In early 1969 when the expansion of Dascon and construction of Bigacon were still in the planning stage, a comprehensive study on the most appropriate tailings disposal system was undertaken. The Parsons Jurden Corporation of New York was retained as consultant to advise and assist the company's engineering and metallurgical staff in the design work for this project.

Mr. Ralph Costantini, Senior Engineer of Parsons-Jurden, came to the Philippines to assess the feasibility of a pipeline system to carry the tailings to the sea. The consultant's recommendations covering preliminary design parameters, pipe sizing, permissible slopes and hydraulic gradient as well as comparisons of alternate pipe combinations, became the basis for the final design and detailing of the system by Atlas.

Construction of a system of four pipelines transporting thickened tailings from both concentrators to the sea by gravity was started in November 1969. The first line (a 20-inch pipeline for Dascon) was complete

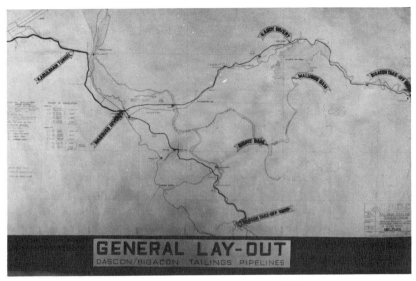

General layout of Dascon/Bigacon tailings pipelines.
Figure No. 1

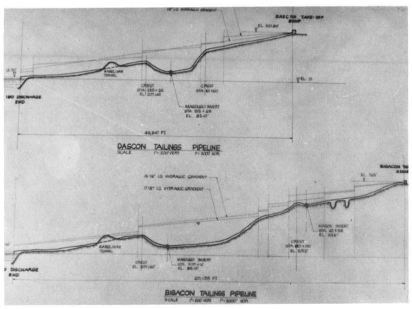

Profiles of Dascon/Bigacon tailings pipelines.
Figure No. 2

and put into operation in April 23, 1971, the second in August 11, 1971, the third in September 14, 1971, and the fourth line in November 14, 1971.

The DAS concentrator system consists of one 20-inch and one 12-inch diameter pipelines, installed in parallel on common supports from Abaca to the discharge point at Ibo, on Tañon Strait, approximately 44,000 feet away. The pipelines have an average slope of 1.06 per cent and handle a total of 35,000 tons per day of thickened tailings at a pulp velocity controlled between 6.5 to 7.0 feet per second. The Biga concentrator pipelines, one 18-inch and one 16-inch in diameter, are likewise installed in parallel on common supports, and carry tailings from a common sump near the thickeners at an average slope of 1.20 per cent. The pipes are approximately 60,000 feet long and operate at about 6.3 to 6.5 feet per second velocity to carry 32,500 tons per day of tailings.

The four pipelines meet at the invert at the Magdug flats, where a sampling sump and two drainlines to the Sapang Daku River had been constructed. The line then follow a common route up to the crest, through a 2,800-foot tunnel cut across the mountain at Kabulihan, and on to a 1,600-foot causeway and pipe pier at Ibo.

The discharge point is located at Ibo Point, approximately one mile southwest of the Atlas port at Sañgi and the mouth of Sapang Daku River. Ibo Point was specifically selected because of the existence of a trench with minus 15 per cent slope. It was anticipated that most of the tailings discharged at this point would continue to flow outwards along the sea bottom into the deeper regions of the Tañon Strait.

It was also expected that the fine solid particles would be carried away by the ocean current, which during most of the year is in the southeasterly direction, away from the company's piers.

At the time of the writing of this report, about 26 million tons of plant tailings had been disposed to the sea bottom through this system. The latest hydrographic survey, which are conducted every 3 months, show that the tailings deposition at the sea bottom has stabilized at 40 feet below sea level in the area immediately below the drop pipes and an equilibrium slope of minus 20 per cent has been established. No further build up of the settled material occurs.

DESIGN AND DESCRIPTION OF THE SYSTEM

Hydraulic Considerations

On the basis of comparable data on tailings pipelines employed in other mines treating similar ores, notably the Kennecott Copper Mine in Chuquicamata, Chile, it was confidently projected that the Atlas plant tailings could be successfully transported by pipeline at a pulp density of 45 to 50 per cent solids by weight, with a hydraulic gradient of about 0.80 per cent.

The Dascon lines have an available gradient of 1.16 per cent while Bigacon has a much higher available gradient of 1.23 per cent. In view of this high head availability, it was felt that the determination of rheology of the material was not necessary and the problem would be one of dissipating the excess head.

The typical screen analysis of the Atlas tailings

from its two concentrators are as follows:

MESH SIZE (TYLER SERIES)	AVERAGE PERCENT RETAINED	
	DASCON TAILINGS	BIGACON TAILINGS
⊬48	11.2	13.0
⊬65	18.5	22.6
⊬100	26.4	33.2
⊬200	43.1	50.6
⊬325	49.9	58.9
−325	100.0	100.0

Specific gravity of solids is 2.65 and pH of the pulp is in the 7.6 to 7.8 range. At the most probable transport pulp density of 48 per cent solids by weight, the free settling rate was determined by standard sedimentation tests carried out at the metallurgical laboratory to be about 0.24 feet per hour.

A 3,900-foot test section of the 20-inch diameter tailings line for Dascon was installed at Abaca, and tests were conducted to observe flow characteristics at various effective hydraulic gradients and different pulp densities. Tailings underflow from the Dascon thickeners were collected in a common sump which fed the test pipeline. At the end of the line, a screw-type plunger was fitted to facilitate closing of the pipe discharge opening at desired settings, which in effect reduced the hydraulic gradient. The pulp velocity was measured by using 3-inch diameter wooden balls which were released at the pipe inlet and the time of travel to the pipe discharge determined. The speed of travel of the ball, equivalent to the pulp velocity through the pipe, was then calculated from the ratio of pipe length to travel time.

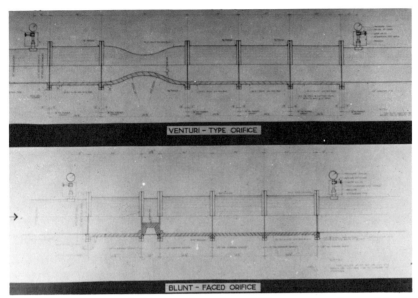

Venturi-type and blunt-faced orifices are installed along the pipeline to handle the balance of head dissipation.   Figure No. 3

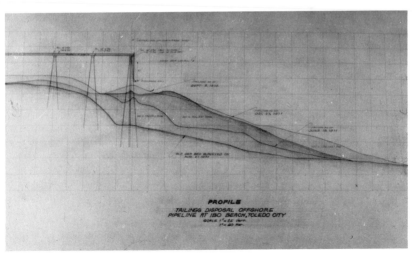

Profile of tailing disposal offshore pipeline at Ibo Beach, Toledo City.   Figure No. 4

485

The test runs were each started with the plunger at zero position so that the discharge end of the pipeline was fully open and the effective hydraulic gradient approximates the actual slope of the pipeline (except for discharge velocity head correction) which was minus 1.14 per cent. The pulp was allowed to flow continuously for sometime before the test balls were introduced.

These tests showed that at pulp densities above 46 per cent solids, no sanding of the line occurs with pulp velocities above 5.3 feet per second. A certain amount of particle-size segregation was observed in the pipeline, which became pronounced at a density of 42 per cent solids or lower, with the coarse fraction of the tailings tending toward the bottom section of the pipe.

Thus, it was projected that the Atlas thickened tailings could be transported by pipeline at a velocity as low as 6.0 feet per second with an ample factor of safety.

Handling of Raw Plant Tailings

In order to avoid settling and possible sanding of the lines, thickening of the raw plant tailings becomes a pre-requisite to tailings disposal by gravity pipeline to the sea. Heretofore adopted in the final steps of the ore treating process primarily as a water reclamation measure, the tailings thickeners now play a dual purpose in the Atlas concentrator operations.

For the DAS concentrator, three 250-foot thickeners were constructed at a suitable site at Abaca, about 7,000 feet downstream from the mill plant, in order to handle the additional tonnage of tailings at the expanded milling capacity. The two original 250-foot thickeners located adjacent to the mill plant can handle a maximum of 15,000 tons per day of tailings, which consist only 40 per cent of the total Dascon tonnage.

Sixty per cent of the plant tailings, or approximately 21,000 tons per day, is piped to Abaca and fed to the three thickeners at a pulp density of 32 to 35 per cent solids. To carry this quantity of raw unthickened plant tailings, a 7,000-foot, 20-inch diameter pipeline, supported by short trestles along the Ilag River bank, was initially constructed and completed in March 1970. Subsequently, a 14-inch diameter line was added and put to operation on June 24, 1971.

The three thickeners have a top elevation of 538 feet above sea level, which is about 75 feet lower than the corresponding elevation on the two thickeners near Dascon. Thus, a gradient of approximately 1.0 per cent was available for gravity flow through the pipelines.

The 20-inch and 14-inch lines have a combined maximum designed capacity of 8,500 gallons per minute, equivalent to 22,400 tons per day of tailings, and thus satisfactorily handle the flow of unthickened tailings to the downstream thickeners at partially-full condition. Actual pulp velocity determinations on these pipelines show an average 7.2 feet per second velocity.

To bring the thickened tailings from the spigots of the two thickeners at Dascon, a 16-inch diameter pipeline was laid out at 1.0 per cent gradient along the Ilag River bank. This line has a maximum designe capacity of 4,000 gallons per minute, equivalent to a flow of about 15,000 tons per day at a pulp density of 45 per cent solids. The line actually flows partially-full at an average pulp velocity of 6.8 feet per second

Thus, all Dascon plant tailings, thickened to a pulp density of 45 to 50 per cent solids, are combined into a common sump at the 510-foot spigot level of the Abaca thickeners. This sump serves as the take-off point for the 43,850-foot, 20-inch and 12-inch dia-meter, gravity pipelines to the sea.

The Biga concentrator tailings are equally distri-buted among four 250-foot thickeners constructed near the plant. Spigot products at a pulp density of 45 to 50 per cent solids are collected in a common sump at Elevation 760 feet, which serves as take-off point for the 60,199-foot, 18-inch and 16-inch dia-meter, pipelines to the sea.

Pipe Route and Slopes

The main consideration in pipe routing is the pre-vention of siphonic action. The pipeline has to be below the hydraulic gradient at every point in the en-tire length. Other considerations are: (1) maximum pipe slope to be minus 15 per cent, (2) minimum ra-dius of curvature should be 150 feet with chord lengths designed to give a maximum deflection angle of 5 de-grees, and (3) negotiations with land owners on rights of way. An invert at the Magdugo flats, common to the route of all four pipelines, was deemed necessary to avoid extremely high towers. For the Bigacon lines another invert at Kasoy was included in lieu of a "cut-and-cover" tunnel which would be more expensive to

Air view shows inaccessibility of site. Figure No. 5

One of the hinged arch trusses used in pipeline
construction.   Figure No. 6

construct. Thru-cuts at Tinahas, Bawod and Kabulihan areas were opted to avoid sharp curves and un-
cooperative land owners. Also, the Malubog pondage
area necessitated high towered bridges for the Bigacon
lines.

The Dascon take-off sump at Abaca has an overflow weir at Elevation 511 feet, which lead to a bypass box with an open launder installed with a minus
2 per cent slope to the Ilag River. The pipes are tappe
at Elevation 500 feet. A 750,000-gallon capacity water tank was installed to supply flushing water during
shutdown of the pipelines and dilution water during
periods of low tonnage rate to ensure full flow in the
lines.

The pipelines start with a minus 1.15 per cent slope
and generally maintain that slope up to Station 161 ∤
60 at Bawod, where they start to increase to a maximum of minus 15 per cent and taper down again to
minus 1.15 per cent at Station 186 ∤ 60 in Magdugo.

The topography at the route does not permit a gradual downward slope in the entire length of the lines
owing to high tower requirements through the Magdugo
flatlands. An invert at Station 215 ∤ 65 at Magdugo
was therefore installed, with two drain lines to Sapang
Daku River.

At the crest of the lines at Station 255 ∤ 25 after the
Magdugo invert, a 2-inch air bleeder was installed in
each line to release entrapped air during start-up of
the line and periodically during normal operation.
From the crest, the lines continue at minus 1 per cent
grade, entering the Kabulihan tunnel at Station 299 ∤
55 where the slope flattens to minus 0.5 per cent up
to the exit portal at Station 327 ∤ 65 in Luray where
the lines continue on at minus 0.6 to minus 0.8 per

cent grade to the Ibo discharge point.

The designed capacity of the two Dascon lines is 8,300 gallons per minute at a velocity of 6.0 feet per second, which at 48 per cent solids corresponds to a milling rate of 36,400 tons daily. The operating velocity range is controlled by in-line orifices installed along the line and, for flexibility in operation, spigot orifices at the Ibo disposal point are changed to suit desired flow rate.

Similarly, the Bigacon lines commence from a common sump where thickened tailings from the four 250-foot thickeners are combined. The two pipelines, one 16-inch and one 18-inch diameter, are tapped to the sump at Elevation 760 feet. Emergency flushing water comes from the mill water pumping station about one mile downstream of the thickeners. During periods of slightly low milling tonnages, thickener underflow spigots are controlled to lower density settings to ensure sufficient volume of pulp for full pipe flow.

The slope of the lines which are installed adjacent to each other on common supports, starts with minus 1.20 per cent and generally maintains this slope up to the first invert in Kasoy at Station 161 ∤ 60, where the pipes then ascend at 1.5 per cent to crest at Elevation 552 feet at Station 180 ∤ 00. From the crest, they slope to Station 300 ∤ 00 at Kawayan at minus 5 per cent to minus 10 per cent, from where they generally maintain a minus 1.0 to 1.5 per cent slope until they reach Sapang Daku River, where they assume a slope of minus 0.6 to minus 0.8 per cent until they meet the Dascon line route at the Magdugo invert. From this invert, the Bigacon lines follow the same route and share common supports with the Dascon lines.

The designed capacity of the two Bigacon lines is 8,700 gallons per minute at 6.5 feet per second velocity; at 48 per cent solids, this corresponds to a milling rate of 38,000 tons per day.

In-Line Orifices

As mentioned earlier, for both concentrators, the available head is much more than needed to dispose of the plant tailings at the present milling rates. Fo flexibility, each line has at least one standby drop pipe to allow spigot changes at the Ibo discharge point when the milling rate decreases due to operational needs, such as when relining ball mills. Thus, 20-inch line has four 10-inch drop pipes and the 12-inch line has two 10-inch drop pipes for the Dascon system. The 16-inch line has two 12-inch drop pipes while the 18-inch line has four 10-inch drop pipes for the Bigacon lines. A sufficient number of spigots ranging in size from 2-inch to 7-inch diameter is kept available for the operator at Ibo.

To handle the balance of head dissipation, permanent in-line orifices are installed along the pipeline at pre-determined points. For this purpose, both blunt-faced and venturi-type orifices have been designed and are now installed in the lines.

Thus, the 20-inch Dascon line has four orifices installed in the line, as follows: one 7-inch blunt-faced orifice each at Station 136 ⫽ 50 in Bawod, Station 256 ⫽ 20 in Kabulihan and Station 419 ⫽ 20 in Ibo, and one 10-inch venturi-type orifice at Station 161 ⫽ 00 near Bawod. The 12-inch Dascon line has one 5-inch venturi-type orifice each at Station 161 ⫽ 00 in Bawod and Station 256 ⫽ 20 in Kabulihan.

Four-legged steel towers and bridge trusses support
pipeline on crossings.   Figure No. 7

Sharp turns are encountered along the pipeline route.
                                        Figure No. 8

The Bigacon lines require more in-line orifices to attain the desired low pulp velocities. The 18-inch line has a total of six orifices, as follows: one 6.5-inch blunt-faced orifice each at Station 188 ≠ 00 in Kasoy and Station 332 ≠ 74 in Kawayan, one 7-inch blunt-faced orifice each at Station 236 ≠ 08 in Malubog and Station 429 ≠ 11 in Kabulihan, and one 9.5-inch venturi-type orifice each at Station 83 ≠ 02 in Balansag and Station 220 ≠ 00 in Kasoy. The 16-inch line has one 5.5-inch blunt-faced orifice each at Station 131 ≠ 36 in Abayan, Station 188 ≠ 00 in Kasoy and Station 429 ≠ 11 in Kabulihan, two 5.5-inch blunt-faced orifices at Station 236 ≠ 08 in Malubog, and one 7.5-inch venturi-type orifice each at Station 83 ≠ 02 in Balansag and Station 220 ≠ 00 in Kasoy.

The blunt-faced orifice causes higher head losses (about 16 to 28 pounds per square inch pressure drop depending on the ratio of orifice diameter to pipe diameter) but the wear rate at the immediate discharge end extending up to 12 feet of pipe length was excessive. The venturi-type orifice has lower head losses (about 3 to 6 pounds per square inch only) but the wear rate is uniform and of much lesser magnitude. To minimize the wear problem, orifices are cast in high chrome iron alloy (15-2-1) with the following metal composition:

Carbon	- 2.8 to 3.2	per cent
Manganese	- 0.52 to 0.80	" "
Silicon	- 0.60 to 0.70	" "
Chromium	- 14.0 to 16.0	" "
Molybdenum	- 1.9 to 2.2	" "
Copper	- 0.9 to 1.1	" "
Sulfur	- 0.05 per cent maximum	
Phosphorous	- 0.05 " "	"

and heat treated to a hardness of 700 Brinell Hardness Number for maximum wear resistance. The section of the pipeline at the discharge end of blunt-faced orifices are replaced with 1-inch thick cast pipe nipples of the same alloy. These special alloy castings are made in ACMDC's foundry shops at less than half the cost of equivalent ceramic moldings.

Air entrapment is also experienced in orifice installations, especially in steep downgrade slopes. Proper fitting of rubber gaskets at bolted flanged joints therefore becomes an important precaution.

Ibo Disposal Point

The disposal point is located 1,600 feet from the beach where the sea bottom at 100-foot draft has an average slope of minus 15 per cent. Drop pipes with 90 degree bend nozzles extend 30 feet below mean low sea water level.

Periodic hydrographic surveys show that the deposition of tailings in the immediate vicinity of the drop point has stabilized at 40 feet below sea level and the equilibrium slope of settled material is determined to be approximately minus 20 per cent. At this gradient, density current appears able to maintain flow towards the deeper shelf which is over 200 fathoms deep about one mile from shore. It is observed that the tailings deposition vanishes at about 800 feet from the discharge point where tidal action and/or littoral currents across the Tañon Strait tend to dissipate it farther away.

Deposition occurring at the back of the discharge point has stabilized at a very flat gradient and there is no evidence of tailings surfacing along the beaches.

Pipe Specifications

All pipes originally specified for use in the system are electric resistance welded (ERW), conform to ASTM A-53 Grade B specifications and have 0.25-inch wall thickness. This pipe has a metal composition similar to mild steel, with a maximum limit on phosphorus content set at 0.045 per cent, tensile strength of 60,000 pounds per square inch, yield point of 35,000 pounds per square inch and hardness of 170 Brinell Hardness Number.

The pipe joints are butt-welded. Dresser couplings are used for long, straight runs to take care of any thermal expansion of the pipe. The pipelines are supported at maximum spans of 40 feet.

CONSTRUCTION WORK

The construction of the pipelines is premised on minimal on-site work and more emphasis placed on pre-casting and pre-fabrication work. The inaccessibility of the route from the existing roads and difficulty in procuring land for access purposes dictated this approach.

Pipes are supported generally at 40-foot spacing. The on-grade supports are pre-cast concrete saddles with cast-in-place spread footings. Low towers (up to 12 feet high) are pre-fabricated steel towers and, depending on the load requirement, are single pylon, two-legged trestles, or three-legged space frames. Tie-rod catenaries with 100-foot to 160-foot spans are adopted to save on tower and foundation costs, espe-

Discharge point, showing causeway with working platform in foreground.   Figure No. 9

Tailings lines reach strait at Ibo Point.
Figure No. 10

cially on portions where continuous long spans are feasible.

On extremely high towers (over 45 feet) where horizontal loads from wind and earthquakes play a significant factor, four-legged steel towers and bridge trusses with spans up to 200 feet are employed.

At the main river crossing at Kawayan, for the Bigacon lines, where flash floods are frequent, the thru-bridge trusses rest on concrete-filled pipe piles. At the Balansag area where the river makes a sharp 90-degree turn and the pipelines cross the river twice in a relatively short stretch, three hinged arch trusses were adopted to take advantage of the competent rock foundation, resulting in substantial savings in superstructure cost.

At the Ibo discharge point, a heavy fill-material causeway was built over coral reef formation with grouted rip-rap slopes and a 6-inch concrete slab topping as wave protection during stormy weather. Beyond the coral reef, concrete-filled pipe pile clusters were driven with an internal drop hammer, topped with reinforced concrete caps to serve as piers at 120-foot spacing. The tailings pipelines are utilized as top and bottom chords, and web and lateral members are added to form the trusses that span the piers up to the disposal point where a platform supports the headers, spigots, drop pipes and a roofed maintenance floor.

The main problem encountered during the construction phase was the hauling of materials and supplies to the inaccessible portions of the pipe route. Carabao (water buffalo) sleds and, where possible, Caterpillar D-4 tractors were used. The finished portions of the pipeline were also utilized as trolley ways for transporting pipes and supplies.

Part of the field construction work for the system was undertaken by several private contractors from Manila and Cebu. These construction firms include the Erectors, P. J. Kiener and Empire Construction who were each assigned specific portions of the pipelines and pier construction. Atlas' Underground Mine Department undertook the driving and concrete lining of the 2,800-foot tunnel at Kabulihan. Supply of materials and construction supplies, and the coordination and over-all supervision of the project, however, was handled by ACMDC's own Construction Department.

OPERATION OF THE SYSTEM

Since start-up upon completion of construction work, the four pipelines have transported and disposed of to the sea a total of 25.8 million tons of plant tailings to date. Following are current operational data:

DASCON LINES

	20-inch	12-inch
Date commissioned	April 23, 1971	Nov. 14, 1971
Number of in-line orifices installed	4	2
Number of discharge spigots open	4	1
Discharge header pressure, pounds per square inch	17.2	atmospheric

Average pulp density,
    per cent solids   46.5   46.0

Average pulp velocity,
    feet per second   6.46   7.03

Tonnage handled to-date,
    million tons   11.7   2.7

BIGACON LINES

	18-inch	16-inch
Date commissioned	Aug. 11, 1971	Sept. 14, 1971
Number of in-line orifices installed	6	6
Number of discharge spigots open	4	2
Discharge header pressure, pounds per square inch	43	25
Average pulp density, per cent solids	45	46
Average pulp velocity, feet per second	6.7	6.3
Tonnage handles to-date, million tons	7.2	4.2

Organization

The operation and maintenance of tailings disposal system is part of the functions of the concentrator organization. The section placed in charge of the system is headed by a foreman and is composed of a maintenance supervisor, two mechanics, two men who patrol the pipelines daily, two operators each shift at Ibo, and one operator each shift at each take-off point in Dascon and Bigacon.

Communication between the men on operational matters is effected through Motorola radio transceiver units which are in operation on 24-hour basis. The set-up employs radio units at Dascon, Bigacon, Ibo Point, and on the mobile truck assigned to the maintenance crew. These radio units are hooked up on the same frequency as the mines' radio communication network, which consists of three base stations and more than 30 mobile units installed on cars, service vehicles and trucks, and covers the entire area of Atlas operations in Cebu.

Operating Procedures

The pipelines are normally started up with the inverts filled with water. For the Dascon lines, the pre-start-up checklist of procedures therefore include the drain valves at the bottom point of the invert at Magdugo kept fully closed and the water level at the flushing water tank at Abaca kept full. Then the water from the flushing tank is introduced by gravity flow into the take-off sump to fill the pipelines. A man at Ibo calls the Abaca operator on his radio communication unit to signal cutting off of the flushing water flow as soon as the water starts to come at the discharge point. Then the tailings thickener underflow streams are directed to the take-off sump and feeding of tailings to the pipeline commences.

Two air bleeders are installed at high points in the line: one at Bawod area and another at Kabulihan at the crest of the line after the invert. A man in each station keeps the air bleeder open until the tailings spurt out to indicate that the line is full up to that point. After closing the air bleeder, he leaves the post unmanned during the normal operation of the line.

A similar procedure at start-up is followed at the Bigacon lines. However, instead of gravity flow of water from a storage tank, flushing water for these lines come from a water pumping station located about one mile downstream of the thickener area.

Only two men per shift actually man the two lines of each concentrator during normal operation: one man at the take-off sump, who also attends to the thickeners, and another man who stays at Ibo Point. The tailings level in the take-off sump is maintained between 8 to 10 feet high, to ensure full flow in the pipelines. Pressure at the Ibo discharge header is maintained at the specified level by installing the proper size of spigots at each of the discharge drop pipes.

Samples of tailings flowing through each pipe are taken every hour at the discharge point, and determination of pulp density and wet screen analysis are conducted. These operational data are promptly relayed by radio to the tailings disposal and mill foremen on duty. These are compared with corresponding data on hourly samples taken at the take-off point to serve as an indication of any sanding which may have started in the line, or of a possible break or leak in the line. These data are recorded on the daily log-sheet for subsequent review by the mill superintendent.

When it becomes necessary to shutdown a line, the take-off sump is emptied of tailings by redirecting the thickener underflow streams to the bypass. Flushing water is then immediately fed to the take-off sump and into the pipeline. The drain lines at the invert are fully opened until the flushing water reaches this point. The drain valves are then closed and water flushing is continued until the line is cleared all the way to Ibo.

Pulp Velocity Determination

Actual determinations of pulp velocity through the pipelines are periodically made with the use of radioactive tracers. All work during these determinations is conducted under the supervision of the Research and Development Division of the Philippine Atomic Energy Commission. This Philippine Government agency operates a nuclear reactor and makes available to both public and private organizations the facilities of the reactor and its laboratories, and the technical services of its staff, free of charge.

When conducting pulp velocity tests on the Atlas tailings pipelines, at ACMDC request, the PAEC Research and Development Division supplies the required radioactive materials and provides the injectors and detection instruments. The work is personally supervised by their highly-trained staff led by Dr. Alberto Campos, Ph. D., and Col. Ver Albano, radiation officer. These services are given at no cost to Atlas.

During the tests, a controlled amount of Bromine
82 radio-isotope is introduced into the pipe inlet at
the take-off sump through appropriately designed injectors. Detection instruments to record the exact
time the radioisotope passes a point are deployed at
different points along the pipeline. Thus, the speed
of travel is computed from the ratio of the distance between the points and the time of travel. The distances
along the pipeline are determined through actual measurements.

These data, confirmed through many successive test
and trials, have greatly assisted ACMDC's engineering staff in the design of in-line orifices which were
installed to dissipate the excessive gradient available
and thereby reduce pulp velocity to desired low levels.

Pipe Wear

The operation of the lines is relatively simple but
the major problem that remains subject of continuing
study is the wear on certain sections of the pipelines

As part of their routine procedures, the maintenance
crew takes thickness measurements of the sides, top
and bottom sections of each pipeline at designated
stations once a month. A KRAUTKRAMER meter, which
is an ultrasonic device specifically calibrated to determine pipewall thickness, is used in these measurements.

These periodic measurements show that pipe wear
is pronounced at the bottom one-third portion of pipe
sections where the line slope is more than 5 per cent.
This observation indicates that a certain degree of segregation occurs, with the coarse sand fraction of the
tailings tending to settle at the bottom portion of the

pipe. On relatively steep downslopes, this coarse sand fraction cascades down and, in the process, abrades the pipe wall.

To reduce pulp velocities on downgrade portions, orifices are installed at strategic points determined by pipewall thickness surveys and hydraulic gradient calculations. The orifice set-up, however, creates turbulence in the pulp flow which causes fast wear on the discharge section which extends to about 12 feet length.

In addition, when air is entrained in the pipeline, the pulp velocity increases due to the reduced cross-sectional area of pulp flow, and results in relatively fast wear on the pipe wall. This observation is confirmed by actual pulp velocity determinations which show that pulp velocity is not constant throughout the pipeline and pulp velocities critical sections reach more than 8.0 feet per second.

For the 20-inch and 12-inch Dascon lines, the critical portion, where fast wear is observed, extends from the Abaca sump to the Pandong Bato area, approximately 8,000 feet in length, and from Station 144 ≠ 00 in Bawod to Station 174 ≠ 00 in Climaco area, about 3,000 feet long.

The high-wear portion of the Bigacon lines extends from Station 33 ≠ 05 to the water pumping station, 3,000 feet away, and from the air bleeder at Kasoy to the orifice at Malubog, 6,100 feet farther downstream.

Pipewall thickness determinations show that wear averages 0.02 inch per month for these sections of the lines. Replacements therefore become due after 12 months of continuous use.

Various remedial measures continue to be adopted to alleviate the situation. Since wear is observed on one-third of the pipe circumference only, periodic rotation of the pipe has been adopted as standard practice to extend life of the pipe. The monthly pipe wall thickness determinations keep the concentrator staff posted on the progress of pipe wear. When the thickness reaches 0.10 inch, the pipe section is rotated. In this connection, installing the pipe segments in curved portions of the pipeline in the form of 20-foot tangents with 5-degree deflection angles facilitates rotation.

Pipe materials specifically intended for slurry transport applications, such as Transol II pipe and its equivalent, have been purchased to replace worn-out sections of the pipelines. Recent arrivals of such purchase from Sumitomo Metal Industries of Japan conform to the following specifications:

Metal Composition:

Carbon	-	0.44 to 0.52 per cent
Silicon	-	0.10 to 0.35 per cent
Manganese	-	1.05 to 1.35 per cent
Phosphorus	-	0.04 per cent maximum
Sulfur	-	0.04 per cent maximum
Copper	-	0.20 per cent maximum

Yield Point	-	55,000 pounds per square inch
Ultimate Strength	-	100,000 pounds per square inch
Hardness	-	180 to 200 Brinell Hardness Number
Pipe Wall Thickness	-	0.375 inch

Currently being tried are centrifugally-cast iron pipes, which are manufactured in Manila and sold at prices competitive with imported steel pipes. With thicker pipe walls (0.68 inch) and a hardness value of 240 Brinell Hardness Number, these pipes are expected to last double the life of steel pipes.

Neothane coating was likewise considered, but was not adopted because of the high cost involved in employing mechanical joints. "In-Situ" coating of welded joints and curved sections is also prohibitively expensive; in addition, this procedure could result in doubtful quality of the coating if done in the Philippines.

Spirally welded pipes, which are manufactured locally and sell at slightly lower prices, had also been tried but results were unsatisfactory. Relatively fast wear appears to be induced by the welded seams. A 1,000-foot section installed in the Bigacon 18-inch line had to be replaced after transporting about 2 million tons of tailings in only 5 months of service. Another section installed at Kasoy lasted barely 7 months after transporting 2.8 million tons.

Further Studies

Current operations indicate that elimination of air entrainment and better head dissipation will significently reduce pipe wear. As a more permanent solution to the wear problem, the installation of intermediate drop boxes at points with sufficient heads to transport tailings over the crest of each invert is now under serious consideration.

High drop boxes will entail re-routing of the lines with drastic revisions on pipe slopes, which require major alteration work and acquisition of additional rights-of-way.

Low drop boxes of about ten feet height, on the other hand, will require minimal slope revisions on the upstream side. Discharge into the low drop boxes will be at atmospheric pressure and can be controlled by spigots. The discharge velocity head will be dissipated completely and will reduce or eliminate the in-line orifices.

Elimination of long loops in the line by tunnel driving is likewise being studied. This concept, if adopted will substantially reduce the length of the pipelines. Open launder flow through these tunnels is being considered as a means of positive head dissipation.

CONCLUSION

In solving its problem of tailings disposal, ACMDC has designed, constructed, and now successfully operates a system of gravity pipelines for transporting and disposing its plant tailings to the sea. Built at a total cost of ₱30 million ($4.662 million), this project has demonstrated the following salient points:

1. Incorporation of inverts in the design of long, gravity, tailings pipelines is a practical solution to construction problems and often prohibitive costs of laying out gradually-sloping pipelines across rugged terrain.

2. Use of appropriately designed easy-to-replace spigots at the discharge drop pipes and orifices installed at high-gradient points in the pipeline offer a convenient method of setting pulp velocity at the desired level, thereby allowing flexibility in concentrator operation.

3. Disposal of tailings pulp beneath the sea water level through vertical drop pipes, places the tailings where undercurrents carry the solids to the deeper regions of the strait. Thus, there is no appreciable build-up of settled tailings in the discharge area, and no solids have been observed to surface.

The disposal of Atlas plant tailings at Ibo has no adverse effects on marine life in the area. In fact, the discharge point at Ibo has become a favorite fishing ground of fishermen in small native boats (bancas). This is really not surprising, considering that the mouth of Sapang Daku River at Talavera Bay where the tailings used to be discharged by the river has always been a good fishing ground.

ACKNOWLEDGEMENT

The writers wish to take this opportunity to thank A. Soriano y Cia, General Managers of Atlas Consolidated Mining and Development Corporation, specifically Don Jose Ma. Soriano, President, and Mr. C. D. Clarke, Senior Vice President-Operations, and ACMDC Management, specifically Messrs. H. A. Toelle, Jr., Resident Manager, R. B. Santos and E. D. Navarro, Assistant Resident Managers, for giving us permission to write, present and publish this paper, and for their encouragement, guidance and help in its preparation.

The writers gratefully acknowledge the valuable assistance of ACMDC's engineering and metallurgical staffs in the gathering of technical information and operational data, and in the preparation of drawings and charts, and of the Atlas Copper Magazine staff in the preparation of photographs and color slides which are important parts of this paper.

DISCUSSION

ROBERT M. DARRAH (Cortez Gold Mines): I would like to direct two questions to Mr. Salazar. First, would you elaborate a little further on your decision to go to the orifice method to dissipate energy as opposed to more conventional drop boxes? Second, what are the comparative operating costs of the pipeline to the sea as opposed to your previous tailing dam?

ROGELIO SALAZAR: With regard to the first question, we actually couldn't adapt the drop boxes in all sections of the tailings lines because of the topography of the route. The sufficiency of the orifices in the lines is such that you do have one continuous pipeline for each of the pipe sizes which is about the only kind of system that is allowed by the topography. For the second question, we actually had no other choice except to use the pipeline, because, as I have mentioned, we do not have enough space in the area for a tailing pond. As far as the cost of operating a tailings line is concerned, we have been operating the lines for about a year and a half -- as I have mentioned we have passed through the lines a total of 26,000,000 tons of tailings to date -- and the costs are probably not yet representative. We expect that the costs will go down some more. At the present time we are talking about three to four cents a ton.

QUESTION: What is the velocity in that pipe-line?

ROGELIO SALAZAR: I'm sorry if I failed to mention that, but it is in the paper. We operate our pipelines at an average velocity, controllable reading at the rate of 6.3 feet per second to as much as 7.0. At the present time we're operating the 20-inch line at 6.46 feet per second, the 12-inch line at 7.0, the 18-inch line at 6.3 and the 16-inch line at 6.7 feet per second.

EDUARDO AVILAR (Minera Las Cuevas): What is the temperature of the discharge coming out into the ocean water and what is the temperature of the inland water?

ROGELIO SALAZAR: The tailings normally go out at room temperature, I mean ambient air temperature; ambient air temperature in Cebu is something around 85° F. throughout the year.

QUESTION: How do the actual head losses in your pipelines compare with predicted head losses?

ROGELIO SALAZAR: That's a very good question. Actually, that is one of the reasons why we went into actual pulp velocity determinations with the use of radioactive isotopes. When we started the pipelines, or rather when we were designing the pipeline, we based our projections on a formula similar to the Hayes and Williams formula for transporting slurries. And we did choose some figures, exponents, and constants. When we tried to use these on the pipelines, we found that they were quite off and so we went to actual velocity determination of different sections of the pipeline -- it took several data samples of course -- and tried to fit it into the formula. We also did find out that the formula for each of the different sizes of pipe is different. In other words, we did come up with empirical formulas that are applicable to each size of pipe despite the fact that the tailing that goes to each of the pipes is the same.

THE ESTABLISHMENT AND IMPLEMENTATION OF A

MONITORING PROGRAM FOR UNDERWATER TAILING DISPOSAL

IN RUPERT INLET, VANCOUVER ISLAND, BRITISH COLUMBIA

J. B. Evans, Head, Department of Mineral
Engineering, University of British
Columbia, Vancouver

D. V. Ellis, Associate Professor, Biology
Department, University of Victoria

C. A. Pelletier, Environmental Supervisor
Island Copper Mine, Port Hardy

INTRODUCTION

In October 1971, following an outlay of capital
investment exceeding $73,000,000 commercial
production commenced at the Island Copper mine
located adjacent to Rupert Inlet at the northern
end of Vancouver Island, British Columbia, Canada.
Island Copper is an integrated base metal open pit
and on site 30,000 tons per day capacity flotation
mill, operated by Utah Mines Limited (Utah), a
wholly owned subsidiary of Utah International Inc.

The sub-outcropping, near surface Island Copper
ore body, a pyrite, magnetite, chalcopyrite, and
molybdenite bearing porphyry deposit contained
within an (andesite-felsite and quartz-monzonite)
intrusive complex, is located within one mile of the
Rupert Inlet shoreline. The Island Copper ore body
is known to extend over 1,000 vertical feet to a

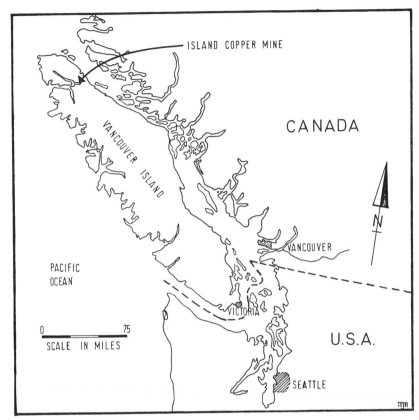

Location of Island Copper Mine.   Figure No. 1

depth some 800 feet below sea level. The presently
known reserve is reported as 280,000,000 tons
averaging 0.52 percent copper and 0.029 percent
molybdenite available from an open pit, the overall
stripping ratio of which is expected to be less than
three tons of waste per ton of ore extracted.

In January 1970, Utah, of its own volition,
initiated an ongoing environmental study of the
Rupert Inlet area to assess the respective merits of
terrestrial and submarine disposal of mill tailing.
Following a Public Enquiry called by the Province of
British Columbia in January 1971, and at which

various groups interested in the preservation of
natural environments expressed their views on the
Utah proposal to discharge mill tailing into Rupert
Inlet, the Province of British Columbia issued a
Pollution Control Permit (the Permit) to Utah in
February 1971.

The Permit sanctions the discharge of Island
Copper mill tailing, premixed with sea water, into
Rupert Inlet from a specified location 150 feet
below the inlet surface, provided stated conditions
of environmental control are maintained during the
pre-operational period and throughout the initial
five years of production.

The Permit, in addition to identifying the
physical and chemical limitations of the permitted
mill tailing discharge into Rupert Inlet, directed
Utah to retain an independent agent to ascertain
the influence of mill tailing discharge into the
receiving waters and specified that an environmental
control field program must be approved and initiated
prior to March 1, 1971.

Recognizing the extent of the environmental
control program that has been undertaken, and having
examined the date generated by that program, it is
postulated that Utah has complied with the provisions
of the Permit during the eight-month preproduction
phase. With respect to the operational period,
October 1971 through September 1972, during which
time interval more than 6,000,000 tons of ore were
milled, it is considered that as yet, October 1972,
no identifiable side effect condition detrimental
to the ecological balance of the receiving environment has developed as a consequence of discharging
particulate mill tailing into Rupert Inlet.

ENVIRONMENTAL CONTROL DURING THE PRE-OPERATIONAL
PHASE

In February 1971, the University of British

Columbia (U. B. C.) undertook to fulfill the duties required of the independent agent as specified by the Permit for at least the ensuing 18 month period. In particular, U. B. C. agreed to make procedural recommendations, offer instructional supervision for specific activities, provide specialized equipment on occasions, undertake or arrange spot sampling procedures when required, collate and assess data, and undertook to prepare periodic reports (1) suitable for publication on the basis of observations and established facts.

During March and April, 1971, U. B. C. assessed the existing environmental study of the Rupert Inlet area initiated by Utah in January 1970, and presented a recommended environmental control program incorporating features of the then existing environmental study. This program, outlined in Table No. 1, was accepted by the Province of British Columbia in June 1971.

Since the prime objective of the environmental control program is to ascertain the impact of mill tailing discharge on the physical, chemical, and biological characteristics of the receiving medium, it is imperative that the natures of these characteristics which exist without the influence of mill tailing be determined prior to the introduction of that discharge. Consequently, the prime restraint of the pre-operational phase of the environmental control program proposed by an interdisciplinary team of faculty members drawn from the U. B. C. Institute of Oceanography and the Departments of Geology, Civil Engineering, and Mineral Engineering, coordinated by the Head of Mineral Engineering, was the time limit available, approximately eight months, within which pertinent physical, chemical and biological data could be obtained in the subject area prior to the introduction of the mill tailing discharge.

As the ecological interrelationships of the subject area had not been established definitively, the decision was taken that initially as many characteristics as possible would be sampled even

TABLE NO. 1

OUTLINE OF PRE-OPERATIONAL ENVIRONMENTAL CONTROL PROGRAM

ISLAND COPPER MINE, MARCH TO OCTOBER 1971

OBJECTIVES	METHODS
Marine Program	
1. Determine bottom topography of receiving waters prior to discharge	24 miles of transecting seismic bottom profiles in Rupert Inlet area
2. Assess benthic conditions prior to introduction of tailing	From grab and core samplings and bottom photography at specific sites within Rupert and adjoining inlets determine:
	a. Physical and chemical properties of the bottom sediments, biannually
	b. Biological properties of sediment dwelling macro species, quarterly
3. Obtain a record of the characteristics of the receiving medium prior to tailing discharge	By appropriate water column samplings at specific locations within Rupert and adjoining inlets, determine on a monthly basis:
	a. Physical and chemical properties - temp., turbidity, colour, transparency, surface condition, pH, salinity, alkalinity, dissolved O_2, anions, cations and heavy metals, total Hg and cyanide
	b. Biological properties of all life forms within the water column - identity, distribution, chemical composition and growth patterns of Plankton, Resident Intertidal Macro species, Resident and Migratory Mobile Macro species
Fresh Water Program	
Establish the physical and chemical character of natural suficial drainage into the receiving medium prior to tailing discharge	Maintain an on site record of meteorological phenomena. At selected sites within the Rupert Inlet watershed, determine the physical and chemical properties of monthly water samples. Estimate rate of dissolved heavy metal surficial run off.
Tailing Simulation	
Indicate composition and properties of proposed discharge	Study the chemical composition, particle size, settling rates, flotation reagent distribution and dispersion rate of simulated Island Copper tailing
Collation	
Present pre-operational data in a format suitable for operational reference	Assemble an interdisciplinary team of specialists to direct the program and assess data as generated.

though, in some aspects, superfluous data could result. A further decision taken was to continue with the service of commercial consulting groups engaged by Utah in the then existing environmental study in areas where their respective capabilities and competences were judged to be acceptable to the U. B. C. team. It was concluded also that a long-term objective would be to achieve a condition whereby Utah personnel would acquire competence to conduct the ongoing environmental control program and thus reduce the contributions from external sources.

To assess the impact of mill tailing discharge in the receiving medium, it is necessary to establish not only the characteristics of that receiving medium and the composition of the tailing discharge, but also to ascertain the characteristics of discharges other than the mill tailing which terminate in that receiving medium. Thus, in this particular environmental control program, in addition to monitoring the Rupert-Holberg Inlet sea water environment and determining the characteristics of the mill tailing discharge, provision has been made for an assessment of the fresh water stream inflow into Rupert Inlet.

For convenience, the discussion of the pre-operational phase of the environmental control program is presented in four divisions, namely:

(A). The Marine Program, in which the sea water environment of Rupert Inlet and adjoining waters is physically, chemically, and biologically assessed.

(B). The Fresh Water Program, in which an assessment of the composition of fresh flow into Rupert Inlet is made.

(C). Mill Tailing Simulation Studies, in which a brief outline of research studies carried out by the Department of Mineral Engineering,

U. B. C. is presented, and

(D). Assessment of Pre-Operational Phase.

The Pre-Operational Marine Program

The marine program consists of a series of samplings and measurements of various physical, chemical and biological parameters taken at scheduled time intervals from stations established in Rupert Inlet and adjoining waters. The locations of the sampling sites were chosen to yield representative data relative to both the marine environment considered to lie within the projected zone of influence of the mill tailing effluent, and the marine environment believed to lie beyond the influenc of the tailing discharge. The time frequencies of the various samplings and measurements are judged to be adequate for determining the trend patterns of the parameters being assessed. The marine sampling stations are located throughout the Rupert Inlet, Holberg Inlet, Quatsino Sound area.

Pre-Operational Physical Surveys, approved by the Province of British Columbia, commenced in March 1971, when a Benthic Physical Survey was conducted. This survey was made up of the following measurements:

1. A bottom profiling seismic survey conducted from a 33-foot-long fish boat in which the following seismic instruments were mounted:

> an EG&G Trigger Capacitor Model 231-H,
> an EG&G Boomer Model 236,
> a Bolt Hydrophone Array Model 7xMP-4,
> a Bolt Amplifier Filter Model PA-7, and
> a Gifft Graphic Recorder Model GRD-IC9.

In this survey some 24 linear miles of continuous profiling were conducted to yield a series of sections across Rupert and Holberg Inlets, and

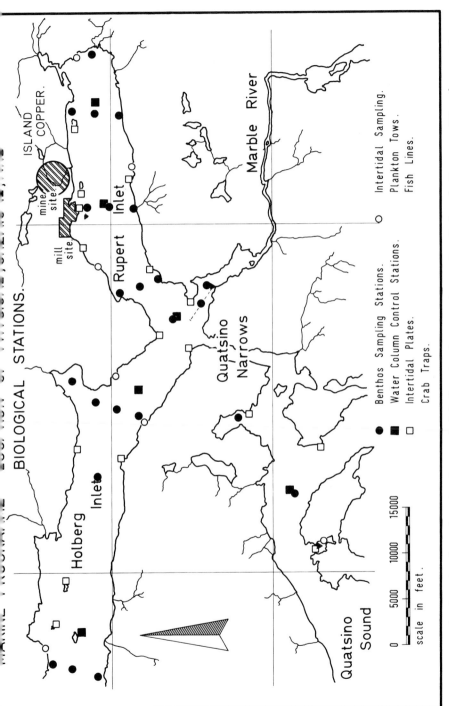

Location of physical, chemical, and biological stations in Island Copper Mine's marine program in connection with discharge of mill tailing into Rupert Inlet, Vancouver Island.

Figure No. 2

longitudinal sections along Rupert and Holberg
Inlets and through the Quatsino Narrows into
Quatsino Sound.

2. In addition, bottom sediment samplings were
    taken from 29 locations using a Petterson grab
    sampler, and, where possible, bottom sediment
    core samples were obtained at the grab sampling
    stations using a Phleger core sampler. All
    grab and core samples were identified, logged
    and, following heavy metal geo-chemical
    analysis, representative samples were placed
    in cold storage for future reference.

3. During this survey, an attempt was made to
    obtain a representative bottom sediment photo-
    graphic record using a submarine camera; how-
    ever, difficulties were encountered in obtaining
    a complete record and, of some 800 exposures
    taken, approximately 100 are considered to be of
    value.

This Benthic Physical Survey has revealed that
the Rupert Inlet bottom profile does not exemplify
a typical fjord bottom condition, a deep V-shaped
bed rock trench, covered by a thick (plus 100 feet)
sequence of flat lying sediments, but rather the
Rupert Inlet bottom profile exemplifies a block
faulted, wedge-shaped, graben structure, the axis
of which is coincident with the Rupert Inlet axis.
On the mine side of the inlet, the gently dipping
basement rock slope surface is covered with a thin
veneer of down-dip transported sediments; whereas
on the opposite slope the bed rock exposure dips
steeply to the wedge apex some 500 feet below sea
level, and is devoid of sediment cover. With
respect to Holberg Inlet, the Benthic Physical
Survey indicated that the bottom profile is a deep
V-shaped trench which has been partially filled
with a relatively thick sequence of flat lying
Quaternary sediments.

Routine measurement of physical parameters
commenced in January 1970, when Utah established
a series of water column monitoring stations within
Rupert and Holberg Inlets and Quatsino Sound at
which certain physical and chemical measurements
of the marine environment were made at periodic
intervals, and when Utah initiated a mine site
station to record basic meteorological phenomena.
In March 1971, the locations of the water column
monitoring stations were revised and the measurements made at these stations modified. The relocated water column monitoring stations yielded
two stations located within Rupert Inlet at which
the influence of tailing discharge was anticipated,
two stations within Holberg Inlet where the
influence of tailing discharge may become apparent
in the future, and two reference stations (one
located in the upper reaches of Holberg Inlet and
the other in Quatsino Sound) considered to lie
beyond the influence of tailing discharge.

The physical parameters measured on a monthly
basis at specific water depths on these water
column stations throughout the pre-operational
program were water temperature, turbidity, color,
and transparency. On each occasion that samplings
or measurements have been taken, the following
basic information has been recorded:

> location, time, weather condition,
> flotage, wave condition, water surface
> appearance, tidal position, personnel
> involved, and equipment employed.

Pre-Operational Sea Water Chemical Surveys,
approved by the Province of British Columbia,
commenced in March 1971. Certain chemical parameters
were measured in the earlier environmental study
initiated by Utah in January 1970 and, where
appropriate, such measurements taken prior to
March 1971 were incorporated into the environmental
control program. The "inorganic" chemical

parameters (i.e. excluding chemical parameters of
a biological nature), taken monthly from appropriate
depths at the water column monitoring stations,
included the following measurements: pH, dissolved
oxygen content; salinity, alkalinity, spent sulphite
content and "dissolved" heavy metals content.

The samples for the sea water "inorganic"
chemical measurements were taken by Utah crews
using a Van Dorn XRB 6.0 liter capacity water
sampler.

In defining the composition of allowable mill
tailing discharge, the Permit specifically restricts
the maximum content of particular "dissolved"
metals to concentration levels which lie in the
parts per billion range. On the basis of personal
experience and awareness of similar studies
conducted elsewhere in the world, the U. B. C.
faculty involved in the Island Copper environmental
control program had difficulty in reconciling the
demands of the Permit with current technology
relating to "dissolved" heavy metal sampling
techniques and analytical methods.

U. B. C. is unaware of the factors considered by
the Province of British Columbia in setting the
upper limits of "dissolved" metal concentrations
permitted to be present in the mill tailing discharged into Rupert Inlet, and it is interesting
to note that pre-operational data considered later
in this report indicate that on occasions the mill
process intake water could contain higher natural
concentrations of certain metals than the Permit
specifies as allowable in the mill tailing effluent.

Considerable difficulty was encountered in
obtaining, storing, and analyzing sea water samples
to obtain valid sea water "dissolved" heavy metal
determination. In addition to conducting analyses
in the Island Copper environmental control
analytical laboratory, suites of replicate sea
water samples were submitted to various laboratories

for "dissolved" heavy metal analyses. These laboratories included commercial facilities, governmental agencies, and University departments. The results of such cross-checking suggests the following:

1. The degree of precision and accuracy of analytical analysis required by the Permit cannot be obtained on a routine basis by many of the laboratories to which sea water samples were submitted.

2. A higher degree of reliability can be placed on the sea water "dissolved" heavy metal analyses performed in the Island Copper laboratory than can be placed on the analyses carried out in the other laboratories.

3. Particular elements and compounds identified by the Permit are believed to have been present in Rupert Inlet during the period June to September 1971, at the following natural levels of concentration:

Element or Compound		Maximum Concentration (p.p.b.)
Cyanide	(total)	32 (a)
Zinc	(dissolved)*	19
Arsenic	(dissolved)	3
Molybdenum	(dissolved)	12
Cadmium	(dissolved)	2
Chromium	(dissolved)	2 (b)
Copper	(dissolved)	4
Lead	(dissolved)	4
Cobalt	(dissolved)	1
Nickel	(dissolved)	10
Manganese	(dissolved)	8 (c)
Iron	(dissolved)	30 (d)
Mercury	(total)	0.5 (e)

Notes:
(a) Cyanide, normally less than 6 ppb, occasional erratic readings up to 32 ppb.

(b) Chromium, one isolated reading at 8.3 ppb.

(c) Manganese, two high readings at surface (20 ppb) recorded at time of an identified plankton "bloom."

(d) Iron, two isolated readings of 150 ppb and high readings exceeding 20 ppb recorded at time of identified plankton "bloom."

(e) Mercury, normally less than 0.05 ppb, but occasional water readings up to 0.45 ppb.

* "Dissolved" - as measured in the filtrate which passes 0.45 micron pore sized filter medium.

4. With respect to routine sea water analysis, as yet universally acceptable sampling techniques, sample storage methods, and analytical procedures have not been developed to yield wholly reliable determination of heavy metal contents at parts per billion levels of concentration.

5. At present, U. B. C. considers the analytical procedures detailed in Appendix No. I, and practiced by Island Copper, to be applicable to sea water metal determination for the Rupert Inlet area.

During the pre-operational environmental control program the monthly sea water analyses for total cyanide and mercury were performed by commercial laboratories using the procedures set down in the American Public Health Association publication "Standard Methods for the Examination of Water and Waste Water." As U. B. C. has not checked the reliability of these determinations, no comment on their validity is offered. Usually the total cyanide content is reported as being less than 6.0 ppb; however, occasional erratics as high as 32 ppb are noted. Likewise in most instances the total mercury content is reported as being less than 0.05 ppb, but again occasional erratics as high as 0.42 ppb are reported.

The determinations of trace elements in bottom sediments were conducted on the samples collected during the March 1971 Benthic Physical Survey, in accord with the U. B. C. standard procedure for soil geochemical atomic absorption analysis. It is believed that sufficient numbers of samples were taken at several stations to be able to estimate the variance. The results of such determinations made on the minus-80-mesh fraction of the Rupert-Holberg Inlet sediments are shown in Table No. 2

TABLE NO. 2

METAL CONTENT, RUPERT-HOLBERG INLETS BOTTOM SEDIMENTS

ELEMENT	METAL CONTENT (ppm)*	
	Range**	Geometric Mean
Cobalt	17 - 24	20
Copper	33 - 59	44
Manganese	542 - 750	638
Molybdenum	1 - 3	2
Nickel	31 - 52	40
Lead ***	1 - 11	1
Zinc	73 - 107	88
Iron (%)	4.0 - 4.7	4.4

*   Ignited Samples

**   Range = geometric mean $\pm$ standard deviation

*** Values less than 2 ppm taken as 1 ppm

Pre-Operational Biological Surveys, approved by the Province of British Columbia, were designed to measure the biota existing in the Rupert-Holberg Inlet and at the head of Quatsino Sound prior to mill tailing discharge into Rupert Inlet. In February 1971, the decision was taken to expand the then existing biological assessment of Rubert and Holberg Inlets, which commenced in January 1970, to yield comprehensive surveys being undertaken at quarterly intervals commencing in March 1971. The quarterly surveys carried out initially by a biological consultant retained by Island Copper involved samplings of the bottom dwelling invertebrates, the intertidal flora and fauna, the resident crabs, the bottom fish, the commercially valuable migratory fish and the plankton present in the subject area. Various sample populations were identified and classified, and for particular representative species the heavy metal contents were determined.

As these quarterly surveys progressed, a conscious effort was made to transfer the duties from the biological consultant to Island Copper staff members as these staff members developed competence in such matters.

As a matter of principle, in addition to conducting the appropriate determinations of each sample and recording the results thereof, sufficient sample material was collected and suitably stored to yield a catalogue of reference material.

By analyzing the samples taken from each station during the pre-operational quarterly biological surveys, the following data were obtained and collated:

1. From the bottom samplings:

> Taxonomic identification of benthic macro invertebrates and estimation of population densities.

Polychaete identification, biomass determination and heavy metal analysis (recorded as ppm "wet" weight).

2. From artificial substrate plates positioned at at fixed intertidal locations:

> Laboratory identification and enumeration of attached macro invertebrate species and estimation of population densities.
>
> A time sequence assessment of algae growth.
>
> A photographic record of attached flora and fauna.

3. From selected intertidal mud flats:

> Taxonomic identification, estimation of population densities, and soft tissue heavy metal analysis of macro invertebrates.

4. From selected intertidal rock pools:

> Taxonomic identification, estimation of population densities, and heavy metal analysis of intertidal fish.

5. From commercial traps located at selected locations for specific time periods:

> Dungeness crab population density, measurement, weight, sex and heavy metal determination of edible tissue of representative specimens.

6. From standardized net samples taken at particular water depth locations and at specific times:

> Taxonomic identification assessment of population densities, and heavy metal analysis of zooplankton.

7. From water samples taken at particular water depth locations and at specific times:

   Chlorophyll "a" content analysis (as a measure of phytoplankton density).

8. From commercial long lines set at selected locations for specific time periods:

   Identification, measurement, enumeration and standard soft tissue heavy metal determination of the dominant fish species caught.

9. From commercial seine nets set at selected locations during the migratory seasons of salmon and steelhead trout:

   Identification and measurement of the species caught, and the determination of heavy metal content of standard tissue segments of representative specimens.

The pre-operational biological heavy metal analyses, conducted by a reputable commercial laboratory in accord with standard analytical control procedures, determined the arsenic, cadmium, copper, lead, mercury, molybdenum, and zinc content of the sample material submitted. Replicate sample tissue has been retained in appropriate preservation as reference material.

The Pre-Operational Fresh Water Program

The prime objective of the pre-operational fresh water program initiated in March 1971 was to determine the natural contributions to the "dissolved" trace metal content of Rupert Inlet derived from inflowing rivers and streams.

Sampling stations were established at midstream locations in 12 streams considered to be the main fresh water inflows to Rupert Inlet and a program of monthly inspections and water sample collection was instigated.

Fortunately a permanent stream flow recording of the Marble River, the principal fresh water flow into Rupert Inlet, has been made by a governmental agency over a lengthy time period, and indicates that the Marble River flow ranges from 151 cusecs. to 4,830 cusecs., with a mean flow of 1,590 cusecs.

Once sufficient records are assembled by the Island Copper mine site meteorological station, it will be possible to determine, within acceptable limits of tolerance, the nature and distribution of fresh water runoff and stream flow into Rupert Inlet.

When these data are obtained and related to the record of stream trace metal contents, a comparison will be made of the "dissolved" trace metal input to Rupert Inlet derived from natural surficial waters and the corresponding input derived from the mill tailing discharge.

Prior to March 1971, Utah had obtained a record of fresh water heavy metal analysis of samples collected over a considerable period of time; however, assessment of the sampling and sample storage methods employed cast considerable doubt as to the validity of such determinations and consequently the record was rejected.

Throughout the pre-operational fresh water program, fresh water samples were collected by Utah personnel and analyzed by procedures similar to those described above in the discussion of the pre-operational sea water chemical surveys.

Check analyses, performed by a commercial laboratory and the U. B. C. Department of Geology on replicate sample splits, indicate that, despite occasional erratic variations, the metal concentrations reported by the three laboratories are in general agreement. Table No. 3 illustrates this degree of agreement.

TABLE NO. 3

INTER-COMPARISON OF FRESH WATER HEAVY METAL ANALYSIS

STATION LOCATION	END CREEK NORTH			END CREEK SOUTH		
LABORATORY	A	B	C	A	B	C
Element	Analysis Unit - parts per billion					
Fe	770	608	900	760	596	985
Cd		0.8		2	1.2	
Cu	5	5	5	13	12	12
Co		2	1		3	3
Cr		4			3	
Mo		3.6	1		3.6	1
Pb	2	7*	1	1	8*	4
Zn	6	7	5	20	29	19
Ni	11**	4	1	12**	5	3
Mn		15	12		95	81
pH		6.30			7.80	

A - Commercial Laboratory

B - Island Copper

C - Geology Department, U. B. C.

* Subsequent introduction of a background compensation attachment to the atomic absorption spectrophotometer produced a decided decrease in signal amplitude when analyzing for Pb of less than 10 ppb concentration.

** Nickel contamination suspected at time of determination.

In addition, Table No. 3, presenting the metal content of End Creek North, on the upstream side of the Island Copper ore body, and End Creek South, on the downstream side of the ore body, separated by a distance less than two thousand feet in length, and sampled within a two-hour time interval, demonstrates the natural increase in heavy metal content that can occur in a stream flowing over a zone containing metallic sulphides.

Another fresh water stream heavy metal content variable indicated by the pre-operational fresh water program is the seasonal variability that can occur. This phenomenum is demonstrated by the

following tabulation of particular sample measurements taken at the same stream location at monthly
intervals.

Measurement	5 July 71	6 August 71	1 Sept. 71	1 October 71
Temperature (^{o} F.)	54	60	64	53
pH	7.25	7.40	7.35	6.70
Total Dissolved Solids (ppm)	48	52	-	126
Dissolved Oxygen (mg/l)	10.0	9.0	9.3	10.9
Bicarbonate (ppm)	26	29	25	7
Iron (dissolved ppb)	84	139	228	80
Copper (dissolved ppb)	1.5	$<$ 1	7	3
Zinc (dissolved ppb)	11	2	127	5

As mentioned above, as yet insufficient program
time has elapsed within which necessary data can be
generated to present a reasonable assessment of
natural "dissolved" heavy metal inflow to Rupert
Inlet from surficial drainage. Table No. 4 presents
a tabulation of the upper and lower limits of
dissolved heavy metal contents of all fresh water
samples taken during the pre-operational program and
considered to be reliable, in relationship to the
corresponding upper limits allowed to be present
in the Island Copper mill tailing discharge as
specified by the current Permit.

Mill Tailing Simulation Studies

Research on the sedimentation behaviors and
chemical stabilities of mill tailings in both fresh
water and sea water has been undertaken in the
Department of Mineral Engineering at U. B. C. (2)

Sedimentation rates of mill tailings are
enhanced markedly in sea water compared to fresh
water. In addition, the supernatant sea water has
much higher clarity than supernatant fresh water.

TABLE NO. 4

SPECTRUM OF FRESH WATER HEAVY METAL CONCENTRATIONS

Element	Permit Tailing Limit	All Fresh Water Stations	Marble River Process Water Intake	Marble River Month
		Analysis Unit - parts per billion		
Fe	200	< 20 - 6,740*	< 20 - 225■	< 20 - 78
Cd	50	0.3 - 13.5	0.4 - 1.0	0.4 - 3.6
Cu	5	< 1 - 21*	< 1 - 6.6*	< 1 - 5.2*
Co	50	< 0.3 - 6.8	< 0.5 - 1.5	0.5 - 6.8
Cr	50	0.5 - 24	0.5 - 1.3	< 0.1 - 3.6
Mo	20	< 1 - 36*	< 1 - 7.2	< 1 - 7.8
Pb	5	< 1 - 23*	< 1 - 5.1*	< 1 - 23*
Zn	22	< 1 -245*	< 1 - 245*	3.4 - 230*
Ni	5	1 -101*	1.9 - 3.2	2 - 24*
As**	8	< 0.2 - 2.0	< 0.2 - 2.0	< 2.0
Hg**	0.3	< 0.05- 0.20	< 0.05	< 0.05-0.14
Mn	5	1 -849*	1 - 4	< 2 - 4
pH	9.5 - 10	5.2 -8.3	6.7 - 8.3	7.0 - 8.0

* "Dissolved" readings which exceed the Permit tailing discharge upper limit

** Total content, i.e. "dissolved" plus suspended.

Both effects are the result of sea water being a
good electrolyte and causing coagulation of the
suspended particulate phase. Such aggregation of the
finest particles to form much larger and faster
settling clusters or "flocs" by coagulation helps
prevent development of turbidity in the upper levels
of the receiving body of water. Study of the distribution of tailing sediment over the bottom of
Rupert Inlet by formation of "turbidity currents"
is planned.

Preliminary studies of the chemical reactivity
or stability of finely ground samples of Island
Copper ore and/or tailing in sea water have been
conducted. In one series of tests, andesite-felsite
type ore assaying 0.52 percent Cu, 0.016 percent
MoS_2 and 9 percent Fe was wet ground to 82 percent
minus - 44 - microns in size. Without removing any
of the metal content these samples were then exposed
to sea water and to fresh water for periods up to 37
days at solids concentrations of 17 percent. No
increase in dissolved heavy metal content was
detected even when the slurry was agitated

continuously. When the solids were allowed to settle and remain undisturbed, it was found that the Cu and Fe contents in the supernatant sea water both decreased. These metal losses were balanced almost exactly by increased Cu and Fe contents in the interstitial water trapped in the sediment. This balance indicates that the fine, freshly ground mineral particles of the sediment abstracted heavy metals from the supernatant and no detectable dissolution of Cu or Fe minerals occurred. Similar extractions of trace metal contents from the sea by fine, particulate sediments have been reported often in scientific literature. (3) (4) (5)

As start-up of the Island Copper mill has been achieved, studies on the sedimentation and chemical characteristics of actual mill tailing are being undertaken. Laboratory tests assessing the ability of freshly ground ore (tailing) to abstract heavy metal ions from sea water of varying metal ion concentrations are continuing.

Assessment of Pre-Operational Phase

A true assessment of the relevance of the pre-operational phase of the Island Copper environmental control program must be delayed until mine production has progressed over an extended time period.

From a monetary viewpoint, Utah estimates the Island Copper environmental control program cost to date and the anticipated future outlays, as follows:

Item	Pre-Operational Jan. 70 - Sept. 71	1st Operating Year Oct. 71 - Sept. 72	2nd Operating Year Oct. 72 - Sept. 73
Capital Equipment	$ 30,000	$ 10,000	$ 5,000
Operating Supplies & Labor	40,000	45,000	60,000
Consultants & Purchased Services	155,000	120,000	55,000
TOTALS	$225,000	$175,000	$120,000

533

TAILING DISPOSAL TODAY

In February 1971, when called upon to prepare an environmental control program appropriate to Island Copper, the program designers had scant knowledge of the key parameters measured in other monitorings of mill tailing discharges to a marine environment, and recognized the virtual absence of fundamental inventories of the physical, chemical, and biological character of the intended Island Copper mill tailing receiving environment. As a consequence the pre-operational phase was designed purposefully to encompass a broad spectrum of indices.

The principal thrust of the pre-production program was to acquire, within the time available, a sufficient coverage of measurements to gauge the food chain eco-system from phytoplankton, through zooplankton and benthos to upper-level carnivores of immediate importance to man, present in the Rupert-Holberg Inlet and Quatsino Sound marine environment prior to Island Copper mill discharge into that system.

At this present time, October 1972, it is postulated that the log of baseline data obtained in the pre-operational phase will permit meaningful comparisons being made of samplings taken during production to discern potentially hazardous environmental effects as they may occur, and with sufficient lead time available to allow remedial action being undertaken before serious environmental damage ensues.

ENVIRONMENTAL CONTROL DURING THE OPERATING PHASE

When Island Copper mill production commenced in October 1971, the data generated by the pre-operational control program was reviewed and, in accord with the Permit, a proposed operating phase program was submitted to, and eventually approved by, the Province of British Columbia.

The accepted operating phase program effective for the first production year is outlined in Table No. 5.

TABLE NO. 5

OUTLINE OF ENVIRONMENTAL CONTROL MONITORING PROGRAM, ISLAND COPPER MINE

INITIAL PRODUCTION YEAR   OCTOBER 1971 to SEPTEMBER 1972

	DESCRIPTION	FREQUENCY	OBJECTIVE
Marine Program			
Seismic Survey	Bottom profile and sediment distribution.	Sept. 1972	Determine tailing distribution
Bottom Coring	Cores at 23 stations - log, determine heavy metals in particulates & preserve cores.	Sept. 1972	Determine tailing composition
Bottom Grabs	Sample at stations where organisms present in last sampling - log, sort to Polychaetes & others, count & weigh (Biomass) preserve samples.	Quarterly	Visual inspection of tailing & monitor of benthic organisms
Water Column	At 6 stations profile temperature, turbidity, color, transparency & suspended solids.	Monthly	Record water column phys. props.
	At 6 stations salinity, alkalinity, pH, dissolved O_2, spent sulphite, "total" cyanide and Hg, and "dissolved" As, Cd, Co, Cu, Fe, Mo, Mn, Ni and Pb.	Quarterly	Record water column chem. props.
	At specific depths on 6 stations sample for chlorophyll "a", identify & preserve phytoplankton, determine biomass and preserve zooplankton, and from vertical hauls at night determine zooplankton heavy metals and preserve samples.	Quarterly	Record water column organisms
Intertidal	From 16 plates identify resident species, estimate growth rate and preserve. From 8 selected sites collect particular species of clams and fish, determine population, growth rates, heavy metal contents and preserve tissue.	Quarterly	Record of intertidal organisms
Edible Species	At specific sites, collect fish by lines and nets and crabs by traps; identify, measure, weigh, determine heavy metal contents and preserve tissue.	Quarterly	Monitor fish and crab population
Fresh Water Program	At 7 mid-stream locations obtain temperature, pH, "total" cyanide and Hg, "dissolved" As, Cd, Co, Cu, Fe, Mo, Mn, Ni, and Pb and retain samples.	Quarterly	Record of fresh water parameters
Meteorological Program	At the mine site record temperature, wind, precipitation, cloud cover, sea water surface appearance.	Hourly	Record of meteorological conditions
Tailing Discharge	From weekly composites of daily samples taken from the thickener underflow determine pH, % solids, "total" cyanide and Hg, "dissolved" heavy metals and retain samples.	Weekly	Record of tailing composition
	From samples taken of tailing/sea water mix conduct 96-hr. TLM bio-assays.	Fortnightly	Record of tailing toxicity
	Determine tailing flow rate continuously, study composition and settling rates.	Continuous	Research activity

535

Following his participation in a Public Enquiry called by the Province of British Columbia in March 1972, to investigate the environmental control requirements of the mineral industry in British Columbia, a marine biologist faculty member of the University of Victoria, B. C., joined the Island Copper environmental control assessment team.

During this initial production year, environmental control activities assigned initially to commercial consultants have been progressively reassigned to Utah personnel as their respective competences have been developed. For example, as from June 1972 all chemical analyses required in the program, except tissue mercury and cyanide determinations, are conducted routinely in the Island Copper environmental analytical laboratory.

Observations Resulting From Environmental Control Monitoring

At this time, October 1972, having a complete record of all measurements taken during the operating phase of the environmental control program up until July 1972, supplemented with a preliminary assessment of samplings taken subsequent to that time, by reference to the pre-operational environmental data, the following observations with respect to the submarine disposal of more than six million tons of Island Copper tailing are made:

1. The limiting specifications of the current Permit have been exceeded in the aspects presented below:

Aspect	Permit Limit Value	Average Tailing Value	Intake Water Range
"Dissolved" Cu (ppb)	5	12	1 - 7
"Dissolved" Mo (ppb)	20	200	1 - 7
pH	9.5 - 10.0	10.0 - 11.5	
Flow Rate (gals. per day)	9.3×10^6	10.7×10^6	

2. No discernible change attributable to Island Copper tailing discharge has been noted to occur at any sampling site within the water column of Rupert and adjoining inlets with respect to the following sea water characteristics:

"dissolved" heavy metal, total cyanide, or total mercury contents, pH, salinity, alkalinity, or dissolved oxygen content.

3. The importance of having monitoring data cross checked independently by various members of the assessment team, and the necessity of retaining reference sample material, were demonstrated when the initial determinations of tissue heavy metal content for March 1972 reported a complete and sudden increase in copper content for the entire spectrum of organisms sampled, from plankton through to upper-level carnivores, at all sampling sites. In this instance the indicated anomalous condition was noted by three members of the assessment team working independently of each other. Check analyses and statistical assessment of analytical results caused the initial determinations to be rejected, as exemplified below:

a) Comparison of average tissue copper contents

Cu in Tissue (ppm "wet" weight)	Sept. 71	Dec. 71	March 72 Init.	March 72 Check	June 72
Zooplankton	4.2	3.5	6.6	4.6	
Clams	1.1	1.0	2.7	1.9	1.3
Dungeness Crabs	8.2	6.9	9.0	6.3	4.2
Dogfish	0.5	0.3	2.2	0.7	0.3
Other Fish	0.5	0.3	1.6	0.6	0.4

b) "Standard" shark tissue sample

	Initial March 72	Known Value
Mean Cu content ppm	1.65	0.54
Statistical Standard Deviation	$\pm$ 1.22	$\pm$ 0.05

4. Using the record of chlorophyll "a" samplings taken at three water depths (above the thermocline, immediately below the thermocline, and 50 feet above the bottom) as a measure of the phytoplanktonic activity in Rupert and adjoining inlets over the period March 19, '71 through July 19, '72, it has been observed that:

a) As expected, the majority of chlorophyll bearing organisms occur in the near surface "euphotic" zone.

b) As expected, and presumed to be related to the extent of daylight hours, a seasonal cycle exists in all the inlets sampled, with lower values noted to occur in the winter months.

c) There tends to be a higher degree of vertical continuity of phytoplankton activity in the winter than in the summer months.

d) Longer periods of increased chlorophyll values occurred in 1972 after mill tailing discharge commenced than in corresponding periods in 1971 which pre-date tailing discharge. It is presumed that such variation results from natural causes unrelated to tailing discharge.

e) Higher absolute values of chlorophyll were found in 1972 than in corresponding periods of 1971 and were identified to occur in association with observed phytoplankton "blooms." When blooms are ignored, the chlorophyll values measured over the pre-operational and operational periods approximate each other, and

f) There is no evidence to suggest that increased turbidity resulting from tailing discharge has decreased the depth of the euphotic zone to an extent which has reduced the amount of phytoplankton present in the water column, or dampened out large natural fluctuations in phytoplanktonic activity in Rupert and adjoining inlets.

5. With respect to zooplankton measurements for the period March 1971 through July 1972.

    a) At present there are insufficient data available to infer any conclusive trends which relate heavy metal content to tailing discharge. A slight decline in zooplankton concentration of As, Cd, Hg, Pb, and Zn is suggested to be occurring at the sampling station near the tailing outfall.

    b) Within Rupert and Holberg Inlets four species make up more than 90 percent of the zooplankton present, and three of these species -- Microculanus pygmaeus pusillus, Pseudocalanus minulus, and Oithona helgolandica -- are normally the most abundant.

    c) Statistical analysis of the deviations from the mean of the station samples presents no evidence to indicate that the tailing discharge has affected adversely the numbers of zooplankton per unit of water volume in the Rupert-Holberg-Quatsino Sound system, and

    d) Likewise similar statistical analysis respecting the distribution of zooplankton species presents no evidence to indicate that the tailing discharge has affected adversely the distribution of zooplankton species in the Rupert-Holberg-Quatsino Sound system.

6. With respect to intertidal biological measurements, as recorded by sampling the organisms resident on fibreglass plates maintained at

shoreline stations for overlapping periods of two-month duration, the productive periods of growth, i.e. the summer months, reveal comparable month-to-month rates of growth variation and similar orders of absolute value of growth present during 1971 and 1972. Study of the intertidal plate record reveals no evidence of adverse environmental effects in the intertidal zone resulting from increased turbidity or sediment deposition attributable to mill tailing discharge.

7. The biological record of intertidal animals so far obtained is judged to be insufficient in the extent required to base specific findings; however, a general trend towards lower heavy metal content is identified to have developed during the period March 1971 through June 1972.

8. With respect to Dungeness Crabs (Cancer magister), a similar observation as presented in item 7 above, for intertidal animals, is offered.

9. With respect to open water fish species, in particular to Dogfish sharks (Squalus acanthius), progressive decreases in heavy metal content, size and weight of specimens caught are evident from the pre-operational period through into the operating phase. It is not known whether or not these conditions result from mill tailing discharge, represent a natural trend, or sampling variation.

10. Consistently throughout the operating phase, the mortality rate of 96-hour static bioassay tests, conducted by a governmental agency using sea water acclimated coho fry in samples of Island Copper mill tailing supernatant as discharged into Rupert Inlet, is reported to be nil.

11. As yet the biological samplings of the September 1972 survey have not been processed completely; however, it is believed that the biological

activity in Rupert Inlet and adjoining waters
will be assessed to be greater during the
summer months of 1972 than the corresponding
period of 1971.

12. The following differences in particular physical
and chemical measurements were recorded for the
summer months of 1971 and 1972:

Parameter	Interval	1971	1972	Difference 72-71
"Average" Ambient Temp. (^{o}F.)	May thru Sept.	52.9	53.0	+ 0.1
Rainfall (inches)	May thru Sept.	20.5	11.6	- 8.9
Total Sunshine (Hours)	May thru Sept.	942	1029	+87
"Average" Sea Water Temp (^{o}C)	June thru Aug.	8.8	9.2	+ 0.4
Sea Water Salinity (as measured near outfall during Sept.; parts/thous.)	At surface	26.15	31.82	+ 5.67
	- 50 ft.	30.62	32.19	+ 1.57
	- 100 ft.	30.88	32.28	+ 0.40
	Bottom	31.82	32.48	+ 0.66

Tailing Distribution and Benthos Effects

The pattern of tailing settlement on the inlet
floor is being monitored at regular intervals, as
outlined in Table No. 5.

The readings obtained in the bottom profiling
seismic survey carried out in September 1972,
using essentially the same instrumentation as used
in the March 1971 survey, are being processed
currently. It is considered that the recording
instrumentation resolution limit is reached when the
settled particulate tailing is less than two feet
in thickness. On this basis a preliminary assessment of the seismic data suggests that a high
proportion of the total particulate tailing so far
discharged, approximately 75,000,000 cubic feet,
occupies a space at least 70,000,000 cubic feet in
extent, located in the apex of the Rupert Inlet
trough within a distance of one mile from the point
of discharge and at a water depth greater than 400
feet. The maximum thickness of settled tailing
is believed to be less than 30 feet. At present the

density of settled particulate tailing to Rupert Inlet is not established.

Phleger sediment corings taken in June and September 1972 indicate that the thickness of tailing sediment in the deepest portion of the Rupert Inlet trough exceeds 20 inches, whereas the maximum thickness in Holberg Inlet is five inches. As tailing discharge progresses it is anticipated that sedimentation will continue to extend further into Holberg depositing along the deep trough of the inlet axis.

Benthic effects of tailing deposition are monitored from counts of organisms obtained from Ponar grab samplings collected from a constant surface area of bottom at specific sites on a quarterly basis. To date, only within the thick sequence of tailing sediment (i.e. plus-20-inches) have the benthos been assessed to be obliterated completely. Over the balance of the depositing area some benthos remain alive. An analysis of benthos tolerance to sub-lethal levels of tailing deposition rate is underway.

The dispersal of suspended tailing within the water column, i.e. "turbidity due to tailing discharge," is being followed by routine monthly sea water station samplings at specific water depths, and by periodic continuous profiling surveys using a recording transmissometer. This particular prototype model instrument which consists essentially of a one-meter long by 10 centimeter - diameter open ended tube equipped with a photo cell light recorder at one end and a light source of known emission strength at the other, when towed by a vessel suitably equipped with depth sounding equipment and a light signal recorder, produces a continuous turbidity reading. The March 1972 continuous recording transmissometer survey detected the presence of suspended tailing within Rupert Inlet at depths below 120 feet. The subsequent monthly routine sea water turbidity

View of mill site from Rupert Inlet.   Figure No. 3

Emergency tailing discharge holding basin.
Figure No. 4

samplings indicate that the tailing turbidity is remaining below that depth, i. e. below the euphotic zone, and as a consequence it is considered that the increased turbidity due to suspended tailing has not affected biological primary production through photosynthetic interference.

At this point in time the extent of Island Copper tailing escape through Quatsino Narrows is unknown. This aspect is being investigated as a portion of a marine geology research project in which the availability of a submersible vessel is being explored.

Data Processing and Collation

In formulating the initial production year environmental control monitoring program, a conscious effort was made to segregate monitorings into two classes, as follows:

"Primary parameters" - monitorings requiring immediate analysis, and

"Secondary parameters"- monitorings which require sample collections at specific times to yield suitable storage sample material, but for which analysis can be delayed until demand is identifie‹

It is contended that savings in time and expense have been achieved by adhering to this policy throughout the initial production year.

Experience gained in conducting the Island Copper environmental control program indicates that sampling routines must be defined in detail, and in particular data report formats must be prepared carefully to ensure that time is not wasted in data analysis.

View of tailing outflow, sea water mixing box.
Mill tailing flows through pipe across the bridge
and is discharged into the vertical mixing column

Figure No. 5

The twin 325-foot-diameter tailing thickeners at
Island Copper Mine. Figure No. 6

TAILING DISPOSAL TODAY

At present the Island Copper environmental assessment team is investigating methods of data recording compatible with computer storage and retrieval systems. When such compatibility is identified, it is proposed that all presently available environmental data, and future data as generated, will be computerized. The implementation of this proposal will facilitate more rapid data cross referencing and statistical assessment than can be achieved at present, even though the total quantity of available data will increase with the passage of time.

CONCLUSIONS

At this stage of the Island Copper environmental control program, following an eight-month period of extensive pre-operational monitoring and the completion of the initial year of mine production, it is concluded that,

1. To date, the sole environmental effect identified as having resulted from the discharge of 6,000,000 tons of particulate mill tailing into Rupert Inlet, is the smothering of benthic mud dwelling organisms.

2. Benthos obliteration, an anticipated direct environmental effect attributable to particulate tailing settlement, has been identified to occur along a section of the Rupert Inlet trough. The inlet floor so far affected is estimated to be not more than 5,000 feet in length and less than 2,000 feet in average width.

3. To date, the particulate tailing sedimentation pattern on the Rupert Inlet floor conforms with design predictions.

4. The environmental monitorings undertaken to date indicate certain specifications of the

current Pollution Control Permit are unnecessarily restrictive. It is suggested that the maximum concentration limits set for dissolved Cu, Fe, Mn, Ni, Pb and Zn in the tailing discharge could be raised without increasing the dissolved trace metal content of Rupert Inlet sea water.

5. During the initial year of production the limits set for maximum dissolved Cu and Mo tailing content and total discharge rate have been exceeded, but no evidence has been found by the independent environmental control agent to indicate that such excesses have had any adverse effect on the ecological balance of the receiving environment.

6. Throughout the period March 1971 to November 1972, Utah Mines Ltd. has displayed an un-reserved willingness to meet the demands of the independent environmental control agent charged with the responsibility of ensuring that the provisions of the Pollution Control Permit are met. Such an attitude is considered to be indicative of responsible corporate citizenship.

ACKNOWLEDGEMENTS

Realizing that this presentation would not be possible without the respective contributions made by all members of the independent environmental control agent team, the authors wish to express their sincere thanks to the following University of British Columbia faculty members:

from the Institute of Oceanography, Drs. Grill, Lewis, Pickard and Taylor,

from the Department of Geological Sciences, Drs. Chase, Fletcher and Murray,

from the Department of Civil Engineering,
Dr. Quick,

from the Department of Mineral Engineering,
Drs. Leja and Poling,

for their participation in the Island Copper
environmental control monitoring programs.

The authors acknowledge the permission granted
by the management of Utah Mines Ltd. and the
President of the University of British Columbia
to present data contained in this paper.

REFERENCES

1. J. B. Evans, Summary Report, Pre-Operational
    Phase, March - Sept. 1971, Environmental
    Control Program, Island Copper Mine, Rupert
    Inlet, B.C., Univ. of Brit. Col. (1972).

2. G. W. Poling, Sedimentation of mill tailings
    in fresh water and in sea water, presented at
    C.I.M. Meeting, Vancouver, Oct. 1971.

3. R. A. Horne, Marine Chemistry, Wiley (1969).

4. J. P. Riley and G. Skirrow, Chemical Oceanography,
    Academic Press (1965).

5. P. G. Kihlstedt, Waste water in metal mining
    industries, Presented at Int. Cong. on Ind.
    Waste Water, Stockholm, Nov. 1970.

APPENDIX I

Sea Water Trace Metal Analyses

a) For the determination of "dissolved" copper, molybdenum, nickel, iron, manganese, cobalt, lead, chromium, cadmium, and zinc. The sample is first filtered through a 2 percent nitric acid washed 0.45 micron millipore filter.

(i) Analysis for dissolved iron, copper, nickel, cobalt, molybdenum, lead, and cadmium.

Two 500 ml. samples of sea water are placed in 1,000 ml. beakers. The pH of the samples is adjusted to 1 by pH meter control. The samples are then transferred to a 1,000 ml. separating funnel. To one sample an addition of 2 mls. of combined standard (Cu 4 ppm, Ni 8 ppm, Mo 16 ppm, Pb 10 ppm, Co 6 ppm, Cr 10 ppm, Cd 6 ppm) is made. One ml. of purified 2 percent ammonium pyrollidine dithiocarbonate (APDC) solution is added to each sample to complex the metals.

The metals are extracted in 20 mls. of water saturated methyl isobutyl ketone (MIBK). The samples are shaken vigorously for two minutes. The organic layer is then collected in 15 ml. graduated centrifuge tubes. One ml. of acetone is added to the sample extract in the centrifuge tubes to eliminate problems caused by any remaining minute droplets of water entrapped in the solvent. The extract is then centrifuged for 5 minutes at 2,500 r.p.m. to complete the separation of water from the extract. The extracts are then analyzed by atomic absorption for copper, molybdenum, nickel, cobalt, iron and chromium. The cadmium and lead atomic absorption analyses are performed on the aqueous portion of the first extraction following an adjustment to pH3. The ratio between (sample + known addition) and sample only is calculated to give sample heavy metals concentration.

(ii)   The manganese determination is done using
a 100 ml. sample adjusted to pH3.   The extraction
is performed in a 250 ml. separatory funnel.
To one sample 1 ml. of 1 ppm Mn is added.
10 mls. of APDC and 10 mls. of MIBK are added
to each sample.   This analysis is done within
one-half hour, as the manganese APDC complex
is not stable in MIBK.

(iii)   Zinc is extracted at a pH of 5.   As zinc
is very sensitive by atomic absorption, the
analysis has to be done on a 100 ml. sample
extracted with 25 mls. of MIBK.   APDC is used as
the chelating agent.

A blank is carried through on each set of
extractions.

b)   The determination of "particulate" copper,
nickel, iron, molybdenum, chromium, lead,
cadmium, cobalt, zinc and manganese.

The particulate portion of the sea water is
analyzed by a simultaneous determination of
the elements collected on a 0.45 millipore
filter.   The filter is placed in a 100 ml.
beaker and digested with 4 mls. conc. HNO_3
and 1 ml. conc. $HClO_4$.   The samples are taken
down to dryness and then cooled.   5 mls. of
conc. HCl is added to each sample and heated
gently to dissolve all residue.   When the
volume of acid decreases to approximately 2 mls.
the samples are analyzed against standards
prepared in the same matrix.   1,240 mls. of
sea water is filtered and the final volume
for analysis is 15 mls. and therefore, the
concentrations read off the graph are divided
by 82.7.   Blank acid washed   filter papers are
carried through and a blank correction is
applied for each element when applicable.

c)   The arsenic analysis is performed on 200 ml.
unfiltered sea water samples.   In an arsine

generator inorganic arsenic is reduced to arsine by zinc in acid solution. The arsine is then passed through a scrubber containing glass wool impregnated with lead acetate solution, to remove any H_2S formed, and then into an absorber tube containing silver diethyldithiocarbonate dissolved in Pyridine. In the absorber the arsenic reacts with silver salt forming a soluble red complex which is measured on a Perkin-Elmer 139 spectrophotometer.

DISCUSSION

QUESTION: I'd like to know if there has been any appreciable increase or noticeable change in the heavy metal content of marine life after placing tailing in Rupert Inlet for one year?

JOHN B. EVANS: The trend that has been noted so far is that there is a decrease in all heavy metals in tissue from zooplankton right up to dogfish. Now whether this is related to the tailing discharge or not, of course, we have no idea, but it may be just in that short trend.

EDUARDO AVILAR (Minera Las Cuevas): What is the temperature of the discharge coming out into the ocean water and what is the temperature of the inland water?

JOHN B. EVANS: This is premixed, as I mentioned before, with sea water which has a temperature of about 8° C. It is premixed before it is discharged. A very interesting thing: the temperature of that area has gone up by about 0.4^{o} this year as opposed to last year. Whether this is a high temperature or a low temperature we don't know.

J. W. GADSBY (Piteau Gadsby MacLeod Ltd.): I'm interested in your comments concerning British

Columbia Pollution Control Boards. Do you think that, after another 20 years of operation, the readings you're getting now may change and perhaps increase? This is an opinion I'm asking for; I know you don't have any facts yet.

J. B. EVANS: Sir, I'm a mining engineer. I personally cannot see that there will be any change but my opinion is not worth much. Changes will be made in the Permit, I can assure you.

ALCAN'S EXPERIENCE WITH DISPOSAL

OF RED MUD TAILINGS FROM THE BAYER ORE PROCESS

K. A. Miners

Senior Engineer

Aluminum Company of Canada, Ltd.

Arivida, Quebec

Since 1936 the Aluminum Company of Canada Ltd.
has been operating mud ponds to dispose of red mud
from the Bayer ore process. Depending on the
quality of the bauxite being processed approximately
2/3 of a pound of red mud tailings must be disposed
of for each pound of alumina produced. Nowadays,
around 2500 tons of red mud are being generated each
day at Arvida Works which are being pumped as a water
slurry (15-30% solids by weight) to the local ponds.

A typical analysis of our tailings is given
below:-

Mesh Size	% Retained	Cumulative
10	2.0	2.0
20	7.5	9.5
35	7.0	16.5
65	7.5	24.0
100	4.1	28.1
200	6.8	34.9
200	65.1	100.0

+ 65 mesh particles are a mixture of bauxite and quartz. Fine material is essentially a ferruginous clay, i.e. the bauxite residue after extraction of alumina.

Early disposal areas were adjacent to the Works and involved clay dykes built across existing ravines. The tailings, including the coarse sands (-10 + 65 mesh) were pumped through buried or insulated lines to the disposal area using centrifugal slurry pumps, such as Wilfley 6C and/or Allis Chalmers, 8" x 6" SRL'S. Initially attempts were made at the ponds to use cyclones and/or settling boxes to separate the coarse fraction for dyke building. However manpower requirements were found to be excessive and this operation was only possible during six months of the year. Thus this idea was dropped for the cheaper operating scheme of a peripheral pipeline with branch lines about every 100 ft.

Pondwater was drawn off via a draw tower and through a pipe going below the dyke to a pumphouse. Centrifugal pumps - Allis Chalmers (S.J.6" x 5") pumped back this water to the ore plant where it was reused in the process to leach out chemicals in a countercurrent washing system of thickeners. Recently Arvida Works has used air agitation successfully around the draw-off tower to overcome freezing problems associated with winter operation.

Disposal areas built after 1948 involved a system of reinforced concrete culverts through existing ravines to carry away surface run-off coming from fields above the new tailings ponds. Dykes were constructed in the normal manner for a conventional water dam using compacted, graded gravel with a layer of clay on the internal face and a rock toe for drainage on the external side. The gravel was top dressed and seeded to grass to prevent erosion.

During the early period when clay dykes were being used several slides occurred. Also we had a couple of cases of overtopping. None of these breaks

CUTTER dredge operating in Pond No. 5, one of the local ponds used by Alcan to dispose of red mud from the Bayer ore process.   Figure No. 1

Pumping station and surge tank.   Figure No. 2

were considered serious. However the red mud
tailings did reach the Saguenay river through our
plant sewer system. We also had several cases of
piping through the gravel dykes but placing of
aggregate as a graded filter stopped this.

Our system of discharging mud around the
periphery of the ponds using branch lines about every
100 ft. gave relatively good separation of the coarse
fraction with the slimes flowing out into the main
pool where they separated eventually giving a clear
overflow at the draw off tower. If desired these
coarse sands on the beach could be scraped up for
upstream dyke construction well within the starter
dyke. Incidentally Arvida Works capped these sands
with waste gypsum to stop erosion and give a hard
surface for transportation and for laying the
peripheral pipeline. However Alcan stopped using
gypsum when it found the gypsum was reacting with
the pond water and thus increasing its sulphate
content.

Over the past two decades the City of Arvida
continued to grow and encroached on the existing mud
disposal area. Consequently Alcan began to get bad
publicity from the dust picked up by the winds in
early spring or late fall when the mud flats were not
wet or snow covered. Thus a study was initiated to
eliminate this dusting problem and construct a larger
disposal area to contain the residues from the
increased production of alumina in the region. This
resulted in our current mud disposal scheme.

In this scheme tailings continue to be pumped
out to local ponds 4 and 5 close to the plant on a
year round basis through buried or insulated pipelines. These tailings are discharged from the
peripheral loop via branch lines where the coarse
fraction forms a beach and the slimes are carried
out into the pond area proper. During the so-called
warm weather months (May to October inclusive) these
local ponds are dredged out using a beefed up Ammco
cutter dredge. Extraneous material is removed from

Slurry is fed from the dredge to a trommel screen
where extraneous material is removed.   Figure No. 3

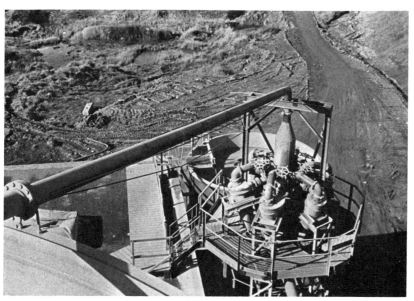

View of cyclones with recirculation line.   Cyclones
separate sands from fine mud.   Figure No. 4

this slurry by a 26' x 5' dia. trommel screen (3/8" openings) prior to separating the plus 65 mesh fraction by a bank of 6, 20" diameter Krebs cyclones. The coarse fraction or underflow is being pumped back to the local ponds using one or more rubber lined 6" dia. Allen-Sherman-Hoff pumps in series. The fines or cyclone overflow is pumped out to the new mud disposal area roughly six miles from the new pumping station using five or six 10" Hazelton CT pumps in series. The water used to transport the fines separates in the distant pond and is pumped back to the local ponds along with all precipitation for reuse within Arvida Works.

The problems associated with development of this scheme were numerous. Help was obtained from many outside sources. The Colorado School of Mines Research Foundation collaborated in determining the flow characteristics and friction factors to be used for pumping the red mud. A.E. Simpson Ltd. took aerial photos and made large scale contour maps of the region to aid in choosing the pipeline route and future settling basins. Precipitation records were obtained from Alcan's hydrology division. Geocon Ltd., soil consultants, collaborated in choosing the dyke sites and suggested an economical method for dyke construction. Alcan's Property Department carried out negotiations with the Quebec Government for crown lands and with private owners for various lots in the future disposal area and for access roads to reach this spot. Our choice of route was influenced by many factors such as, - being able to drain the line if the pumping system stopped; avoid the high costs for crossing swamps, deep ravines or blasting rock outcrops; avoid crossing roadways, railways, etc. Alcan finally ended up buying the ends of farmers lots for the access road to reduce costs and avoid habitations. Most decisions resulted from a team effort by Alcan personnel in Montreal or Arvida.

With a closed water circuit to Arvida Works the amount of precipitation and evaporation or net run off had to be estimated. Precipitation has ranged

Cyclone underflow is disposed of along the mud pond
beach.   Figure No. 5

Cyclone overflow is discharged to fine mud pump
tank.   Figure No. 6

from 1" to 12" per month averaging about 40"per year
during the last 20 years. Our experience since 1972
indicates that our assumptions were conservative.
Either there is less run-off than estimated or the
solids are entrapping more water, i.e. settling at a
lower percent solids. Test borings are required to
obtain factual information to clarify this point.

About the only major problem encountered and
not foreseen was the floating of swamp muck on top of
the mud. With a negative water balance this muck
was therefore drawn back to the floating pondwater
return pump. Relocation of the pump staved off this
problem for two years. A percolation rock filter
took care of another year. Enlargement of the
disposal area in 1970 with relocation of the pondwater return pump in the new settling basin appears
to have solved this problem. The swamp muck was
pushed away from the discharge area and trapped
adjacent to the dykes farthest from the overflow
culvert leading to the new drawn-off basin.

Another problem encountered by everyone
building tailings ponds is seepage through so-called
impervious dykes. Although one can have leaks because
of faulty material, Alcan's major headaches have been
associated with bonding the clay membrane to sloping
rock surfaces. Experience indicates a trench blasted
into the rock and packed with clay and/or slopes less
than 45^0 to permit easy compaction for bonding is the
answer. However sump pumps are usually needed to
collect seepage. Alcan has standardized on the
submersible "Flygt" pumps for this duty.

This scheme has solved most of Alcan's problems
for several decades. The dusting problem in the
local ponds has been largely eliminated by dredging
out the fines and replacing them with coarse sands
only around the beaches. And, these well washed
sands are currently being given away to contractors
for land fill.

In short over the years Alcan has gained

View of fine mud pumping system.   Figure No. 7

Moss floating on ponds threatened to block water
return pump. Pump has been relocated in the new
settling basin to solve this problem. Figure No. 8

considerable knowledge and experience with tailing disposal. It is continuing to improve its dyke construction and disposal techniques to keep ahead of the times and eliminate pollution from its ponding operations in a very economical manner.

DISCUSSION

QUESTION: How do the actual head losses in your pipelines compare with predicted head losses?

K. A. MINERS: We actually did test work before we even put in our experimental run with the Colorado School of Mines Research Foundation. We put up a test loop, 1,000 feet long and actually ran our slurries, red mud slurries, through this and took test information on it. We actually found that the critical velocity for our mud slurry was approximately 6.0 feet per second. As a result, we are operating our pipeline at a little more than that - 1.0 foot more per second. Otherwise, we have set a minimum of 7.0 feet per second for our pipeline to the new disposal area. Does that answer your question? Oh, by the way, in regard to the actual velocity, since we piloted a 6-inch loop and our pipeline is a 14-inch loop, we anticipated we were going to be on the conservative side, which we actually found to be true. Otherwise our pipeline losses were actually less than we anticipated from using the formulas that have been referred to here.

THE USE OF DRIP IRRIGATION

FOR VEGETATING MINE WASTE AREAS

Dan A. Bach

Irrigation Consultant

Dan Bach & Assoc., Tucson, Arizona

The concept of drip irrigation, as it is known
today, originated in Israel about 10 years ago, but
until 3 years ago it was virtually unknown in the
United States. However, since then, approximately
30,000 acres of orchards and vineyards have been
converted from flood or sprinkler irrigation to
drip irrigation. The reason for the explosive rise
in popularity of drip irrigation is understandable.
Drip irrigation has many unique features unequalled
in any other type of irrigation. There is a long
list of advantages associated with the use of drip
irrigation, however, many of them are not relevant
to this discussion. Three of these attributes have
been of significant importance to us in our work
with mine waste areas and merit further consideration.

Drip irrigation most simply defined, is the
application of water at a low rate over relatively
long periods of time. The flow rate of a drip
emitter (orifice) is generally expressed in gallons

per hour. The most common rate of application is 1 GPH per emitter. As the term "drip" implies, this is a steady drip of water from each emitter. Application of water at the rate of 1 GPH per emitter for a 24 hour period, for example, results in a slow deep penetration of water into the berm with some lateral movement, but with no runoff. Researchers have discovered that this type of application leads to a small saturated area under the emitter and from there the movement is a non-saturated flow (1). During this period all soluble materials are washed away from the root zone (2,3,4). This complete washing of the root zone applies to nutrient ions as well as toxic ions, if present. Therefore, all well designed drip installations must have a fertilizer injection pump for nutrient solutions which are used frequently, if not every irrigation, to replace the essential elements leached from the root zone (4). This deep movement of water into the berm cannot be underestimated, not only does it create a non-toxic root environment, but it also helps the plant establish roots deep into the berm where the soil temperature and moisture conditions are more uniform. These roots will be necessary for the plant to survive after the irrigation system is removed.

Drip irrigation is being used in greenhouses for nutrient or hydroponic culture. Here the growing media is inert sand or gravel and all the nutrients and water are applied through the irrigation system(5) It is our thinking that the tailings materials, once leached of toxic materials are nothing more than a sterile media devoid of nutrients. Drip irrigation allows us to apply everything essential for plant growth, water and nutrients, simultaneously. Once the plants have become established they generate their own root environment by adding organic matter and stimulating microbial activity. The principle concern is to generate a root environment condusive for plant growth which remains even after the irrigation system is removed.

In agricultural applications water savings as

high as 90%, when compared to flood irrigation, have been attained (6). The reduction of surface evaporation and the absence of surface runoff, even on the

Mesquite tree planted at Duval Sierrita Corporation on alluvium berm 18 months old.   Figure No. 1

steepest slopes, due to the slow application rate, are in part responsible for the water savings. This is important in the agricultural industry where water is often the limiting resource in arid areas. To a mining company, water, if not limited, is still a commodity to be used wisely, especially where inefficient and ineffective sprinkler irrigation may be avoided. To illustrate the type of water savings, Duval Sierrita Corp. south of Tucson has 42 acres of alluvium berm under drip irrigation at the present time. They realize the value of their water resources and strive to be 100% effective in its utilization. They have approximately 10,000 plants being irrigated with a flow rate of 26.4 gallons per minute continuous 6 days per week during the hottest summer months. This consumption declines to practically nothing during the winter months and then increases with warm weather in the spring.

Our original work was hampered somewhat by emitters that were adequate at best. Industry, however, has responded very effectively and we now have emitters and other hardware which are inexpensive yet dependable.

Mesquite tree similar to tree in Figure No. 1 at planting time.

Figure No. 2

Our philosophy has been that establishing a shallow rooted grass is not the answer to the beautification or stabilization problem. We feel that trees shrubs and ground covers (dense foliage plants which lie prostrate on the berm surface) should first be established. The accumulation of organic matter from such growth would generate an environment where grass seed might be sown or native grasses and annuals could establish themselves naturally at a later date. The foliage from the trees, shrubs and ground covers would diffuse rain drops and reduce water erosion while the root systems would help stabilize the surface from wind erosion. Using this approach one is able to begin to conceal the berm with visible, perennially green vegetation from the outset.

Three-month-old Wild Tobacco Tree, Nicotiana glauca, planted in August 1972 in pure tailings at Duval Sierrita Corporation.   Figure No. 3

Many different types of vegetation have been tried. As expected, some have responded better for us than others. The type of plant material must be carefully selected depending on the surrounding environment, salt resistance, etc. Figure No. 1 shows a mesquite tree, Prosopis chilensis, growing on an alluvium berm at Duval Sierrita Corp. about 30 miles south of Tucson. This tree was planted in May 1971 about 18 months ago; the yard stick (right center) will give you some idea of how large the tree is now. Figure No. 2 shows a similar mesquite tree at the time of planting. All the plant material we have planted thus far has been well established in a one gallon size can and will range in height from 12 to 18 inches tall. Also in this figure you can see the drip hose with an emitter (bottom center) near the base of the plant. Figure No. 3 is a general view

567

of an experimental planting at Duval Sierrita Corp.
on pure tailings. These plants were planted in Aug.
1972 about 3 months ago. All the plants are doing
well, but the Wild Tobacco Tree, <u>Nicotiana</u> <u>glauca</u>, in
the foreground is making exceptional growth. It has
grown about 5 feet tall since planting 3 months ago.
Other Tobacco Trees on the same berm are making
similar growth. A combination of slow release
fertilizers was added to the planting hole on these
plants due to the late summer planting date, but in
the spring a custom formulated liquid fertilizer will
be supplied to these plants through the irrigation
system. Figure No. 4 shows a close-up of an emitter.

Close-up of a drip emitter.   Figure No. 4

The drip emitter has a barbed insert type connection
at either end and can be easily inserted into the
pipe in the field or prefabricated at the factory.
The pencil point in Figure No. 4 indicates the spot
where the water drips from the emitter.

The drip system is composed entirely of ultra-
violet resistant plastics. The drip system lies on

the surface of the berm; this is best illustrated
in Figure No. 3, where the plastic emitter lines can
be seen running parallel to each other along the
face of the berm. The distance between lines and
the distance between the plants depends on the amount
of coverage desired. With the system on the surface,
it can be serviced easily and later rolled up and
reused to establish vegetation at another site.

CONCLUSIONS

Drip irrigation is a new method of irrigation
with many advantages that lend it to use on mine
waste areas. The drip system saves enormous quantities of water yet does a much more effective job of
leaching. The principle of drip irrigation has long
been proven effective in greenhouse culture where an
inert growing media is used. New equipment and
technology has made drip irrigation an inexpensive
dependable method for establishing vegetation on
mine waste areas.

REFERENCES

1. Goldberg, D., and M. Rinot, and N. Karu, "Effect
of Trickle Irrigation Intervals on Distribution and
Utilization of Soil Moisture in a Vineyard", Soil
Sci. Soc. of Am. Proc., Vol. 35(1), 1971, pp 127-30.

2. Goldberg, D., B. Gornat, and Y. Bar, " The
Distribution of Roots, Water and Minerals as a Result
of Trickle Irrigation", J. Amer. Soc. Hort. Sci.,
Vol. 96(5), 1971, pp 645-48.

3. Goldberg, D., B. Gornat, M. Shmueli, I. Ben
Asher, and M. Rinot, "Increasing the Agricultural
Use of Saline Water by Means of Trickle Irrigation",
6th Am. Water Res. Conf., Las Vegas, Nevada, 1970.

4.   Goldberg, D., and M. Shmueli, "Drip Irrigation-A Method Used Under Arid and Desert Conditions of High Water and Soil Salinity", Trans-Am. Soc. Agric. Engin., Vol. 13(1), 1970, pp 38-41.

5.   Jensen, Merle H., "Ring and Trough Culture for Greenhouse Tomato Production", Envir. Research Lab., University of Ariz., Tech. Report No. 1, 1968.

6.   Bach, Dan A., and J. R. Kuykendall, "Trickle Irrigation-For Pecan Orchards", The Pecan Quarterly, Vol. 5(2), 1971, pp 11-15.

ABANDONMENT OF TAILING FACILITIES

E. D'Appolonia, President

Richard D. Ellison, Vice President

John T. Gormley, Assistant Project Manager

E. D'Appolonia Consulting Engineers, Inc.

Pittsburgh, Pennsylvania

INTRODUCTION

Tailing facilities were often planned and operated to solve immediate problems associated with the disposal of solids or clarification of process water. Minor consideration was given to the use of the facility on abandonment. Usually it was left as an unattended "waste" land within an industrial complex, or as a potential financial and safety burden to the owner or the public.

Recent emphasis on safety and environmental regulations, coupled with recognition of the liability of tailing facilities dictate that abandonment be considered as a key factor in the planning and design of a facility. Innovative planning and design for proper abandonment of partially or completed facilities have also become significant because modifications to operating waste areas are difficult.

Before a decision can be made on when and how abandonment is to be implemented, it is essential to optimize capital investment, maintenance and abandonment costs in relation to the projected life and future use of a facility. The proper balance can be realized by staging the construction, thus avoiding excessive initial investment and costly remedial work and providing flexibility during the interim period to make modifications appropriate for the site's conditions and the production of tailings. Regardless of the owner's decision concerning cash-flow alternates, reasonably accurate estimates of abandonment costs should be incorporated in the overall economic analysis of the processed product.

Generally, the primary environmental consideration during both operation and abandonment is the quality protection of surface and subsurface water, particularly when the discharged tailings contain ore leach water which is highly acidic, alkaline, toxic, or exhibit other degrading characteristics. Collection and treatment of leachates often cannot be avoided. However, when the nature of the tailing is such that contamination of water occurs over a long period of time, particularly with material soluble in water, continual planning to minimize the volume of water reaching the tailings is important. Otherwise, the cost of collection and treatment may be exceptionally high for an unpredictable length of time after abandonment.

Other environmental considerations include air contamination in the form of dust or odor, reclamation and long-term land use, and, in some instances, aesthetics. The question of land reclamation should gain importance for industries near population centers where land for expansion is at a premium. Properly planned abandonment of tailing facilities in the areas of unusable low or steep land can yield usable space for plant expansion at little additional cost.

The main design considerations for a tailing disposal area involve staged construction of the embankment using available on-site or solid-waste materials and control of storm water runoff to safeguard against overtopping, excessive erosion, and leachate generation. Often, the most important factor controlling stability is seepage through the embankment. The flow is greatly affected by changes that occur during both the period of operation and after the facility has been abandoned. Seepage control requires careful planning and surveillance throughout the life of the facility.

A consideration relatively unique to the abandonment of impoundments is the stabilization of certain soft sludges. For installations where both solid and slurry wastes are to be disposed, mixing can economically solve the stabilization problem, especially during the late stages of the operation. On the other hand, if only a limited supply of on-site borrow is available for ground cover, planning for stabilization may have to be carried out periodically with disposal of the slurry. Where two or more industries having dissimilar wastes are located in the same vicinity, a joint effort can solve each industry's disposal problem, particularly if one of the wastes is granular.

A safe and economic abandonment can be best attained by surveillance of the behavior of the tailing facility and its environment as the impoundment increases in height and extent. In certain cases, surveillance may be essential to obtain meaningful field data for modification of the filling operations and to avoid building detrimental conditions which could be costly on abandonment.

The following sections discuss (1) the bases for evaluating cost and cash-flow alternatives for operation and abandonment of a tailing facility; (2) comparative examples of facilities where cost and long-term cash flow apparently were not initially considered; and (3) the basic mechanisms which

TABLE I

Alternate No.	Disposal Method	Initial Cost	Operating Cost (Trans-portation)	Operating Cost (Leachate Control)	Cost of Abandonment	Probability of Costs Continuing After Abandonment	Relationship of Cost and Product Sales	Volume of Waste per Acre of Land	Land Use After Abandonment
I	Slurry	High	Low	Potentially High	High	High	Out of Phase	Moderate	Poor
II	Solid Land Fill	Low	High	Low to Moderate	Moderate	Moderate	In Phase	High	Moderate

generally should be considered in prudent planning for eventual abandonment.

ECONOMICS OF ABANDONMENT

If, at the outset, the total cost of a tailing facility is included in the pro forma for product development, then a rational technical-economic program for site preparation; operation, maintenance and repair (OMR); and abandonment can be established. Undoubtedly, there are numerous possible schemes. The valid ones must be based on a study of cash flow for all facets of the construction, operation and demise of the tailing facility. Within this framework, the critical cost items can be identified and alternatives for abandonment can be compared on an economic and technical basis.

An example of major alternatives for many solid waste projects is presented in Table I which qualitatively compares disposal as a slurry and as a solid.

Table I shows that in the general case, disposal as a solid landfill has a potential advantage in all respects except for operating costs associated with transport of waste to the disposal area. If disposal as slurry is chosen, say because of volume of waste and transport distance, the higher potential for long-term abandonment costs should be "escrowed" throughout the life of the site and should be reflected in the cost of the product.

Although abandonment normally occurs when the available waste area is filled or when generation of the waste ceases, abandonment plans should be started early in development of a site. For example, (1) major changes in water courses could result in considerable savings in placement of waste and long-term environmental control, (2) the stockpiling of available on-site cover materials could eliminate costly input at the time of abandonment, and

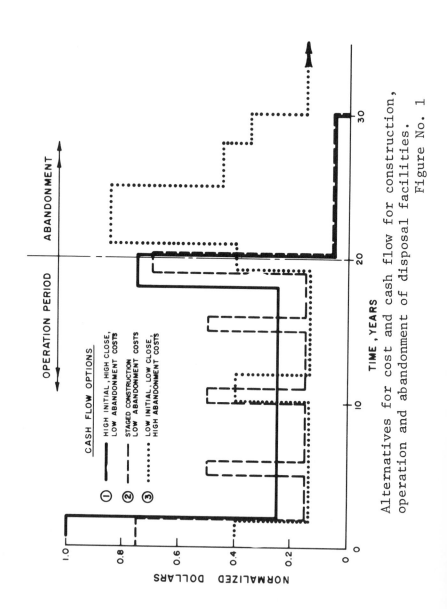

Alternatives for cost and cash flow for construction,
operation and abandonment of disposal facilities.

Figure No. 1

(3) maximization of volume can only be obtained by constantly building toward that configuration which will be satisfactory upon abandonment. The optimum solution would be one where the costs cease when the facility is no longer needed as a part of the processing of the product. However, the OMR costs will not automatically cease then. They will stop when the measurable influence of that impoundment (in its abandoned state) on the surrounding environment is determined not to be adverse. Of direct significance here is the relationship of the abandonment costs to existing regulatory standards and the anticipation of probable future revisions. History during the past several years has shown that the end to stricter regulations is not yet in sight.

Considering the foregoing, it is important to establish means for determining cost of abandonment. Without these, product costs cannot be assessed and market analyses may be invalidated. Given the means, cash-flow alternatives appear to be warranted in preplanning staged construction of a tailing facility. These cost and cash-flow alternatives are shown in Figure 1 and are discussed below:

1. Major commitments at the onset of development are made to site selection and preparation. The rationale behind this would be that it costs more to build or modify facilities at a later date than it does at the present time. Operations costs for this option would include continued corrective measures for environmental control, both in the disposal area and the overall site. There probably would be more structures to maintain than are actually required for a particular operation at any given time. Under this option, it may be difficult to implement revisions to the preplanned development of the site because of changes in the type and amount of waste material being generated. A high closing cost for abandonment is applied at one time to the whole

577

site.

Since deliberate expenditures were made
to establish a controlled system and to
close out the facility, it is expected that
the costs following abandonment would be
negligible or small. Abandonment expenditures would practically cease at the same
time that the tailing disposal ceases. The
maintenance costs, if any, would continue
until the impoundment has become stable
within its environment. The stabilization
period would depend on the planning and
implementation that goes into the site
preparation and abandonment measures.

2. Construction costs consistent with the
   volumes of waste materials generated are
   staged throughout the operating life of
   the facility. Site preparation is kept one
   step ahead of disposal. Abandonment measures are staged to follow closely each completion stage of filling of the disposal
   area. Major capital expenditures occur
   periodically throughout the operational life
   of the facility. Nevertheless, initial and
   close-out costs may still constitute a large
   portion of the total expenditure.

   Staged construction is normally more
   costly than the previously defined option
   because of the periodic mobilization of men
   and equipment to extend structures for decanting and surface runoff, etc. However,
   staging operations provide the best means
   for environmental control and adaption to
   revised regulations. In particular, the
   facility can be readily altered to changes
   in type and amount of waste material
   generated.

   Since planned expenditures were implemented to contain and control the generated

waste, the abandonment costs should be relatively low, and throughout the post-
abandonment period surveillance and maintenance costs should be fairly well defined
and small.

3. The third cash-flow option may be considered
the traditional approach to abandonment.
That is, minimum of site preparation, placement, control and surveillance is given to
the impoundment during and following completion of waste disposal. During the period of waste generation, operating costs of
the facility are low. However, with abandonment, close-out expenditures would be
high when no product is being processed
against which the abandonment costs could be
assessed. This type of high close-out cost
should be avoided because it is uncontrolled,
and detrimental site conditions may develop
that could require large maintenance and
surveillance expenditures over long periods
of time after abandonment.

EXAMPLES

Example No. 1: Combined Solid Refuse-Slurry Waste
Disposal

A. Without Abandonment Plans. Figure 2(A) shows
a typical cross section of a combination slurry
solid waste disposal facility on steeply sloping
ground. Many of these coal refuse heaps were simply
dumped into a gully without intending to totally or
partially fill the valley, and little attention was
given to impoundment of water. It was assumed that
runoff from small watersheds temporarily collected
behind the embankment would flow readily through the
relatively pervious rock fragment refuse. In the
intervening years, coal preparation and clean stream
requirements led to the practice of depositing coal
washings in the reservoir formed by the refuse pile.

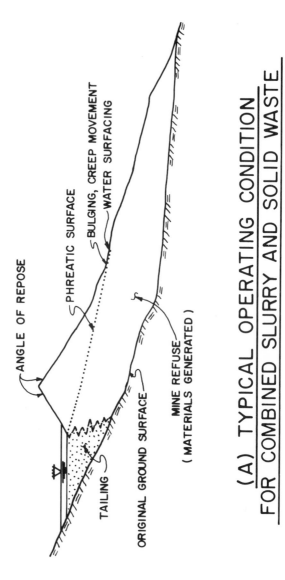

ANGLE OF REPOSE

PHREATIC SURFACE

BULGING, CREEP MOVEMENT
WATER SURFACING

TAILING

ORIGINAL GROUND SURFACE

MINE REFUSE
(MATERIALS GENERATED)

(A) TYPICAL OPERATING CONDITION
FOR COMBINED SLURRY AND SOLID WASTE

Mine refuse-slurry disposal facility. Figure No. 2

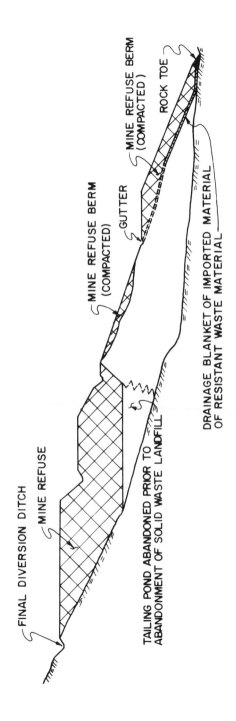

FINAL DIVERSION DITCH

MINE REFUSE

MINE REFUSE BERM (COMPACTED)

GUTTER

MINE REFUSE BERM (COMPACTED)

ROCK TOE

TAILING POND ABANDONED PRIOR TO ABANDONMENT OF SOLID WASTE LANDFILL

DRAINAGE BLANKET OF IMPORTED MATERIAL OF RESISTANT WASTE MATERIAL

(B) ABANDONMENT SCHEME
USING PRIMARILY WASTE MATERIALS

Solids settled out and the clarified water simply percolated through the refuse embankment.

The refuse dumped from a high line or tailgated from trucks produced a heap whose configuration depended primarily on the angle of repose of the refuse and the slope of the valley bottom. Normally, such an embankment was stable. However, the increasing depth of slurry and constantly rising level of impounded water, and internal phreatic pore pressures, jeopardized the stability of the embankment. Further, weathering of the shales which make up much of these refuse piles resulted in loss of permeability and shear strength. These changes in a large number of cases have caused accelerated creep of the refuse pile and, in some instances, major slips.

A detrimental effect of the coal slurry impoundment is the contamination of the water, which becomes acidic and high in iron as it flows through the coal and pyritic shales of the refuse.

Figure 2(B) illustrates proposed remedial measures for the embankment shown in Figure 2(A). Rock or other granular material provides a drainage system to control seepage from the embankment and rip-rap for erosion protection in diversion ditches and gutters. The coal refuse placed and compacted in layers is used as a stabilizing buttress and as fill over the slurry to consolidate the slurry and to completely fill the reservoir, precluding impoundment of surface runoff.

A diversion ditch at the head of the refuse pile and intermediate gutters on the surface of the embankment control runoff to minimize infiltration into the refuse heap and flow over its surface, and the resultant leachate which may require treatment.

The requirements for placing a final soil cover and vegetation over the entire exposed surface of the pile will depend on its resistance to erosion and on the quality of water passing over its surface.

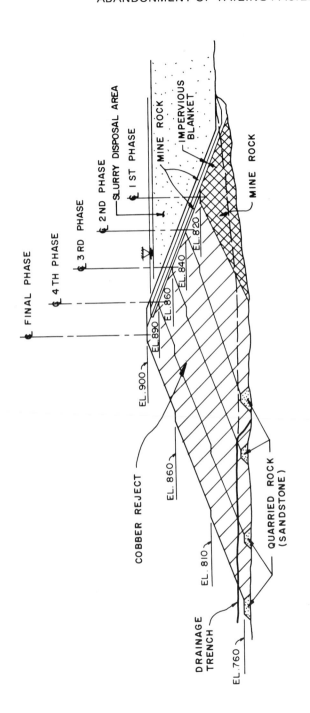

Section of flow-through dam.   Figure No. 3

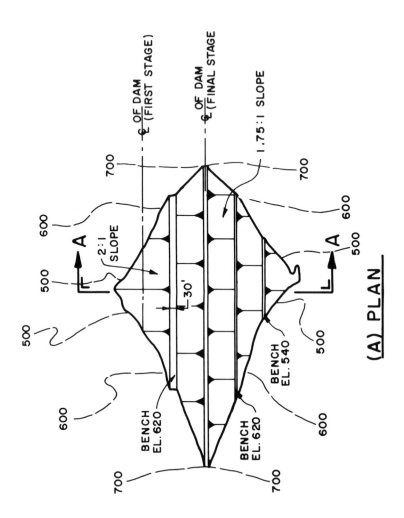

(A) PLAN

Flow-through rock fill dam.   Figure No. 4

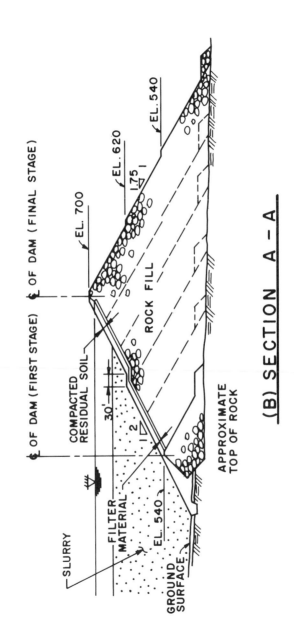

(B) SECTION A - A

The major unanticipated cost factors associated with abandonment of this type of facility are:

1. The relatively high cost of transporting or double-handling the material required to construct the downstream slope berm;

2. The high cost of obtaining off-site borrow materials for final covering, if required,-- particularly in light of the amount of available on-site soil and weathered rock beneath the pile;

3. The potential long-term requirements to collect and treat groundwater flow through the embankment which could otherwise have been effectively diverted through a constructed underdrain system.

B. Flow-Through Embankments with Abandonment Plans. Figures 3 and 4 illustrate two examples of slurry disposal retention embankments which are being constructed in stages with provisions for safe abandonment at any time. The case shown in Figure 3 is of interest as it effectively contains solid and slurry wastes. The embankment, except for the starter dam, is being constructed entirely of cobber reject generated with an iron ore pelletizing process. The initial embankment was built of on-site soil and rock. Each stage is added to best satisfy the scheduled requirements of both the solid and slurry wastes.

Surface runoff and process water flow over a broad weir formed on the crest of the impervious layer and through the pervious main body of the dam. Spillways in the form of decant towers or side hill cuts, which are costly to build, modify and maintain, are not needed with flow-through dams. Water flows safely through the embankment and emanates at the toe where it can be collected as needed and recirculated to the plant for process water.

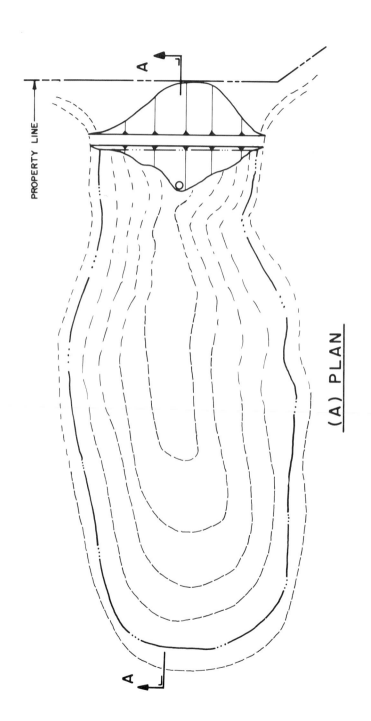

(A) PLAN

Fly ash/oxide tailing slurry disposal facility. Figure No. 5

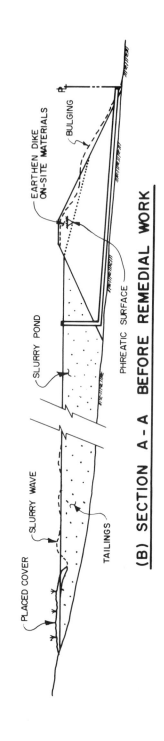

(B) SECTION A - A BEFORE REMEDIAL WORK

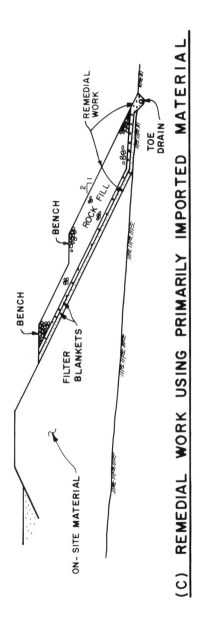

(C) REMEDIAL WORK USING PRIMARILY IMPORTED MATERIAL

Figure 4 illustrates a similar staged configuration, except that the embankment was constructed
from resistant rock taken from on-site borrow.

Example No. 2:   Slurry-Waste Disposal Behind On-Site
                 Borrow Embankment

A.   Without Abandonment Plans.   Borrow, rather
than solid waste, as discussed in the previous examples, was used for the embankment to confine a flyash slurry as shown in Figure 5.   The site was selected solely for maximum volume and convenience of
disposal adjacent an industrial complex.   Figure 5
(B) shows the toe of the 160-foot-high embankment
located next to the property boundary for full valley
use, with negligible consideration given to slope
stability, nature of the embankment materials and
their compaction, toe drainage, seepage and ground-
water flow.   The reservoir was filled, covered, and
the facility abandoned.   Shortly thereafter, an unstable condition developed as a result of a continually rising phreatic surface and the embankment
face illustrated in cross section in Figure 5(B) began to bulge.

Remedial measures shown in Figure 5(C) consisted
of a rock buttress at the toe and graded drainage
filters over a major portion of the embankment face.
All of the materials had to be imported and placed
under costly and difficult conditions because of
access and property line constraints.

B.   With Abandonment Plans.   As a consequence of
the high cost of unplanned abandonment at the above-
discussed site, the owner planned a new tailing impoundment within the same industrial complex which
incorporated the following considerations for abandonment:

1.   Adequate storage volume and site access at
     various stages of filling.

2.   Availability of soil and rock which would

govern embankment construction.

3. Control of drainage of groundwater and seepage from the reservoir.

4. Changes in the amount and nature of the seepage with time and for different levels of slurry waste in the reservoir.

5. Staged construction of the embankment.

6. Cover and stabilization of the waste on completion of filling of the reservoir.

In this case, design for abandonment assured safety of the embankment and an impoundment compatible with its environment and with the facility's operation and future use. Rock and soil were taken from within the reservoir to increase its capacity, and the sequence of borrowing and reservoir filling was preplanned to optimize cash flow in the event early abandonment became necessary.

Example No. 3: "Dry" Fly Ash Disposal

A. Without Abandonment Plans. Figure 6(A) shows a fly ash and bottom ash disposal area in which the materials were placed in a relatively dry state. The site was a wide valley and filling was started high in the valley's reach immediately after clearing and construction of an access road. Materials were end-dumped across the valley, forming a plateau bounded by the steep rising valley walls. As filling progressed, the front advancing face of the embankment increased in height, without consideration of the strength of the fill, nor to changes in the natural drainage. As a result, a major landslide occurred causing the ash to flow down the valley, covering wide expanses not prepared for the waste. Scarps on the surface of the fill interrupted further dumping of the ash.

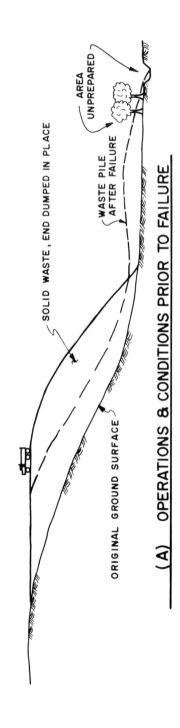

SOLID WASTE, END DUMPED IN PLACE

AREA UNPREPARED

WASTE PILE AFTER FAILURE

ORIGINAL GROUND SURFACE

(A) OPERATIONS & CONDITIONS PRIOR TO FAILURE

Solid waste disposal facility, ash and mine refuse. Figure No. 6

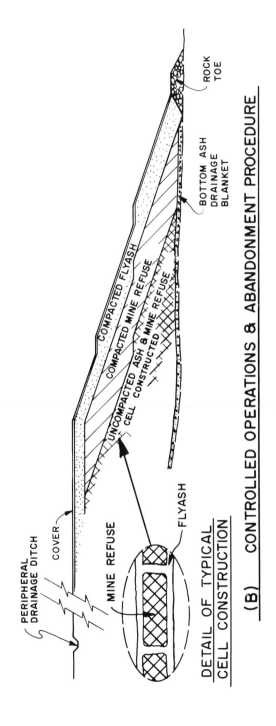

ROCK TOE

BOTTOM ASH DRAINAGE BLANKET

COMPACTED FLYASH

COMPACTED MINE REFUSE

COMPACTED ASH & MINE REFUSE

UNCOMPACTED CELL CONSTRUCTED MINE REFUSE

PERIPHERAL DRAINAGE DITCH

COVER

MINE REFUSE

FLYASH

DETAIL OF TYPICAL
CELL CONSTRUCTION

(B) CONTROLLED OPERATIONS & ABANDONMENT PROCEDURE

Investigations disclosed that surface runoff and uncontrolled groundwater seepage had infiltrated the fill, resulting in extensive piping of the fly ash and high pore pressures which ultimately brought about the flow slide.

Remedial measures required the construction of peripheral drainage ditches, the costly removal of the fill from wet areas and the difficult construction of rock underdrains through the displaced material to prevent the build-up of saturation zones. A main pipe underdrain was placed in the valley bottom and a program for placing the more permeable bottom ash between the valley floor and fly ash was instituted. Major portions of the existing embankment face were stabilized by constructing a new compacted earth and ash slope. End-dumping operations were discontinued and a procedure of placing and compacting the waste in lifts was used.

B. <u>With Abandonment Plans</u>. The counterpart of this example is a fly ash and mine refuse disposal area that has been designed to contain more than 100 million cubic yards of waste. Upon completion of the fill, the waste pile will require minimum maintenance, including controlled leachate treatment, and will form a usable land area.

The fill will cover a 450-acre valley having a long axis distance of 7,000 feet and an overall vertical relief of approximately 450 feet. The site was investigated to establish pertinent geologic and hydrologic conditions with particular attention given to the surface drainage, location, type and amount of soil and rock, and groundwater flow. These data were used in the development of a staged-construction scheme. Figure 6(B) shows a typical section of the embankment. The installation of the underdrainage system, in this case, significantly offset costs of intermediate drainage systems. The drainage system included a main pipe in the original stream bed, a two-foot-thick bottom ash drainage blanket over the entire site and pipe-rock lateral drains to conduct major springs to the main drain. A staged program was developed for clearing, grubbing, stripping and stockpiling of topsoil for cover to control dust and surface runoff.

Example No. 4: Disposal of Slurry Soluble in Water – Without Abandonment Plans

A particularly interesting example of excessive abandonment costs is shown schematically in Figure 7. An earthen dike was placed around the perimeter of an abandoned rock quarry depression for the purpose of disposing of a slurry which is highly soluble in water. In this case, the clarified water was decanted while solids settled to the bottom. With time, the 60-acre impoundment was filled and the site was again abandoned, with no attention given to the long-term effects of solubility of the solid material. Water from the slopes surrounding the reservoir passed into the impoundment and a highly contaminated seepage emanated from the embankment and rock, discharging into the river, as shown in Figure 7.

Presently, this problem is being partially solved at a high cost by collecting the leachate at the decant structure and at several of the nearby leaks and discharging it directly into the river through a diffusive system. However, continually changing water quality standards and emphasis on protection of the environment will very likely require, in the near future, either elimination of the leachate or collection of all of the leachate and treatment at an excessively high cost. Schemes for eliminating practically all of the inflow to the impoundment through ditching, grouting, surface sealing and combination of these alternatives, have resulted in cost estimates ranging between $1.5 to $4 million. Schemes of collection and treatment would be expected to be at least of the same order of magnitude, if at all possible, due to the anticipated difficulty in treatment.

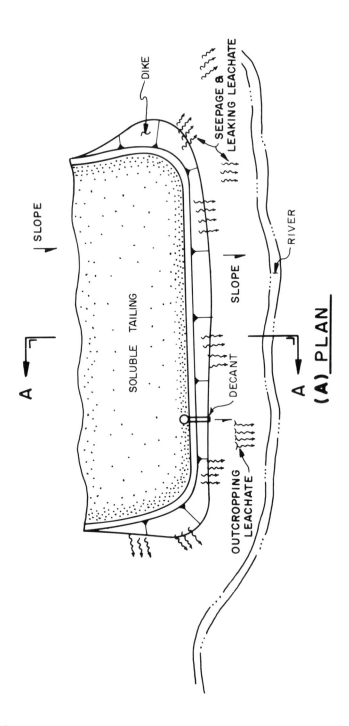

Slurry pond for highly soluble waste. Figure No. 7

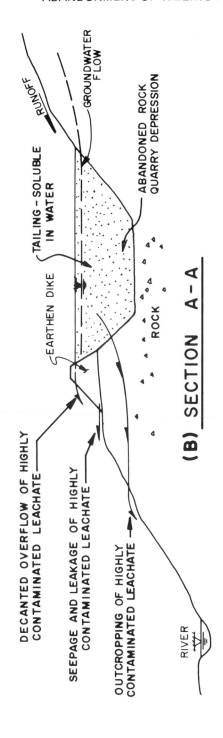

(B) SECTION A-A

Hindsight with this case stresses, when a highly soluble solid is to be disposed, care should be exercised in choosing and developing the disposal site so that surface water and groundwater flow through the waste is minimized or eliminated. Probably a primary economic consideration would be that of sacrificing low disposal costs as a slurry against higher costs for disposal as a solid. In this particular case, had the material been placed and compacted as a solid in a specially prepared landfill with intermediate and final relatively impermeable soil layers and with a surface water diversion scheme, the abandonment cost would have been small compared to that incurred to date and particularly to that which may be incurred under forthcoming environmental regulations.

THE MECHANICS OF ABANDONMENT

From the foregoing examples, it is apparent that abandonment plays a significant role in the planning and operation of a tailing facility; and that there are basic technical guidelines for the abandonment of a tailing disposal area. A check list for site preparation, operation, and abandonment includes, but is not limited to, the following:

I. Waste Materials to be Handled:

Physical and chemical characteristics
Possible variations with time
Available means of transport
Schedule of disposal volumes
Requirement and/or advantages of segregation or combining different waste materials

II. Geology and Mineral Extraction:

A. Geologic History and Present Activity

Significance of topographic features

Potential of natural hazards
Basis for locating and designing
major structures

B. Bedrock

Benefit for erosion-resistant chan-
nel construction
Deterrent for costly excavation and
leakage
Important parameters include:
Location, type and thickness of
strata
Resistance to weathering
Resistance to chemical attack
Cost of excavating
Dip and strike, as it affects
siting and groundwater flow

C. Regional Groundwater Conditions

Location and direction of flow
through pervious strata
Flow-restricting characteristics of
interbedded non-pervious strata
Separation effect of surface runoff
and regional groundwater by overburden soils
Initial water quality

D. Past and Future Mining

Fracturing of bedrock due to past or
future mining
Existing or probability of subsi-
dence or sinkhole development due
to past or future mining
Effect of waste overburden on stability of past or future mining
Effects of mining on surface water
or groundwater quality

III. Soil Characteristics and Availability:

    A. Origin of Soils

        Residual
        Glacial
        Colluvial
        Alluvial

    B. Location and Quantities

        Adequacy as natural blanket
        Availability as intermediate or
          final cover material
        Requirement for stockpiling
        Suitability as drainage material
        Effect on stability if left in place

    C. Effects of Weathering

        Can shales be stockpiled to weather
          for soil cover
        Changes in soil characteristics with
          time and exposure

    D. Mineralogy

        Cation exchange and leachate reno-
          vation capacity

IV. Surface Waters:

    A. Streams

        Storm runoff and stream control can
          be most expensive initial long-
          term cost item
        Consider effects of reasonable design
          flow in locating embankments and
          structures
        Develop baseline quality data for
          streams prior to placement of
          wastes

B. Local Surface Runoff

> Rule - where possible, divert sur-
> face waters away from waste
> disposal area
> Use stream diversion, peripheral
> ditches, underdrain pipes

C. Infiltration of Rainfall onto Disposal
Area

> Consider the use of impervious cover
> material
> Provide final grading for rapid run-
> off
> Provide impervious and erosion-
> resistant intermediate ditches to
> direct water off of the waste area

V. Groundwater:

A. Seepage from Waste Area into Ground-
water

> Remedial measures to eliminate
> leachate seepage to groundwater
> is costly or practically impossible
> Minimize groundwater construction by
> sealing original ground, sealing
> waste surface and collecting in
> underdrain prior to entering
> groundwater

B. Groundwater Seepage into Waste Area

> Construct adequate underdrain system
> Provide rock and/or pipe collectors
> at major spring areas
> Consider separation of uncontaminated
> underdrainage and leachate to min-
> imize treatment

TAILING DISPOSAL TODAY

SUMMARY AND CONCLUSIONS

New state and federal regulations will place the design and construction of tailing embankments and refuse piles on a par with those currently applied to earth and rock-fill dams for water impoundment. Rapidly changing attitudes of the regulatory government agencies under public pressure will force strict compliance and enforcement of the regulations, soon to be applied to the coal mining industry, that are comparable to those of the Federal Power Commission for hydroelectric dams and the Atomic Energy Commission for nuclear power plants. Already the Health, Education and Welfare Department is reviewing existing veteran hospitals in relation to earthquake hazards, following a pattern set forth by the AEC for nuclear plants.

Regulations of the Bureau of Mines will, within a short period of time, be applied uniformly throughout the whole of the mining industry. High on the priority list of regulatory control are tailing impoundments and refuse piles. One item receiving particular attention is abandonment of a waste pile. Two factors considered paramount are the quality of water emanating from the impoundment and the stability of the waste pile. Many state and federal agencies have already concentrated their efforts on the former. The latter--stability--is under study. The current survey (1972) by the Corps of Engineers of the nation's non-government dams and detailed recent investigations of coal refuse piles and slurry impoundments by the Bureau of Mines are but the first steps in the enforcement of forthcoming regulations. These regulations will require physical investigations embracing the geology, seismology, hydrology and meteorology of a site; numerous environmental impact reports for different agencies will be demanded; detailed chemical and biological studies and soil and foundation investigations will be required with comprehensive laboratory and field testing for the formulation of parameters for design, construction and operation of a facility; field instrumentation and surveillance programs will have to be undertaken and reports prepared, as often as daily, will have to be submitted to different agencies to assure compliance with safety and compatibility of the facility with its environment.

Abandonment will no longer be a neglected item, nor one to be considered at the end of the operating life of the plant. Plans for abandonment will have to be developed during the feasibility stage of a project and will be submitted with the applicant's first request for a permit. Implementation for abandonment with allocated funds to assure a satisfactory, safe shutdown of a facility will have to be demonstrated.

The key factor for abandonment of a tailing facility is ultimate compatibility of the disposal area with its environment. Critical at all times is control of the surface and subsurface flow of water. Stability of the embankment can be readily assured by applying currently accepted procedures for placing and compacting embankment materials--either those from the site or the waste.

It is essential to plan for abandonment from the inception of a project. To optimize the cost of waste handling and disposal, alternatives for site preparation, operation and abandonment should be critically evaluated as an environmental, technical and economical multi-disciplined system.

Undoubtedly, the increase in cost for abandonment will be dramatic. For those plants where abandonment plans and funds are neglected or disregarded, the effect on that industry will be shocking.

DISCUSSION

DAN KEALY (U. S. Bureau of Mines): Could you tell us what basic design changes industry will have to make in their current disposal practices to accommodate these new abandonment regulations – some of the basic changes you see?

E. D'APPOLONIA: Well, there are basically two. The first basic change – and this, of course, applies to the wetter areas of the United States, and probably to the east more than to Arizona – is the question of the leachates from the piles. As I illustrated in one slide the toxic material coming out is flowing into the piles. This will imply that the owner, the company, will have to spend a fair amount of money in either treating the water that comes out, or preventing the passage of surface and underground water through the tailings themselves. As it was pointed out here earlier, there is already legislation underway requiring the treatment of water. So this is item Number 1.

The second, of course, is stability. In the stability of the embankments, since there is so little information and data on why these refuse piles and embankments are performing as they are, especially from the point of view of the phreatic line, there will be need for field investigation, probably a considerable amount of instrumentation. The pressure will be placed on the industry to gather these data for the U. S. Bureau of Mines. I see this coming. In certain cases, where the pile has been abandoned, disclaimed by the owner, where he does not intend to go back and get material, I think the government agencies will take steps to find out what parameters should be used in making it safe, or bringing it to the safety level they want. Just one closing comment: there is dis-cussion of having factors of safety comparable to earthen dams, which is 1.5 – I won't go into that – and many of these piles have factors of safety of 1.0, and to go from 1.0 to 1.5 or 1.2 demands a fantastic cost.

LEE APLIN (Clarkson Company): Mr. D'Appolonia,

if I understood what you said, in the situation where they were passing something like 2,000 second feet through the embankment dam, I thought the section that you showed had an impervious blanket on the upstream face. Would you elaborate on that a bit, please?

E. D'APPOLONIA: Well, there's the freeboard on the rock fill section of the dam, and the one shown there was about a 10-foot height of freeboard and the impervious section, of course, stopped short of that. In the center section there was a depression of about two feet into the impervious blanket which acted as a broad clefted spillway over which the water flowed through the rock material. Incidentally, that particular material is copper reject and is all made up of material ranging in size from about 1/4 inch to 1 inch, with the predominant size in the 5/8 to 3/4 inch range. The rock in the bottom and toe drains was the development rock from mining·

TAILING AS AN ORE BODY

James J. Bean

Consulting Engineer

Miami, Arizona

There are tailing piles all over the world. Some
are old and some are new. All are monuments to the
dreamers who made mineral deposits into ore bodies
by milling them. All too often the dreamer's economics were bad and when they were the piles are
small, but some were sound economists and their dreams
have come true in magnificent fashion and it is because they succeeded that this symposium is being held
to discuss how best to build such piles, how to make
them more acceptable to the general public once they
are built and, I hope, how to preserve them for the
use of future generations, for they are potential ore
bodies.

Every mill superintendent since the one cracking a whip over slaves collecting gold in the sheep-
skins of the original "Golden Fleece Concentrator"
has had the thought, perhaps unexpressed, that "No
One is going to re-work my tails." Nearly all of
them were wrong and I suppose those of us here who
have had that thought are wrong too.

To me, a metallurgist, an old tailing pile is a challenge because they are assets; they do contain values which may not be economically recoverable now but which may be in the future. Many ore bodies now being mined were not considered ever "possible" ore a few years ago. New knowledge and new equipment have made them ore today. Is it not possible that the new discoveries of tomorrow will lead to processes that will extract the values in old tailings economically and convert the piles into real assets? Real ore bodies?

From the time of Agricola to 1890 ore dressing depended almost wholly on the principle of gravity. Then came chlorination, cyanidation and flotation, all entirely new in concept. They revolutionized metallurgy and made "ore bodies" out of a lot of hitherto "refractory" mineral deposits.

In the 80 odd years since their introduction all have been highly perfected and their very perfection seems to rule them out as the means of treating the tailings being made in most mills today.

But, is it unreasonable to expect new ways to appear as revolutionary in principle as flotation and cyanidation were 80 years ago? Since 1900 the world has acquired more knowledge of the nature of things than in all the centuries preceding and the rate is still accelerating. Surely some answers that are needed are going to come out of this progress.

It is entirely possible that the worth of the dumps will not be in their originally sought for minerals, though these may be recovered incidentally, but instead will lie in some of the gangue minerals.

For instance, the porphyry gangues frequently contain appreciable amounts of potassium and phosphorus. The extraction of these elements may become not only desirable but necessary when the present phosphate and potash deposits are depleted. The means of extraction may be improved non-metallic flotation schemes, or better chemical means, or entirely new processes using principles not even suspected at present.

Similarly, the trace elements may be extracted by new, more efficient, processes than are available now. It is well known that many of the copper ores have in them appreciable quantities of uranium and/or thorium. Palabora is currently extracting uranium and producing thorium sulfate from a heavy metal concentrate before discarding its tailings. As the demand for atomic materials increases there seems little doubt that some of the readily available old tailings will become usable sources.

The future also may find uses for other trace elements which may be in tailings but whose presence is hardly suspected now. If this occurs the possibility of obtaining such elements from tailings no doubt will be thoroughly investigated.

As mentioned earlier the advent of flotation and cyanidation stimulated re-working old tailing dumps and the depression of 1930-40 added additional incentive in the United States.

An instance I recall easily, because I was associated with it in its early stages, is the retreatment of the Ohio Copper Company of Utah tailings at Lark, Utah. Those 5 million tons, made prior to World War I, assayed around 0.37% Cu. They were successfully and profitably retreated, beginning in 1936, by hydraulicking them into a flotation mill where they were treated by L. P. F. (Leach- Precipitation-Flotation).

The old cyanide tailings at Manning and Mercur, Utah, were minus one inch in size and yielded a good profit after grinding further and supplementing re-cyanidation with flotation. The Manning tails were from the first cyanide mill in the United States.

Other cyanide tailings at such places as Delamar,

Nevada, and Marysville, Montana were profitably retreated by re-cyaniding them following regrinding.

During World War II old tailings in the Coeur d'
Alene river in Idaho responded well to Heavy Media
treatment. Not only were the lead-zinc-silver
values recovered but to a considerable degree the
river was cleaned up.

Coarse tailings such as those in the Tri-State
and eastern Tennessee find a ready market as railroad
ballast and agricultural limestone.

Recently the Kennecott Copper Corporation has
announced that its Utah Division is cooperating with
Utah Highway Department in an experiment using tailings for road construction.

The possible use of tailings for agriculture,
ballast, road material, raw material for bricks or
light weight aggregate is, of course, quite obvious,
but likely will not be general for such use depends
on a good, large, continuing market, something not
usually found near mining camps.

But economic depressions are not the only stimul-
ants to re-work tailings. Economic booms such as
our present one with their higher metal prices can
and do make such projects possible and some are now
in process and others are proposed.

In Mexico tailings retreatment is a fact at Parral
and Pachucca. Tailings are hydraulicked into mills
and the values lost in earlier, less efficient, operations are recovered.

The Cyprus Island Division of Cyprus Mines Corporation is currently extracting copper by pressure
leaching the slime fraction of their ore. Prior to
World War II the slime fraction was impounded in
ponds. In early 1960 retreating of the slimes which
had oxidized in the meantime was begun with some 60%
recovery of the more than 1% of copper they contained

being made as water - soluble copper. Exhaustion of the pre-war material led to the development of a low pressure leaching process capable of handling both pre-war and current slimes with recoveries ranging from 83-87%. The plant is now in continuous operation treating 1000 tons per day. Following leaching a fine pyrite product assaying 49% sulfur is made by floating the leach residue.

In the United States the Cities Service Company is evaluationg the Miami Copper Operations No. 5 tailing pond for possible retreatment by the L. P. F. process in the relatively near future. This pond holds the tailings from the earliest operations. It contains more than 32 million tons, averaging more than 0.35% Cu. It is mined, crushed and largely ground. It is not just an eyesore! It is not just a sand pile! It is an ore body of consequence!

Regardless of whether old tailings piles are retreated to recover additional original values or, as I have postulated, new, unsuspected ones, there are certain problems, that are now apparent and which probably will remain and will require careful consideration if there is to be success. Most apparent among these are sampling, reclamation and disposal after retreatment. Perhaps a little discussion of such foreseen difficulties is in order.

When tailings are being ponded usually records of tonnage and assays are kept and in many cases these records remain, if indeed they were ever kept.

Whether or not records are available it is not prudent to base an operation of any magnitude on them entirely and it will be necessary to check as far as possible the tonnage to be expected, the amount and kind of minerals that it is planned to recover and determine if any alteration of them has occurred. Sulfide minerals of course are especially prone to alter upon standing in the pond and such changes can seriously affect the metallurgy to be expected. The association of the minerals will also be of import-

ance and little attention may have been given to that
phase when the tailings were deposited. Of course the
most important of all is the method of treatment and
to determine this accurately fully representative
samples will be required.

This means that a sampling and measuring program
is in order very early in the project.

It would seem on the face of it that the sampling
of a tailing pond, especially one from a flotation or
cyanide mill, would be simple in the extreme. Experience
proves that this is not necessarily so. The presence
of segregated slimes and sands and mixtures of
both often makes special techniques necessary. Free
gold, as is well known to those who sampled placers,
may be exceedingly difficult to sample accurately.
Coarse mine dumps and coarse tailings are notorious
for being hard to sample because of their segregation.

In the past, drifting under both coarse and fine
piles has been tried with at best, indifferent success.
Costs have been high, accurancy poor and many
times it has been impossible to complete the operation
because the ground simply could not be held safely.

Churn drilling has been a popular choice. As a
rule costs of this method have been acceptable, except
where much casing has been required and recovery
of it has been impossible. This latter is likely to
happen in very slimy situations, which hold the casing
in an almost unbreakable grip. But more important is
the fact that churn drilling gives, at best, only an
approximation of the character of the stratification
at the pond and where soluble values exist it may be
very difficult to determine the amount because of loss
of solution through leakage or in the case of soluble
copper because of precipitation on the steel of
the bit.

Hand augers give good results in shallow deposits
of fine materials but have limited application because
holes of more than 40 or 50 feet are very hard

to drill and even harder to pull. Accordingly labor requirements are high.

The "Klam" drill is an air operated clam-shell mounted on a wire of a churn drill. It will sample coarse as well as fine ponds, but the spread of the open "Klam" is nearly two feet so the hole is very large with a corresponding large sample. This can be either an advantage or a disadvantage. In fine dumps and especially in slimy ones about 50 feet is the limit of hole depth without casing. The required large casing is difficult to handle and is costly and nearly always not recovered.

Probably the best means now available of sampling fine dumps is the hollow auger and core samplers that have been developed by the soil engineers. These devices give accurate knowledge of strata and require no water so that soluble values are more easily obtained though some precipitation can still occur. Also, since it is essentially a pipe-sampling technique it starts to fail when really wet, slimy material such as is frequently present at the dump bottom is encountered. The size of the hole and of the sample tube of course limits the coarseness of the material to be sampled and limits to some extent the amount of sample that can be taken. If a pilot plant is contemplated this may be a serious limitation.

Technology has already contributed to improved sampling by providing plastic bags in which samples are easily stored without loss or gain in moisture or change in soluble values through precipitation and with minimum incipient oxidation. Nor is freezing a hazard as it is when bottles may be required because soluble values are important.

Tonnage can be determined by the usual surveying methods, particularly when topographical maps of the original surface are available. When such information is not, then additional drilling may be required. Since we are dreaming of the future is it too much to hope that some variation of sonar will be available then?

The nature of tailings is such that they never "dryout". They are, in fact, a species of aquifer and as such they range from moist to wet, top to bottom, and in addition , at the bottom are often quite plastic and will flow if given an opportunity. The sandy portions are frequently interspersed with slime layers that not only resist reclamation because of their slippery, plastic nature but also present problems in re-pulping.

The upper foot or two of a pond is usually easily dealt with by almost any means but any wheeled or tracked vehicle quickly becomes bogged down once this upper, thin layer is removed. While it is possible to move to new areas and allow a new shallow layer to dry out, this requires close scheduling, much moving, and unfortunately even in Arizona the drying out does not occur rapidly. In wet climates such a solution is impractical, and even in arid regions the infrequent torrential rains will bring the whole operation to a sudden quite undesirable halt of uncertain duration.

Where tailings can be attacked from the face rather than the top conventional shovels and trucks can be used. The sticky clays present may make discharging the dipper difficult, sometimes requiring assistance from a water hose. Scrapers, bucket wheels, draglines and front end loaders may also be considered. Any of them will have some difficulty with slimes and even trucks may have trouble discharging their loads.

Where tailings are so located that a hydraulic giant may be used against the face, reclamation is relatively simple and cheap with repulping and density control coming as a matter of course. It is probably the most desirable of all solutions for it uses little expensive equipment and labor requirements are small.

Dredging seems a natural for tailing reclamation.

However if it is considered, the possibility of not
being able to hold the pond should be investigated,
the contrariness of nature being such that a pond
that might be too impervious for in-place-leaching
will be too porous to hold a dredge pond.

Whatever excavation method is used, whether it is
shovels, scrapers, draglines or something else, the
problem of repulping is acute. Regardless of what
type of repulper is used some sort of feeder is required under either bins or open piles. No matter
which is used hang-ups of the feeders will occur with
all their usual attendant difficulties magnified by
the often sticky nature of the tailing. Open piles,
of course, become wet, compounding the problems.

Repulping in ball mills or in drums loaded with
stones has been used and has done a good job of handling the clay fraction which often gives difficulty
when screens or trommels and sprays are used. Many
other combinations are possible of course, for instance, high solids conditioning combined with screens,
trommels, sprays etc.

And finally, regardless of how you sample, reclaim,
repulp and retreat a tailings pond the problem of
where to put them when you have finished is perhaps
the most difficult of all. Even when a suitable site
is available the invironmentalists are going to scream
about destroying nature's beauty. But, tails are an
asset! They deserve preserving! They are ore bodies!
There are solutions to all of the problems, including
re-disposal! Beauty is not everything! The first
man to eat an oyster raw certainly couldn't have been
struck with its beauty but millions of millions of
people since have agreed with him that it was worth
closing his eyes to its appearance in order to enjoy
its taste!

REMINING OF TAILINGS BY HYDRAULICKING

AND OTHER METHODS

W. Norman Sims

Vice President - MARCONAFLO Division

Marcona Corporation, San Francisco, California

When the opportunity presented itself to give this paper and when I read the title assigned to it, I gave considerable thought about accepting. "Remining of Tailings by Hydraulicking and Other Methods" puts no restrictions whatsoever on what I can talk about. That "Other Methods" is what really became difficult to define.

Before looking at methods of remining of tailings, my investigations indicated that there are a number of reasons why this is being considered. Some of the older ponds have been found to contain recoverable metal values that more than justify the cost of remining. It is important to remember that many of the major tailings ponds were started at the turn of the century. The mining of high-grade ore was the accepted practice, and the process or recovery technology was neither efficient nor necessarily advanced. As a result, it was not uncommon to dispose of tailings which, with the passage of time, have become of ore grade. This is particularly true in the copper industry where many of the older impoundments contain in excess of 0.5 percent copper. This is often higher grade than much of the copper ore being mined. Technology has changed so that these mineral values can and should be recovered. Mining technology has seen more advancement, however, than the remining of tailings. There are many unknowns about the behavioral characteristics of tailings that make it difficult to make reasonable estimates of costs. This is changing now and need for remining will speed the development of systems for economic recovery.

It goes without saying that the long-range planning of tailing disposal systems was not always evident when mining operations started at many locations. There is always present some element of expediency, but this was particularly true 50 to 75 years ago. Mining operations have far exceeded the then expectations, mining systems have changed and lower grade ores have become viable. As a result, some tailings must be moved to uncover recoverable ore bodies that once were considered to be uneconomic or too low in value. The remining problems are just as complex in such instances as if the material were being reprocessed. In some instances, the reprocessing for the recovery of metals justifies the moving of the tailings. This is a happy set of circumstances. The need to move old tailings ponds has highlighted a problem that fortunately is now receiving due attention. That is the long-range planning of tailings disposal.

The third serious concern necessitates the remining of tailings to obviate the safety hazards and overcome the requirements of the environmentalists. This is a very complex problem and one that is hard to evaluate property. Many of the older impoundments were never really engineered, they just "growed." As mining activity expanded, the dams were raised. Little scientific or engineering study was evidenced, and some major impoundment failures have resulted. Everyone has become more concerned with this potential problem, and all impounding areas will have to

be determined to be safe or made safe. In some instances, this will not be possible, and remining will
be required.

Along with the safety requirements, concern is now
being evidenced about appearance that was not expected
to be a problem. It is necessary to understand that
the general public and the government are going to in-
sist that the mining industry be involved in environmental improvement whereby the legacies of this generation must and will be better than those of the past.
Serious consideration will have to be given to these
problems, and they should be evaluated into a total
equation when thinking of tailings disposal problems
and when studying the remining and reprocessing of
old impoundments.

In more recent years, another reason has become
evident. With better planning for tailings disposal,
there have been a number of pipelines installed to
transport the tailings greater distances to remove
them from the concentrator area to meet environmental
requirements, to stay away from ore bodies or for
reasons of safety. No pipeline is so foolproof that
it will stay in service 100 percent of the time. It
is, therefore, necessary to have some impounding area
near the concentrator to ensure continuity of operation. Without emergency storage ponds, the plant is
idled when the pipeline is out of service. These
emergency ponds are quite often limited in size and
soon become full. A company does not always have the
opportunity or the space to create new ponds or to
enlarge older ones; therefore, remining must be a
part of the overall disposal system. It is unfortunate that this has not always been considered, with
resulting downtime and costly interruptions in production. Generally, this will require some different technique than the remining of the older and
larger impoundments.

The next question after determining that a pond
may be moved is to determine just what it is that is
going to be moved. Many estimates of just what is in

the ponds have been made. The studies have included
a review of old mining practices, but the history is
not always conclusive. Again, the expediency of the
times and the real lack of planning has been a serious handicap. It is only in comparatively recent
times that serious study has been given to what
really happens when tailings are impounded. Several
companies have drilled and taken cores to determine
the characteristics of the material, but variations
are so great that an accurate predetermined behavioral pattern cannot be established. These ponds contain wooden trestles, various degrees of saturation,
a wide range of particle size and various layers of
"caking" causing some impervious areas. This is quite
evident when clays are present in some quantity.

As a result of the studies and of the limited experience in remining, there exist serious conflicts
within the mining industry as to how to remine, what
will happen under given sets of circumstances, and
the cost of remining programs. In talking with many
industry personnel with some exposure in remining,
it was found that little or no agreement in an overall system is present and will not be until more
conclusive evidence and data is available for appraisal. The next few years are going to supply the
badly needed data on what happens in remining tailings, although each pond will exhibit its individual
characteristics. Most of the work on remining systems has not been published because the failures
have been greater than the successes.

Many systems have been considered. There is
ample reason to think that a dredge would be an ideal
device for remining of tailings; however a small
dredge was constructed and placed on top of a copper
tailings pond. It was not a success, and part of
the old relic can still be seen. The older ponds
are rather large, and the material is generally non-
consolidated. The high degree of saturation that
might exist should mean that little water would have
to be added. It should be possible to dredge from
the pond to a thickener for reprocessing. It is

unfortunate that this analysis is not supported in fact.

As previously indicated, the nature of old tailings ponds is unpredictable, and the test program with the small dredge indicated that it would be impossible to control the water in the pond on which the dredge operated. At times, the material would appear to be impervious and operations could proceed, but more often the percolation of the water through the tailings in an uncontrolled fashion indicated that the hydraulic head on the dam itself could possibly reach dangerous levels. It must be recalled that many of these older dams were built without today's scientific knowledge; the risks of having one of these dams fail outweigh any benefit that might be accrued from operating a dredge.

While the lack of control of the water was the main deterrent, several operating problems were evidenced. Dredges generally pump a low percentage of solids, which has a serious effect on the operating costs. It must be manned at all times, and in the presence of corrosive conditions, maintenance becomes a problem. This results in an overall economic condition that makes dredging somewhat less attractive.

Hydraulic monitors have been tested and used with some degree of success. In fact, of the various systems that have been tried, the monitors have given the greatest promise of continued success. No system is free of problems, however, and monitoring is no exception. If it were possible to start at the berm or the deepest part of impoundment and remove it and then have all of the tailings flow down grade to the pumps, a monitoring system could be very successful. This is not possible because no one will recommend a system which could cause a dam to fail and which could then result in an uncontrolled flow of tailings. Monitors, then, must start from up grade and work down from the surface, an operation which is much less efficient for materials removal.

This provides the same concerns over the uncontrolled input of water, how much seepage occurs and what head is built up at the dam itself.

Another problem that is quite evident is that the shear characteristics of tailings that have been standing a long period of time are very unpredictable. The main danger is that of removing large quantities of material and being required to have the pumps and monitors in close proximity of the resulting high wall and then have that high wall collapse and cover all of the equipment and personnel that might be involved.

Dry removal methods have also been receiving serious consideration. At this particular time, a rather extensive test program is under way on a copper tailings pond where low ground pressure D-7 Cats are being used to move the tailings to front-end loaders for trucking out of the pond. I have seen some of the work, but have not had the economics of the system made available to me. Studies indicate that this is a high cost method both from original investment and operating costs. Such a system is both capital and labor intensive.

There are two main problems related to bulldozers and trucks over and above the economics involved. The actual percentage of moisture and the variations in the type of material tend to make the operation of such equipment uncertain. A pond area may look dry on the surface, but the effective depth of a bulldozer appears to be less than ten feet before the conditions restrict their use. It is then necessary to go to another area and wait for a period of time to permit drying of the previously exposed surface. During a period of rain, such drying does not occur and all of the equipment may come to a halt. This alone may not be a problem, unless a consistent operating schedule of reprocessing is to be maintained

The second problem is that of maintenance. Many of the copper tailings ponds, particularly in Arizona,

are very acid in nature. It is not uncommon to en-
counter a pH of less than 3. There is little data
available that will allow the prediction of the life
expectancy of motorized equipment when used under
such conditions. It is necessary to plan on a rapid
writeoff and to provide for high maintenance costs
during operation.

Sauerman scrapers have been attempted, but the
results have left much to be desired. Many of the
ponds are of such size and design that an installation of Sauermans is not even feasible. Because of
the many limitations of such a system, it is not
considered to be viable for general consideration.

I would, therefore, like to address the rest of
this paper to a specific system and to an installation of this system. When I accepted the opportunity
to present this paper, I hoped that it would be possible to present conclusive information regarding
the operation of this installation, but the best laid
plans sometimes go awry; therefore, I must present
design data.

I am referring to MARCONAFLO as a system and
about an installation at Atlas Consolidated Mining
and Development Company at their operations on the
island of Cebu, Philippines. The disposal system
at this operation has been so ably described in the
paper by Mr. Roger Salazar.

MARCONAFLO was developed to answer some of our
own corporate needs in materials handling, and
simply it involves the use of slowly rotating or
oscillating jets of high pressure water working beneath the solids material, causing it to be undercut
and to collapse into this high pressure stream and
be slurried. The slurry flows into a sump from
which it is pumped for transportation to the desired
location. Marcona is using this system to pump iron
ore and magnetite sands to and from ocean-going ships.

There are many designs and applications of the

system, but the principle as described above remains
the same; jets working beneath the solids to slurry
the material and then pumping to a desired location.

At Atlas' Biga Concentrator, the emergency storage
ponds were approaching maximum height, and the question of remining or pumping through new lines over
the hill to another disposal area was considered. I
might add that Atlas might well have had a third alternate, and that is to wait for a typhoon and hope
for a failure to wash the impounded tailings down
the fertile valley below so that the pond could be
rebuilt and the cycle started over, but that approach
was not even considered.

The material that exists in this particular pond
was represented to be as shown in the first table,
(Table No. 1), which I assume is typical of many

Table No. 1
MARCONAFLO **Tailing** Reclaim System
for
Atlas Consolidated Mining & Development Corp.

Material Specifications

Material - Tailings From Copper Concentrator
Specific Gravity - 2.7
Screen Analysis   + 48 - 36%
- 48 +100 - 33%
-100 +200 - 16%
-200   16%
Moisture in Pond   15% to 30%

---

copper tailings. Please note that the estimate of
contained moisture varies from 15 to 30 percent.
Such finite information is also typical of what is
available from most tailings ponds. It was indicated
that a recovery of up to 440 tons per hour of dry
solids as 50 percent slurry was desired. This pond
is approximately 1000 feet in diameter and 70 feet

deep. To meet these requirements, a slurry pump with a capacity of 2400 gallons per minute at 100 foot head was selected. This pump requires 150 horsepower. This data is shown in Table No. 2

Table No. 2

MARCONAFLO TAILINGS RECLAIM SYSTEM
for
Atlas Consolidated Mining & Development Corp.

MARCONAFLO Slurry Pumping System

Slurry Pump Capacity - 2400 GPM @ 100 ft. head
Designed Slurry Density - 50% solids
Slurry Sp. Gr. @ 50% solids - 1.46
Solids Rate @ 50% Solids - 440 tons/hr.
Slurry Pump Power - 150 HP

With these parameters, a remining system was designed, presented by Marcona and accepted by Atlas. An artist's view of this system is shown here in Figure No. 1 It consists of a capsule 10 feet in diameter and 30 feet high, which contains the high pressure water lines to the MARCONAJETS which direct the water into the tailings for slurrying. This slurry flows back through the grizzly, which is constantly cleaned by the jet itself, and into the sump and slurry pump, all of which are in the capsule, along with drives, hydraulic gates and other necessary operating devices.

Because this unit is permanently installed for use whenever needed, it is mounted between four pilings driven into bedrock and connected to the berm of the pond by means of a bridge. This affords access to the unit for operation and maintenance and also the means of supporting both the water and slurry lines. A view of this is best shown in Figure No. 2.

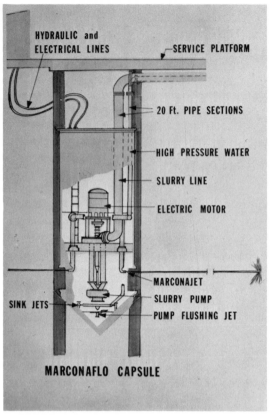

Artist's view of remining system for Atlas Consolidated at its Biga tailing reclamation operations.
Figure No. 1

In operation, the capsule is lowered into the tailings pond by means of sink jets placed in the bottom. These slurry the material directly beneath the capsule and as it lowers into this material, the resulting slurry is pumped away. Once it is lowered to its desired position, the sink jets are turned off, the capsule secured to the pilings and one or more of the MARCONAJETS are started. Each has the capacity to meet the requirements of 440 tons per hour so that control is exercised over the removal in such a way that the berm will remain intact. As the material is pumped from the pond, it

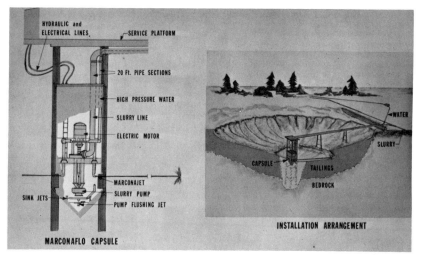

Capsule containing the high pressure water lines to the Marconajets is mounted between four pilings driven into bedrock and connected to the berm by bridge.   Figure No. 2

goes into a drop box for insertion into the tailings disposal pipeline. Once the pond is emptied, the capsule can be raised to the top and the pond refilled as needed.

To give you a better view of the capsule which is now on the site and installation under way (it was started up during December 1972), a photograph is shown of the capsule at the MARCONAFLO Manufacturing Center during construction (Figure No. 3). This view is the bottom of three sections so designed and manufactured for ease of shipment. The jets operate through openings in the side of the capsule, each being able to oscillate through 120 degrees. The material as slurried enters through these same openings which contain grizzlies to prevent foreign material such as trees or rocks from entering into the pump. As previously stated, the jets are designed to keep the grizzlies clean.

The next table (Table No. 3) gives a little more

Capsule at the Marconaflo Manufacturing Center in
San Francisco, California, during construction.

Figure No. 3

of the design features also water and power requirements, and the next (Table No. 4) are the best estimates of operating costs based on design parameters.
I should like to point out that these numbers do not
include engineering, design, capital, depreciation
or know-how. They are based on the circumstances as
represented at the location using the Philippine
labor costs. Each installation must be considered
on its own merits and conditions.

Table No. 3
MARCONAFLO TAILINGS RECLAIM SYSTEM
for
Atlas Consolidated Mining & Development Corp.

MARCONAFLO Repulping System

No. of MARCONAJETS - 4
High Pressure Water Required - 1250 GPM @ 450 PSI
High Pressure Water Pump Power - 460 HP
Designed Repulping Density - 50% solids

Table No. 4

MARCONAFLO TAILINGS RECLAIM SYSTEM

for

Atlas Consolidated Mining & Development Corp.

Direct Operating Costs/Ton of Solids

Power*
High Pressure Water Pump -	$0.0085
Slurry Pump --------------	0.0025
Misc. Power --------------	0.0003
	$0.0113/ton
Labor -------------------------------	0.0011
Maintenance** ----------------------	0.0032
Total	$0.0156/ton

 * Power Cost based on $0.01/Kw-Hr.
** Maintenance Costs based on 1,250,000
   tons of material reclaimed per year

For example, we expect to be testing early next year a unit of a different design in one of the ponds here in Arizona; but because of the poor quality of acid water with a pH of less than 3, the materials of construction and resulting costs will be different. It will be tested in a larger pond and will not be a permanent installation, so different operating characteristics are required.

I mentioned earlier that there are different designs utilizing the same principles and I would like to show two that are presently receiving serious consideration. The first (Figure No. 4) is a toboggan that can be pushed around and into the tailings. Bulldozers can move the material to the device containing the jets, pumps, controls, etc., and the front-end loaders and trucks are eliminated. This is a modification that might be required because of pond restrictions on the use of water. A more posi-

tive control is possible, although good control can
be maintained at all times.

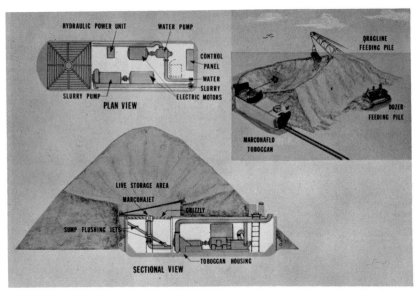

Suggested design for portable unit which can be
pushed around and under the tailing. Figure No. 4

The next one (Figure No. 5) is very special because the material in this pond contains some elemental phosphorus, enough that when exposed to the
air, explosions can occur. It is, therefore, necessary to retain a level of water above the slimes at
all times. This unit is designed to remove the
slimes from beneath the water in a slurry form to
eliminate the hazards of the other possible techniques.

It is rather obvious that the remining of tailings presents some very serious problems in materials handling. If it were easy and if it could be
done by conventional methods, many of the existing
ponds would have been remined prior to this time.

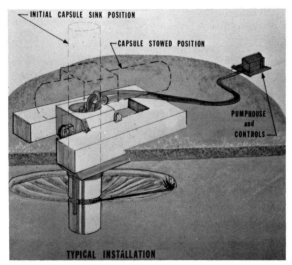

Unit designed for installations where material contains elemental phosphorus. It removes slime from beneath the water in a slurry form to eliminate hazards. Figure No. 5

This paper has been a rather quick exposure of the MARCONAFLO system of remining of tailings ponds. It has proven to be a very flexible system with a wide range of capacities, adaptable to a variety of remining applications. It is now being used or being considered for use in the remining of copper tailings, calcium carbonate, gypsum, culm banks and other such tailings impoundments. The system has been manufactured to handle from 100 tons per day to several thousand tons per day, is capable of being used in corrosive as well as non-corrosive environments, it is not necessarily restricted by adverse climatic conditions, and is applicable in ponds where there are many unknowns and hazards. This is particularly true when a reasonable control of water is required to reduce the possibility of dam failure.

It has been a pleasure to prepare this paper and to present to this Symposium some information regarding the MARCONAFLO remining system.

DISCUSSION

B. W. RUHFUS (Engelhard Minerals & Chemical Company): I have a question about the Marconaflo system. How do you control the consistency of the slurry and in what range does it vary on different projects? Can you say anything as to that?

NORMAN SIMS: A good question...one that's often asked. We find that in our own operations now, where we have these systems operating, working underneath the materials and having it collapsing into the stream's water, that this is an easy way of controlling percentage of solids. It depends -- the percentage of solids contained in the slurry is going to vary considerably with the particle size, and the material that you are slurrying. With fine iron ore, such as we're talking about here, it is in the 50 percent order of magnitude. We run into some variations in this. If we have no material above the stream of water that is collapsing into it and it has to reach out further, it then starts to approximate a regular hydraulicking system. This is why we try to keep our jets under the solids. When the jet is caving the solids there is the tendency to have a much higher percentage of solids. The particular capsule shown has flush jets which we do turn on for dilution if the slurry gets too dense for pumping purposes. We can control the flow of water in and out, and this is our basic means of control. We keep monitoring the system to see what the percentages are. We're working now to try to find a good, consistent, continuous recording device that gives us easy data on percent of solids in a slurry stream.

JOHN DAVID PARKER (N.C.C.M. Chingola Division): What Mr. Sims has mentioned so far appears to be the type of caisson mining of tailings dams. Has Mr. Sims any knowledge of the normal monitoring type systems that are used in South Africa and, hopefully, in the future in Zambia in the reclamation of tailings dams at Chingola?

NORMAN SIMS: I really think I ought to ask Jim Bean to comment on this. He's had a great deal more experience in monitoring than I. We have another gentleman in the audience by the name of John Miscovich who invented an Intelligiant which is used for monitoring; he has operated one all his life. I don't know what information you'd like to have on this, so maybe if you would elaborate a little on your question, please.

JOHN DAVID PARKER: I wonder whether you could go through any idea of monitoring a wide face, the whole face of the dam. If you were reclaiming the entire dam, a dried out dam, sort of monitoring from the side wall of that dam into the dam itself, reclaiming at something like 1,000 tons an hour.

NORMAN SIMS: This has been considered, talked about. Jim Bean, I'd like to ask you to comment on this one too. There are some real problems when you go into the dam itself. You almost have to work from the shallow end back toward that dam so that you don't disturb the dam while you remove the material, particularly when you have a little bit of uncontrolled water flow that might be building up some hydraulic head problems itself. So, Jim, would you want to comment on it, please?

JAMES J. BEAN (Consultant in Mineral Processing, Miami, Arizona): I'm not familiar with the African situation that you mentioned, but perhaps this comment will answer part of it. In retrieving the Ohio Copper tailing, we worked at the face of the dam, with the giant. The control was quite easy. Flotation density was supposed to be 20 percent solids, or thereabouts. We had a very sophisticated way of arranging this. We had a claxon horn near the man that was running the giant. We had a shaft bottle in the mill. The mill operator would take a density sample, and if the density was above what he wanted, he gave a long

toot and the number of points that it was above.
For instance, if it was 22, it was a long toot and
2 short toots. If it was below, it was a short toot
and a couple of long toots. And so, by this tooting
method we were able to hold the density at 20
percent solids quite easily. Now you might wonder
how the man at the nozzle controlled this. It was
as you might suspect. If the density was low, he
undercut the bank. If the density was high, he
undercut less. And he became quite expert at this.

The experience in Cornocopia, Oregon, was a
little different, because here the nozzle was
unattended. The mill foreman -- there was a second
mill running at the location of the dam -- made
about three trips a shift out to move the nozzle.
In this case, we had a thickener. But the thickener
was about two and a half miles from the dam itself,
and the tailing had to flow in a ditch around the
hillside and down through about a 300-foot inverted
siphon, 300 feet vertical, which was covered by
40 feet of snow all winter. So there was quite a
time loss between the time density could be
measured at the mill and the man at the nozzle.
But even so, we were able to maintain a nice, even
flow and run the mill very successfully.

Now, if you have 1,000 tons an hour or 2,000
tons an hour, I think that -- and this is guesswork
of course, because I never tried it -- it appears
to me that the same general situation would arise,
particularly if the monitor was manned and
controllable, which, of course, it would have to be.
You might have to have several others. I understand
from your description that you were going to sluice
from the top of the dam down into a well; this is
one thing that I've been advocating at Miami,
Arizona, and I haven't succeeded in selling. I'm
not sure I will, but I think it will work. There
has been a little work done along this line in our
area, which indicates that it will work and that
you can control the densities and reclaim tailing with
a density of something between 40 and 50 percent solids

AL WALLACH (Kaiser Engineers): About 20 years ago, here in Arizona, we remined tailing -- it was a relatively small operation, about 500 tons a day. The density was maintained very closely. The way it was done was that water was metered into the pond at the pumping rate of the discharge; monitoring was done from a barge right in the middle of the pond. The density was kept within about 2.0 percent by this method, that is, all the monitoring was done with pulp instead of with water. There was a slight amount of wear on the slurry pumps, but it worked very well.

UNKNOWN COMMENTATOR: There are some good examples, and I'm not an expert on the mining in Kalgoorlie, Australia, but the means that they used and developed in actually recirculating the slurry through the monitors, then through the pumps is an easy means of controlling the density. Also, in Tasmania at the Electrolitic Zinc Company's operations, they're reclaiming pyrite tailing. That's an interesting reference. In some of these cases there are pumps used that have integral motors that can drop 100, even 200 feet below the surface of the dam and, hopefully, keep themselves protected and eliminate the need for a caisson. Especially in Tasmania, in some of these operations where....caissons and causeways have been built, there are some difficulties. There is a great deal of experience in that part of the world, also in Malaysia. I haven't been there, but I imagine there are people in the audience who have.

MODERNIZATION OF COEUR d'ALENE

TAILINGS DISPOSAL PRACTICES

Roy E. Williams
Professor of Hydrogeology
College of Mines
University of Idaho, Moscow

ABSTRACT

The Coeur d'Alene Mining district in North Idaho
(primarily lead, zinc, silver, antimony, copper)
has served as a field laboratory for evaluating
several methods of disposing of mine wastes. This
paper deals with investigation of the effect of
different practices on ground water and surface water.
In all cases the water table in the Coeur d'Alene
valley bottom is within a few feet of the ground
surface, and most of the waste disposal sites are
situated above zones of predominantly lateral ground
water motion.

The disposal practices evaluated consist of,
1) spreading tailings over a valley bottom, 2) disposal of mill wastes alone in a tailings pond, 3)
disposal of mill wastes plus acid mine drainage and
process effluents in a tailings pond, 4) disposal of
tailings in a pond using a point inflow system, 5)
disposal in a pond using a peripheral discharge

system, and 6) disposal in more than one tailings pond connected in series, using a peripheral discharge system.

The results of the study indicate that: 1) old tailings which have been spread on a valley floor can be expected to be leached and have a detrimental effect on ground water and surface water quality, particularly if the tailings were produced by the poor recovery processes of the early days of mining; 2) properly designed and managed tailings ponds can be expected to treat mill wastes adequately; 3) tailings ponds alone cannot be expected to treat mining wastes other than mill wastes. Additional treatment in the tailings pond or of the pond effluent is required if most process effluents and some types of mine drainage are mixed with mill wastes; 4) point discharge systems frequently result in the discharge of poor quality water to the water table, and perhaps more importantly the practice facilitates the formation of a continually dissipating ground-water mound within the tailings pile after abandonment; 5) the use of a peripheral discharge system eliminates several problems with respect to ground-water quality and abandonment, even if the water held in the pond during operation is of poor quality. Ponds in series, using the peripheral discharge system, can be expected to produce the best effluent and to minimize lixiviation and the recharge of poor quality water to underlying ground water, both during operation and after abandonment.

INTRODUCTION

Mining has been the main industrial activity in the valley of the Coeur d'Alene river of northern Idaho for over 80 years (Figure 1). During this period several mining methods and waste disposal practices have been employed. Consequently the valley constitutes an unusual field laboratory wherein the long term effectiveness of various mining and disposal methods can be evaluated. The mining indus-

Map of Western United States showing the Coeur
d'Alene River Basin study area.   Figure No. 1

try, the U. S. Bureau of Mines, the Idaho Bureau of
Mines and Geology and the University of Idaho have
cooperated in such an evaluation for the past four
years.

At the present time there are nine large operating
mines and several smaller working mines in the Coeur
d'Alene basin. In addition to the regular mining
operations there is an antimony plant, a lead smelter,
and electrolytic-zinc plant, a phosphoric acid plant,
and several sulphuric acid plants. The area is noted
as one of the major silver, lead and zinc producing
areas in the world. In addition, the area yields
cadmium, copper, antimony, and gold, and has an overall mineral production of some 2.5 billion dollars.

The Coeur d'Alene Mining district produces all of
the antimony taken from Idaho and a major portion
of the state's gold, lead, silver, copper, iron,
and zinc. In 1968, 57 percent of the total mineral
production for the state of Idaho was from the Coeur
d'Alene area. On a national basis in mineral production, the State of Idaho ranked first in silver
and antimony, second in lead, and third in zinc. The
Sunshine Mine, located on Big Creek in the Coeur
d"Alene district, produced nearly all of the antimony
in 1968 for the nation (U. S. Bur. Mines, p. 172, 235,
644, 1013, and 1164)[1]. In addition, the district
contains the first, second, third, and fifth ranked
silver mines in the United States. The importance
of the South Fork of the Coeur d'Alene River to the
economy of Idaho and the U. S. should not be underestimated.

During the early days of mining tailings were
distributed over valley bottoms or in piles. Many
of these tails were metal rich because hand or
gravity separation techniques were employed. Some
of these tails have been reworked but in some locations the old tailings are still present and are
high in metal content. All recovery is now done by
flotation and since 1968 all mill wastes have been

collected in tailings ponds.

GEOLOGY

The rocks of the area consist mainly of the Precambrian Belt Series which is composed of fine-grained argillites and quartzites associated with smaller amounts of carbonate-bearing, dolomitic rocks. Quartz and sericite are the principal minerals within the Belt Series; accessory minerals include feldspar, muscovite, magnetite, illmenite, zircon, tourmaline, rutile, and titanite.

Tertiary Columbia River Basalt extends from Coeur d'Alene Lake ten miles up the Main Stem of the Coeur d'Alene; the main basalt outcrops occur around the mouth of the river. (See Figure 2 for map of basin). The river valleys are partially filled with alluvial deposits which vary in thickness from less than one foot to several hundred feet. The deepest and most extensive alluvial deposits occur along the Main Stem. The alluvium consists mostly of unconsolidated sand and gravel. Tailings from previous mine milling operations have formed a veneer over much of the valley areas. One of the most extensive of these areas is located at Cataldo Missions Flats.

At the head of the Coeur d'Alene basin there is evidence of glaciation which occurred during Pleistocene time. Glacial material can be found in scattered patches on the upper reaches of both forks of the Coeur d'Alene River. Some of the alluvial deposits which comprise the main aquifers of the basin are of glacial origin.

HYDROGEOLOGY

The flows of the streams of the Coeur d'Alene basin are extremely variable so that flow rate must be considered when evaluating water quality data. Winter and spring floods caused by rain and melting snow are common.

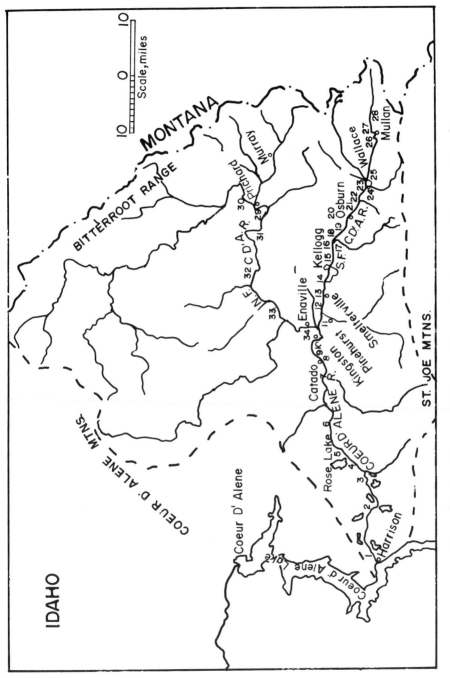

Map of the Coeur d'Alene River Basin.   Figure No. 2

TAILING DISPOSAL TODAY

Along the main stem of the Coeur d"Alene river the water table is above the surface of the adjacent valley floor during the spring months. The flooding exposes large areas of old tailings to river flow during these months. The river subsequently becomes laden with sediment derived in large part from old mine tailings distributed on the valley floor. It remains so laden during most of the spring and early summer.

PREVIOUS WORK IN AREA

Much of the work of the past has reflected the condition of the Coeur d'Alene river prior to the establishment of tailings ponds (completed in 1968) and with raw sewage being dumped into the river.

Kemmerer, et al., (1923)[2], Ellis (1940)[3], Chupp (1955)[5] and a study by Cornell, Howland, Hayes observed conditions which would be expected of this type of disposal practice.

Mink, Williams and Wallace (1971)[6] reported on the condition of the river after the installation of tailings ponds by all mines. They observed that the main problem currently is metallurgical process effluents which find their way into the river. This conclusion is portrayed by the high peak in Figure 3 which shows the zinc content of the river versus distance from its mouth. The secondary peak at station 24 on the South Fork is the result of leaching of old tailings by ground-water which will be discussed subsequently.

EFFECT OF FLOW RATE AND OLD TAILINGS ON THE VALLEY FLOOR ON RATE OF MASS TRANSPORT

The curve shown in Figure 3 changes considerably with the flow rate at the time of sampling. To visualize the effect of flow rate on zinc concentration during periods of high flow, a graph was prepared showing flow rate and zinc concentration plotted against time. (See Figs. 4 and 5). The

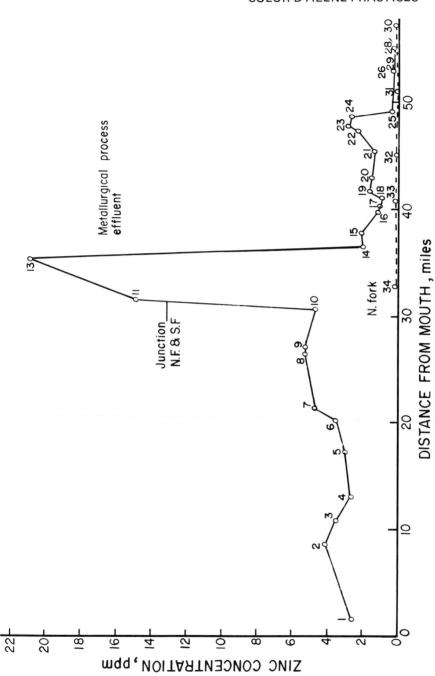

Zinc concentration vs. distance for stations on Coeur d'Alene River, September 14, 1969.

Figure No. 3

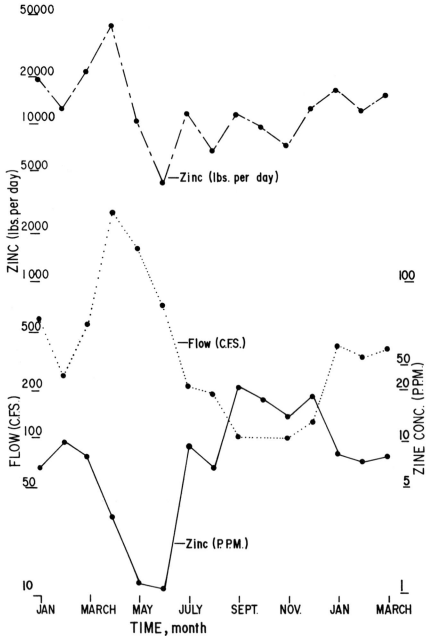

Zinc mass transport, zinc concentration and flow
vs. time for Station 13, Coeur d'Alene River,
1969-1970.   Figure No. 4

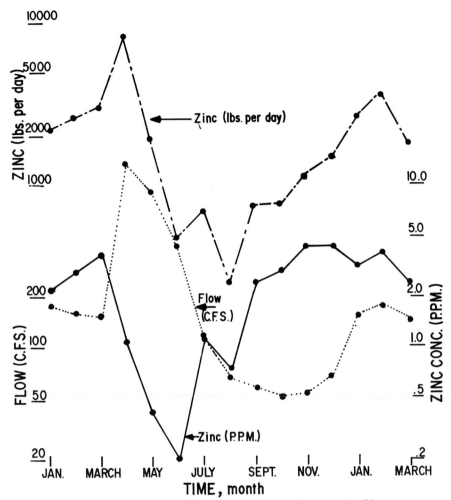

Zinc mass transport, zinc concentration and flow
vs. time for Station 22, Coeur d'Alene River,
1969-1970.   Figure No. 5

graphs show a relationship of lower concentration during high flow and higher concentration during low flow, but the increase in flow during flood stage overrides the importance of the decrease in zinc concentration due to dilution. Consequently, greater values of pounds per day of zinc going down the river occur during periods of lowest concentrations of zinc. This relationship indicates that flood waters introduce a source of zinc in addition to present day waste disposal operations like the one causing the high peak in Figure 3. It was observed that during the high flow stage the suspended load in the river first increased noticeably upon flowing through a flat area below station 21 where old tailings have been deposited by the river. We conclude, therefore, that the exposure of old tailings to the river during flood stage constitutes an important source of heavy metals to the river in addition to the industrial sources currently operating. Fortunately the practice of spreading tails over valley floors is no longer employed.

DESIGN OF TAILINGS PONDS TO MINIMIZE LEACHING OF OLD MINE TAILINGS BY GROUND WATER

This phase of the Coeur d'Alene district studies deals with the interpretation and a proposed solution to the presence of heavy metals in the ground water and surface water of a basin which joins the South Fork and causes the zinc anomaly at station 24 in Figure 3. The causes and sources of high heavy metal concentrations observed within the ground water and adjacent surface water of the tributary basin were investigated. The problem was particularly perplexing initially because the ground water and surface waters are higher in metal concentrations and lower in pH than the effluent from the only significant mine tailings disposal system located upgradient in the valley.

Soil and sediment samples (much of which consist of old jig tailings) collected from the stream channel and along the sides of the stream in the valley were found to contain up to 6.0 percent lead and 4.4 percent zinc. Copper concentration of the sediments had a mean value of approximately 430 ppm. More detailed analyses of the samples of intermixed soils and old mine tailings are presented by Galbraith, Williams and Siems (1972)[7]. This mixture of natural sediments and old jig tailings proved to be the source of heavy metal ions present in the ground water and surface water which causes the zinc anomaly at station 24 shown in Figure 3. Our proposed solution consists in part of a tailings pond design which minimizes tailings pond leakage, thereby providing for minimum raising of the water table into the old jig tailings. Laboratory and mathematical model output which provide the basis for this design are presented herein.[8] The details of the models are given by Kealy (1970) and the entire problem is discussed in greater detail by Mink, Williams and Wallace (1972)[9] and by Williams, Kealy and Mink (in review)[10].

Many of the mountain valleys in the Coeur d''Alene mining district of northern Idaho have been incised by erosion into the metamorphic rocks of the belt supergroup. Some of these valleys are partially filled with outwash from pleistocene glacial activity. The belt rocks have low permeability, except where faulted; large, deep mines in the area customarily have minimal problems with mine drainage rates. On the other hand, the glacial outwash which partially fills many of the valleys is commonly a permeable aquifer.

As stated previously the early day mining operations which used gravity separation did not recover zinc from the ores. Lead bearing minerals were recovered by "jigging". The tailings from the jigging process were spread over the top of the sand and gravel outwash in the valley under investigation. The jig tailings were produced by concentrators upstream in the canyon from the late 1880's until the late 1920's and early 1930's when it first became economically feasible to recover zinc. Tailings for this period showed lead assays of 0.9 percent to 1.5+ percent. No assays were conducted for zinc, but the soil analyses mentioned previously indicate that the zinc content was high.

In August, 1968, two tailings ponds were installed in series in the sand and gravel aquifer alongside the tributary to the Coeur d'Alene river. Residents of the area downgradient from the tailings ponds reported a rise in water levels in their wells shortly after the ponds were put into use, suggesting that the tailings ponds contribute water to the ground-water flow system. The tailings pond inflow is a point source and leakage to the sand and gravel aquifer occurs through the embankment walls. In addition, the decant system discharges onto and presumably into the sand and gravel aquifer. Analyses of ground-water samples collected downgradient from the ponds after they were installed revealed that the ground water in portions of the aquifer is acid and contains higher than normal concentrations of lead and zinc.

Twelve sampling points were established and monitored from June, 1969 through April, 1970 with major emphasis on the summer months. These dates include only the period after tailings ponds were put into operation. No satisfactory sampling point was found for ground water in the sand and gravel aquifer above the ponds. The water table does not "crop out" at the ground surface as it does below the ponds, and no wells are available at acceptable locations. The zinc, lead, and cadmium concentrations in ground water not associated with old mine tailings or ore deposits in the Coeur d'Alene basin is normally .1 ppm.

Samples from tailings pond inflow and outflow, seepages, springs, and wells were analyzed to obtain information on the ground water quality below the pond. Details of the analyses are presented by Mink, Williams and Wallace (1972)[9].

The samples revealed that the ponds are not the direct source of high zinc concentrations observed in the creek and in ground water. The pond water contains approximately one-fourth as much zinc as the creek.

But based on 14 samples, a lower zinc concentration
was observed in the creek above the tailings pond
(3.1 ppm) than below the tailings ponds (5.9 ppm).
The outflow from the tailings pond decant system
has a mean zinc concentration of 1.1 ppm (based on
5 samples). The seepages from the basin's sand and
gravel aquifer reflect a high zinc concentration in
ground water a considerable distance from the ponds.
These concentrations reach 31.0 ppm to 37.2 ppm zinc.
Values of pH and lead and cadmium concentration
display similar distributions. These data indicate
that the quality of the tailings pond effluent re-
charging the ground-water flow system degenerates
after it has entered the sand and gravel aquifer
occupying the valley bottom.

GROUND-WATER FLOW SYSTEM

Figure 6 shows a longitudinal cross section of the
valley wherein the tailings ponds are located; also
shown is an interpreted flow system which is influenced by recharge from the tailings ponds. The
thickness of the aquifer is estimated but seismic
lines have recently been run to determine the exact
thickness. These data will be available shortly.

Before the tailings ponds were installed, it is
believed that the major ground water discharge area
was at the lower end of the valley where the valley
narrows and the alluvium thins out. The proposed
flow system shown in Figure 6 indicates that a
discontinuous discharge area now exists from a point
directly below the settling pond to the lower end of
the valley. Evidence for this conclusion consists
of several springs which now emerge between the ponds
and the downgradient end of the valley even during dry
weather. The discharge area below the tailings ponds
brings ground water into contact with the jig tailings
in the upper portion of the sand and gravel aquifer.
Lixiviation of the jig tailings then occurs. Virtually
all ground-water discharges into the creek before
leaving the valley because the thickness of the sand
and gravel aquifer thins to zero in a narrow con-

striction above the confluence of the creek and the
main river. Water level measurements show the water
table to be near the surface throughout the valley.
This ground-water discharge mechanism transfers the
poor quality ground water to the stream which flows
into the South Fork of the Coeur d'Alene river at
station 24 in Figure 3. Mechanisms by which the
ground water acquires dissolved ions from the old
tailings in the aquifer are discussed by Galbraith,
Williams and Siems (1972)[7].

SOLUTION TO THE PROBLEM

The tailings ponds used in the valley under study
have a single point inflow for tailings. The ponds
are installed in a sand and gravel aquifer, the
upper portion of which is intermixed with old jig
tailings. Under the present design, clear water
lies against permeable embankments causing leakage
and recharge of the ground-water flow system. The
decanted effluent also flows onto and presumably into
the aquifer. Consequently, the water table is raised
into contact with the old jig tailings, causing leaching
of metals. If contact of the ground-water table with
old jig tailings in the upper portion of the sand
and gravel aquifer is to be minimized, both sources
of recharge water must be minimized. Elimination
of ground-water recharge from the decant system
effluent is straight forward.

The rate of leakage by seepage from these and other
tailings ponds can be minimized by utilizing a technique
developed by Kealy (1972)[11] during an investigation
of a tailings pond located in northern Washington. The
physical features of that pond are described in detail
by Kealy (1970)[8], Kealy and Busch (1971)[12], and Kealy
and Williams (1971)[13]. The pond contains tailings
from a lead-zinc mine which produces approximately
standard-grind mill tailings. The pond has a peripheral
discharge system and the water is decanted from the
clean portion of the free water area.

A lower permeability occurs at depth, and there is

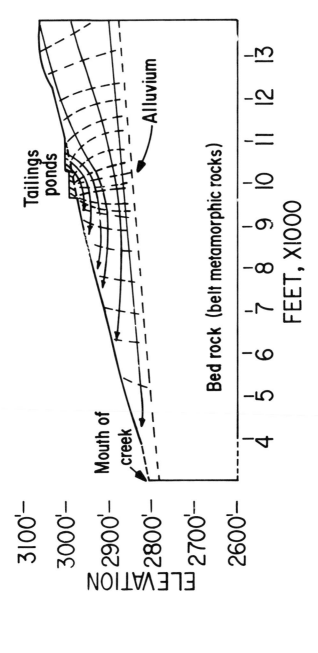

Proposed ground-water flow system in valley fill material beneath tailings ponds.
Figure No. 6

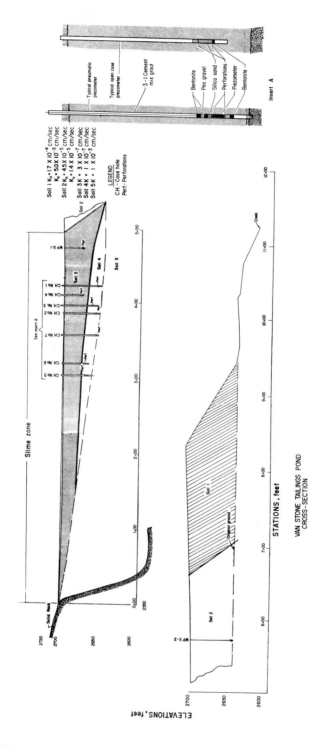

Cross section of tailings pond modeled showing permeability distribution. Figure No. 7

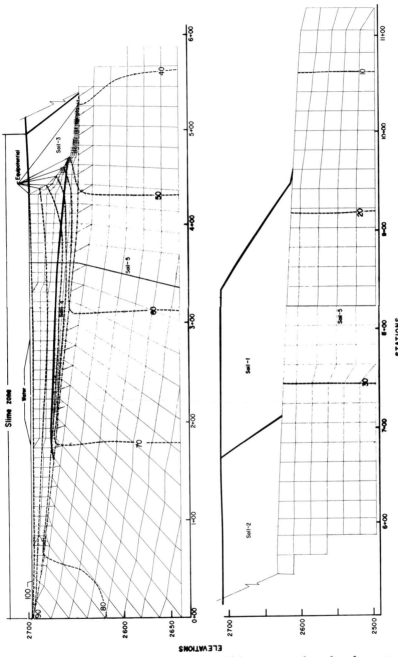

Finite element model of tailings pond embankment
(all dimensions in feet).   Figure No. 8

a lateral variation in permeability. The permeability distribution considered as being most representative is shown in Figure 7. Permeability values from every Shelby tube sample extracted can be obtained from Kealy and Busch (1971)[12] and Kealy (1972)[11]. Piezometers were installed at selected locations on the tailings pile so that field fluid potential values and the configuration of the free water surface could be measured.

The permeability distribution and boundary conditions shown in Figure 7 were used as a basis for the construction of a finite element mathematical model as shown in Figure 8. Details of the application of the mathematical model to problems such as this are presented by Taylor and Brown (1967)[14], by Kealy and Williams (1971)[13], and Kealy and Busch (1971)[12]. The objective of the application of the model to this particular tailings pond was to examine the structural and environmental characteristics of the pond and to investigate ways of improving the design of this and other tailings ponds if necessary.

Observed field ground-water conditions indicated two basic types of ground-water flow systems exist beneath the tailings pond depending on the time of year: (1) a saturated connected system; that is, tailings, embankment, and substrata are hydraulically connected during high ground-water conditions; and (2) a disconnected system during low ground-water conditions in which an unsaturated zone exists directly beneath the tailings. Both the hydraulically connected and hydraulically disconnected systems were modeled using the finite element method. The fluid potential distribution for the connected system is shown in Figure 8. However, the model output showed that maximum flow occurs with the hydraulically disconnected system. The discharge from the bottom of the two-dimensional model (unit width in the third dimension) is portrayed in Figure 9. If the flows from each of the elements at the bottom of the slime zone (soils 3 and 4) are summed and the unit width of the two-dimensional cross section extended to

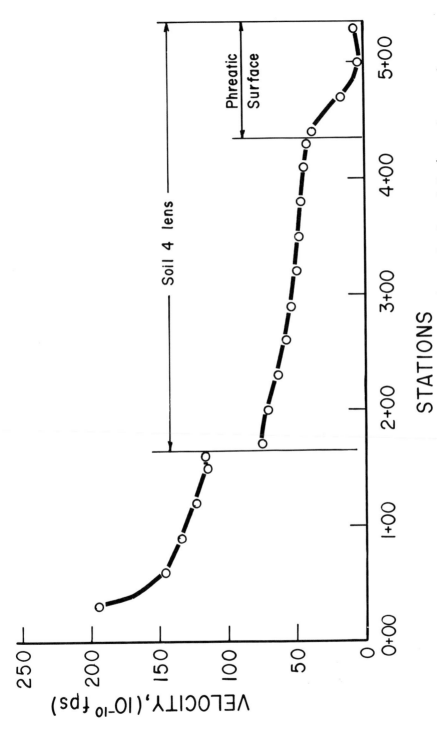

Velocity profile for pond losses as predicted by mathematical model (station numbers represent hundreds of feet). Figure No. 9

cover one acre, then the rate of leakage from the bottom of the pond, as predicted by the model, is only 140 gallons per day per acre.

Further, manipulation of the free water body in the mathematical model of the tailings pond revealed that the most significant ground-water outflow beneath the pond must come from the natural-ground-- tailings contact and from the soil 3 (slimes)--soil 2 interface (see Figure 10). Therefore, by controlling the pond water level, the leakage along the soil 3-soil 2 contract can be minimized, if not eliminated. In addition, proper preparation of the natural ground- pond contact would eliminate leakage along this contact also. Therefore, the transmission from the pond of water or water containing detrimental substances can be essentially eliminated. However, it is critical that this condition results only if the pond water level and permeability (slime distribution) at the two contact areas are controlled. Control can be maintained with a peripheral discharge system and with a decant system designed to maintain the free water surface over the slime zone. A system so designed is also more stable structurally because the phreatic line in the embankment is near the base of the embankment thereby providing for a maximum factor of safety. The relation between the phreatic line delineated by the mathematical model and slope stability is presented by Kealy and Williams (1971)[13].

The field piezometer water levels are in close agreement to pressures produced by the mathematical model. Most of the mining companies in Coeur d'Alene valley are currently adopting the design criteria derived from this study in order to maximize stability and to prevent leakage and recharge of the ground- water flow system which may leach old tailings or which may contribute poor quality water to the water table directly.

TAILINGS PONDS AS A TECHNIQUE FOR TREATING WASTES

This phase of the Coeur d'Alene district studies

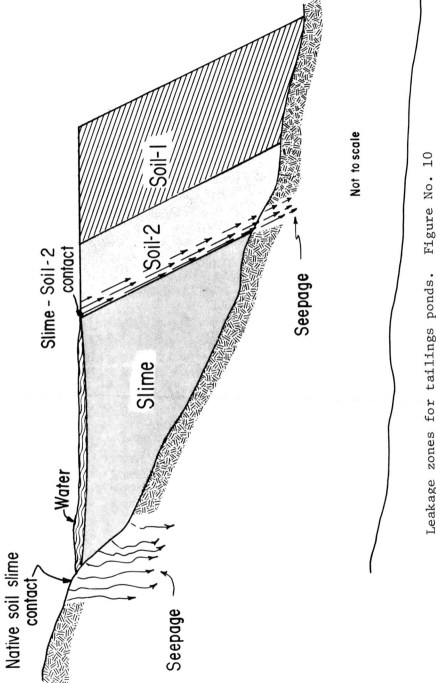

Leakage zones for tailings ponds. Figure No. 10

was designed to evaluate tailings ponds as a means of renovating various types of mining and metallurgical process wastewaters. It was also the purpose of this phase to determine whether other types of treatment are necessary to improve the efficiency of tailings ponds in the reduction of constituents under certain unusual conditions. Other problems associated with design of mine tailings ponds were investigated concomitantly.

DATA COLLECTION

Conclusions in this phase of the Coeur d'Alene studies are based on samples collected from the waste operations of three major mines in the Coeur d'Alene district. Seven mines were studied but only three representative ones are discussed herein. The data were collected from June 12, 1969 through June 22, 1971, a period after the mining industry of the district constructed tailings ponds to curb pollution. The tailings ponds were established by the mining industry by the fall of 1968; the exact dates for the establishment of each pond will be given later under the discussion of each individual mine.

Points of data collection reported herein include inflows and outflows to and from each settling pond for each of the mines. A description of each sample point and its location is presented along with the discussion of each mine. More detailed information on the three mines discussed herein, as well as on the other mines in the basin, will be presented by Mink, Williams, Wallace and McNay (in review)[15].

POND DESIGN

Most of the tailings ponds used by the mining industry are the classical type and consists of a dike, an inflow,and a decant system. Two main differences among the ponds in the district are the type of waste being discharged into the ponds and the method of discharging waste into the ponds. The majority of the mines studied are discharging only concentrator waste into the tailings ponds; but two mines are discharging both industrial waste and concentrator effluent.

The method of discharging waste into the pond is either through a peripheral discharge system or a point discharge system. Mine 1 now uses a peripheral discharge system for the main portion of its pond but other types of systems have been used in the past; mine 2 used a point discharge system until recently when a movable point discharge system was installed; mine 3 uses a peripheral discharge system with the main tailings pond located in series with polishing basins.

MINE 1

The tailings pond for Mine 1 is a 160 acre pond which receives wastewater and solids from the mine, concentrator, phosphoric acid plant, and raw sewage from a nearby community (see Fig. 11). The center portion of the pond, consisting of approximately 40 acres, was established in 1930 and has received concentrator waste and mine drainage since that time. In 1968 the pond size was increased to a total of approximately 160 acres. A pond for gypsum waste from the phosphoric acid plant, approximately 60 acres, was built to the west of the old pond, and a pond of about 60 acres was built to the east of the old pond to handle mine drainage and sewage. The concentrator effluent is now distributed in a peripheral discharge system around the eastern portion of the pond to help strengthen and seal the dike around the pond. A decant system was installed in the east half of the pond, and this discharges into the South Fork of the Coeur d'Alene River. The phosphoric acid pond outfall flows into the pond containing mine drainage, concentrator effluent, and sewage. In the future, the entire pond area will operate as a single unit along with a two-stage treatment of the effluent.

The discussion of the tailings ponds for Mine 1 will be presented in two parts. The first discussion

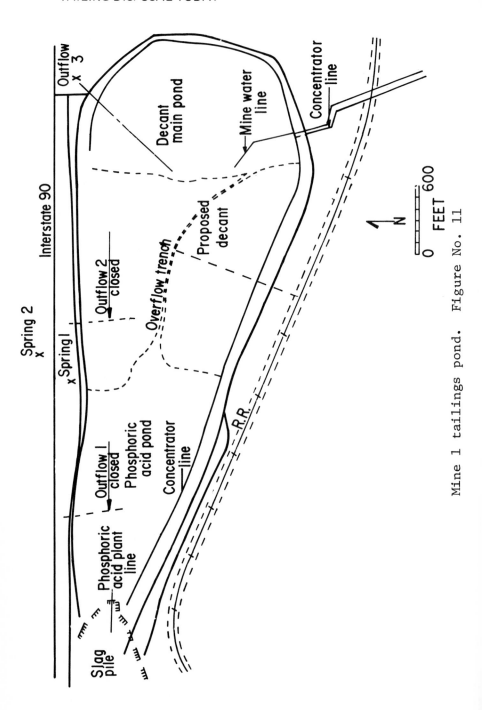

Mine 1 tailings pond. Figure No. 11

deals with the pond receiving only phosphoric acid
plant discharge, and the second discussion deals with
the pond receiving discharge from the phosphoric acid
pond, mine drainage, concentrator effluent, and domestic
sewage.

The phosphoric acid pond displays a statistically
significant decrease in pH, fluoride, suspended solids,
cadmium, and copper between inflow and outflow. A
significant increase at the .05 level was observed
for electrical conductivity and lead concentration.
Zinc concentration was also observed to increase
within the tailings pond, but the increase was found
to be non-significant at the .05 level. The antimony
concentration was below the detectable limit for both
the phosphoric pond inflow and outflow. (See Table I).

TABLE I

MINE 1 PHOSPHORIC ACID POND MEAN INFLOW AND OUTFLOW
CONCENTRATIONS (ppm)**

Parameter	Inflow	Outflow
pH*	2.6	2.4
E.C.*	4241	5239
F*	503.6	348.3
S.S.	46086	125
Cd*	0.4	0.2
Cu	0.3	0.1
Pb*	0.2	0.5
Sb	5.0	5.0
Zn	12.2	16.9

*Significant difference at .05 level between inflow
and outflow mean values.

**ppm except pH and E.C.

The main tailings pond receives the effluent from
the phosphoric acid pond along with effluent from
mine drainage, concentration process, and domestic
sewage. Samples were collected and analyzed from all
mine related inflows and the pond outflow. The
sewage inflow was not sampled, but a few tests have

been conducted for coliform counts in the pond outflow;
all were negative.

Mean pH of the tailings pond outflow is low. The
high pH of the concentrator effluent does not offset
the low pH of the other two inflows to the main pond.
The low pH, high conductivity, and fluoride values of
the pond are caused by the phosphoric acid pond outflow
and mine drainage, which also contributes a large
portion of the cadmium, lead, and zinc to the tailings
pond. The highest copper concentration occurs within
the concentrator effluent, which along with mine
drainage causes copper to be present in the pond outflow. The tailings pond is effectively reducing the
suspended solids but is inefficient with respect to
all other parameters except possibly coliform organisms
This is due to the nature of the inflows, primarily the
acid water entering the pond which causes an acid
condition to exist (see Table II). Preliminary tests
on the ability of the combined mine wastes to eliminate
coliform from the sewage entering the pond have revealed no coliform organisms leaving the pond.
However, these tests must be viewed as preliminary
in nature. Possible elimination mechanisms are now
under investigation.

Table II

MINE 1 MAIN POND MEAN INFLOWS AND OUTFLOW CONCENTRATIONS (ppm)**

Parameter	Mine Drainage	Concentrator Effluent	Phosphoric Acid Pond Outflow	Outflow
pH	3.3	10.1	2.4	3.0
E.C.	2122	919	5239	2615
F	0.8	2.4	348.3	116.8
S.S*	3700	277206	125	41
Cd	0.4	0.02	0.2	0.3
Cu	0.6	1.9	0.1	0.8
Pb	2.9	0.1	0.5	2.1
Sb	<5.0	<5.0	<5.0	<5.0
Zn	133.6	0.2	16.9	109.2

* Significant difference at .05 level between inflow and outflow mean values.

**ppm except pH and E.C.

MINE 2

The tailings pond system for Mine 2 was installed in February 1968. The effluent from Mine 2 is piped approximately one and one-half miles to the settling basin located in the lower portion of a valley (see Fig. 12). The highly alkaline solution from an electrolytic antimony plant enters the tailings pond together with tailings from the flotation process. The 14 acre pond embankments are constructed of valley fill material (glacial outwash) and waste rock from the mine. The dike at the lower portion of the pond currently is approximately 35 feet high. The inflow system now utilizes eight inch inflow pipe from which tailings can be discharged along the lower portion of the pond. During the first two years of operation, a single point inflow at the upper end of the pond was used. Two decants are located along the west edge of the pond, and effluent is discharged into a stream flowing beside the west edge of the pond. Inefficient sealing of the pond allows much leakage to occur through the bottom and sides of the pond because of the high permeability of the dike and valley floor material. The leakage forms a pool at the toe of the lowermost embankment and causes anomalous seepage into the Coeur d'Alene River.

Analysis of pond 2 inflow and outflow water revealed a 99.92% reduction in suspended solids within the tailings pond. A significant increase was observed for pH and antimony concentration within the tailings pond. Upon further investigation it was determined that this increase is due to wastes with high pH and antimony concentration entering the tailings pond during the early morning hours (See Figs. 13 and 14) when samples were not ordinarily collected. A slight but non-significant increase was also noted in electrical conductivity. The elements cadmium, copper, lead, and zinc were observed to be below detectable limits in both the inflow and outflows (See Table III).

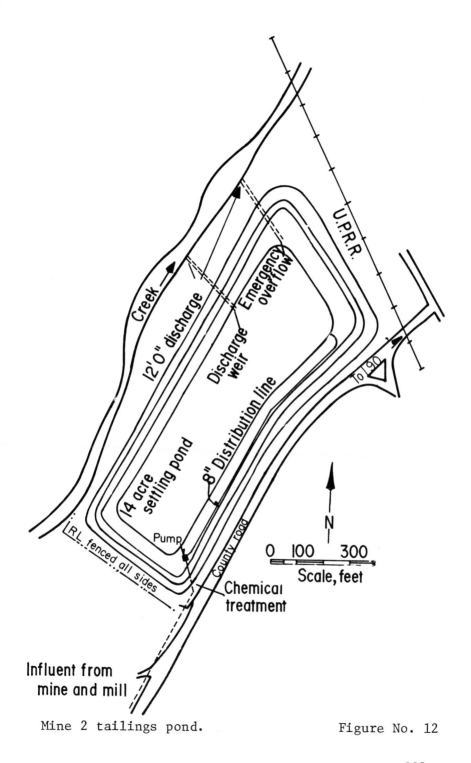

Creek

12'0" discharge

Emergency overflow

U.P.R.R.

Discharge weir

8" Distribution line

To 90

14 acre settling pond

R.L. fenced all sides

Pump

County road

Chemical treatment

N

0   100   300
Scale, feet

Influent from
mine and mill

Mine 2 tailings pond.   Figure No. 12

663

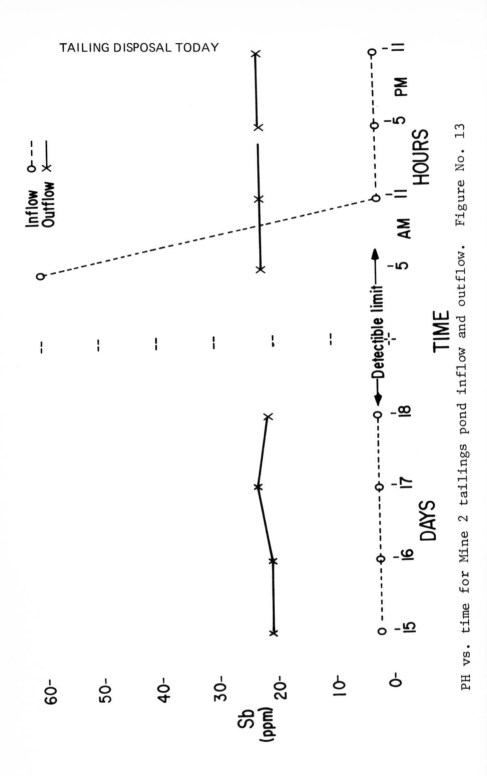

PH vs. time for Mine 2 tailings pond inflow and outflow. Figure No. 13

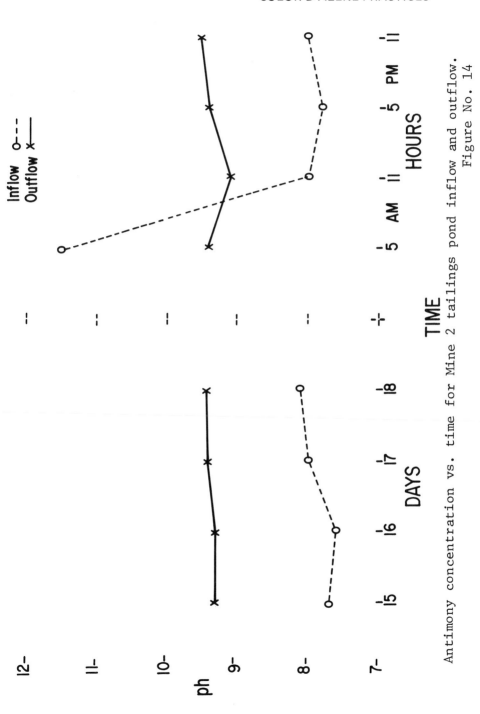

Antimony concentration vs. time for Mine 2 tailings pond inflow and outflow.
Figure No. 14

TABLE III

MINE 3 INFLOW AND OUTFLOW CONCENTRATIONS (ppm)**

Parameter	Inflow	Outflow
pH	8.8	10.1
E.C.	1045	1063
S.S.*	88457	70
Cd	0.02	0.02
Cu	0.1	0.1
Pb	0.1	0.1
Sb*	8.9	33.3
Zn	0.1	0.1

* Significant difference at .05 level between inflow and outflow mean values.
**ppm except pH and E.C.

MINE 3

There are four tailings ponds in the waste disposal system for Mine 3. They are in series (See Fig. 15), but are operated as independent ponds. Each pond is capable of receiving tailings independently of the other three ponds.

When a given pond is in use, tailings are fed into it and water is decanted from that pond into a common collection pipe which either transports the decant water to a reclaim sump or to a small polishing basin referred to in Figure 15 as the clarification pond. In our data collection and analysis program, we refer to this pond as pond number 5, however, it is not to be confused with a classical tailings pond. Its purpose is merely to provide for removal of any suspended solids which might leave tailings ponds 1, 2, 3, or 4 via the decant system.

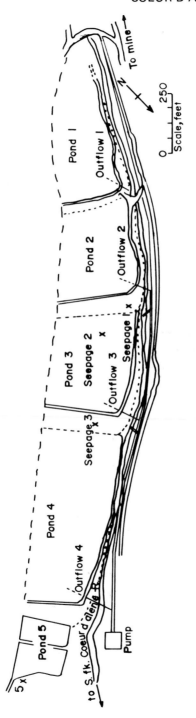

Mine tailings pond system. Figure No. 15

A peripheral type discharge system is used to in-
ject the tailings into ponds 1, 2, 3, or 4. Tailings
are distributed via the system along the embankment
on the northeast end and northwest side of each
pond. The southwest sides of ponds 2, 3, and 4
consist of the toe of the embankment of ponds 1, 2,
and 3 respectively. The southeast side of pond
number 1 is the valley wall. All ponds lie along
a creek which flows along the northwest of the entire
series of ponds including the clarification pond.
The effluent from the clarification pond, which may
constitute the effluent from any of the four tailings
ponds at a given time, is discharged directly into
the creek.

A significant reduction between inflow and outflow
mean values was observed for pH, electrical conductivity and suspended solids, the latter having
a 99.99% reduction within the settling pond. The
other parameters analyzed, including cadmium, copper,
lead, antimony, and zinc, were below their respective
detectable limits for both the inflow and outflows
(see Table IV). Williams, Wallace and Mink (1971)[16]
determined that the effluent from Mine 3 tailings ponds
has an insignificant effect on the creek and on the
South Fork of the Coeur d' Alene River.

TABLE IV

MINE 3 MEAN INFLOW AND OUTFLOW CONCENTRATIONS (ppm)**

Parameter	Inflow	Outflow 1	Outflow 2	Outflow 3	Outflow 4	Outflow 5
pH*	7.8	7.5	7.3	7.4	7.6	7.4
E.C.*	477	266	324	352	318	293
S.S.*	392786	17	38	79	43	31
Cd	0.02	0.02	0.02	0.02	0.02	0.02
Cu	0.1	0.1	0.1	0.1	0.1	0.1
Ph	0.1	0.1	0.1	0.1	0.1	0.1
Sb	5.0	5.0	5.0	5.0	5.0	5.0
Zn	0.1	0.1	0.2	0.1	0.1	0.1

* Significant difference at .05 level between inflow and outflow mean values.
** ppm except pH and E.C.

SUMMARY OF RENOVATION CHARACTERISTICS

The quality of certain wastewaters discharging from a mining operation can be greatly altered through the use of a tailings pond. This change in water quality is, in the majority of cases, an improvement. Comparison of inflow and outflow values for tailings ponds in the Coeur d'Alene district has provided insight into what can be expected to occur within a tailings pond.

Mineral extraction in the district at the present time consists of selective flotation to concentrate the ore. Effluent from this process is the only material received by the tailings ponds at one of the mines discussed herein. The pond at a second mine receives effluent from the concentrating process, along with effluent from a phosphoric acid plant, mine drainage, and raw sewage from a nearby town. A third mine uses its pond for effluent from a concentrator and an electrolytic antimony plant.

The tailings pond receiving only concentrator effluent was observed to reduce suspended solids by 99+% when properly managed. The outflows of this pond do not contain toxic elements in dangerous concentrations provided a small amount of dilution is available. The tailings ponds receiving acid mine drainage and metallurgical process effluents were observed not to be effective in adequately reducing concentrations of fluoride, cadmium, lead, antimony, and zinc. The pH of the pond receiving acid drainage and process effluent is very low while pH of the pond receiving effluent from an electrolytic antimony plant is considerably above neutral. Antimony is also detrimentally high in this effluent.

Ponds having inflow systems which permit the coarser tailings to accumulate in the interior of the pond area can be expected to produce a tailings pile underlain by a ground-water mound. The mound persists in a humid climate because such tailings piles permit the infiltration of essentially all precipitation falling on the tailings after abandonment. The existence of such a mound may be harmless or harmful depending on the availability of ions that may be leached from the tailings as the mound recharges the regional ground-water body.

Proper design and maintenance of tailings ponds utilizing the peripheral discharge system will create an acceptable effluent for ponds receiving only effluent from the concentration process. Tailings ponds being considered for metallurgical process effluents or acid mine drainage should undergo careful study to find an effective and economical way of producing an acceptable effluent. This could involve chemical treatment of the inflows or outflows, or recycling of the water. In rare cases it may be possible to combine high pH and low pH effluents to minimize treatment costs. However, it is the opinion of the writer that the best approach is an intensified research effort to develop metallurgical processes which are more efficient. Such processes would not only prevent pollution of the environment, but would provide for better recovery of the metal in question. The long term result would be an improved metal supply picture for the United States.

REFERENCES CITED

1. U. S. Bureau of Mines, 1969, Minerals Yearbook,
    v. I, II, and III: U. S. Govt. Printing Office,
    Washington, D. C. 1013 p.

2. Kemmerer, G., J. F. Bovard and W. R. Boorman,
    1923, Northwestern Lakes of the United States;
    Biological and Chemical Studies with Reference
    to possibilities in Production of Fish: Bull,
    Bur. Fisheries, Vol. 39, No. 944, 138 p.

3. Ellis, M. M., 1940, Pollution of the Coeur d'
    Alene River and Adjacent Waters by Mine Wastes:
    Special Scientific Report 1, U. S. Bureau of
    Fisheries, 61 p.

4. Chupp, N. R., 1955, An Evaluation of the Lower
    Coeur d'Alene River Waterfront Habitat in
    Kootenai County, Idaho: M.S. Thesis, Dept.of
    Wildlife Management, Univ. of Idaho, Moscow,
    Idaho, 119 p.

5. Cornell, Howland, Hayes, and Merryfield, 1964,
    Mine, Industrial and Domestic Waste Disposal
    Study for the South Fork Coeur d'Alene River;
    Engineers and Planners, Corvallis, Oregon, 102p.

6. Mink, L. L., R. E. Williams, and A. T. Wallace,
    1971, Effect of Industrial and Domestic Effluents
    on the Water Quality of the Coeur d'Alene River
    Basin: Idaho Bureau of Mines and Geology, Moscow,
    Idaho, Pamphlet No. 149, 95 p.

7. Galbraith, J. H., R. E. Williams, and P. L. Siems,
    1972, Migration and Leaching of Metals from
    Old Mine Tailings Deposits; Groundwater, vol. 10,
    No. 3

8. Kealy, C. D., 1970 Seepage Patterns in Mill
    Tailings Dams as determined by Finite Element

Models: M.S. Thesis, Department of Mining
Engineering and Metallurgy, University of
Idaho, Moscow, Idaho, 160 p.

9. Mink, L. L., R. E. Williams and A. T. Wallace,
   1972, Effect of Early Day Mining Operations
   on Present Day Water Quality: Groundwater,
   vol. 10, No. 1, p. 17-27

10. Williams, R. E., and C. D. Kealy, 1972, Cause
    and Prevention of Ground-water Pollution by
    Tailings Ponds: (In Review)

11. Kealy, C. D., 1972, Structural-Environmental
    Analysis of the Slime Zone of a Tailings Pond:
    ph.D. Dissertaion, College of Mines, University
    of Idaho, Moscow.

12. Kealy, C. D., and R. A. Busch, 1971, Determining
    Seepage Characteristics of Mill-Tailings Dams
    by the Finite-Element Method: U.S. Bureau of
    Mines, Report of Investigations 7477, 113 p.

13. Kealy, C. D., and R. E. Williams, 1971, Flow
    Through a Tailings Pond Embankment: Water
    Resources Research, v. 7. no. 7, p. 143-154.

14. Taylor, R. L. and C. Brown, 1967, Darcy's
    Flow Solution with a Free Surface: Amer. Soc.
    Civ. Engrs., J. Hydraulics Div., Vol. 93,
    No. Hy 2, p. 25-33.

15. Mink, L. L., R. E. Williams, A. T. Wallace and
    L. McNay, Renovation of Wastes by Mine Tailings
    Ponds, (in review).

16. Williams, R. E., A. T. Wallace, and L. L. Mink,
    1971, Impact of a Well Managed Tailings Pond
    System on a Stream: Mining Congress Journal,
    v. 57. no. 10, p. 48-56.

THE DISPOSAL OF MICACEOUS

CHINA CLAY WASTE IN SOUTH WEST ENGLAND

Michael J. Ripley

Assistant Chief Geologist

English Clays Lovering Pochin & Co. Ltd.

St. Austell, Cornwall, England

1. INTRODUCTION

a) General

The formation of china clay or kaolin in an apparently unique geological environment has given rise to an Industry which has been required to develop much of its own technology. Large scale hydraulic mining of china clay can only be seen in the counties of Devon and Cornwall in South West England.

The paper is concerned primarily with the workings of the Clay Division of English China Clays, which produces over 80% of the china clay. It extracts over 22 million tons of material per year. Of this total, approximately 2,000,000 tons is micaceous waste. This is disposed of in wet form.

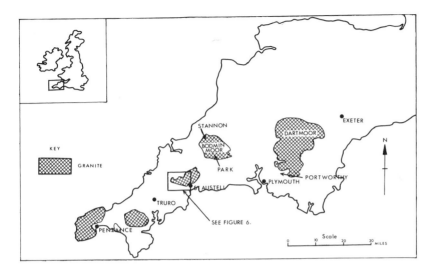

Map of South West England showing position of major granite intrusions. Figure No. 1

b) Geology of the kaolin deposits

i. Formation. The kaolin has been formed by hydro-thermal alteration of the feldspar minerals in the original granite (1). Location of the granite bosses of South West England are shown in Figure No. 1. Kaolinisation has occurred to varying degrees in all of these areas. The largest deposits are, however, found in the western part of the St.Austell granite. The alteration, which is thought to have been prin-cipally hypogene, was produced by solutions migrating through the granite. The deposits of clay extend to considerable and unproven depths.

ii. Associated Minerals. Kaolin forms on average about 11% of the ground removed during mining. The remainder, which is almost all waste, is formed primarily of sand, silt and clay size particles, unaltered granite, lode material of various types and overburden. Numerous other minerals occur in very

675

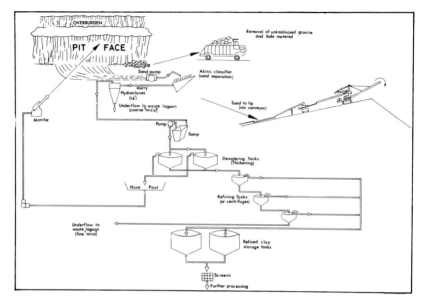

Sketch diagram showing mining and initial stages of china clay processing.　　　　　　　　Figure No. 2

small quantities.

c) Mining of Kaolin

The clay is mined hydraulically by high pressure water hoses, known as monitors. Pressures of up to 300 pounds per square inch can be developed at the ceramic lined monitor nozzles. A simplified flow sheet showing the mining and part of the processing operations is shown in Figure No. 2. The slurry produced by the hydraulic monitors at the pit face gravitates to the lowest part of the pit where it is pumped to Akins spiral classifiers. These remove the sand from the slurry, 90% of which grades between 0.1 millimetres and 10 millimetres. The sand is then fed onto a conveyor and carried to the tip. The slurry is pumped away for further refining and processing.

Pre-treatment of the pit slope, before hydraulicking by either blasting or ripping, is necessary in areas where difficulties resulting from "hardness" are encountered in maintaining a sufficiently high density clay/water slurry in order to meet production requirements.

Materials which are too large to gravitate in the slurry stream are removed from the pit by truck.

d) Refining of Kaolin

The clay slurry passes through three, and in the case of the highest quality products, four, stages of refining. Stages 1, 2 and 3 are shown in Figure 2.

The stages of refining are as follows:

Stage 1. Removal of sand by Akins spiral classifiers as described above.

Stage 2. Removal of coarse micaceous material by hydroclones.

Stage 3. Removal of fine micaceous material by gravitational settling tanks.

Stage 4. Separation of coarser clay by Bird or Dynacone centrifuges.

e) Waste Product Disposal

Most of the coarser fraction produced at each of the four stages detailed above is disposed of as waste. Only the coarser clay produced at Stage 4 is sold in large quantities.

The sand is tipped into waste piles which range up to 300 feet in height. The micaceous material, or "mica" as it will be referred to in this paper, is disposed of in wet form into either rivers or waste lagoons. As a result of anti-pollution legislation the former method, which has been used for nearly two hundred years will have stopped by 1974. All "mica" will then be retained on land.

In addition to the waste products derived from the slurry stream there are also the waste products from the pits. These are overburden and non-productive ground. The latter is either lode material or un-kaolinised granite, which frequently requires blasting or ripping and is known locally as stent.

2. PHYSICAL PROPERTIES OF MICACEOUS WASTE

a) Introduction

Only in recent years has detailed work been under-taken in determining the physical properties of "mica". Knowledge of the behaviour of "mica", both in slurry and solid form, is far from complete. Considerable study has still to be carried out, both in the laboratory and the field. The physical properties vary considerably, being dependant on numerous factors, such as the mineralogy of the original granite, the efficiency of the refining equipment, the type of bund construction and the depositional position in the lagoon relative to the in-flow and out-flow points. For example, the physical properties of the materials at the in-flow and out-flow areas of the lagoon, all other factors being equal, differ consid-erably because of the concentration of -2 micron E.S.D. (Equivalent Spherical Diameter) particles at the out-flow area.

Today, because of the lack of knowledge of the behaviour of "mica" under various conditions the lagoon bunds are possibly being built to conservative designs.

The variable behaviour of the material is illust-rated in Section 3. Two failures are described in which the "mica" behaved in different ways. In one, the bund failed and the "mica" remained unsupported within the lagoon whilst in the other the "mica" flowed as a wave down the valley.

b) Mineralogy and Particle Size

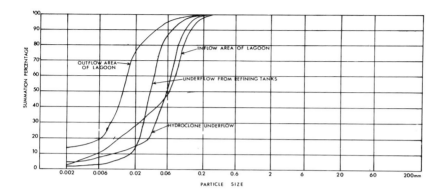

Particle size distribution curves for hydroclone
underflow, refining tank underflow, inflow area and
outflow area of "mica" lagoon.   Figure No. 3

Particle size curves for material taken from
different positions in a lagoon are shown in Figure
No. 3. These samples were taken from an old lagoon
no longer in operation. The -2 micron content is
sufficiently high in the area of the out-flow to
justify re-working. Also shown in Figure No. 3 are
particle size analysis curves of the underflow from
the 14" hydroclones and the grading of the underflow
from the gravitational settling tanks. These curves
represent the two types of waste which are deposited
in approximately equal quantities in the tailing
lagoons.

The mineralogy of the "mica" is very variable but
in general it is composed of 50%+ "coarse" kaolinite,
the remainder being essentially muscovite or lithion-
ite mica with small quantities of biotite mica,
quartz, tourmaline, potash and soda feldspar. Quartz
forms the bulk of the non-mica material.

c) In-situ Density and Shear Strength Characteristics

In-situ densities have been measured both on the
surface and in boreholes. Dry densities average 75
pounds per cubic foot with a range of 67 to 93 pounds
per cubic foot. The water content ranges from 36% to
56% with an average of 48%.

On geotechnical considerations the properties of
the "mica" are comparable with those of a laminated
soil formed of laminae of silty sand, silt and silty
clay. As a result of these laminations the properties
of the "mica" are markedly anisotropic.

In-situ vane tests have been carried out in a
number of boreholes. The results from two boreholes
drilled in the coarser and finer areas of a lagoon
are shown in Figure No. 4. The grading of the material in the two areas is similar to that shown in
Figure No. 3. The vane was pushed into the ground
and the maximum depth that could be reached in the
coarser area was 25' below surface. The penetration
resistance was less in the finer material and the
vane penetrated to a depth of 54' below surface.

In laminated soils containing sand, silt and clay,
there is some doubt about the true relation between
vane test readings and the shear strength parameters
of the soil. However, both vane test probes show an
increase in shear strength with depth although the
plot for the coarser material is more erratic than
that for the finer material.

Tests on samples carried out in a Soils Mechanics
Laboratory indicated that the effective shear strength
parameters gave friction values $\emptyset'$ ranging between 20°
and 23° and a small or zero effective cohesion value c'.
Total stress shear strength tests are of doubtful
value in material of this type but triaxial tests
carried out in the more clayey material from the lagoon
gave cohesion values comparable with those of a soft
clay in the range of 300 to 400 pounds per square foot.

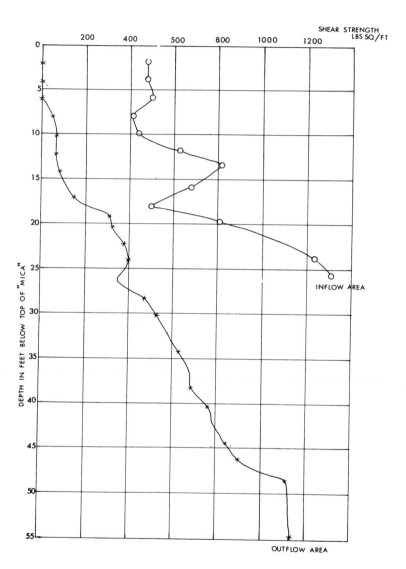

Graphs of shear strength against depth for the relatively coarse and fine areas of Maggie Pie lagoon.

Figure No. 4

d) Slurry Properties

In Section 4 a very brief account is given of a new "mica" disposal scheme presently being implemented. This utilises twelve miles of pipeline and numerous pumping stations. Knowledge of the physical properties of the "mica" in slurry form was of critical importance in designing this disposal network.

It is not within the scope of this paper to discuss these properties in detail but sufficient to say for general completeness of this account that the micaceous material is highly abrasive and that the solids rapidly settle to the bottom of the pipe if the flow ceases. These two factors have played a considerable part in determining the type of pumps and pipelines required, the density and speed at which the slurry is transported, the gradients on the pipelines and the siting and control of the emergency pipeline valves. The latter are needed in case of sudden pump failure in order to prevent blockage of the pipelines.

3. BRIEF CASE HISTORIES OF THREE LAGOON FAILURES

During the winter of 1969/70 failure occurred in three tailing lagoons within a period of five weeks. Experience gained from these incidents has played a large part in determining the method of bund construction and the types of in-flow and out-flow systems which are now being used by the Industry. Unlike many mining operations this Industry at the moment does not build its lagoons from the tailings themselves but utilises other waste products. Bund building using "mica" was, however, until recently, a common method of construction and it is quite possible in certain isolated areas the method could be re-introduced.

Park. Park pit is on Bodmin Moor (see Figure No.1). It is in an isolated area divorced from any other China Clay workings. The adjacent river is used as a water supply for a large area in Mid-Cornwall. There is, consequently, strict control on the effluent

flowing into the river from the china clay operation.
The maximum allowable concentration of suspended solids
is 250 parts per million at a pH of between 3 and 8.
This means it is necessary to have a two-stage tailing
impounding system in order to prevent "mica" overflowing
into the river (see Table No. 1).

Failure occurred as the result of overtopping of a
10 foot high bund constructed of waste sand. Fortunately as it was a secondary structure of very small
dimensions the degree of river pollution was relatively
slight. The failure developed from ice blockage of the
overflow system. Floating ice became lodged in the
overflow pipes in sufficient quantity to produce a
build up of water behind the bund. It eventually over-
flowed the bund and rapidly down cut through the granular sand thus allowing much of the impounded "mica"
to drain into the river.

As a result of this failure the lagoon has been
permanently closed.

Portworthy. This lagoon is situated near Plymouth in
South Devon (see Figure No. 1). It would be described
as a downstream structure by Kealy (2), as part of the
bund raising procedure involves adding material to the
downstream slope. It receives all the micaceous
residue from the Dartmoor pits of English China Clays
and is located about one and one-half miles south of the
mining area (see Table No. 1). Other waste products
are not readily available and the bund has been built
from excavated slate. The use of this construction
material has also produced additional storage capacity
as the "mica" is now overflowing into the excavated
area. The bund has been built across the valley.
Also a diversion channel has been constructed to carry
the river which originally occupied the valley floor.
This type of bund is defined as a cross-valley structure.

A cross-section of the overflow system used at this
lagoon is shown in Figure No. 5. As the water level
rose the rectangular sectioned concrete culverts were
sealed so as to prevent overflow of "mica". The

Table No. 1.

Details of the Tailing Lagoons used by English China Clays

Lagoon	Bund Materials	Type of Bund	Maximum Height	Rate of Deposition (Tonnes per annum)
Kernick	Sand, Rockfill, Overburden	(P) Cross-Valley Down-Stream	300'	
Dubbers	Sand	(P) Cross-Pit Down-Stream	65'+	
Great Treverbyn*		(P)		
Lower Ninestones	Sand, Rockfill	(P) Cross-Pit and Cross-Valley Down-Stream	30'+	2,000,000
Treviscoe*		(P)		
Gilleys	Sand	Perimeter Down-Stream	65'	
Trethosa Moor (E)	Sand, Rockfill	Perimeter Down-Stream	30'	
Carbis Moor (E)	Sand	Cross-Valley Down-Stream	35'	
Carpalla (E)	Old pit	(P)		
Stannon (3 lagoons)	Sand	Perimeter Down-Stream	100'	75,000
Park (2 lagoons)	Sand	Perimeter Up-Stream	75'	75,000
Portworthy	Slate x	Cross-Valley Down-Stream	100'+	300,000

E   Emergency Use Only

*   Details Not Yet Finalised

P   Old Pit Incorporated Into Lagoon

x   This Bund May be Raised by Using the Tailings

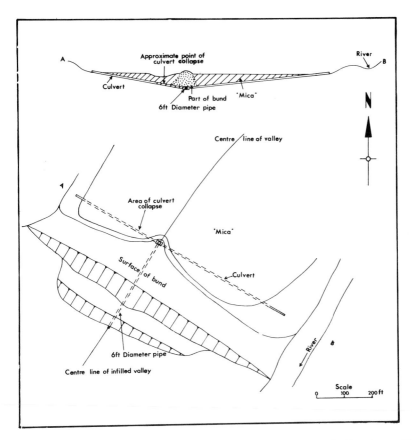

Plan and cross-section of the bund area at Portworthy lagoon.
Figure No. 5

culverts were built at right angles to the contours on both sides of the valley before the initial deposition of 'mica'. The culverts met in the central part of the valley and discharged into a 6 foot-diameter-circular re-inforced concrete pipe which carried the water under the bund. Both culverts consequently were overlain by deposited "mica".

Failure occurred as a result of a collapse of part of the western culvert beneath some 50 feet of "mica" and overlying lagoon water. A wave of water and "mica" emerged from the 6-foot circular pipe and flowed into the Laira estuary at Plymouth. The flow continued for an unknown period of time (less than 12 hours) before the pipe became blocked by debris. The movement of "mica" and water into the collapsed culvert caused some slumping of the upstream part of the slate bund, and this material helped to plug the breach.

The reason for the collapse of the culvert is unknown. Corrosive attack, differential settlement or faulty materials could have produced a condition whereby the stress produced by the overlying "mica" and water was sufficient to induce collapse.

The overflow system has now been sealed and discharge is from a point at the upstream end of the lagoon. In-flow of waste occurs at the down-stream end.

Maggie Pye. This lagoon is located in the major china clay area north-west of St. Austell in Cornwall (see Figure No. 6).

Failure occurred along a 300-foot section of this 60-foot-high bund. The bund, which completely encircles the depositional area, is built in part of "mica", in part of clayey overburden and in part of waste china clay sand. This type of lagoon, where the bund encloses the depositional area, is defined as a perimeter bund. The toe of the bund moved out 115 feet completely covering the adjoining road. 25,000 tons of bund material were involved in the slide. The notable feature of this failure was the behaviour of the "mica" In contrast with the Portworthy culvert collapse only a very small amount of wet "surface mica" flowed through the breach. The majority of the material remained unsupported within the lagoon (see Figure No. 7). The position of the slide was in a part of the lagoon where the "mica" was relatively fine grained.

Construction of the lagoon in the area of failure began in the 1930's. In those days the bund was built

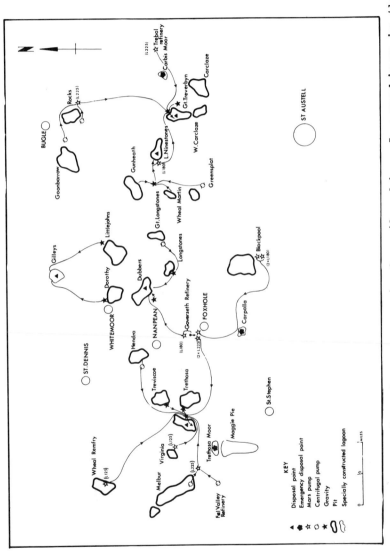

Disposal network for micaceous waste from the china clay workings in the St. Austell area.

Figure No. 6

Photograph showing the breach in the Maggie Pie "mica" lagoon. The contact between the impermeable and relatively permeable bund material is shown by the black line.   Figure No. 7

manually from the "mica". As the level rose in the lagoon, so more "mica" was dug from the lagoon and used to increase the height of the bund. From time to time clayey overburden from the adjacent pits was also incorporated into the bund. These two types of material were used to build the bund to a height of 30 feet. This can be seen in Figure No. 7.

Above this level the bund was raised a further 30 feet by the addition of waste sand. The sand has a higher coefficient of permeability than the underlying materials. The permeability of the sand is of the order of 10^{-3} centimetres per second whilst that of the underlying non-lamina "mica" is of the order of 10^{-5} centimetres per second. The sand was tipped by truck and placed into position with a D4 bulldozer. In order to increase the height of the bund it became necessary to overstep the deposited "mica" with the material being used to raise the bund. This type of construction is described as up-stream by Kealy (2).

It has resulted in a dog tooth contact between the deposited "mica" and bund material on the up stream side of the bund.

After weeks of heavy winter rain, cracks and small slips, indicating instability, began to show on the eastern side of the bund north of the eventual area of collapse. It was decided to temporarily close the lagoon. However, bund building continued in the section of the bund where there were no visible signs of movement. This was carried out by spreading dumped sand with a D4 bulldozer. Less than twelve hours after the bulldozer had completed its work the bund failed along a section corresponding exactly with the area over which it had been working.

Immediately after the slip piezometers were installed in the bund in order to determine the piezometric level within the bund. It was found that the water level was 30 feet above the base of the bund.

Failure is considered to have occurred because of the relatively poor permeability of the lower 30 feet of the bund. As a result of the heavy rainfall high pore water pressures developed which were sufficient to reduce the shear strength to the point of failure.

The exact correlation between the working area of the bulldozer and the area of failure was probably not a coincidence. It is thought that either the addition of the further material or the vibratory action of the bulldozer or a combination of both factors were sufficient to finally induce failure in the bund which was already in a critical condition. Correlations between vibration produced by earth moving equipment and slope failure have been recognised on other occasions in the China Clay Industry.

A further noteworthy feature of the slip is that the major collapse occurred along a section of the bund that gave no visual indication of instability. Those sections of the bund where the initial cracks and small scale slips had been noticed did not in fact suffer large scale failure. A tentative suggestion is that in this instance small scale failure could have indicated a gradual release of stress which was sufficient to prevent catastrophic failure.

As a result of this failure the lagoon has been permanently closed.

Conclusions

Many lessons have been learnt from a study of these failures. The most important is that all lagoons and overflow systems must be designed and built to strict engineering standards. Use should be made of soil mechanics and earth dam technology.

Detailed recommendations are as follows:

i. Wherever possible pipes or culverts should not be placed through or under the bund. In some instances this may be unavoidable, in such cases considerable care must be taken in selecting a design and materials.

ii. Each lagoon should have two independent water discharge systems. In instances where pump discharge is the primary method the secondary system should be based on water overflow and not a stand-by pump.

iii. Different types of material should not be placed in a random manner during bund construction. Ideally bunds should be built of permeable waste china clay sand. Where this is not possible there must be strict control of the placement of the material and the following rules should be applied:

1. The more permeable material should not be placed up-stream of the less permeable, unless either:

(a) the less permeable is protected by a

filter, or

(b) the more permeable has been placed as a thin skin on the downstream slope of the bund in order to facilitate plant growth.

2. The more permeable should not be placed above less permeable so that both outcrop on the down-stream face of the bund.

Failure to observe these rules, particularly the second, can result in a rapid build up of pore water pressures during heavy rainfall.

iv. Before designing the bund there should be a full evaluation of the engineering properties of the construction materials and the bund foundations.

v. The tailings should be fed onto the lagoon from the highest parts of the bund. This ensures that the coarsest fraction of the "mica" is deposited adjacent to the potentially weakest section of the bund. Also it prevents the over-lying water from standing in contact with this section of the bund.

vi. There should be strict control of earth moving equipment working on the bund.

4. MICACEOUS WASTE DISPOSAL

a. Introduction

Currently the micaceous waste is disposed of either into one of seven lagoons or into local rivers. This river disposal method has been in use for nearly 200 years. Legislation passed during the past decade has meant that this practice must cease. The alternatives were disposal at sea by pipeline or retention on land. The Industry has decided that on environmental considerations the latter method will be most suitable. Consequently, by 1974 all micaceous residue will be retained on land.

This decision has meant that the Industry is now in the process of constructing a ten million dollar disposal network. This will accommodate all "mica" disposal until the beginning of the next decade within the St. Austell area and permit further extension of the scheme for in excess of 60 years. Six new lagoons are being, or will be built. They will be fed by a twelve mile pipeline system. Existing lagoons will also be used as emergency disposal areas.

Five of the new lagoons are associated with pits, two of which will be progressively run down so as to accommodate the waste. In each case bunds will be constructed either to increase the disposal capacity of the old pit or to separate the working from the non working areas of the pit.

b. Disposal in the St. Austell area

A brief account is given in this section of the scheme for the St. Austell area. It is expected to have a life of about ten years, when new lagoons will be required for its extension. The location of the major parts of the disposal network such as the china clay pits, disposal areas, pipelines and pump positions are shown in Figure No. 6.

i.   The lagoons. There will be nine disposal areas, three of which will only be needed in case of emergency. Details of these areas are shown in Table No. I and Figure No. 6.

ii. Transportation. The micaceous waste will either be pumped or gravitated into the settling areas. Pumping will be either by double acting, duplex reciprocating Mars pumps manufactured by the Mitsubishi Metal and Mining Co. Ltd., or by rubber lined centrifugal pumps. The former will be used for the majority of the work.

The slurry will be transported at 40% solids

in pipes ranging from 3 inches to 6 inches inside diameter depending upon the velocity required. The steel pipes connected to the Mars pumps will be lined with quarter inch poly- urethene using a process patented by English China Clays. It is estimated that the pipeline life should be 20 years. The pH of the slurry will be approximately 5. The gravity lines will be made of $\frac{1}{2}$ inch thick walled high density polythene pipe. Ten Mars pumps (2 x L125, 3 x L180 and 5 x L225) will be used on a regular basis. Each pumping system will operate at a critical velocity of between 5 and 6 feet per second and will start and stop on water. The Mars pumps will work continuously at rates of between 80 and 950 U.S. gallons per minute depending on their size and requirements. Automatic valve release mechanisms have been built into the system so as to prevent pipeline blockage should pump failure occur. Three spare pumps, one of each size, will be available in emergencies. The location of these pumps is shown in Figure No. 6.

It is estimated that when the scheme is completed in 1974 that it will be disposing of approximately 2,000,000 tonnes of micaceous waste per year.

c. Disposal in other areas

English China Clays have a number of additional lagoons which service the more remote mines on Bodmin Moor and Dartmoor. Mention has already been made of the workings at Park on Bodmin Moor and on Dartmoor. There is also a third area, at Stannon on Bodmin Moor. The lagoons in all these areas will continue to function for the indefinite future. Details of the lagoons are given in Table No. I.

d. Bund construction

This section outlines the designs for three lagoons

in which different construction methods have been used primarily because of the restrictions imposed by the availability of materials.

i. _Kernick._ This cross-valley embankment will be 300 feet high on completion. It is being built in order to increase the disposal volume of Kernick pit. Construction is designed to keep pace with the in-flow of waste and the work should be completed by about 1980. All construction materials, including the specialised filters, will be produced from local waste products. Boreholes and trenches were used as part of the site investigation programme. At present stripping of the foundations is taking place. The overflow design has yet to be finalised.

A cross-section at the highest point of the final bund is shown in Figure No. 8a. The bund will be built essentially of sand and rock-fill with transitional filters between these two types of material. The disposition of these materials can be seen in the cross-section.

The sand will be waste china clay sand. It must be well graded with not more than 8% passing the 200 mesh sieve (0.075 millimetres) and 95% finer than 3 inches (76.2 millimetres). The rock fill will be waste stent which will not contain more than 10% below 2 inches (50.8 millimetres) and no lumps larger than 30 inches (762 millimetres).

A thin blanket of overburden will cover the downstream slope of the bund in order to facilitate plant growth.

The filter layers will lead into drains underlying the bund.

All materials after placement will be compacted as and when required. The procedures and specifications to be used will be finalised after site trials by the Consulting Engineers.

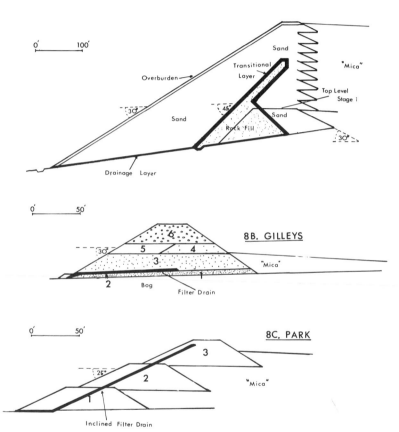

8A. KERNICK

8B. GILLEYS

8C. PARK

Diagrammatic cross-sections showing the method of
bund construction at Kernick, Gilleys and Park lagoons.
Numbers indicate order of construction. Figure No. 8.

Deposition of the "mica" will be against the inner slope of the bund so as to form a beach around the inside of the embankment. Casagrande type piezometers will be installed at sites selected by the Engineers during and after completion of the bund.

ii. Gilleys. This lagoon is being formed by a perimeter bund. It will be built entirely of waste sand, grading 80% + 0.2 millimetres, 15% + 6 millimetres approximately. This sand, which was tipped many years ago unknowingly on deposits of kaolin, has to be removed and consequently as much as possible is being incorporated into the bund. It would have been possible to design the bund using less sand.

A cross-section of the bund is shown in Figure No. 8b. It can be seen that internal drains have not been used as at Kernick. Also the full trapezoidal cross-section is built of sand. "Mica" deposition is taking place from the highest section of the bund. The water is being pumped off the lagoon and re-cycled.

Problems were encountered during the site investigation because of the boggy nature of the ground. It was not economic to remove the bog or to investigate the bog before construction. Consequently, it was decided to build the first seven feet of the bund with sand directly on the bog without any site investigation (see cross-section in Figure No. 8b). Boreholes were drilled through the sand and the information obtained used to plan the subsequent lifts of the bund.

The essence of the following lifts has been to leave sufficient time for dissipation of any pressures that developed in the bog as a result of bund construction, before commencing on the next lift. This has meant that the section of the bund overlying the bog has required very careful monitoring during construction. Very detailed surveys have been carried out in order to detect any movement.

The bund has been built almost completely by Euclid TS 24 scrapers. These have spread and compacted the

sand in thin layers to an in-situ dry density of at least
110 pounds per cubic foot and in some instances as
high as 125 pounds per cubic foot.

iii. Park. This lagoon is being formed by an up-stream
perimeter bund built from sand of similar grading to
the Gilleys sand. The water is being pumped from the
lagoon. A cross-section of the bund is shown in Figure
No. 8c.

Undoubtedly the down-stream method produces a more
stable structure, all other factors being equal, but
because of the lack of suitable construction material
in this area it has not been possible to use this
method. Consequently the design for the Park bund has
incorporated features necessary to produce an adequate
safety factor which were not required at Gilleys.
The differences are as follows: The Park bund has both
an inclined and basal filter. Gilleys only has a basal
filter. The down-stream slope angle at Park is 25°
whereas at Gilleys it is 30°. (The natural angle of rest
of waste sand is about 35°). At Park there is an in-
situ dry density specification of 114 pounds per cubic
foot whereas at Gilleys the only stipulation is that
the bund is built in thin layers by scrapers.

The bund at Park is being built, as at Gilleys, by
Euclid TS 24 scrapers.

5. RE-WORKING OF TAILING LAGOONS

Considerable thought has been given to the possibility
of re-working "mica" particularly the material deposited
when separation techniques were not as effective as
they are today.

Re-working had started on two old lagoons when a
temporary recession affected the Industry in 1971 and
the re-working operation was postponed.

Sufficient experience had been gained to indiate
that it could be a practical possibility to treat the

lagoon as a clay pit and to hydraulically mine the tailings with a high pressure water hose. Difficulties can be expected when working in the bund areas but these will probably be overcome by removing the "mica" in layers and immediately afterwards removing an equal depth of bund by earth-moving equipment.

6. GOVERNMENT LEGISLATION

Before a lagoon can be built the Government has to be satisfied that the lagoon will be a stable structure and meets its design and planning requirements. The latter cannot be met by applying any scientific formula and is determined from human and environmental considerations.

a. Mines and Quarries (Tips) Act, 1969

As a result of the Aberfan disaster in 1966, legislation has been passed which controls the tipping of all types of Mine and Quarry waste. Generally lagoons and tips have to be registered with the Inspectorate of Mines and Quarries (a Government body) and have to be certified as safe by a competent person.

The Inspectorate also has to be notified of any changes in waste disposal procedures and various records have to be kept. Liaison is maintained between the Inspectorate and the Industry during both design and construction stages.

b. Town and Country Planning Act, 1971

Formal Government permission is required from the Local Planning Authority before any lagoon can be built. This statutory body, which is formed of local representatives elected by the people, and supported by Professional Officers, has many factors to consider before passing judgment. It has to balance the benefits that will accrue to the local and national economies as a result of the generation of wealth from the mining operation against the possible damage to the environment. If necessary, an appeal can be made to a higher authority against its decision.

c. Rivers (Prevention of Pollution) Act, 1951

Permission to discharge the water from a lagoon into any nearby river or stream is required from the River Authority under the provisions of the Rivers (Prevention of Pollution) Act, 1951. There is a right of appeal against the decisions of the Authority.

I am indebted to my many colleagues in English China Clays and T.R.M.Wakeling of Foundation Engineering for discussion and information on numerous aspects of this paper.

REFERENCES

1. Bristow, Colin M., "Kaolin Deposits of the United Kingdom and Northern Ireland," XX111 International Geological Congress (1968), Vol. 15, pp. 275 - 288.

2. Kealy, Charles D., "Design of dams for mill tailings by C.D. Kealy and R.L. Soderberg" (Washington), U.S. Dept. of the Interior, Bureau of Mines (1969). Information Circular 8410, 49p., illus.

PROS AND CONS OF COMBINED

TREATMENT OF MINING AND DOMESTIC WASTES

Floyd L. Matthew

Project Engineer, Brady Consultants, Inc.

Spearfish, South Dakota

ABSTRACT

Homestake Mining Company and the cities of Lead
and Deadwood have discharged their untreated wastewaters to Whitewood Creek since 1876 when the Gold
Rush began in the Black Hills of South Dakota.
Spent tailings, cyanide and heavy metals in the
industrial wastes and bacteria, solids and organic
materials in the domestic wastes contributed to
severe pollution problems in the receiving stream.
In 1965 the Lead-Deadwood Sanitary District was
formed to make it possible to solve both the industrial and domestic waste problems through a unified
action.

An engineering study completed by Brady Consultants, Inc. in 1970 recommended an 8 mile interceptor sewer and a 290 acre, 90 foot deep, treatment-
storage unit to treat the combined industrial and
domestic wastes. Laboratory and pilot plant studies

indicated that the treatment provided by interrelated chemical and biological processes in the
storage-treatment impoundment produced an effluent
capable of meeting specified stream standards. The
impoundment volume will be adequate to store all
tailings from Homestake Mining Company for an estimated 27 years.

Combining the mining and municipal wastes produced several design problems, but the combined treatment facility proved to be the best solution after
comparing all alternates.

TAILING DISPOSAL TODAY

HISTORY

Homestake Mining Company began operations in Lead in 1876. At the current time, the mine processes approximately 1,900,000 tons of ore per year using the cyanidation process for both sand and slime. Cyanide solutions are applied by gravity to the sand fractions (60% of the total tonnage) in Lead. Slimes are piped to Deadwood, about 3 miles away, where cyanide solutions are applied in filter presses. Spent slimes are sluiced directly to Whitewood Creek in Deadwood. Approximately 80% of the spent sands are returned to the Mine and 20% are discharged to Gold Run Creek, a tributary to Whitewood Creek.

Construction is presently underway in Lead on a char-in-pulp process unit. The filter presses in Deadwood will be abandoned when the char-in-pulp units are placed in operation in early 1973 and the entire operation will be located in Lead.

The cities of Lead and Deadwood and several scattered residential developments in the area discharge all storm and sanitary sewage to Whitewood Creek without treatment. Domestic wastes are very dilute because of excessive groundwater infiltration into the municipal sewer systems. Treatment of domestic wastes in conventional units is not possible because of their dilute nature and the extreme flow variations produced by storm flows.

In 1965 the Lead-Deadwood Sanitary District was formed to provide an administrative authority to investigate and carry out a unified wastewater treatment project. Several studies were completed by the South Dakota State Health Department and Homestake Mining Company from 1959 through 1969. In 1969, the District hired Brady Consultants, Inc. of Spearfish to conduct a preliminary engineering study and make recommendations for a wastewater treatment system which would eliminate the pollution problem in Whitewood Creek.

DESIGN CRITERIA

Design criteria for the proposed Lead-Deadwood
Sanitary District wastewater treatment facilities
are as follows:

1. Design Life for Treatment Facility   20 years
2. Design Life for Interceptor Sewer   50 years
3. Design Population - Lead, Deadwood
   and Contiguous Area   1970 -   10,170
                         1990 -   12,080
4. Design Flows in Cubic Feet Per Second

	Maximum	Average	Minimum
Homestake Mining Company	14.1	5.0	3.2
Domestic Wastes	19.0	9.9	4.8
Storm	30.0		
Total	63.1	14.9	8.0

5. Tailings Characteristics

Homestake Mining Company will discharge approximately 1,012,000 tons per year of sand and slimes to
the proposed system. The solids will consist of
780,000 tons of slimes and 224,000 tons of sand with
the following typical size distribution:

Mesh	Percent Retained Sand	Slimes
+48	0	
+80	6	
+100	8.3	
+150	17.4	
+200	22.4	0.5
-200	45.9	
+325		12.5
-325		87.0

Specific Gravity of Rock   3.12 pounds/cubic foot
Specific Weight of Rock   195 pounds/cubic foot

Unconsolidated Specific Weight of Sand	81 pounds/cubic foot
Unconsolidated Specific Weight of Slime	55 pounds/cubic foot
Specific Weight of Sand After 72 Hours Settling	106 pounds/cubic foot
Specific Weight of Slime After 72 Hours Settling	91 pounds/cubic foot
Consolidated Volume Per Ton For Sand	19 cubic feet
Consolidated Volume Per Ton For Slimes	22 cubic feet
Storage Volume Required Per Year	500 acre feet

6. Domestic Wastes
   Suspended Solids   1,845 pounds/day
7. Biochemical Oxygen Demand

Industrial	Insignificant
Domestic	1,890 pounds/day

8. Chemicals

Homestake Mining Company Cyanide Concentrations (Refluxed Samples)

Sand	1.2 - 17.6 milligrams/liter (CN)
Slime	1.6 - 5.2 milligrams/liter (CN)
Mercury	Naturally occuring only, amalgamation is no longer practiced in the Mine.

Iron, zinc, arsenic and other heavy metals in varying concentrations.

9. Effluent Requirements

Parameter	Limiting Value
5 Day Biochemical Oxygen Demand	30 milligrams/liter
Suspended Solids	30 milligrams/liter
Process Mercury	0

10. Stream Water Quality Requirements

Parameter

Cyanides	0.02 milligrams/liter (CN)
Dissolved Oxygen	5.0 milligrams/liter
H_2S	1.0 milligrams/liter
Iron (Total)	0.2 milligrams/liter
pH	6.3 - 9.0 milligrams/liter
Fecal Coliform	1000/100 milliliters
Alkalinity	750 milligrams/liter as $CaCO_3$
Total Dissolved Solids	700 to 1500 milligrams/liter
Electrical Conductivity	1000 to 2500 micromhos/centimeters
Nitrates	50 milligrams/liter as NO_3
Sodium Adsorption Ratio	10 to 26
Soluble Sodium Percentage	30 to 70%
General -	No toxic materials greater than 0.1 times the 96 hour median tolerance limit for short residual compounds or 0.01 times the median tolerance limit for accumulative substances.
-	No taste or odor producing substances.

PROPOSED SYSTEM

A. Restraints

Several combinations of waste handling and treatment systems were evaluated during the preliminary engineering study. Dominating problems associated with the various alternatives were:

1. Tailings transport and storage.
2. Removal of cyanide and other heavy metals from the industrial wastes.
3. Bacterial removal.

4. Extremely variable flow rates produced by storm waters from Lead and Deadwood.

5. Absence of suitable sites in the immediate vicinity of Lead and Deadwood.

Any proposed wastewater system had to transport and store the tailings; transport and treat stormwater; and remove bacteria, solids, cyanides and certain heavy metals. These service functions had to be satisfied within a cost effective structure.

B. Preliminary Findings

1. Laboratory studies indicated that cyanide removal using conventional methods was impractical because of side reactions, extremely high chemical requirements and non-uniformity of the chemical characteristics in the industrial wastes.

2. An investigation of pipes and flumes in the Homestake mill indicated that concrete was very resistant to abrasion by sand. Slimes were not abrasive to any significant degree. When slimes were mixed with sand, the abrasiveness of the sand was further reduced.

3. Chlorine demands for the combined wastes were very high because of the reducing characteristics of the pyrrhotite in the ore. The demand remained high even after liquid-solid separation had been accomplished. This presented a problem since bacterial reduction in the domestic wastes would be very expensive unless the domestic wastes were pretreated before mixing with the mining wastes.

4. Free cyanide in the mining wastes is rendered non-toxic because of a reaction with pyrrhotite which, in the presence of free oxygen, produces non-toxic thiocyanate. Cyanide is also destroyed by direct oxidation and conversion to relatively non-toxic ferro and ferricyanides. Whitewood Creek was found to be extremely toxic to test fish below the outfall from Homestake Mining Company's slime plant,

but bioassays using water from approximately 8 miles below the slime plant indicated that cyanide toxicity was absent. Stable populations of catfish, carp and other warm water species in the Belle Fourche River below its confluence with Whitewood Creek (29 miles from the slime plant) also verify the non-toxic nature of the Homestake Mining Company wastes after adequate aeration and contact with the spent tailings.

5. Treatment of domestic and mining wastes could be accomplished satisfactorily together if an adequate detention period could be provided.

6. Experiments with an 8 inch steel pipe and a 30 inch diameter wooden flume indicated that the sands could be transported without deposition under open channel conditions by maintaining an average cross-sectional velocity of approximately 4.5 feet per second. A slope of 1% provided an adequate safety factor for the 30 inch diameter flume. Transport reliability was determined to be a function of critical depth as well as velocity.

7. Observations made on the receiving waters and during previous investigations indicated that impounding the combined wastes for an adequate period would produce an acceptable effluent. A pilot study was conducted in 1970 using a 12,000 gallon tank and chemical plus bioassay procedures to evaluate the treatment effectiveness of an impoundment and to establish the detention period required. Results were very conclusive. After 7 days detention, the effluent was non-toxic to brook trout, bacterial and heavy metal reductions were nearly 100% and biochemical oxygen demand and suspended solids concentrations were safely within the effluent requirements specified for the project.

C. Proposed System

The final recommendation was to combine domestic and municipal waste treatment in a treatment-storage impoundment located on a divide between Polo and Whitewood Creek about 8 miles downstream from Lead.

The proposed system consists of the following components:

1. A 10,000 gallon storm water metering dam in Lead which will store peak storm flows and meter them back into the interceptor during low flow periods.

2. An inlet facility with flow measurement devices for Lead domestic wastes and Homestake Mining Company sand and slime flows.

3. A 43,000 foot long, 24 inch to 36 inch diameter, precast concrete interceptor sewer laid on a minimum slope of 1% grade. (A minimum slope of 1% was determined as necessary based on a study completed using a 75 foot section of 30 inch diameter redwood flume.)

4. An impoundment with 290 surface acres, a 90 foot maximum depth and a storage volume of 13,000 acre feet.

The pipeline follows highway and railroad right-of-way for approximately 6 miles where it passes through a 3000 foot tunnel under the Polo Creek-Whitewood Creek divide. At the exit to the tunnel, the interceptor discharges to a screening unit and head box. During normal flows, the wastes enter an 18 inch diameter ductile iron pressure pipe which carries the wastes to the dam inlet. An overflow is provided at the head box to carry storm flows through a gravity storm flow inlet that discharges at the edge of the pond.

Inlet facilities are presently under design. At this time a high pressure bottom discharge is being considered for the primary inlet. A manifold will also be installed along the main dam with valved discharges at 200 foot intervals.

The treatment-storage impoundment is formed by 3 dams. A 120 foot high main dam across the Polo Creek drainage forms the impoundment. Two back dams located on the Polo Creek-Whitewood Creek divide allow gravity flow of the effluent back into Whitewood Creek. A fourth dam within the impoundment isolates a polishing impoundment which will provide 15 days detention of the wastewater flows away from the stored tailings.

The treatment-storage unit will provide over 350 days detention, initially, and approximately 50 days detention when the storage volume is depleted.

The impoundment will be operated at full water depth. Sands and slimes will be discharged beneath the surface and the effluent will be returned directly to Whitewood Creek without further treatment.

At the end of the design period, the filled impoundment will be reclaimed or the dam heights will be increased as required to accommodate future wastewater loads.

PROS AND CONS

Experiences at Homestake, Lead and Deadwood indicate that mining and domestic wastes can be treated in a single unit to the mutual benefit of both the industry and the municipality. This will not always be the case, of course, since the solutions may not always be compatible in other situations.

Those mining operations having the option of joining with a municipality or a district for a joint wastewater project should thoroughly investigate the problems and advantages of the joint operation before proceeding.

Advantages of a joint venture include:

1.   The power of eminent domain gives more latitude for site selection.

2.   Financing is normally easier and interest rates are lower for a governmental entity.

3.   Administrative and overhead costs can be shared with the community.

4.   Federal and State assistance programs may be available. The trend, however, is to make the industry repay their portion of any grant made to the governmental entity constructing the system.

Disadvantages of a joint wastewater project are:

1.   The industry loses a great deal of flexibility because of legal restraints and red tape involved with municipal operations. In the current environment a mining company could find themselves shut down due to an enforcement action while the red tape is being unsnarled.

2.   Design periods are normally longer for municipal projects. Consequently, a mining company may have to plan and pay for a 20 year wastewater project when their mine life projections are for a shorter period.

3.   Mining companys may have to provide guarantees which can be very expensive if ore grade, market fluctuations or union demands dictate a mine closure. Any repayment guarantees should be considered very carefully before they are formally committed.

4.   Because of the public nature of a municipal operation, environmental considerations can become a dominant problem. An industry may be able to construct a much more economical facility than a municipality could construct.

5. A mining company may just be assuming additional administrative and financial problems by joining with a small community or a new district. Responsibilities should be clearly defined before a cooperative program is initiated.

6. The industry may lose certain tax advantages by joining a municipal operation. It certainly loses the accounting flexibility associated with an independent operation.

7. It is very difficult to equitably apportion costs. Before entering into a joint project, cost apportionment criteria for the project should be established.

The combined treatment method was the best solution for Homestake Mining Company and the communities of Lead and Deadwood. Mining companies who are situated to take advantage of joint community-industry wastewater treatment projects should thoroughly investigate the advantages of such an association.

SUMMARY

In 1965, the cities of Lead and Deadwood formed a sanitary district which included Homestake Mining Company. The District was formed to eliminate a severe pollution problem on Whitewood Creek caused by spent tailings, cyanide, heavy metals, bacteria and organics contained in the industrial and domestic wastes.

A preliminary study was completed by Brady Consultants, Inc. in 1970 which recommended a combined wastewater facility for the industrial and domestic wastes. The proposed system consists of 8 miles of 24 inch to 36 inch diameter interceptor sewer and a 290 acre treatment-storage impoundment which provides 13,000 acre feet of storage for spent tailings. Laboratory and pilot plant studies

coupled with stream observations indicate that this
unit will effectively remove all polluting materials
and produce an effluent which can be returned directly to Whitewood Creek without further treatment.
The impoundment will be operated in a full condition
and wastes will be discharged below the water
surface.

The proposed facility is currently in the design
phase. Bids are expected to be let in the fall of
1973 and the unit will be placed in service in the
fall of 1975.

Advantages and disadvantages accrue to both the
industry and the community on joint venture
wastewater projects. This alternative should be
thoroughly evaluated, however, by all mining operations which have the opportunity to join with a
governmental unit for a joint project.

DISCUSSION

D. W. McDONOUGH (New York Trap Rock Corporation):
Mr. Matthew, this zero discharge has me a little
worried. You say that we must eat it, even so we
have a lot of extra help eating it. I can't quite
understand how any industry can operate with zero
discharge, or any municipality either, for that
matter.

FLOYD MATTHEW: You'll have to ask Senator
Muskie what he's going to do with it in 1985. I
don't know. I've been fighting this, and it
doesn't make any sense at all. This is the thing
that's talked about, the environmental issues.
Mr. Evans talked about the problem north of
Vancouver. The rules and regulations that are
being promulgated today are going to stand in the
way of efficient resource development for years and
years to come. I think we're being remiss in our
duties when we don't educate the lawmakers to the

practical, technical and engineering restraints
on the things they're proposing that we do. Now
they're setting this as a goal: no discharge by
1985. This is totally impractical because water
quality management is a water resource management
tool. What we want to do is reclaim that water and
reuse it. To have the concept, even, that we're not
going to redischarge it back into the water courses
is absolutely ridiculous, and it does not conform
to any common-sense approach to water resource
management. I cannot go along with it myself and
all I can say is, I don't know what we're going to
do with it by 1985.

DESIGN, CONSTRUCTION AND OPERATION OF

OZARK LEAD COMPANY'S TAILINGS DISPOSAL SYSTEM

Milton A. Lagergren

Process Engineer
Engineering Center, Metal Mining Division
Kennecott Copper Corporation
Salt Lake City, Utah

Arthur W. Griffith
Mill Superintendent
Ozark Lead Company
Sweetwater Rural Branch, Missouri

ABSTRACT

Tailings from the 6,000 tons per day Ozark Lead concentrator are deposited in a small valley about one mile distant. The tailings dam serves a triple purpose: tailings disposal, water storage and stream regulation. Tailings are deposited along the crest of the dam using hydrocyclones. Unusual features of this installation are the use of a 60 inch pipeline through the dam to control storm run-off and an underdrainage system to control the phreatic water level together with a shutoff valve to insure water storage. A reservoir and pump station downstream of the tailings dam receives water decanted from the lake upstream of the tailings to furnish the entire mill water supply.

In four years of operation, the dam has been raised twenty-one feet above the starter dam level. Runoff from several storms has been handled with a substantial reduction in peak flows below the dam.

The mill has had an adequate supply of water at all times, entirely from the storage lake above the tailings. Tailings disposal and water supply operate as a closed system with no release to the stream below under normal operating conditions.

INTRODUCTION

The Ozark Lead Company, a wholly-owned subsidiary of Kennecott Copper Corporation, is located near the southern end of the "New Lead Belt" in southeast Missouri. The general area is hilly and wooded with relatively narrow valleys unsuitable for agriculture except on a very small scale. The nearest community is Bunker, population 300, located about 10 miles by road from the mine site. Annual precipitation in the area averages about 24 inches. The orebody being mined at present was discovered in 1962 about 1,200 feet below surface. Further drilling outlined its value and extent, following which a development shaft was drilled, ore samples were subjected to metallurgical testing and a flowsheet for ore treatment was developed. The tailings disposal system was planned with safety and negligible environmental impact as prime objectives. Engineering and construction of a 6,000 tons per day lead-zinc mine and concentrator was completed in mid-1968. By September 1972, approximately 3.7 million tons of tailings had been produced by the concentrator and deposited in the tailings disposal area.

DESIGN CONSIDERATIONS

The mine headframe, hoisthouse, service buildings and concentrator are located on the crest of a ridge about 200 feet higher in elevation than nearby Adair Creek, a small stream in a narrow, steep-sided valley. Surface soil is weathered dolomite and clay containing a fair proportion of rocks and boulders. The terrain in the general area is not favorable for disposal of large volumes of tailings or for storage of the mill

water supply. An investigation was made of several
possible sidehill sites which proved to be imprac-
ticable because high dikes would be needed for small
and inadequate storage volumes. Two alternate sites
were investigated on Adair Creek, one about a mile
from the concentrator, where a narrow portion of the
valley made possible a relatively short retaining
dam, another about 1,000 yards downstream providing
more ultimate storage but requiring a much longer
and lower initial dam. The first site (Figure No. 1)
was chosen because of lower first cost and better
provision for mill water storage, particularly during
initial start-up. The other site can be developed
in later years when additional storage will be needed.

Both sites permit gravity flow of tailings to the
disposal area by concrete pipeline. If desired,
pumping of tailings can be initiated when the limits
of gravity flow are reached in order to gain more
tailings storage capacity. Eventually, after exhaustion of the orebody, the upper end of the disposal area will become a recreational lake.

Use of the upstream end of the tailings pond as
a mill storage reservoir had several advantages,
mainly the provision of several times the amount of
storage that would be practicable at any of the
available hillside storage sites and the maximum
usage of stream runoff water for mill supply. However, this affected the design by requiring a higher
dam to provide the necessary freeboard and making
necessary an impervious starter dam. In order to
permit drainage of tailings behind the starter dam
and prevent the future phreatic line from reaching
the dam face when built up with tailings, an underdrain system was provided just upstream of the
starter dam. The drain system terminates in a pipe
outlet and valve below the downstream face of the
dam. The purpose of the valve was to permit water
storage during initial plant start-up. Pervious
tailings cyclone underflow material on the upstream
face of the starter dam permits water flow to the
drain system when the valve is open.

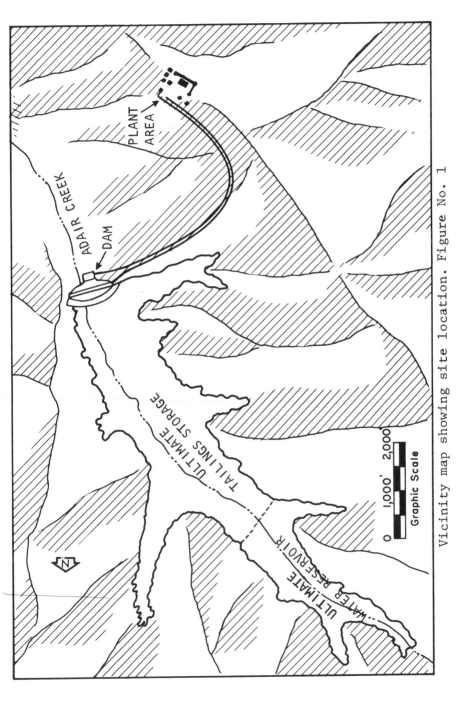

Vicinity map showing site location. Figure No. 1

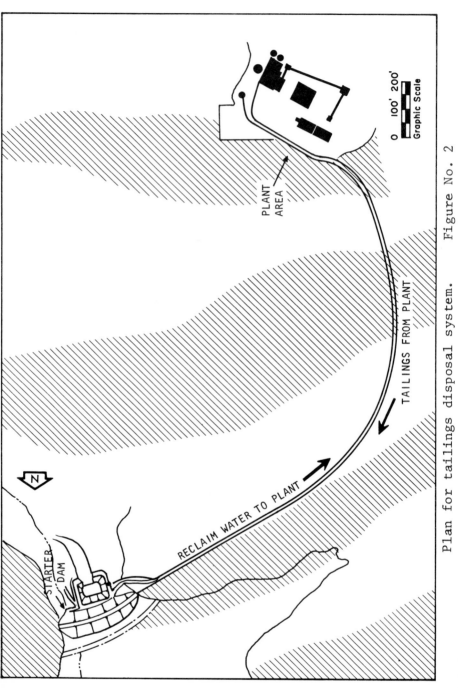

Plan for tailings disposal system.   Figure No. 2

The drainage area above the tailings dam is about
6 square miles. Normal stream flow in Adair Creek
between rains is about 100 to 150 gallons per minute,
but in order to cope with flood flows, it was decided
to design for a 50-year storm. Considerable thought
was given to the design of a system to handle peak
storm run-off with maximum safety and minimum disturbance to operations and the environment. A
diversion channel or tunnel was not practicable because of the terrain. A spillway at one end of the
dam was considered but this would require periodic
raising as the dam was built up. A circular spillway tower 1,500 feet upstream from the dam feeding
a large pipeline through the dam was studied and
this led to the final design. For a spillway, the
upstream end of the pipeline is extended up a steeply
sloping hillside and provided with a trash screen
over the open end. Raising of the spillway can
easily be accomplished by adding lengths of pipe as
needed.

Comparative estimates were made of several sizes
of pipe ranging from 96 inches, which could carry
the peak flow as it developed, down to 60 inches
which would require holding a portion of the flood
behind the dam and releasing the impounded water over
a 76-hour period. Reduced costs of smaller pipe
sizes were offset somewhat by required increases in
the height of the starter dam. In all cases, a clear
freeboard of 5 feet was considered to be the absolute minimum. A decision was made in favor of a
60 inch pipeline which would have as an added benefit
the reduction of peak flood flows downstream of the
dam.

The tailings water decant system would be required
to supply all of the mill process water and thus,
reliability was a prime consideration. A comparative
study was made of: 1. a floating pump barge, with a
floating section of pipeline and a fixed pipeline
to the plant site, and 2. a fixed decant pipeline
through the dam to a stilling pool and a fixed pump
station with a pipeline to the plant site. This

study showed first cost to be about a standoff. The
fixed pump station arrangement was considered to be
a better operation, lower in maintenance costs and
more reliable so it was chosen.

The Ozark Lead tailings solids are dolomitic
limestone ground to 10 percent to 15 percent plus
100 mesh. No clay or slime-forming minerals are
present and deposited tailings drain rapidly to a
very firm state. The method of dam building with
tailings hydraulically deposited at the crest of the
dam has been successfully used for many years at
mines in the U. S. and foreign countries. The
coarser sands form a stable free-draining zone on
the downstream side (Figure No. 2) and the finer
fractions are naturally classified as they flow
away from the dam. The result is a very stable
structure with the coarsest particles at the downstream face gradually grading to finer particles
with the extreme fines most remote from the dam.
A number of dams are in existence well over the projected maximum height of 100 feet for Ozark Lead.
As further assurance of safety, the stability of
the dam as designed was checked by stability analyses.
Cyclones were adopted as a means of insuring free
drainage of the material on the upstream face of the
starter dam merging into the downstream face of the
tailings built dam above.

DESCRIPTION OF THE TAILINGS SYSTEM

The unthickened mill tailings plus overflow water
from the concentrate thickeners are combined and are
carried in a gravity flow pipeline to the tailings
disposal area about 6,000 feet away. About 1,000
feet from the concentrator, the mine water is discharged to the same pipeline. The first 4,500 feet
is 21-inch concrete pipe which flows partly full and
discharges to a concrete drop box. From this drop
box an 18-inch steel pressurized pipeline slopes to
the dam crest and then is carried level across the
dam. Outlets are provided every 50 feet for feeding
cyclones which are mounted on wooden stands. A

control valve is provided so that tailings may be sent either to the cyclones or discharged directly to the tailings pond. The cyclone underflow furnishes coarse material for dam building and the overflow discharges by gravity behind the dam.

The starter dam (Figure No. 3) is 37 feet high above the valley floor with a crest length of 1,200 feet. The dam is constructed of impervious material compacted to 95 percent optimum density, except for the downstream toe which is of permeable material. A core trench along the axis of the dam was excavated to a clay base about 20 feet below surface, then backfilled with clay. The dam base is 215 feet wide maximum, both upstream and downstream faces slope at 2.5 to 1 and the top has a 30-foot wide roadway as a service road for the cyclones.

In the area about 200 feet upstream of the starter dam, there is a drainfield (Figure No. 4) with collector drains leading to an outlet pipe under the dam. Drain pipes are 6-inch perforated steel pipe and the outlet pipe is 6-inch steel pipe with four welded seepage collars. A gate valve at the outside end of the outlet pipe permits water storage as desired. Drain pipe trenches are backfilled with clean gravel topped off with clean coarse sand.

The stormflow outlet system conducts normal and storm runoff, plus decanted water, under the dam to the stilling pool where the outlet structure assists in dissipation of hydraulic energy. The 60-inch storm conduit is corrugated metal pipe, asbestos bonded and bituminous coated inside and out. The interior lining is applied to fill the corrugations and make a smooth surface. Four galvanized metal seepage collars at 25 foot centers are provided. The 60-inch pipe slopes toward the outlet on a 1 to 2 percent descending grade for 1,400 feet. The upper end, as extended during operations, is laid on a steep hillside on a 60 percent grade. A temporary inlet structure was established initially at the bottom of the hill at an invert elevation 18

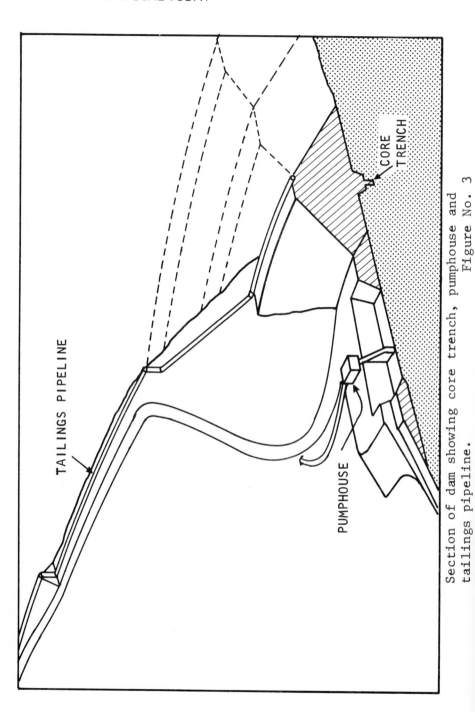

Section of dam showing core trench, pumphouse and tailings pipeline.

Figure No. 3

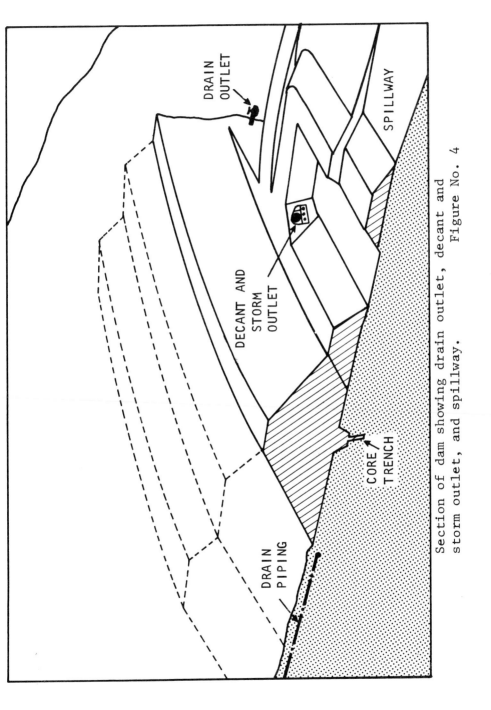

Section of dam showing drain outlet, decant and storm outlet, and spillway.   Figure No. 4

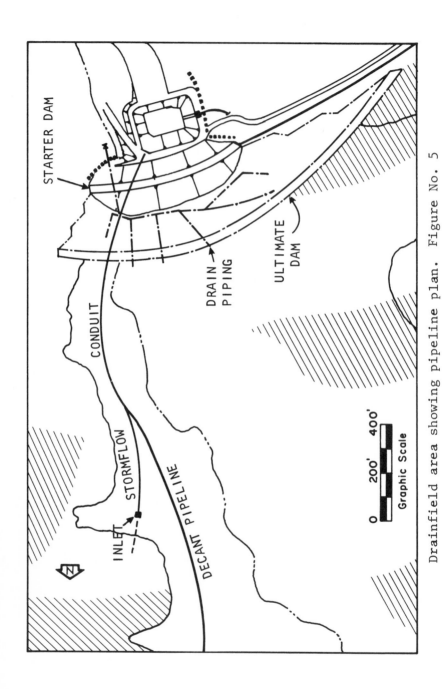

Drainfield area showing pipeline plan. Figure No. 5

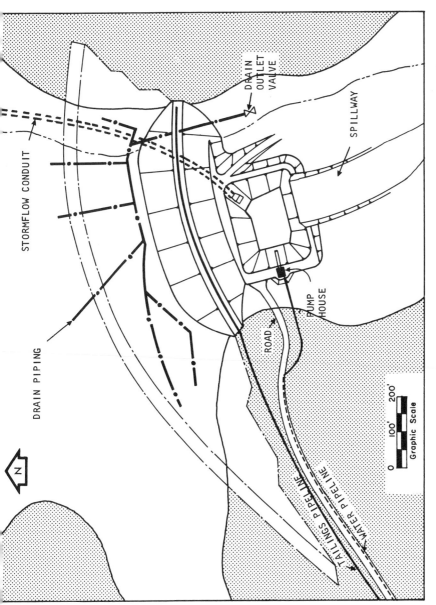

Drainfield area showing plan of dam and pipelines. Figure No. 6

feet below the crest elevation of the starter dam.

The decant pipeline is a 24-inch corrugated metal pipe connected to the top of the 60-inch pipe about 1,000 feet upstream from the outlet. This 24-inch pipe is extended upstream along the valley floor to the clarified water decant pool upstream of the deposited tailings. This pool also functions as a mill water storage reservoir. A valve with accessible operator is provided in this decant pipe for regulation of water flow from the decant pool to the reclaim water reservoir.

Just below the downstream side of the dam is a reclaim water reservoir of 4 million gallons capacity. Input to this reservoir is clear water from the decant pool conducted through the 24-inch and 60-inch pipelines. A weir, which is 24 feet wide, has been installed to measure and record the amount of water being returned to the stream below as surplus water or storm water.

A pump station is located at one side of the reclaim water reservoir to deliver water through a 16-inch steel pipeline to a 200,000-gallon elevated water storage tank adjacent to the concentrator. Three 300 horsepower, 2,000 gallons per minute vertical turbine pumps are automatically sequentially operated by electronic level controllers at the water tank. Water level in the tank is also recorded at the mill central control panel. Hydraulically cushioned check valves protect the pumps which have an operating head of 460 feet.

SYSTEM OPERATION

In May 1968, the Ozark Lead concentrator began operating at a limited production rate. The tailings produced were diverted, at a point near the end of the concrete pipeline, to a small valley above the starter dam. These tailings flowed down this valley and deposited at the edge of the storage lake which was formed by impounding runoff water before start-

View of tailing dam with water reclaim pond to the
right.   Figure No. 7

Downstream side of the dam, showing vegetation.
                                          Figure No. 8

up. In May 1969, the tailings were directed to the
cyclones and the underflow sands were used to raise
the height of the dam. Cyclones and associated pipelines and valves are not operated during about four
months of each winter to avoid damage from freezing.
For the remainder of the year, cyclones are operated
about 60 percent of the time, tailings otherwise
being diverted directly to the tailings pond from
the diversion point near the end of the concrete
pipeline. As cyclone underflow sands build up,
cyclones and stands are raised and also moved hori-
zontally to fill valleys between the cyclones.
Raising is normally done by mobile crane, although
horizontal moves are sometimes done manually. Today,
after more than four years of operation, the dam has
been raised 21 feet by building with cyclone sands.
A bulldozed roadway is planned for this level and
the main 18-inch pipeline will be raised to this new
level. Cyclone dam building will then continue for
another 20 feet. The road, pipe and cyclones will
then be moved up to this higher elevation. These
steps will be repeated until a maximum height of
about 100 feet above the valley floor is reached.

Cyclone performance is very good with a minimum
of fines in the cyclone underflow product as shown
in Table I.

Table I - Typical Screen Analyses

Mesh	Cyclone Feed (20% Solids) Weight %	Cumulative %	Mesh	Cyclone Underflow (65% Solids) Weight %	Cumulative %
+ 48	0	0	+ 48	0	0
+ 65	7.5	7.5	+ 65	18.5	18.5
+100	8.4	15.9	+100	19.6	38.1
+150	9.9	25.8	+150	23.5	61.6
+200	12.2	38.0	+200	18.9	80.5
+270	9.5	47.5	+270	9.6	90.1
+400	13.1	60.6	+400	7.4	97.5
-400	39.4	100.0	-400	2.5	100.0

Inlet to water diversion line has a trash rack to keep out debris.   Figure No. 9

Looking down on the water reclaim pond. Pumping plant, seen at right, recirculates water to the mill.
                         Figure No. 10

To date, the 24-inch decant pipeline has been extended upstream a total of 5,000 feet and will be extended again in the near future. Normally, the decant pipeline is submerged below the lake surface. The level of the lake upstream of the deposited tailings is controlled by a valve in the decant pipeline. Release of decant water is generally regulated to keep the water level in the reclaim water reservoir below the overflow spillway elevation. The maximum level of the lake is limited by the elevation of the storm drain inlet. The quantity of water stored and the lake elevation fluctuate depending on the amount of natural precipitation but an ample supply of water for concentrator operations has been available at all times. The distance from the dam to the nearest part of the lake varies from one-eighth to one-half mile and the length of the lake ranges between one-half and one mile.

The 60-inch storm drain conduit has been extended twice since operations began for a total raise in elevation of 12 feet. Three major storm floods have been experienced to date. The most severe storm, after a period of unusually heavy rainfall during the winter of 1968, backed up water to five feet above the storm drain inlet. Release of that water took about two days' time. Peak flow downstream of the dam was reduced accordingly, but because of the relatively small drainage area involved, the effect on the general stream system below was small.

Some turbidity occurs with flood flows but sufficient settling takes place in the decant lake and in the reclaim water reservoir so that the mill water supply is tolerably clear. The reclaim water reservoir has accumulated some silt and will require cleaning out in the near future.

The underdrain system has functioned as expected, although the level of the decant lake and the phreatic line has not yet reached the elevation of the starter dam crest. Presently, the 6-inch drain pipe is kept open all winter as a safeguard against freezing and is closed all summer for maximum storage of water. The 6-inch pipe flows about one-fourth full when open. In the future, the drain outflow will be regulated to keep the phreatic line in a safe position as measured by piezometer tubes installed near the dam face.

Whenever it becomes necessary to release water to the stream below the dam, flow measurements are taken at the 24-foot-wide weir discharging from the reclaim water reservoir. Periodic tests are made on the quality of reclaim water and of water discharged to Adair Creek. All tests to date indicate that this water is of excellent quality. As final proof, a number of fish, up to 12 inches long, have made the reclaim water reservoir their home.

In conclusion, operating experience with the Ozark Lead tailings disposal system has demonstrated that sound planning and good management can result in an efficient and safe operation with negligible impact on the environment.

DISCUSSION

E. D'APPOLONIA (E. D'Appolonia Consulting Engineers, Inc.): I notice that you have a great deal of instrumentation and construction control in your dams; at least, this was implied. However, are you also taking these data and trying to turn them around and see whether you can't gain economy in the next stage of construction? That is to say, gaining economy, either by decreasing the amount of materials that may be required, reducing the section, or trying to get more economy into your structure from your control and your data? Or is this further down the pike in the next project?

MILTON LAGERGREN: I think at Ozark Lead Company we are about as economical of labor and materials as we can reasonably expect to get. As the dam builds up and gets higher very slowly, I think we may institute some procedures as it builds. We intend to find out as much as we can about the phreatic water line and density and so on. We will try to learn from the operation as it proceeds. We'll try to get enough information that may relate to future projects of like nature. And, naturally, we try to operate just as economically as possible, within safety and environmental considerations. I really can't cite anything specific, other than the piezometers and the density measurements and things like that which we'll no doubt use and make as the deposition proceeds.

C. A. RABLING (Minera San Francisco del Oro, S.A. de C.V.): In Mexico, we were faced with this problem that I wish somebody could answer. We were going to treat 9,000,000 tons of tailing in our ponds for fluorspar, also five other tailing ponds. And we had to sample the tailing ponds for moisture content, screen analysis, as well as the contents. We tried, we drilled about 40 holes, but the average of all these holes did not check with what the historic data that we had showed about these tailings. The screen analysis products were altered, so were the moisture contents in the different areas, and we were forced to make bigger trench holes with front end loaders in order to sample the faces for moisture and get samples for screen analysis. I wish somebody could have had this experience and propose a better system than this. It was very expensive so that we couldn't do this in the entire area of the tailings.

MILTON LAGERGREN: I'd like to give a short commercial. I have a patent on a sampling system. It's a thing that was conceived when we were doing some investigations on the possibility of remining some of our tailings, trying to sample very soft tailings materials. This is a freeze sampling system, where we actually freeze the material and then withdraw it in order to get a sample. We haven't really applied it yet on a full scale.

We've made some pilot scale tests and it looks pretty good. I think it probably has some limited application. However, it will give a complete sample, even of water layers in the tailings which actually get frozen, so that you get a real sample of moisture as well as the solids.

ED BECKER (Kaiser Engineers): I found it interesting that the cutoff on the dam was on the downstream toe and, secondly, that it looked as if the water discharging from the underdrainings bypassed the reclaim water pond.

MILTON LAGERGREN: No, the water does not bypass the reclaim water pond. It comes out through the five-foot storm drainage pipe right into the reclaim water reservoir. The cutoff wall is in the middle of the starter dam, of course, and the starter dam is the toe of the future dam as it is built up. The drainage system is purely a means of providing drainage and preventing buildup of water pressure which would subsequently escape over the top of the starter dam at the interface between the built-up portion and the starter dam -- a situation that we did not feel we wanted.

NEW TAILING DAM CONSTRUCTION

AT WHITE PINE

FRANK E. GIRUCKY, P. E.

THE MINE

The only active underground copper producer in
Michigan is the White Pine Copper Company, a
subsidiary of Copper Range Company. It is located
in the northwest part of the Upper Peninsula
adjacent to the east boundary of the Porcupine
Mountain State Park.

Construction at the plantsite started in 1952.
The first ore was brought to the surface in 1953
and the first copper was poured in 1955.

Mining of copper sulphide chalcocite (80 percent)
and native copper (20 percent) is by room-and-pillar
method from a strata-bound deposit in the base of the
Nonesuch shale and the top few feet of the Copper
Harbor formation. The ore column in the Nonesuch is
divided into the parting shale, upper sandstone,
and upper shale. In full column mining (13-foot

high rooms-and-pillars) the ratio of sandstone to
siltstone is 1 to 4. Production schedules call for
approximately 25,000 tons of 1 percent copper ore
to be mined daily.

Elevation at the plantsite is 882 feet above mean
sea level or 280 feet above Lake Superior. North
of the plantsite the area slopes gently towards the
lake six miles away. It is covered with a heavy
second growth of aspen, hemlock, and tamarack.
Annual temperatures range between 100° F. and -40° F.
with the mean high and low of 60° F. and 30° F.

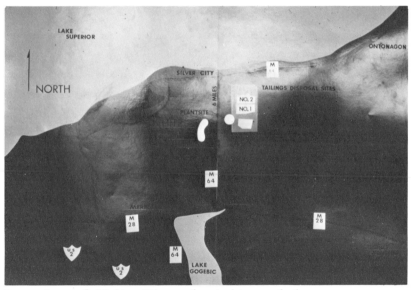

Location of White Pine plantsite and dams.
Figure No. 1

Precipitation averages 35 inches a year and the
annual snowfall averages 180 inches. The recreational
facilities of this area will satisfy the needs of the
most ardent sportsman.

TAILING DISPOSAL TODAY

All construction at White Pine is in an area which
has been extensively glaciated. The sequence of
glacial deposits suggests that they were laid down
by an ice sheet that retreated into an ice marginal
lake and then readvanced leaving the following
arrangement: (1) clayey till, (2) layers of till
and laminated silt and clay, and (3) stony till.
In places the upper clayey till is overlain by
strongly laminated clay, silt, and sand lacustrine
deposits which were laid down in preexisting glacial
lakes that occupied the area. Drainage patterns formed
on the fluted till surface have been little changed
by headward erosion or stream-piracy since their
inception in post glacial time.

ORIGINAL TAILING DAM

General tailing was impounded on the surface
behind a rolled earth filled dam until late 1971.
This structure was first used in 1953, extended
eastward to twice its original size in 1963 and
raised to its present elevation in 1965. Tailings
were last transported to this disposal site at the
rate of 18,000 gpm of 17 percent solids and velocities
of seven feet per second.

The dam was dewatered by means of six reinforced
concrete decant towers located adjacent to the
headwall (north dike) and an equal number of decant
lines which passed beneath the embankment to empty
into a collection ditch. Water from the collection
ditch was either returned to the plantsite or to
Lake Superior.

Relationship between Lake Superior, in the foreground, the new tailing dam, original tailing dam and plantsite, far right of the original tailing dam.   Figure No. 2

Elements of the new tailing dam from left to right: peripheral road, collection ditch, downstream starter dike sand core and underdrain system, upstream starter dike and

The dam embankment encompassed 1,860 acres. It developed a capacity to store approximately 90,000,000 dry tons of waste rock behind the handwall which was topped out at 50 feet above the original ground elevation. The south dike was located 1.1 miles upstream of the north dike and topped out at approximately 12 feet above the original ground elevation.

The designed 10 foot difference between crest elevation of the north and south dikes was equal to the vertical drop (angle of repose) for hydraulically deposited general mill tailing flowing 1.1 miles northward towards the handwall. It made the dams' total developed capacity available for the storage of mill tailing when the dam was filled to its designed limit of five feet below its crest. The east and west dikes were located 215 miles apart. All dikes were constructed with 1 vertical on 2 horizontal slope with one exception. The east dike was constructed with 1 vertical on 3 horizontal slope because the borrow found east of the dam contained comparatively more silt than clay.

The nearly rectangularly shaped tailing disposal site was located west and north of the plantsite. Its southwest corner was approximately 1,200 feet due east of the tailing pumphouse. All tailings were discharged into the dam from the south dike. They were transported to the point of discharge in either a 22-inch or 30-inch 3/16 inch walled steel pipeline. General tailing was last discharged into the eastern portion of the original dam from an outfall located 13,500 feet east of the pumphouse. Pipeline wear was never a problem.

Total tailings were directed into the new tailing dam in late 1971. Construction of this disposal site had started three years earlier. As of

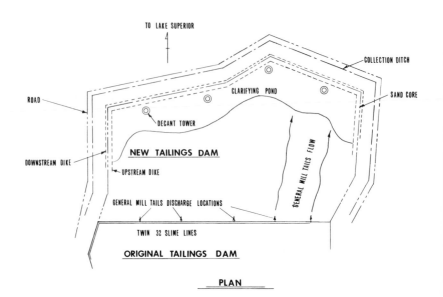

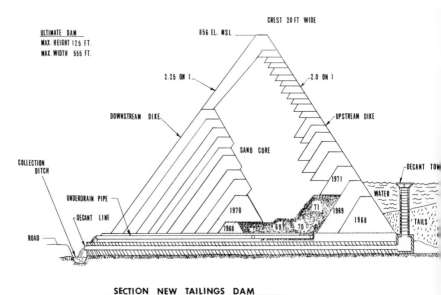

Schematic of the ultimate structure.   Figure No. 4

January 1972, the crest of the new tailing dam was approximately 17 years away from topping out.

NEW TAILING DAM

The area north of and adjacent to the original dam was selected as the site for the new tailing dam. It is a rather heavily wooded area which gently slopes downward at approximately a one percent grade from an elevation of 800 feet above sea level northward to Lake Superior, four miles away.

The headwall of the original dam will be the south dike of the new tailing dam. The east and west dikes of the original dam will be extended northward to become the east and west dikes of the new dam.

Site development is in an area cut by north-northeastward flowing drainage-ways spaced about half a mile apart. Soils referred to locally as glacial lake beds are a red dense sandy clay containing scattered rocks ranging in size from small pebbles to occasional boulders up to four feet in diameter. The soils are generally impermeable and quite strong. They become extremely slick when wetted and very difficult to traverse with heavy equipment.

Design of Ultimate Structure

The new tailing dam did not closely resemble the successfully designed rolled earth structure of the past. The most significant differences were the result of utilizing rolled earth fill together with sand from the mill as embankment materials. Construction rate is contingent upon the availablility of mill sand and total construction is keyed to the annual production level. Its date of completion and total life are only two years apart.

Bechtel Corporation of San Francisco, California was retained to design a new tailing disposal site. Its design incorporated the technological advances of 20 years to most effectively utilize all of the available construction materials and to minimize those dangers inherently associated with the upstream and downstream method of constructing a tailing dam.

The original dam embankment was homogeneous. The new dam embankment is heterogeneous. Bechtel utilized an upstream and downstream rolled earth shell to sandwich between them a cycloned mill sand core that was kept dewatered by means of an extensive underdrain system.

The difference in permeability of the upstream dike, downstream dike and sand core, plus an extensive underdrain system were used to advantage in designing a stable 125-foot-high embankment containing the smallest amount of material. The slime covered impervious rolled earth fill upstream dike minimizes the seepage into the embankment, whereas the comparatively more permeable dry random filled downstream dike provides the required stability. The embankment's structural integrity is maintained by controlled seepage through the pervious sand core which directs the passage of both seepage water and sand transportation water from the interior of the embankment to the collection ditch.

Sand for the embankment is hydraulically transported from the mill to the dam site where it is dewatered by three sets of cyclones and the underdrain system. The cyclone overflow contains 3 percent to 10 percent solids. It is impounded behind the upstream dike. The cyclone underflow contains 70 percent solids. It is deposited between the upstream and downstream starter dikes. About three days later the underflow is moved into place in the embankment by heavy earth moving equipment.

General mill tailing minus the sand fraction are hydraulically transported from the mill to the south

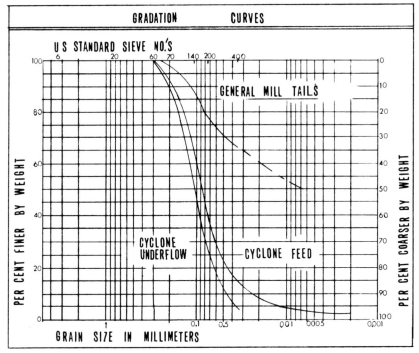

Gradation of mill products and classified sand.

Figure No. 5

side of the dam for disposal. The solids are retained
in the dam. The transportation water is decanted
from the dam after it has clarified. Water thus
removed and the water removed from the sand core
by the underdrain system empties into the collection
ditch located adjacent to the downstream dike. Flow
from the collection ditch travels northward 2-1/2
miles to Lake Superior.

The axis of the ultimate embankment will be 161 feet
from the axis of the upstream starter dike and 65 feet
from the axis of the downstream starter dike.
Distances from the centerline of the ultimate embankment and the centerline of the upstream and downstream
rolled earth dikes vary annually as they are dependent
on the foundation elevation and the year in which
construction occurs. Maximum height of the ultimate
structure will be 125 feet above original ground; its
width 555 feet. The upstream slope is 1 vertical on
2 horizontal and the downstream slope is 1 vertical

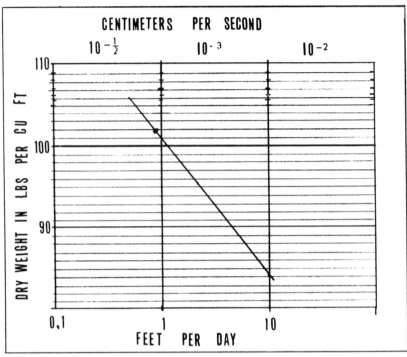

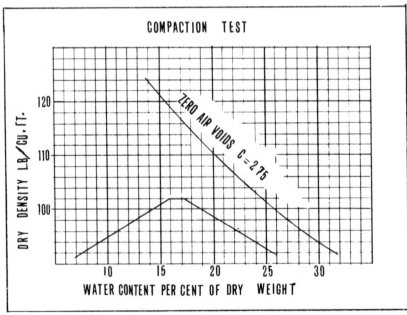

Engineering properties of the twice cycloned mill sands.   Figure No. 6

on 2.25 horizontal.

Approximately 14,000,000 cubic yards of borrow and 10,500,000 cubic yards of twice cycloned mill sand will be placed in 29,000 lineal feet of embankment to encompass 2,500 acres. The north and south embankments are 1.5 miles apart. The east and west embankment are 2.5 miles apart. The ultimate structure will have the capacity to store 280,000,000 dry tons of tailing. Storage capacity at White Pine is calculated on the basis of 26 cubic feet per dry ton.

Exploration for Rolled Earth Fill

An exploration program was developed by White Pine to control total borrow cost, i.e., the cost to develop borrow pits, a function of clearing, grubbing, stripping and depth and quality of borrow, and the cost to place rolled earth fill, a function of haul distance and borrow conservation. The program was the definition of both quantity and quality of borrow adjacent to the collection ditch for a distance of 2.5 miles from the dam. The quality of borrow is determined by its engineering properties, permeability, water content, density, compressive strength and Atterburg Limits. Utilizing these data, it became possible to determine where to borrow and when to borrow to minimize total borrow costs.

Exploration for borrow is accomplished by using a small backhoe and a soil resistivity meter. Holes are dug at 1,000-foot intersection, logged and related to the resistivity meter readings taken prior to digging. Reliability of data interpretation is enhanced by augmenting the 1,000-foot data points with resistivity readings taken at 400-foot grid inter-sections. Anomalies were rechecked with a 100- or 50-foot resistivity grid or backhoe holes. Predicted quantities and qualities correlated closely with findings in the field.

Secondary control of borrow cost is directly related to the conservation of materials or total borrow recovery. Haul distance was minimized and the in situ cost of borrow was reduced when a ripper was used in each pit to ensure the maximum recovery of material before pit abandonment or flooding.

Float boulders were generally encountered prior to bottoming out a borrow pit on bed rock. The ripper became the means of removing the maximum amount of borrow with only normal wear on the scraper blades.

Utilizing these techniques, long-term plans and schedules were developed to ensure the annual place-ment of rolled earth fill at a reasonable cost.

Sand for the Embankment

Mill wastes will account for about 40 percent of embankment materials. Milling at White Pine produces two separate waste products, a sand fraction and a slime fraction. Formerly, these were recombined in the pumphouse and transported to the disposal site as general mill tails. Currently sand from the mill passes through the old pumphouse into a new addition, the sand house. The sand fraction is classified in this building and the processed sand is pumped to the dam site by a battery of 18 rubber lined pumps. When the temperature falls below 32° F. the sand fraction is again recombined with the slime fraction and transported to the disposal site as general mill tails.

The sand fraction is classified by pumping it through six 20-inch Krebs cyclones with hydrocyclones attached. The cyclone overflow is returned to the slime house (old pumphouse) while the 70 percent solids underflow is diluted to approximately 35 percent solids. This is hydraulically transported to the project site through three 8-inch-diameter pipelines to be deposited at locations varying between 8,000 to 29,000 feet from the sand house. The pumps in the

Sand buggy depositing classified sand from the mill between the upstream and downstream dikes.

Figure No. 7

Completed section of underdrain system downstream of the upstream starter dike waiting to receive classified sand from the mill.

Figure No. 8

sand house have the capacity to move 1,400 gallons per minute of 35 percent solids at 400 pounds per square inch when six pumps are connected in series to each 8-inch pipeline.

Distribution of sand at the project site is accomplished by means of a sand buggy which is attached to each of the three 8-inch pipelines. A sand buggy is a four-wheel trailer upon which three 15-inch Krebs cyclones were mounted primarily for dewatering the classified sand. These are pulled from place to place on the crest of upstream dike to distribute the 70 percent solids underflow between the upstream and downstream dikes. Overflow from the sand buggy, 3 percent to 10 percent solids is wasted upstream of the upstream dike to be retained for clarification as are the general mill tailing which is pumped into this disposal site from the north dike of the original dam.

Water in the sand buggy underflow seeps downward through the classified sand core into the underdrain system which directs it into the collection ditch. Water from the underdrain system has the clarity of the best bottled water.

Twice cycloned sand is moved into place between the upstream and downstream dikes by two rubber-tired dozers after it has been dewatered for approximately three days. The sand is compacted in 12-inch lifts. Compaction is obtained with a seven-wheel static type compactor having a gross vehicle weight of 36,000 pounds. Experience has shown that 95 percent Proctor could be obtained with one pass when the water content was close to optimum.

Underdrain System

Interconnected perforated pipe was imbedded in the foundation beneath the sand core. This is the heart of the underdrain system. Two 8-inch-diameter pipes were installed parallel to and 10 feet away from the

upstream and downstream starter dikes. These were
interconnected every 125 feet by perforated pipe
laterals and unperforated pipe which passed beneath
the downstream dike to terminate in the collection
ditch.

Perforations are four lines of 3/8-inch holes drilled
in the bottom one-third of the galvanized, 16-gauge
bituminous hot dipped corrugated metal pipe. Underdrain
pipe was installed in 2-1/2-foot-wide trenches to a
minimum depth of 2-1/2 feet, holes down.

All perforated pipe was imbedded in filter
material. The trench was filled first with a 4-inch-deep
layer of fine concrete aggregate sand curved to the
fit of the pipe. This was overlain with six inches
of crushed stone curved to the fit of the pipe. The
pipe was bedded and covered with crushed stone to the
top of the pipe. The balance of the trench was
filled with fine concrete aggregate. All filter
material was power tamped to 95 percent Proctor
during its placement. The result was a non-plugging
underdrain system installed beneath a classified sand
core.

The portion of the underdrain system which passed
beneath the downstream starter dike was unperforated
bituminous hot dipped corrugated metal pipe. It was
installed in a similar sized trench but back filled
with materials removed from the trench.

The underdrain system functions regardless of
very low temperatures. The icicles get longer and
thicker but water continues to flow unabated from the
pipes into the collection ditch.

Decant System

The dam is dewatered by means of four 30-inch Internal
Diameter encased concrete pipes crossing under the
embankment to four 54-inch Internal Diameter reinforced concrete towers located adjacent to the upstream

Installation of the underdrain system downstream of
the downstream starter dike.   Figure No. 9

Decant tower with first concrete ring and trash
rack attached.   Figure No. 10

toe of the upstream starter dike. This arrangement
is similar to the system used in the original dam.
The location of the decant towers divides the water
impounded against the upstream dike into five fairly
equal zones.

As the dam's capacity is reduced by incoming
tailings, the decant towers are raised to provide
additional storage capacity and to maintain the depth
of water over the settled slimes necessary for the
successful operation of the dam. Decant towers are
raised by adding 8-inch-high precast concrete rings
(containing eight tapered holes) to those already in
place. Each ring must be firmly connected to the
underlying ring. This is accomplished by seating
the ring over eight preanchored threaded
reinforcing bars (No. 18) which are torqued to 1,000
pounds per square inch and grouted into immobility.
When the grout has cured, the retaining nuts and
bearing plate on each threaded rebar can be removed,
the rebars extended, and another decant ring added.
Although two decant rings can be added to a tower at
one time, it is the more costly practice as the
grouting requires more time.

Because a decant ring cannot be removed without
difficulty once it is grouted into place, pumping,
siphoning or the construction of spillways become the
methods whereby the pond level can be lowered below
the elevation of the lowest decant ring.

Each of the decant towers is capped with a circular
galvanized steel water control lid and a trash rack.
The latter prevents the entrance of large pieces of
floating debris which could plug the tower when
decanting is in progress. The lid is simply a circular
steel plate hinged on two sides, with one or both sides
being lifted to permit clarified water to flow from
the dam. The weight of the lid and the overlying
water seats it tightly on the topmost concrete ring
to prevent the uncontrolled escape of water from the
dam.

The water control lid is equipped with a lifting eye attached to a vertical rod welded to the center. On either side of this rod, three 6-inch-diameter pipes, each 30 inches high, have been welded to the lid in a vertical position. These function as vacuum breakers and permit the easy removal of the inundated hinged cover whenever it becomes necessary to add a concrete ring.

All decant towers are constructed and operated from a barge specially designed for this purpose; however, the lids are also operated from a 12-foot boat. In the winter decant tower lids are opened and closed from a boat skidded into position. No concrete rings are added to the towers when the temperature is too low to ensure the proper curing of grout.

Placing a concrete ring on a decant tower from the barge specially desiged for this purpose.

Figure No. 11

Concrete rings are trucked from a stockpile to the dam and unloaded on the slope nearest to a decant tower. Using the barge winch, these rings are transferred to the deck and then to the decant tower. The barge is propelled between towers by means of two 5-horsepower outboard engines. The engines are sized to minimize the possibility of the barge berthing at speeds which would damage a decant tower. Travel time between decant towers averages two hours, but is considerably slower against substantial winds.

Clarified water decanted from the dam via decant line. Several cutoff walls and bedrock foundation are visible.   Figure No. 12

The balance of the decant system is the decant line, the concrete encased concrete pipe which carries the water beneath the dam embankment to the collection ditch. The 30-inch Inside Diameter decant line is enveloped by 18 inches of reinforced concrete. All decant lines were constructed on bedrock. Each has three reinforced concrete cutoff collars beneath

the embankment to prevent piping through the
foundation. Bed rock beneath the upstream starter
dike was pressure grouted adjacent to the decant line
to minimize seepage and piping. Water flow through
the line is regulated to prevent a pulsating discharge. This minimizes dynamic stressing.

Water Standards

Water quality control which is, in this case, the
fundamental reason for the existence of the dam, starts
at the mill and terminates at Lake Superior. Water
returned to Lake Superior from the tailing dam
complies with the standards set by state and federal
agencies. Water quality determinations are made
twice daily at the four decant towers and in the
stream which carries water from the tailing dam to
Lake Superior. Periodic checks are made for metallic
ion concentrations and all other possible contaminants.
The resultant water is of very high quality and
supports a normal suite of plant and animal life in
the carrier stream.

In order to clarify the water, the mill adds
approximately two pounds of lime to each dry ton of
tailing impounded behind the dam. The effectiveness
of lime as a flocculent is influenced by a number of
variables, including temperature and dilution by snow
and rain. It is increased and decreased accordingly.
In the winter months, when pool quiescence has been
developed by an ice cover, lime is reduced without
significantly increasing the retention time necessary
to clarify the transportation water. During the
spring runoff, it becomes necessary to add more
lime to maintain an adequate settling rate. However, if it should be found that the required
clarity is not attained by increasing the lime,
the decant towers are raised to increase retention
time and construction logistics are adjusted
accordingly.

Field density test is one of the several methods employed to control the quality of embankment construction.   Figure No. 13

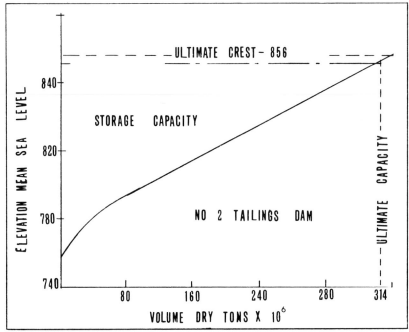

Relationship between embankment crest elevation and storage capacity for the ultimate structure

Figure No. 14

755

Secondary water quality control is accomplished by minimizing watershed siltation attributable to the construction projects. Banks of the collection ditch and borrow pits through which water flows towards Lake Superior have been revegetated with grass planting and/or natural seeding. Test plantings and growth studies are currently in progress to determine the optimum method of stabilizing various soils.

Dam Construction

Construction of the tailing dam is controlled by five permanent employees. Quality control is the responsibility of a two-man soils team. Quantity control, field layout, and the determination of contractual pay quantities are the responsibility of a three-man survey team. Both teams cooperate in the exploration for borrow during the winter months, and the year-round monitoring of piezometers and the dam embankment. The permanent team is assisted by four to six engineering students from nearby colleges and universities during a part of the construction season.

The transportation, placement and compaction of the twice cycloned mill sand is accomplished with inhouse resources.

Sand is pumped to the tailing dam at the rate of 3,200 cubic yards per day, seven days per week, seven months of the year starting about mid-April.

The slime house and sand house operate on a 24-hour-a-day basis. This requires four men with the cost distributed proportionately between tailing dam construction and slime disposal. Maintenance is done as needed on a high priority basis and charged to tailing dam construcation.

Three heavy equipment operators work 40 hours a week moving the sand deposited by the sand buggies and compacting it into place. This work is accomplished with two Michigan 280s and a Michigan R-81 compactor.

Sand buggies are moved, monitored and sampled during one eight-hour shift, seven days per week. They are intermittently monitored and sampled during the remaining two eight-hour shifts, seven days per week. Four men are required to control the sand buggies.

Placement of rolled earth fill in the embankment has previously been awarded to an outside contractor on a year-by-year basis. This phase of the construction generally starts about the first of June and is completed by mid-October. Approximately 600,000 cubic yards of borrow are placed annually.

Studies are in progress to determine the feasibility of utilizing inhouse resources for total construcation.

Costs

Currently inhouse resources are utilized for all construction work at No. 2 dam except the placement of natural borrow. During the past several years inhouse costs were 50 percent lower than bid prices received from local contractors for corresponding construction.

There are a number of reasons which accounted for an annual savings of 50 percent. The most significant ones are the result of differences in the union agreement under which each group must operate. By comparison, White Pine's union agreement is more favorable.

Heavy Equipment operators at White Pine receive approximately two-thirds the hourly wage paid by local contractors. Operators are, however, employed the year around.

Local contractors are working under a 40-hour guaranteed work week with no option to reassign the work force to other tasks during times of inclement weather. Inhouse, employees are moved as needed to maintain the highest rate of production. Our union agreement provides for the flexibility of multi-trade crafts.

The maintenance on the job that is available to all White Pine personnel is comparatively more extensive than what is available to a local contractor working 50 to 100 miles away from his permanent shop facilities.

The profit of the local contractor is only a small percentage of the total savings possible by utilizing inhouse resources for construction purposes.

Construction costs through 1971 totaled approximately $8,500,000 for the sand house and pumping equipment, 90,000 feet of 8-inch sand lines, three sand buggies, 140,000 feet of underdrain system, 500 concrete tower rings, four decant lines, a decant tower barge, two Michigan 280s, a compactor, 38,000 feet of 32-inch slime pipeline, 1,500,000 cubic yards of cycloned mill sand, 2,800,000 cubic yards of rolled earth fill, and miscellaneous support field equipment such as: a soils field laboratory, two field trailers, Broncos, pickup trucks, boom truck, and snowmobiles. These costs are continuing presently at about (or over) $1,100,000 per year.

This dam was designed to provide storage capacity for mill tailing in balance with mill production requirements and in compliance with state specifications for water quality without disturbing the beauty of the area. It is a major part of White Pine Copper Company's extensive environmental control program.

DISCUSSION

E. D'APPOLONIA (E. D'Appolonia Consulting Engineers Inc.): I notice that you have a great deal of instrumentation and construction control in your dams -- at least, this was implied, certainly in the White Pine dam. Of course that is one thing -- you have designed, you have a plan, you are controlling it. Are you also taking these data and trying to turn them around and see whether you can't gain economy in the next stage of construction? That is to say, either by decreasing the amount of materials that may be required, reducing the section, or trying to get more economy into your structure from your control and your data? Or is this further down the pike in the next project?

FRANK GIRUCKY (White Pine Copper Company): There are two things that have happened. One is, very simply, we have what we thought was a good plan to start with. Second, because we are learning, we have modified this plan slightly to gain the economies that were available to us. We have approximately 24 piezometers installed in the upstream berm. We monitor them. This is our second year of monitoring and, consequently, we have not had the opportunity to take advantage of the data that were available to us, to realize any economies that might be associated with the piezometer. But, believe me, there are many managers in our organization who sleep a lot sounder because of the piezometers.

I. SINTENIS (Sherritt Gordon Mines Ltd.): During the field trip, as well as during the lectures, I noticed that the ground was not prepared -- let's say because the organic matter was not removed -- and I'd just like to ask Mr. Girucky what investigation is necessary to find out if there is a leakage problem in the long run? "Leakage" may not be the right word, maybe "seepage" is better because of the settling through the ground.

FRANK GIRUCKY: One of the things that was asked was real simple: "What do I do when I find seepage?" Or is the question, "How do I prevent seepage to begin with?" Let me handle the first one. One of the methods that we've used to find out where some water disappears on occasion has been the interjection of fluorasine or rhodamine dyes and then monitoring these later on with black light. This tells us that there is indeed some seepage. So if you're not sure and you have a way to put the material, these dyes, into your dam, you can find out if the dam is actually seeping. You can do the same thing with the ground. Now, one of the things that bothers me is that we talked about "seepage." I think any seepage is good, as long as you are controlling it. It is when it becomes uncontrollable that you have your problem.

NOEL W. KIRSHENBAUM (Marcona Corporation): In view of the extreme frigid conditions you experience and enjoy during the winter at White Pine, could you perhaps describe some of the problems and solutions of operating the ponds during those periods?

FRANK GIRUCKY: I'm delighted to answer this one. Our dams operate best in the winter. Very simply, we do not have the problem of wind. You get a two or three-foot-thick layer of ice over the pond; the wind does not disturb it and, consequently, we enjoy winter from the standpoint of operating a dam.

NOEL W. KIRSHENBAUM: How about your clothes?

ANSWER: Wear lots.

W. A. WAHLER (W. A. Wahler & Associates): I'd like to make a comment relative to the foundation stripping problem. I think when you're talking about a dam, whether it is in the water industry or the mining industry, the technology has to be about the same. The two most important

elements of a dam are the embankment and its
contact with the foundation or the natural ground.
If you do a good job at the contact zone, between
the embankment and the foundation, you've probably
eliminated two-thirds of the post-construction
troubles that you'll have. If you don't do a good
job at that interface, you're really asking for it.
I think that is a much more critical barrier than
higher up within the embankment. Many people like
to take the position that if they get rid of this
messy little job of the foundation quickly, cover
it over and then do a real good job on the embankment, everything will come out all right. This
idea that doing an average-good job might produce
a satisfactory solution is fallacious.

TAILING DISPOSAL - ITS HIDDEN COSTS

Charles E. Johnston
Mining Engineer
Arthur G. McKee & Company
Western Knapp Engineering Division
San Francisco, California

INTRODUCTION

The possible cost to the mining industry of public concern for ecology is staggering. One of the many parts of a mining operation where these added costs appear is the tailing disposal system. In fact, the added cost resulting from the multiple restrictions now placed on waste disposal may be the controlling factor for the acceptance or rejection of a potential mining operation. This money outlay can well be termed "hidden costs". All too frequently, as witnessed in past operations, expenditures for tailing disposal were considered insignificant from the very start of a preliminary appraisal of the deposit or site.

This paper presents guidelines for the preliminary evaluation of operating costs of a planned tailing disposal system. A simple two-step procedure is suggested for estimating the cost of each section of the system.

To develop disposal costs for the economic evaluation of a potential mining operation, the several basic variables influencing these costs must be considered. These variables relate to the site location, features of the surrounding area, ore characteristics and other factors affecting waste disposal. For example; is there a natural basin that can serve as a depository or must an enclosure be provided? Can the tailing slurry flow by gravity or must it be pumped? Is there an adequate supply of make-up water or must the liquid portion of the slurry be recycled? Can the clear liquid be discharged or must it be retained? What are the settling characteristics and how acidic or basic is the slurry? It is almost impossible to arbitrarily fix all of these variables to represent any specific situation. Each section of the system must be considered individually.

A review of each section of a disposal system is included. These reviews will aid in defining the variables encountered in; 1) slurry thickening, 2) slurry transport, 3) tailing containment, 4) tailing treatment, 5) effluent transport, 6) evaporation, and 7) area restoration. A typical system may not require all these sections, but careful consideration should be given to the possible effects of alternatives and of future planning that may require additions to the system.

As a basis for an appraisal, a preliminary evaluation of the location, pollution control regulations, and characteristics of tailings is necessary. There is no substitute for a detail engineering study of a tailing system; ultimately every mine operator is faced with this requirement, and with the need to prepare environmental impact studies to satisfy the several regulatory agencies. However, with only the basic data established, it is possible to develop a preliminary estimate of costs for the usual sections of a tailing disposal system by following the evaluation procedure presented in this paper.

SLURRY THICKENING

Where direct disposal of the tailings is not practicable, thickeners are usually installed. Thickeners are specialized pulp settling tanks using mechanical rakes to discharge the settled solids to an underflow and a peripheral launder to overflow the clarified liquid. Thickening reduces the volume of slurry to be handled. This reduces the sizes of pipes and launders, pumping power requirement, and size of the tailing dam area, thus decreasing the disposal cost. Recycle of the clarified liquid overflow from the thickener reduces the amount of new water required by the plant.

Thickener requirements can be estimated by measuring slurry settling rate in a graduated cylinder and by applying empirical formulas based on experience. Thickener manufacturers will often provide this service. However, it should be included as a part of the initial bench tests on the ore. In the absence of test data the following average values of thickener area can be used in the evaluation procedure:

Solids	Thickener Area Required sq ft/ (ton solids/24 hrs)
Amorphous or Colloidal	7 to 9
Granular	3 to 5

Cost factors have been developed based on thickener diameters ranging from fifty to five-hundred feet.

SLURRY TRANSPORT

In waste disposal systems the tailings are frequently slurried in water and transported by either pipeline or launder with gravity flow. The slurry under certain conditions may be discharged into a natural drainage channel and collected at a lower elevation for distribution to a pond area. The system becomes much more complicated when gravity flow is not possible, requiring a pump station or stations, with single-stage or multi-stage centrifugal pumps. Long distance transport may require positive displacement pumps and a high-pressure pipeline. To minimize costs, the pumps and piping must be designed for handling an abrasive slurry. The selection and design of pumps is beyond the scope of this paper.

Tailing slurries are typically heterogeneous, two-phase mixtures, from which coarse particles settle rather rapidly. During transport by pipeline the velocity must be kept above the critical value to avoid deposits that constrict the flow and increase energy losses. The critical flow velocity is simply the velocity below which solid particles begin to drop out of suspension and form a deposit on the bottom of the pipe. Critical velocities at various solids concentrations are best determined by pump tests of the slurry being considered. However, preliminary evaluations can be based on experience without the use of test data. Operating velocities of slurry pipelines are typically in the range of three to seven feet per second.

Slurry concentrations are in the range of 35 to 50 percent solids by weight, provided the concentration has not reached the range where a small increase in percent solids results in a drastic increase in the apparent viscosity of the slurry.

The water leaving the plant as tailing slurry is usually a major part of the total plant water requirements. The cost of water, the possible need to reduce heat requirements, the characteristics of the tailing slurry, and the slurry transport distance must be considered in evaluating the need to reclaim a reusable effluent from the tailing disposal system.

In a preliminary appraisal evaluation the total amount of water in the tailing slurry is usually charged to the plant operation at the estimated cost of new water. The effect of a reclaiming scheme to reduce the quantity of water is generally deferred until more detailed evaluations are required. Recovery of heat should also be considered in such a final evaluation. For example, heat may be effectively reclaimed by recycle of overflow from the thickener.

The slurry transport cost factors are based on a slurry specific gravity of 1.46, solids specific gravity of 2.7, slurry concentration of 50 percent solids by weight, and a flow velocity of four feet per second. The evaluation formula provides an adjustment for different specific gravity and solids content. Prices are based on unlined steel pipe with no provision for a corrosive condition. Wood and non-metallic pipes are frequently used, especially for gravity lines. Spare pumps and electrical feeder lines are included.

TAILING CONTAINMENT

There are two approaches for constructing tailing containments; construction with either the mill tailings themselves, or with excavated material.

When using tailings for construction a small starter dam of excavated material is constructed first, followed by gradual buildup of the dam with coarse material from the tailings.

Dams built with excavated material can be either completed at the start of the project, or can be partially constructed in the beginning and finished at a later date when the need arises. Material can be obtained from a selected borrow-pit or from mine wastes. Overburden from an open-pit operation is a common source. In many situations the use of mine wastes for construction of the tailing containment will offer appreciable cost savings.

Dams constructed of tailings will cost much less than those constructed from excavated material. The disadvantage of using tailings lies in controlling the material so that a safe design criteria for the dam can be met. Failures of dams built of tailings are not unusual. However, with proper design and control, safe containments can be built using tailings.

Other site factors have a major effect on the cost of the tailing containment. These factors are: topography, hydrology, seismic conditions, geology, availability of dam material, and distribution of this material.

Basically there are three dam configurations. First, there is a dam to block a trough or valley. This is the ideal situation. Second, there is a three-sided dam to meet conditions represented by a gradual slope. Third, there is a four-sided dike or dam to fit a level or nearly level site.

The acceptability of a site is frequently stated as the "return ratio". This ratio is defined as the unit volume of waste stored per unit volume of fill in the dam.

Where a valley exists that can be dammed as a single side of a trapezoid, the return ratio becomes several hundred to one. Some perimeter dams may have a return ratio as low as 2:1. For this reason it becomes very important to consider alternative disposal areas and dam details. Although an alternative site may require a longer tailing pipeline the cost of additional slurry transport may be less than the dam cost for a nearby site with a low return ratio.

The height of the dam and area of the pond will depend on the plant production rate and the area available for the tailing pond. With an established tailings rate, the available area will have the greatest influence on the cost of the dam.

The control of seepage through a dam and its effect on surrounding areas must be considered. Minimizing seepage through a dam or dike containment has long been considered desirable, but not necessarily economically justified for many installations where regulations did not require rigid control. This situation is rapidly changing, brought about by the impact of strong environmental programs.

Many sealing methods are used to reduce seepage to an acceptable low rate. The most common approach is the placement of an impervious clay core in the dam or dike. Other methods include the placement of membranes, selected impervious soil lining, sealing with the fine tailings, and use of concrete, asphalt or grout. In addition, wells, collection basins, and cut-off trenches are frequently installed downstream from the pond area. The objective is to monitor or collect any seepage.

For a containment constructed with excavated material a basic factor has been developed using a cost of $1.00 per cubic yard. This factor is further refined by a second term, the material availability factor, that adjusts for such variables as source of material, ease of obtainment and distance hauled. For example, an earth structure built with mine waste material will cost only the added expense of longer haul and specialized handling. This can be as low as $0.20 per cubic yard. A somewhat higher cost in the range of $0.50 per cubic yard can be expected for material borrowed within a one-half mile distance and requiring no blasting or ripping. At the other extreme, costs will range up to $3.00 per cubic yard if distances are long and blasting is required. Where tailings are to be used the cost is much lower; in the range of $0.15 per cubic yard. This cost includes a small starter dam of excavated material.

The basic cost factor, shown in Figure 3a, allows for 26 cubic feet of storage per ton of dry tailings. This ratio is probably on the high side, but is reasonable to provide for adequate storage capacity. The second factor, shown in Figure 3b, modifies the cost of excavated material to reflect anticipated construction costs of the area. All costs include provisions for seepage control, filter material and other construction features, but no allowance has been made for land acquisition, natural stream diversion or pond floor clearance and preparation.

TAILING TREATMENT

Chemical treatment of the tailings can be done at one or more points in the disposal system. The usual locations are immediately before or just after the thickener, just prior to discharge into the tailing pond, and on the decant side of the tailing pond.

Several important advantages for treatment at the thickener are:

a)   Convenience of locating treatment facilities at the plant site rather than a remote tailing pond area.

b)   Reduction in possible corrosion of slurry pipelines.

c)   Opportunity to treat tailings prior to possible quantity increase caused by rain and runoff into tailing pond.

d)   Provides an acceptable quality liquid in tailing pond where animals may be in contact.

e)   Reduces problems resulting from seepage of untreated liquid.

The principal disadvantage of treatment at the thickener is that the total tailings must be treated. In many cases, only that portion of the effluent required for special uses, or going to natural drainage, need be treated; with a large portion of the effluent being returned to the plant with little or no treatment. It is possible to take advantage of the smaller effluent quantity where treatment is on the decant side of the tailing pond. In some cases there may be advantages in recovery of water and reagents by recycling clarified liquid from the pond.

For both alkaline and acidic tailings, treatment is in most cases a neutralization process. Basic, or high pH solutions, can be acidified, or in many cases neutralized by carbon dioxide from the atmosphere. Lime or powdered limestone is typically used to correct an acidic condition.

A knowledge of the range of the pH of the tailings is required to develop costs of tailing treatment. This can be established during bench testing or estimated on the basis of experience with similar operations. Also helpful is an understanding of what might cause a continuing basic or acidic condition.

Costs developed in this study for neutralizing acidic tailings represent typical treatment of the effluent using lime at one cent per pound. For alkaline tailings, costs are based on a normal application of sulphuric acid costing 1.7 cents per pound.

While not included in the cost factors presented by this paper, there are cases where radioactive material, cyanide, or other harmful materials are present and require special treatment. Barium chloride can be used to reduce radioactive material while chlorine will help rid the tailings of dangerous amounts of cyanide.

For special cases, ion-exchange can be used to remove heavy metals. Also, additives may be added to the effluent to reduce or prevent scaling.

EFFLUENT TRANSPORT

Handling of decanted liquid from a tailing pond area is usually a simple gravity flow or pumping problem with one or more of the following objectives:

1. Recycling effluent to the plant. It frequently can be used for plant process water and is cheaper than the cost of acquiring make-up water from a fresh source. This plan reduces the environmental impact that might result if the liquid is wasted.

2. Sending the effluent to a special treatment pond.

3. Discharging the effluent to a location for use other than plant process water. Agricultural irrigation is an example.

4. Sending the effluent to evaporation ponds.

5. Discharging the effluent into a natural drainage, either with or without treatment. This last approach is possible only if the quality of the effluent meets today's increasingly rigid standards.

The liquid decanted may be much less than the total input to the tailing pond area since liquid entrapment in the tailings, evaporation, and seepage all reduce the amount of effluent. Evaporation is frequently relied upon to rid the disposal system of unwanted water. This assumes that provision will be made to bypass any natural runoff from entering the tailing pond. Also, if rainfall is high the annual evaporation may not exceed the precipitation and the volume of effluent will be increased.

There are three common methods of collecting the effluent. One method is to decant the liquid from the tailing pond to a pump located at the base of the dam. The decantation system offers the advantage of a permanent pump location, and is capable of handling a sudden flow of natural drainage. It permits natural drainage through the pond area after abandonment and provides simplicity of operation. The disadvantages of this system are in the construction costs, and the problems of a decant tower and pipelines beneath the dam.

The other two methods incorporate the use of pumps and siphons. Both methods have essentially the same advantages of eliminating the cost of decant towers and pipelines through the dam. There are also disadvantages. The more important ones include:

1. Requires care to raise and position the pumps as pond level rises.

2. Power outage or siphon failure leaves no place for water to go and can cause overtopping of the dam.

3. Freezing weather can be troublesome. (Compressed air or circulating water may be required to keep ice from the barge.)

4. There is no way to take care of surface drainage after abandonment except with a special overflow channel.

5. In a siphon system the pond water must be against the dike unless special arrangements are made.

Cost factors have been developed for pipeline gradients between gravity flow and 7 percent grade (Figure 5a). The transport distance is introduced as a second factor (Figure 5b).

The effect of evaporation on the reduction of the quantity of effluent must also be considered. Evaporation can take place in two sections of the disposal system; the tailing pond area and any special evaporation ponds.

To account for evaporation in the tailing pond, adjustment

factors (Figures 5c, 5d and 5e) have been included as adjustments to the cost of effluent pumping. A modifying factor has been included in the evaluation formula to account for variations of input of water caused by different slurry solid concentrations. The cost of a special evaporation pond is part of the next section.

EVAPORATION FACILITY

A tailing disposal system which recycles the maximum amount of effluent to the plant may have an undesirable effect on plant operation. There will be a build-up of soluble material in the plant flow streams. This is frequently avoided by returning only part of the effluent and wasting the remainder as a bleed stream. If 90 percent of the effluent is returned to the plant and 10 percent is wasted, the build-up of soluble material in the plant is limited to ten times the amount of soluble material if all effluent is wasted and none returned. This is usually a satisfactory limit.

Solar evaporation can be used as a means of bleed stream disposal. Part of the effluent from the tailing pond flows to a second pond where the combination of seepage and evaporation exceeds the inflow of effluent. The cost of tailing disposal is increased by any added pumping costs and by the cost of the second pond.

The required pond area depends primarily on local weather and site conditions. The rate of evaporation from a pond depends on temperature cycles, sun exposure time, wind conditions, humidity, depth of pond, and characteristics of the effluent. The average evaporation rate for a large area is difficult to define. A review of historical data and an evaporation test program is necessary to define the evaporation rate for a selected site. However, a net evaporation rate, total evaporation less rainfall, of 24 inches per year is a typical condition which is reasonable for a general cost factor. On this basis the pond area required to evaporate 10 percent of the tailing effluent is as follows:

Daily tonnage of dry tailings	Evaporation pond size
1,000	9 acres
10,000	90 acres
30,000	270 acres
50,000	450 acres

In addition to the evaporation loss in the evaporation pond there are losses by seepage and by evaporation in the tailing pond. There may also be an inflow of surface water to the tailing pond which should be minimized. The combined result usually has small influence on the size of evaporation pond required. An exception to this is when seepage losses in the tailing pond are unusually high; the evaporation pond area may be reduced by as much as 10 to 15 percent. A sizable part of the construction cost of evaporation ponds is for seepage control. Rigid regulations may require sealing of pond area, resulting in high initial costs.

Pumping requirements for evaporation ponds of this type may generally be neglected in a preliminary evaluation. Gravity flow of effluent is frequently possible from the tailing pond to the evaporation pond. Otherwise, low-head pumps are satisfactory. A more significant cost is the pumping system for return of the effluent to the plant, which is included under effluent transport.

Figure 6 shows cost factors for the addition of evaporation ponds to a typical tailing disposal system. Costs for three conditions have been developed. In the first case, costs include the construction of low peripheral dikes with impervious cores, interior dikes with weirs to control flow, and a nominal size pumping system for transfer of effluent. In the second case, the cost of sealing the pond floor with selected earth material has been added. In the third case, the cost includes an impervious membrane to seal the pond floor. In each case the allowance for evaporation is 24 inches per year, with a provision for adjusting the factor to other evaporation rates.

AREA RESTORATION

Area restoration is presently required by federal and state agencies in the United States. Organized conservation groups are also active in pinpointing critical areas, often including remote sites where no present other use can be envisioned.

Restoration of the waste disposal area has three objectives:

(1) Soil stabilization to prevent wind and water erosion.
(2) Pollution control; includes water percolation into the downstream drainage, with special attention to conditions such as radiation from uranium tailing areas.
(3) Landscaping of tailing areas so that appearance blends with the surrounding landscape.

It does not necessarily follow that all three of these objectives will be easy to accomplish. Soil stabilization today is in most cases a "must" and a great deal of effort has been directed toward this objective. The other objectives are important but may not always be of major concern.

There are three principal methods to stabilize a tailing area:

(1) Vegetative - The promotion of plant growth.
(2) Physical - The covering of a tailing area with soil, slag, or other material.
(3) Chemical - The formation of a top crust by the use of chemicals to interact with fine-sized minerals.

Vegetative stabilization should produce a self-perpetuating plant cover. Frequently this involves furrowing or other surface preparation, the planting of a preliminary growth called a nurse crop, fertilizing, and introduction of chemicals to minimize sand movement, retain moisture and produce a dark heat-absorbing surface. A resinous adhesive type material is most effective. Landscaping, if required at all, will be minimal. The vegetative process may be aided under some conditions by a soil cover, matting, and irrigation. Neutralization of acid soils with limestone and treatment of basic soils with gypsum may prove beneficial. However, tests have indicated that neutralization is frequently not necessary and in some cases may adversely affect plant growth. Of greater importance is the control of blowing sand during germination of the nurse crop.

The nurse crop will commonly be a variety of domestic grain or legume; its purpose is to promote a microhabitat for native growth. In some cases a nurse crop may not be necessary.

Under wet conditions the planting of water-loving plants and shrubs to remove excess water by transpiration may be effective. These include tamarisks (salt cedars), watercresses, mints, hyacinths, and reeds.

Physical stabilization is used to protect fine tailings against wind erosion and to provide an attractive habitat for plant growth. The most commonly used material is rock or soil from borrow areas. Mine wastes and slag are also used. Though less common, a cover of bark or the harrowing of straw into the top few inches of the tailings have been used.

A physical cover without vegetation will not always produce the esthetic effect that is demanded. It is usually important that the physical cover be amenable to plant growth.

Chemical stabilization is brought about through the formation of an air and water resistant crust with a thickness of a few inches. The purpose is to minimize wind and water erosion and to prevent pollution. It is particularly applicable in an arid climate, or with acidic or basic conditions. Because the crust will prevent plant growth, this approach will normally meet full acceptance only where vegetation is either not possible or is not wanted.

Tailings may be treated for the recovery of mineral values. This approach, though effective in reducing the immediate site restoration problem, is more in the field of economics rather than environmental control and will not be considered in this discussion.

Many combinations are possible for developing general costs. However, for the purpose of a preliminary appraisal, five basic approaches warrant consideration. The costs will vary greatly depending on type of tailings, location of disposal area, weather conditions, and terrain. The initial appraisal of a tailing disposal problem may not have sufficient information available to pinpoint applicable methods and requirements for proper restoration. For this reason, only an approximation can be made of the expected costs. Current information suggests the following individual restoration costs for stabilization. Other modifications will not greatly change such costs.

Methods	Dollars per acre
Seeding and Fertilizing	40 - 60
Chemical - Vegetative	100 - 250
Four-inch Physical Cover with Seeding	300 - 650
Twelve-inch Physical Cover with Seeding	750 - 1750
Chemical	250 - 750

The cost factors developed in this study are averages of the above values. However, if specific field data is not available, an allowance figure of $300 to $400 per acre is suggested for site restoration costs for appraisal purposes. This allowance is typical of the third category; a four-inch physical cover with seeding to start vegetation. The costs do not include a surety bond, sometimes required by governmental agencies, or the cost of maintaining restrictions on the property over a period of years following its restoration.

EVALUATION PROCEDURE

The objective of an evaluation is to develop preliminary operating cost figures in dollars per ton of tailings, including both direct and indirect costs. The direct operating costs include labor, labor benefits, maintenance, power, fuel, and supplies. Indirect operating costs include controllable costs, non-controllable costs, and 10 percent of initial capital costs as depreciation.

The evaluation procedure consists of two steps:

(1) Obtain information to complete the Field Check List (Table I).
(2) Complete a Cost Tabulation Summary (Table II) using factors (Figures 1 through 7) to estimate a cost for each section of the disposal system.

The check list permits information collected in the early stages of field investigations to be conveniently recorded and applied to the cost estimate. The physical layout, design criteria, and public regulatory influences are included in this information by the completion of column 4 of Table I. The values recorded should reflect preliminary design as shown by columns 1 through 3 of Table I. In the determination of costs the values are used in two ways; they serve as guides to the proper selection of the cost factor, or they are transferred directly to the final tabulation summary to modify the basic cost factor. In this way, the specific characteristics of the planned system are introduced into the cost study.

The cost curve factors, Figures 1 through 7, provide a means by which the experience of industry can be introduced into the study. Basic design criteria and construction costs are reflected in these factors.

The tabulation summary (Table II) brings together the field reference data (Table I) and the experience factors (Cost Factors, Figures 1 through 7) to determine the unit cost for each section of the tailing disposal system. This is done by following the instructions of column 2 of the tabulation summary. Here the

777

proper factors and field reference data are introduced into the formula of column 3. From this step-by-step process the individual unit costs are developed for each section. The unit costs as shown in column 4 of the tabulation summary are recorded in the summary box at the end of the tabulation.

The summation of these unit costs is the total unit cost of the tailing disposal system. By analyzing the cost summary it is possible to identify sections with unusual costs. It gives extra purpose to the appraisal by calling attention to sections where abnormally high or low costs are expected. This situation is illustrated in the example following Figure 7. The high cost of the tailing containment dam is easily singled out in the summary on the last page of the example.

Table I

FIELD CHECK LIST

Sheet 1 of 6

Code No.	Basic Field Reference Item	Description of Sub Items	Data Entry Record	Reference Number of Sub Item
Column 1	Column 2	Column 3	Column 4	Column 5
FR-1	Tailing feed rate	Dry feed rate in short tons to the tailing disposal system per 24 hours.	Short tons	FR-1
FR-2	Precipitation-evaporation data	When evaporation exceeds rainfall show net loss in inches per year.	Inches/year	FR-2a
	Select one	When evaporation does not exceed rainfall show net gain in inches per year.	Inches/year	FR-2b
FR-3	Thickening	Thickening area required per ton per 24 hours in sq. ft.	Square feet	FR-3
		Slurry transport distance in miles	Miles	FR-4a
FR-4	Slurry transport	Av. % grade of slurry pipeline if uphill or if (-1% or greater) downhill show as gravity flow. Base grade on total lift in feet divided by total distance in ft. x 100.	Percent	FR-4b

779

Table I
FIELD CHECK LIST

Sheet 2 of 6

Code No.	Basic Field Reference Item	Description of Sub Items	Data Entry Record	Reference Number of Sub Item
Column 1	Column 2	Column 3	Column 4	Column 5
FR-4 contd.		Expected percent solids in slurry by weight.	Percent	FR-4c
		Average specific gravity of dry tailings.		FR-4d
FR-5	Containment Area	Available disposal area for tailing dams and ponds in acres.	Acres	FR-5
		Level area requiring containment on four sides		FR-6a
FR-6	Containment area configuration	Sloping area requiring containment on 3 sides.		FR-6b
	Select one and check	Basin configuration requiring containment at lower end only.		FR-6c

Table I

FIELD CHECK LIST

Sheet 3 of 6

Code No.	Basic Field Reference Item	Description of Sub Items	Data Entry Record	Reference Number of Sub Item
Column 1	Column 2	Column 3	Column 4	Column 5
FR-7	Method of constructing containment	Construction with tailings		FR-7a
	Select one and check	Construction with excavated material under one of following conditions—select one and check (use FR-7d unless otherwise known).	/////	
		Material requires blasting or ripping. Haul distance between three and six miles.		FR-7b
		Material requires blasting or ripping. Haul distance between one and three miles.		FR-7c
		Material requires blasting or ripping. Haul distance under one mile.		FR-7d
		Material easily excavated. No blasting or ripping required. Haul distance one to 3 miles.		FR-7e
		Material easily excavated. No blasting or ripping required. Haul distance under one mile.		FR-7f
		Material to be obtained from mine waste. Haul distance three to six miles.		FR-g

Table I
FIELD CHECK LIST

Sheet 4 of 6

Code No.	Basic Field Reference Item	Description of Sub Items	Data Entry Record	Reference Number of Sub Item
Column 1	Column 2	Column 3	Column 4	Column 5
FR-7 contd		Material to be obtained from mine waste. Haul distance under three miles.		FR-7h
FR-8	Tailing treatment	Show expected pH of tailings (use 2.0 unless otherwise known).		FR-8
		Effluent transport distance in miles.	Miles	FR-9a
FR-9	Effluent transport	Av. % grade of effluent pipeline if uphill; if downhill show as gravity flow.	Percent	FR-9b
		Show percent total effluent to be pumped. If information is not available select one of the following values (see Item FR-10): 1) With evaporation ponds use 90% 2) Without evaporation ponds use 100%	Percent	FR-9c
		Note: In determing percent effluent to be pumped do not allow for evaporation in tailing ponds. Provision for this condition is included elsewhere.		

Table J

FIELD CHECK LIST

Sheet 5 of 6

Code No.	Basic Field Reference Item	Description of Sub Items	Data Entry Record	Reference Number of Sub Item
Column 1	Column 2	Column 3	Column 4	Column 5
FR-10	Evaporation facility	Insert other available evaporation area or area from schedule below, whichever is smaller. Then select either FR-10b or FR-10c below. Insert 0 if no evaporation ponds are planned.	Acres	FR-10a
		If available evaporation area exceeds requirements as per schedule below, insert 1, otherwise insert 0.		FR-10b
		If rainfall exceeds evaporation, insert 0.		FR-10c
		Schedule of Area Requirements (Acres) Tailings-TPD 24"/y 48"/y 72"/y 1,000 9 5 3 10,000 90 45 30 30,000 270 135 90 50,000 450 225 150	/////	/////
FR-11	Seepage control for evaporation facilities.	Minimum seepage regulations- Average clay core in dams with small collection facility below pond areas.		FR-11a
	Select one and check	Nominal seepage regulations-Pond floor sealed with selected earth material.		FR-11b
		Rigid seepage regulations-Pond floor sealed with membrane or equivalent.		FR-11c

783

Table I

FIELD CHECK LIST

Sheet 6 of 6

Code No.	Basic Field Reference Item	Description of Sub Items	Data Entry Record	Reference Number of Sub Item
Column 1	Column 2	Column 3	Column 4	Column 5
FR-12	Tailing area restoration requirements Select one and check	Seeding and Fertilizing		FR-12a
		Chemical - Vegetative		FR-12b
		Four inch Soil Cover with Seeding		FR-12c
		Twelve inch Soil Cover with Seeding		FR-12d
		Chemical forming hard crust on surface		FR-12e

Table II

COST TABULATION SUMMARY

Sheet 1 of 3

Section	Evaluation Instructions	Evaluation Formula	$ per dry ton of tailings.
Column 1	Column 2	Column 3	Column 4
/////	Symbol explanation: 1. FR-XX-Field Record Data from column 4 of Field Check List. 2. fxx-Factor from Cost Curve, Figures 1 through 7.	/////	/////
SLURRY THICKENING C-1	Apply feed rate value of FR-1 and thickening settling rate FR-3 to Figure 1 to obtain f1 factor for use in formula	$C1=f1$	$C1=$
SLURRY TRANSPORT C-2	Apply feed rate value of FR-1 and slope value of FR-4b to Figure 2a to obtain f2a factor for use in formula. Apply slurry transport distance value of FR-4a to Figure 2b to obtain f2b. For FR-4c and FR-4d use values of FR-4 (c and d).	$C2 = f2a \times f2b \times \sqrt{\dfrac{50}{FR\text{-}4c} \times \dfrac{2.7}{FR\text{-}4d}}$	$C2=$
TAILING CONTAINMENT C-3	Refer to FR-7 and use procedure X below if construction is with tailings (FR-7a will be checked in List) or use procedure Y if construction is with excavated material (one out of FR-7b through FR-7h will be checked). **PROCEDURE X** - Apply feed rate of FR-1, containment area value as shown in FR-5 and configuration selection as shown in FR-6 (a,b, or c) to Figure 3c to obtain f3c factor.	$C3X=f3c$	$C3X=$

Table II

COST TABULATION SUMMARY

Sheet 2 of 3

Section	Evaluation Instructions	Evaluation Formula	$ per dry ton of tailings.
Column 1	Column 2	Column 3	Column 4
C3 (contd)	PROCEDURE Y - Apply feed rate of FR-1, containment area value as shown in FR-5 and configuration selection as shown in FR-6 (a,b, or c) to Figure 3a to obtain f3a factor. Apply selection from FR-7 (b,c,d, e,f,g, or h) to Figure 3b to obtain f3b factor.	$C3Y = f3a \times f3b$	$C3Y=$
TAILING TREATMENT C4	Apply pH value of FR-8 to Figure 4 to obtain f4. Use average condition for curve selection unless chemical condition is known. Apply feed rate of FR-1, area of FR-5, and evaporation rate of FR-2a or FR-2b to nearest appropriate rate as shown by Figure 5c, Figure 5d or Figure 5e to obtain f5 (c,d, or e) factor.	$C4 = f4 \times f5 \; (c,d, \text{ or } e)$	$C4=$
EFFLUENT TRANSPORT C5	Apply feed rate of FR-1, and slope value of FR-9b to Figure 5a to obtain f5a factor. Apply effluent transport distance value of FR-9a to Figure 5b to obtain f5b factor. Apply feed rate of FR-1, area of FR-5, and evaporation rate of FR-2a or FR-2b to nearest appropriate rate as shown by Figure 5c, Figure 5d or Figure 5e to obtain f5 (c, d, or e) factor. For FR-9c use value as shown in FR-9c. For FR-4c use value as shown in FR-4c.	$C5 = f5a \times f5b \times$ $f5 \; (c,d, \text{ or } e) \times$ $\dfrac{FR-9c}{100} \times \sqrt{\dfrac{50}{FR-4c}}$	$C5=$
EVAPORATION FACILITY C6	Apply feed rate of FR-1 and seepage control selection of FR-11(a,b or c) to Figure 6 to obtain f6 factor. For FR-10 use value of selection of FR-10b or FR-10c (1 or 0). (If "0" is value then C6=0.) For FR-2a use value of FR-2a(if evaporation exceeds rainfall, otherwise C6=0). Note: A value of 0 for C6 indicates "No evaporation ponds".	$C6 = \dfrac{24 \times f6}{FR-2a} \times FR-10 \; (b \text{ or } c)$	$C6=$

Table II

COST TABULATION SUMMARY

Sheet 3 of 3

Section	Evaluation Instructions	Evaluation Formula	$ per dry ton of tailings.
Column 1	Column 2	Column 3	Column 4
TAILING AREA RESTORATION C7	Determine total area to be restored by adding areas of FR-5 and FR-10a. Apply to Figure 7 this total area value and the selection as shown in FR-12 (a, b, c, d, or e) to obtain f7 factor.	C7=f7	C7=

TABLE II
COST TABULATION SUMMARY

$/ton

Slurry Thickening	C1=___
Slurry Transport	C2=___
Tailing Containment	C3=___
Tailing Treatment	C4=___
Effluent Transport	C5=___
Evaporation Facility	C6=___
Tailing Area Restoration	C7=___
TOTAL TAILING DISPOSAL COST	$___

COST CURVE FACTORS

A.   Cost Curve Parameters

    a)   Cost curves are shown as single lines. However, it should be understood that a band of plus or minus 15 percent is a true representation of the factor.

    b)   The annual tailings rate equals the daily rate shown on the curves multiplied by 365 days.

    c)   The capital cost has been included in the cost factor by applying a ten year depreciation charge as an operating cost.

    d)   Construction will take place in the continental United States with 1972 prevailing costs. No future escalation is included.

    e)   The operating labor rate, including all fringe benefits, is $5.00 per hour.

    f)   The power rate is $0.01 per kwh.

    g)   Costs of disposal site acquisition, initial engineering, and environmental project study are not included.

    h)   The cost of treatment is based on the quantity of effluent from the tailing pond.

Additional parameters for the cost factors are included in the discussion of each section.

B.   Example Symbol

The symbol $\rightarrow$ denotes a point of reference to the example evaluation described later.

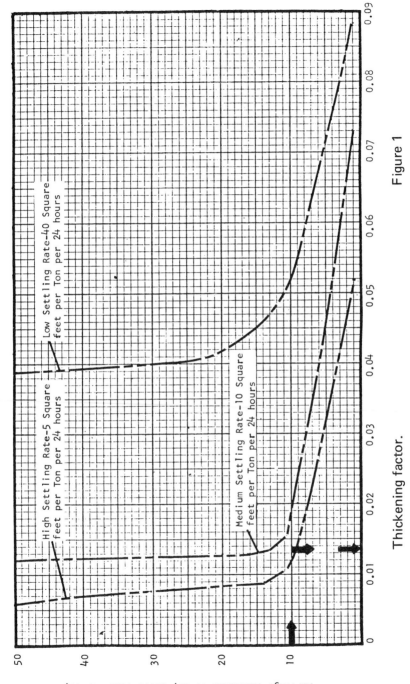

Figure 1

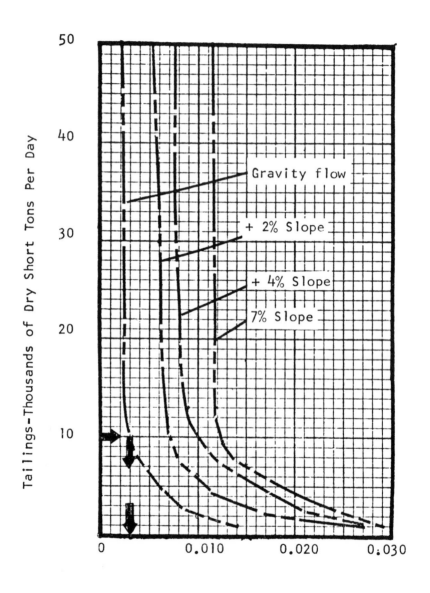

Slurry transport factor.

Figure 2A

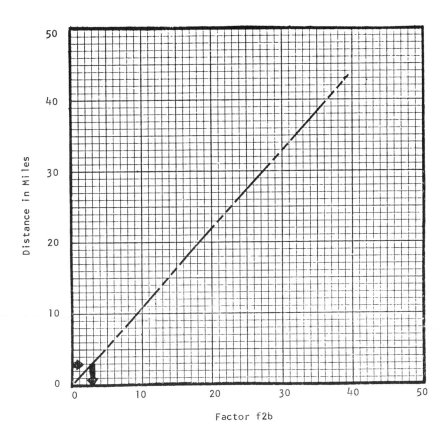

Slurry transport distance factor.   Figure 2B

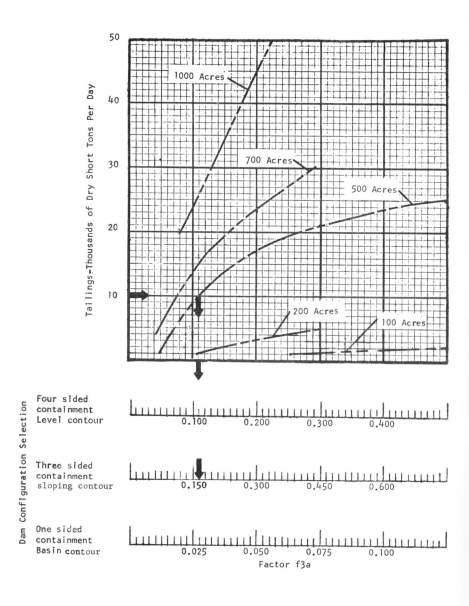

Tailing containment factor using excavated material.   Figure 3A

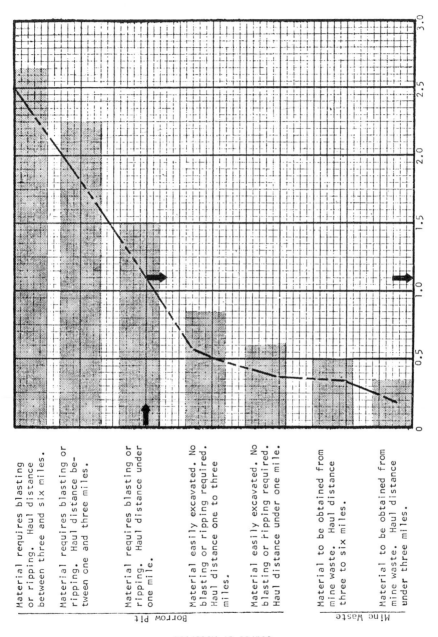

Material availability factor using excavated material.   Figure 3B

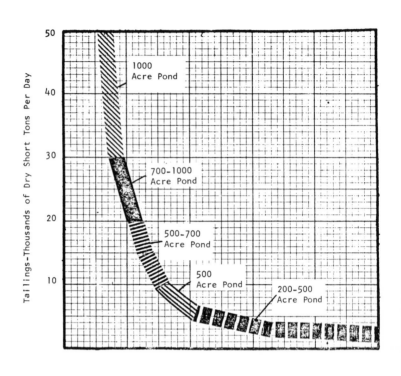

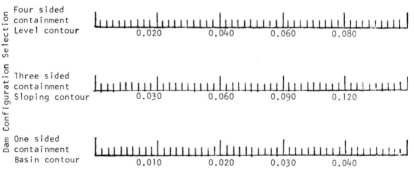

Tailing containment factor using tailings.   Figure 3C

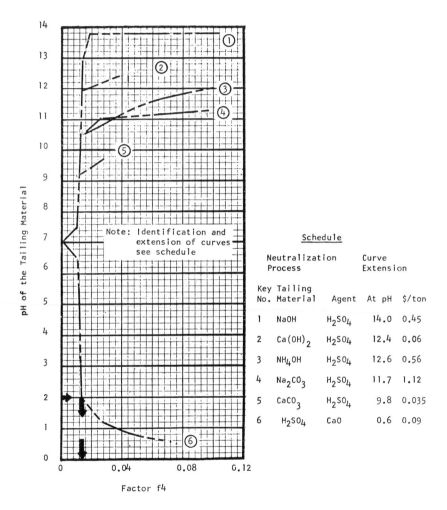

Tailing treatment factor.

Figure 4

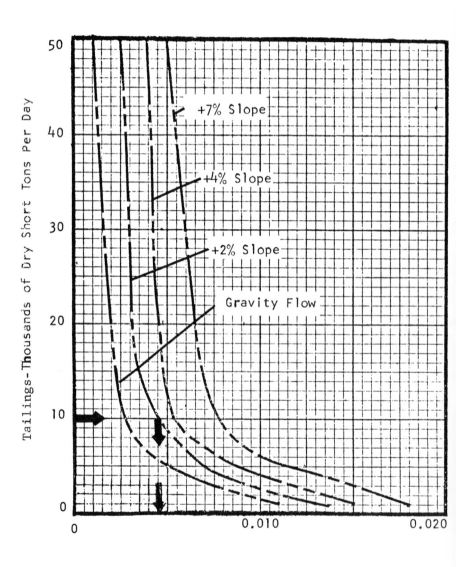

Effluent transport factor.   Figure 5A

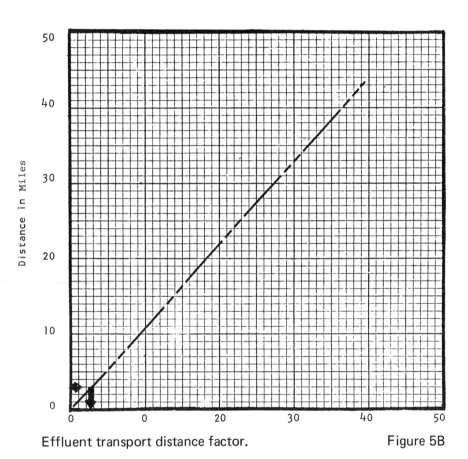

Effluent transport distance factor.　　　　　　Figure 5B

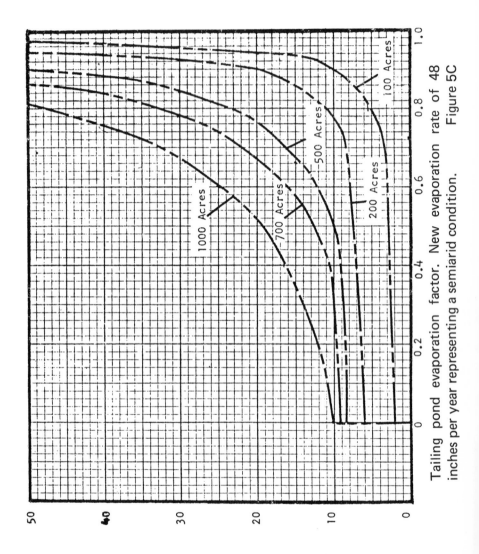

Tailing pond evaporation factor. New evaporation rate of 48 inches per year representing a semiarid condition.   Figure 5C

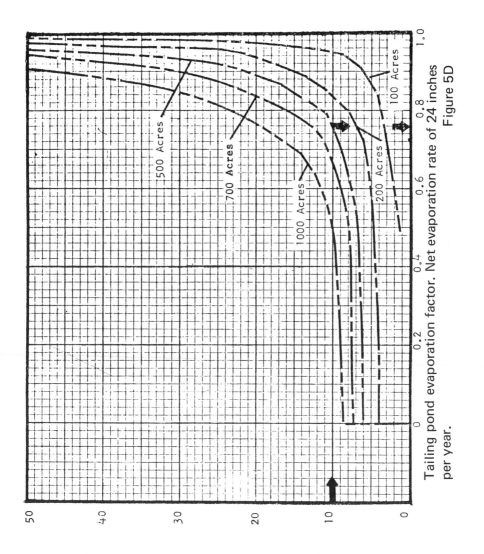

Tailing pond evaporation factor. Net evaporation rate of 24 inches per year.

Figure 5D

Tailings-Thousands of Dry Short Tons Per Day

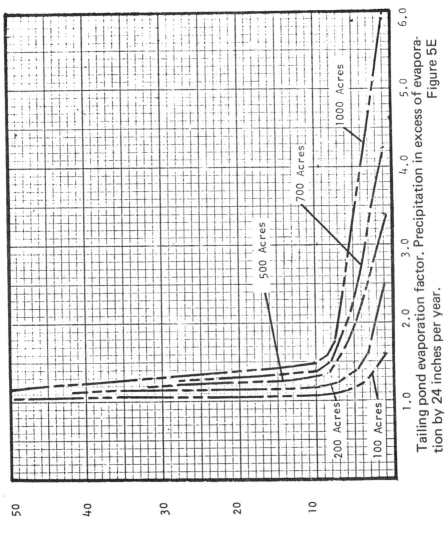

Tailing pond evaporation factor. Precipitation in excess of evaporation by 24 inches per year.

Figure 5E

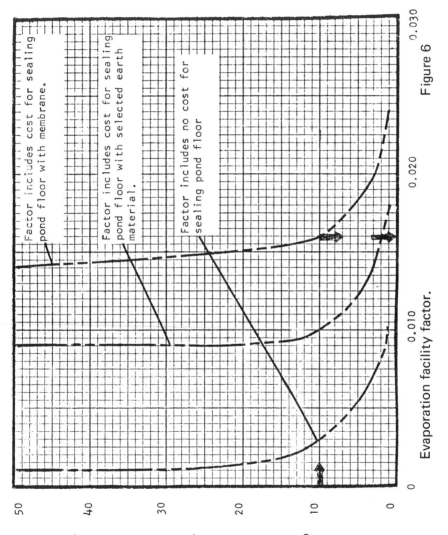

Factor includes cost for sealing pond floor with membrane.

Factor includes cost for sealing pond floor with selected earth material.

Factor includes no cost for sealing pond floor

Figure 6

Evaporation facility factor.

Tailings-Thousands of Dry Short Tons Per Day

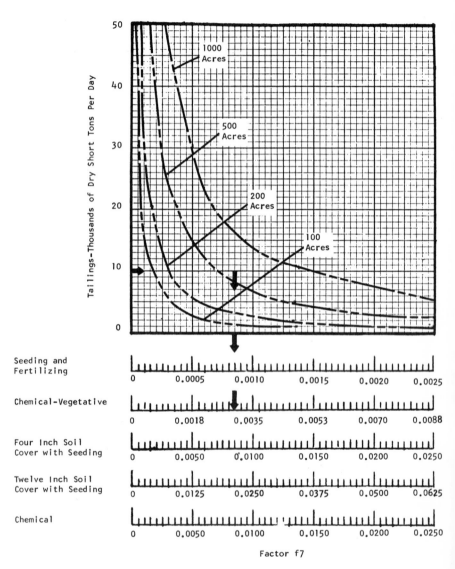

Area restoration factor.   Figure 7

EXAMPLE

The procedure described by this paper is illustrated by the following example. It is a study of a hypothetical tailing disposal system using the step-by-step procedure to estimate the preliminary cost for each section of the proposed system. For this example the following field conditions are assumed:

The market potential and the ore reserve suggest a daily dry tailings discharge of 10,000 tons. The specific gravity of the dry tailings is 2.8. The preliminary site investigation reveals that the most logical tailing disposal area is three miles from the plant site, and there will be approximately 500 acres available for the tailing pond, with an additional 150 acres for evaporation ponds. This disposal area is open and gradually sloping. It will require a dam on three sides. The elevation is below (2 percent grade) the plant site, permitting transport of tailing slurry by gravity flow. The slurry will contain 50 percent solids by weight. All available effluent, reduced by evaporation, will be neutralized and returned to the plant. It is planned to install evaporation ponds to rid the circuit of 10 percent of the effluent. General construction requirements and rigid regulations will probably dictate construction of the dam from excavated material rather than from tailings. Mine waste is not available; material must be excavated and hauled three-quarters of a mile. Blasting will be required. Geological studies of the disposal area indicate the possibility of excessive seepage.

Weather data at the nearest station shows a net evaporation rate of 24 inches per year. A preliminary settling test was run disclosing a thickener area factor of seven square feet per ton per 24 hours. Little is known about the pH of the tailings except that it is acidic. At the end of the operation the disposal area must be restored by chemical treatment, fertilizing and seeding.

Following the step-by-step procedure this information has been recorded on the standard check list, and a tabulation summary has been completed. From this summary the section costs can be compared. This hypothetical study shows that the tailing containment cost is much higher than the other sections and is the major part of the total cost of disposal. This illustrates the value of a preliminary appraisal to pinpoint areas requiring careful evaluation. In this example, if a basin area requiring a dam on one side only can be located, the cost of disposal can by reduced by approximately 15 cents per ton. This saving assumes the same transport distance for the slurry.

This approach can be used to study various alternatives as part of the preliminary evaluation and to determine realistic costs of disposal without an extensive engineering study.

Table 1

FIELD CHECK LIST

Sheet 1 of 6

Code No.	Basic Field Reference Item	Description of Sub Items	Data Entry Record	Reference Number of Sub Item
Column 1	Column 2	Column 3	Column 4	Column 5
FR-1	Tailing feed rate	Dry feed rate in short tons to the tailing disposal system per 24 hours.	10,000 Short tons	FR-1
FR-2	Precipitation-evaporation data	When evaporation exceeds rainfall show net gain in inches per year.	24 Inches/year	FR-2a
	Select one	When evaporation does not exceed rainfall show net gain in inches per year.	Inches/year	FR-2b
FR-3	Thickening	Thickening area required per ton per 24 hours in sq. ft.	7 Square feet	FR-3
		Slurry transport distance in miles	3 Miles	FR-4a
FR-4	Slurry transport	Avg grade of slurry pipeline if uphill or if (-1% or greater) downhill show as gravity flow. Base grade on total lift in feet divided by total distance in ft. x 100.	gravity flow Percent	FR-4b

805

Table I

FIELD CHECK LIST

Code No. Column 1	Basic Field Reference Item Column 2	Description of Sub Items Column 3	Data Entry Record Column 4	Reference Number of Sub Item Column 5
FR-4 contd.		Expected percent solids in slurry by weight.	50 Percent	FR-4c
		Average specific gravity of dry tailings.	2.8	FR-4d
FR-5	Containment Area	Available disposal area for tailing dams and ponds in acres.	500 Acres	FR-5
		Level area requiring containment on four sides	X	FR-6a
FR-6	Containment area configuration	Sloping area requiring containment on 3 sides.	1	FR-6b
	Select one and check	Basin configuration requiring containment at lower end only.	X	FR-6c

Table I

FIELD CHECK LIST

Sheet 3 of 6

Code No.	Basic Field Reference Item	Description of Sub Items	Data Entry Record	Reference Number of Sub Item
Column 1	Column 2	Column 3	Column 4	Column 5
		Construction with tailings	X	FR-7a
	Method of constructing containment	Construction with excavated material under one of following conditions--select one and check (use FR-7d unless otherwise known).	(hatched)	
FR-7	Select one and check	Material requires blasting or ripping. Haul distance between three and six miles.	X	FR-7b
		Material requires blasting or ripping. Haul distance between one and three miles.	X	FR-7c
		Material requires blasting or ripping. Haul distance under one mile.	✓	FR-7d
		Material easily excavated. No blasting or ripping required. Haul distance one to 3 miles.	X	FR-7e
		Material easily excavated. No blasting or ripping required. Haul distance under one mile.	X	FR-7f
		Material to be obtained from mine waste. Haul distance three to six miles.	X	FR-g

Table I

FIELD CHECK LIST

Sheet 4 of 6

Code No.	Basic Field Reference Item	Description of Sub Items	Data Entry Record	Reference Number of Sub Item
Column 1	Column 2	Column 3	Column 4	Column 5
FR-7 contd		Material to be obtained from mine waste. Haul distance under three miles.	X	FR-7h
FR-8	Tailing treatment	Show expected pH of tailings (use 2.0 unless otherwise known).	2.0	FR-8
FR-9	Effluent transport	Effluent transport distance in miles.	3 Miles	FR-9a
		Av. % grade of effluent pipeline if uphill; if downhill show as gravity flow.	2 Percent	FR-9b
		Show percent total effluent to be pumped. If information is not available select one of the following values (see Item FR-10): 1) With evaporation ponds use 90% 2) Without evaporation ponds use 100%	90 Percent	FR-9c
		Note: In determining percent effluent to be pumped do not allow for evaporation in tailing ponds. Provision for this condition is included elsewhere.		

Table I

FIELD CHECK LIST

Sheet 5 of 6

Code No.	Basic Field Reference Item	Description of Sub Items	Data Entry Record	Reference Number of Sub Item
Column 1	Column 2	Column 3	Column 4	Column 5
FR-10	Evaporation facility	Insert other available evaporation area or area from schedule below, whichever is smaller. Then select either FR-10b or FR-10c below. Insert 0 if no evaporation ponds are planned.	90 Acres	FR-10a
		If available evaporation area exceeds requirements as per schedule below, insert 1, otherwise insert 0.	1	FR-10b
		If rainfall exceeds evaporation, insert 0.	X	FR-10c
		Schedule of Area Requirements (Acres) Tailings-TPD 24"/y 48"/y 72"/y 1,000 9 5 3 10,000 90 45 30 30,000 135 90 50,000 450 225 150		
FR-11	Seepage control for evaporation facilities.	Minimum seepage regulations- Average clay core in dams with small collection facility below pond areas.	X	FR-11a
		Nominal seepage regulations-Pond floor sealed with selected earth material.	X	FR-11b
	Select one and check	Rigid seepage regulations-Pond floor sealed with membrane or equivalent.	✓	FR-11c

Table I

FIELD CHECK LIST

Sheet 6 of 6

Code No. Column 1	Basic Field Reference Item Column 2	Description of Sub Items Column 3	Data Entry Record Column 4	Reference Number of Sub Item Column 5
FR-12	Tailing area restoration requirements	Seeding and Fertilizing	X	FR-12a
		Chemical - Vegetative	✓	FR-12b
	Select one and check	Four Inch Soil Cover with Seeding	X	FR-12c
		Twelve Inch Soil Cover with Seeding	X	FR-12d
		Chemical forming hard crust on surface	X	FR-12e

Table II

COST TABULATION SUMMARY

Sheet 1 of 3

Section Column 1	Evaluation Instructions Column 2	Evaluation Formula Column 3	$ per dry ton of tailings. Column 4
	Symbol explanation: 1. FR-XX–Field Record Data from column 4 of Field Check List. 2. fxx–Factor from Cost Curve, Figures 1 through 7.		
SLURRY THICKENING C-1	Apply feed rate value of FR-1 and thickening settling rate FR-3 to Figure 1 to obtain f1 factor for use in formula	$C1 = f1$ $C1 = 0.0135$	$C1 =$ 0.0135
SLURRY TRANSPORT C-2	Apply feed rate value of FR-1 and slope value of FR-4b to Figure 2a to obtain f2a factor for use in formula. Apply slurry transport distance value of FR-4a to Figure 2b to obtain f2b. For FR-4c and d use values of FR-4 (c and d).	$C2 = f2a \times f2b \times \sqrt{\dfrac{50}{FR\text{-}4c}} \times \dfrac{2.7}{FR\text{-}4d}$ $C2 = 0.003 \times 2.87 \sqrt{\dfrac{50}{50}} \times \dfrac{2.7}{2.8} =$ 0.0082	$C2 =$ 0.0082
	Refer to FR-7 and use procedure X below if construction is with tailings (FR-7a will be checked in List) or use procedure Y if construction is with excavated material (one out of FR-7b through FR-7h will be checked).		
TAILING CONTAINMENT C-3	PROCEDURE X – Apply feed rate of FR-1, containment area value as shown in FR-5 and configuration selection as shown in FR-6 (a,b, or c) to Figure 3c to obtain f3c factor.	$C3x = f3c$	$C3x =$

811

Table II

COST TABULATION SUMMARY

Section	Evaluation Instructions	Evaluation Formula	$ per dry ton of tailings.
Column 1	Column 2	Column 3	Column 4
C3 (contd)	PROCEDURE Y - Apply feed rate of FR-1, containment area value as shown in FR-5 and configuration selection as shown in FR-6 (a,b, or c) to Figure 3a to obtain f3a factor. Apply selection from FR-7 (b,c,d, e,f,g, or h) to Figure 3b to obtain f3b factor.	C3Y=f3a x f3b $C3Y= 0.165 \times 1.1 = 0.1815$	C3Y= 0.1815
TAILING TREATMENT C4	Apply pH value of FR-8 to Figure 4 to obtain f4. Use average condition for curve selection unless chemical condition is known. Apply feed rate of FR-1, and of FR-5, and evaporation rate of FR-2a or FR-2b to nearest appropriate rate as shown by Figure 5c, Figure 5d or Figure 5e to obtain f5 (c,d, or e) factor.	C4=f4 x f5 (c,d, or e) $C4 = 0.014 \times 0.76 = 0.0106$	C4= 0.0106
EFFLUENT TRANSPORT C5	Apply feed rate of FR-1, and slope value of FR-9b to Figure 5a to obtain f5a factor. Apply effluent transport distance value of FR-9a to Figure 5b to obtain f5b factor. Apply feed rate of FR-1, area of FR-5, an evaporation rate of FR-2a or FR-2b to nearest appropriate rate as shown by Figure 5c, Figure 5c or Figure 5e to obtain f5 (c, d, or e) factor. For FR-9c use value as shown in FR-9c. For FR-4c use value as shown in FR-4c.	$C5=$ f5a x f5b x f5 (c,d, or e) x $\frac{FR-9c}{100} \times \sqrt{\frac{50}{FR-4c}}$ $C5 = 0.0045 \times 2.8 \times 0.76 \times \frac{90}{100} \times \sqrt{\frac{50}{50}} = 0.0086$	C5= 0.0086
EVAPORATION FACILITY C6	Apply feed rate of FR-1 and seepage control selection of FR-11 (a,b or c) to Figure 6 to obtain f6 factor. For FR-10 use value of selection of FR-10b or FR-10c (1 or 0). (If "0" is value then C6=0.) For FR-2a use value of FR-2a (if evaporation exceeds rainfall, otherwise C6=0). Note: A value of 0 for C6 indicates "No evaporation ponds".	$C6= \frac{24 \times f6}{FR-2a} \times$ FR-10 (b or c) $C6 = \frac{24 \times 0.016}{24} \times 1 = 0.0160$	C6= 0.0160

Table II

COST TABULATION SUMMARY

Sheet 3 of 3

Section	Evaluation Instructions	Evaluation Formula	$ per dry ton of tailings.
Column 1	Column 2	Column 3	Column 4
TAILING AREA RESTORATION C7	Determine total area to be restored by adding areas of FR-5 and FR-10a. Apply to Figure 7 this total area value and the selection as shown in FR-12 (a, b, c, d, or e) to obtain f7 factor.	$C7 = f7$ $C7 = 0.0030$	$C7 =$ 0.0030

TABLE II
COST TABULATION SUMMARY

$/ton

Slurry Thickening $C1 = 0.0135$

Slurry Transport $C2 = 0.0082$

Tailing Containment $C3 = 0.1815$

Tailing Treatment $C4 = 0.0106$

Effluent Transport $C5 = 0.0096$

Evaporation Facility $C6 = 0.0160$

Tailing Area Restoration $C7 = 0.0030$

TOTAL TAILING DISPOSAL COST $ 0.2414

Rounded —— $0.24

E X A M P L E

813

SUMMARY

What are the hidden costs of your planned tailing disposal system? A typical tailing disposal system will cost somewhere between 4 and 80 cents per ton of dry tailings. This is a wide range of possible costs. A precise estimate of disposal cost requires an extensive engineering study. However, for the preliminary appraisal of a new project you can determine the approximate cost of a tailing disposal system by a two-step approach.

First, divide the tailing disposal system into sections and consider each section as a unit for which costs can be estimated.

Second, narrow the range of cost by relating the estimate for each section closely to actual site conditions. The procedure outlined by this paper shows how to quickly make a preliminary estimate for each section of your system.

To those of you who have completed an engineering study of your tailings disposal problem, you have the answers. You know what the hidden costs are. To those of you who are in the preliminary stages of contemplating an installation that will require a sophisticated tailing disposal system, you have a challenge to take a good look at the hidden costs of disposal.

Tailing problems are not in themselves insurmountable obstacles to the success of a venture, but with modern environmental trends the veil must be lifted. The costs are of a magnitude that can no longer be hidden.

DISCUSSION

W. A. WAHLER (W. A. Wahler & Associates): After you've heard some of the comments here, will you revise your form to include engineering and investigative fees and the inspection fees? And also, on tailings dams, when you are comparing one built of tailings vs. one built of earth, how far do you go in handling the operating costs, so as to bring this into a true perspective?

CHARLES E. JOHNSTON: Answering your first question regarding engineering fees, if I understand your question, I believe there should possibly be more emphasis placed on the cost for all types of pre-investigations. I agree that this should be done most likely. Answering your second question as to operating costs, which includes depreciation which I've set at 10 years, these operating costs have been adequately included in the cost of a dam -- of building a dam with tailing material. I will say one thing: to try and derive these operating costs is very difficult. You go to one operation with maybe four men operating a tailing pond and, right next door, there will be no one -- or maybe the foreman is looking at it once a day or something like that -- if you're talking about labor of operating. I have analyzed the cost of moving the cyclones, or the spigots, or the main line. That has all been included in the tailing containment factor. As to the cost of building a dam with borrow material or, as I call it, excavated material, this is pretty well put in as a flat rate per cubic yard, rather than a detailed operating cost.

ARIZONA'S DAM SAFETY PROGRAM AND ITS

IMPLICATIONS FOR TAILING DAMS

Wesley E. Steiner

Executive Director and State Water Engineer

Arizona Water Commission
Phoenix, Arizona

INTRODUCTION

Of the structures that man builds, dams and reservoirs perhaps have the most awesome potential for producing sudden and catastrophic loss of life and property damage. Considering the number of dams that have been built, disastrous failures represent a very small percentage of this total. Arizona has had its share of dam failures but fortunately none that have been of majo. proportions. Speaking generally, there have been enough failures to make people aware of the potential hazard and to enact protective legislation for the general public. With our increasing population, not only here in Arizona but throughout most of the world, dams which may once have been considered remote and of a very low hazard can no longer be so classified. The problem is further compounded by the fact that most of the good damsites have been utilized and dam builders are left with increasingly marginal type damsites upon which to construct the new dams.

Dams and reservoirs are a way of life in the western United States. A large percentage of the total land area of these states is arid with an insufficient quantity of natural water to sustain life as we like to think of it. However, by careful management of the water resources that are available, the people in these areas have been able to create prosperous civilizations in an environment that otherwise could support only a handful of people.

A scarcity of water and the long dry periods that are characteristic of this country, confined original settlement to those areas where flowing water was available. When the populations were very small there was no need for large storage systems even though occasional very dry years worked a hardship on every-body. As the population increased, the larger storage facilities became a necessity.

Now, some 100 years after the first major dams and reservoirs were built, there are in these eleven western states over 6,500 dams, without inclusion of the many hundreds of small farm ponds and stock tanks. Not all the States have effective programs for regulating the safety of these dams, but most of the states do have statutes providing for some kind of control over water storage facilities.

WATER IN ARIZONA

Arizona, the most arid of our western states, comprises almost 114,000 square miles of which only 334 square miles are water surface. The state is a complex of plateaus, mountains, deserts and plains with elevations ranging from 100 feet above sea level near Yuma to 12,600 feet at the summit of Humphrey's Peak in the San Francisco Mountains north of Flag-staff. Annual precipitation in Arizona varies from as low as three (3) inches in some areas in the desert to more than 30 inches in certain small areas in the mountains. Stream flows are erratic and fluctuate widely from year to year. Because of this variability, storage of these available waters is vital to water management in Arizona.

The vast majority of Arizona's dams are small, less than 100 feet high. The large structures, with few exceptions, are Federally owned dams that were built by the U. S. Bureau of Reclamation or the Corps of Engineers. The majority of the non-Federal water storage dams are located in the mountainous and timbered areas of four northern counties, Apache, Coconino, Navajo and Yavapai. Geographically this area runs roughly from an area just north of Williams and Flagstaff in a southeasterly direction toward the New Mexico line at about the mid-point of the State. Most of the dams are located here because this is where the water is--this is where the highest rainfall occurs and the major drainage systems of the State originate. In addition to storage dams, there are a large number of flood retarding dams that have been built to protect agricultural or urban lands from the flash floods that are characteristic of Arizona weather. As the name implies, this type of structure does not store water but merely retards it during high flows. The reservoir is empty most of the time.

DEFINITION OF A DAM

Any program for the safety of dams has to start with the definition of a dam which will include a height and/or capacity combination. In the western states ten (10) feet is a fairly common figure for height, combined with minimum capacity ranges from ten to fifty acre feet. In Arizona it is an either/ or situation, either 15 feet high or exceeding ten acre feet.

By dictionary definition a dam is a barrier built to hold back flowing water. Arizona laws'[1] state that a dam is for the impounding or diversion of water. There is no mention of a water course or a natural stream in Arizona's definition, nor is anything said about the use of the water. It is safe to presume, I believe, that the Arizona lawmakers, when they proposed legislation in 1929, envisioned much the same as you or I, a conventional barrier across a natural watercourse, but it would also appear they may have purposely left the definition general.

ORIGINAL LEGISLATION

In 1928 the St. Francis Dam on San Francisquito Creek in Southern California failed suddenly with a loss of several hundred lives. At the same time, in Arizona, Lake Pleasant Dam, the largest multiple arch in the world, was under construction. Only partially built, it was already experiencing structural failure. Also at this same time the United States Bureau of Reclamation was preparing designs for the largest dam in the world, Hoover Dam on the Colorado, to be over 700 feet high.

Legislation protecting the general public from loss of life and property damage through failure or malfunction of dams was a logical outgrowth of this combination of circumstances. Legislation defining a State program for jurisdiction over the Safety of Dams became law on March 22, 1929. All dams in the State were placed under jurisdiction including Federally owned dams. Responsibility for administration of the law was assigned to the State Highway Department, the only State agency at that time with the required engineering capabilities.

EXCEPTIONS TO JURISDICTION

Exceptions to the law soon began to develop. The Attorney General ruled, in a decision dated December 10, 1930, that the law did not apply to structures which we now class as offstream storage facilities. At that time there were, and still are, two such reservoirs in Phoenix and two in Flagstaff.

Although the State law applied to all dams within the State, the Federal Government did not recognize State jurisdiction over their dams, particularly Hoover Dam. However, engineers from the staff were permitted to inspect these Federal structures, but only as interested technical observers.

In 1931 the Legislature decided that stock watering dams were not as dangerous as other types of dams and, therefore, should be excluded from the State's law

for jurisdiction over dams. Even though vetoed by
the Governor the agriculturally oriented Legislature
was successful in making this exception to the law.

THE DAM SAFETY PROGRAM

Once the jurisdictional status of a dam has been
determined, a typical safety program such as Arizona's
functions in several major areas of responsibility.
For a new dam, an application is filed describing the
location of the dam and accompanied by pertinent
backup data such as plans, specifications, and
foundation and materials information. Additionally
there may be a filing fee that accompanies the
application. Arizona charges such a fee which is
based on a percentage of the total cost of the dam.
It starts at 1% of the cost, gradually reducing to
one-tenth of one percent for cost in excess of
$5,000,000.

The application and the accompanying engineering
data are subjected to a review and independent
analysis by the staff of the State agency. Arizona's
staff has three professional engineers and a geologist,
all experienced in dams. Dependent upon the size and
complexity of the proposed structure, this review will
include inspection of the damsite for foundation
adequacy, examination of construction materials,
analysis of embankment design, analysis of the
hydrology and spillway hydraulic design, and structural analysis of the spillway and outlet facilities.
The construction drawings and the specifications are
also evaluated to determine adequacy with respect to
a safe dam. Construction is not permitted to start
until the application has been approved and the owner
so notified.

Once construction is underway, engineers from the
State periodically inspect the construction progress,
particularly at the highly critical stage where the
foundation is being prepared for placement of earth
or concrete. In their supervision of construction,
the engineers carry out their regulatory function
through contact with the owner or his engineer. If

construction is not according to approved plans and specifications, corrections are made or work ceases. Under no circumstances though, are orders given directly to the contractor. Once construction has been completed, but before certification for use, a final inspection is made to verify that all work has been in conformance with the approved plans.

The other major part of a typical safety of dams program, and particularly here in Arizona, involves assurance that safe conditions are maintained during the operating life of the dam and reservoir. While the owner always retains responsibility for maintaining a safe dam, he is often an individual who is not experienced in detecting unsafe conditions in dams and it is necessary for the State engineers to periodically inspect the operating dams.

The State's engineers are trained to detect signs of unsatisfactory operation performance that may indicate distress of some sort in the structure. The frequency of these periodic inspections is related to the hazard potential of the dam. A complex structure or one that has had a long history of trouble, will warrant more frequent inspections. Instrumentation installed in the dam to help monitor performance is an invaluable detection aid for both the owner and the State's engineers.

Unsatisfactory conditions noted in an inspection are passed on to the owner with a request to comply. In the event it is serious enough to be dangerous, the State Water Engineer has the authority to require immediate action by the owner or, upon his refusal, to take emergency action on his own.

DAMS BUILT IN VIOLATION OF LAW

When a dam has been built without knowledge of the State it is obviously in violation of the law. Once discovered, the owner has a choice of removing the dam or bringing it under the Safety of Dams Program with payment of fees and necessary remedial work.

A dam built in violation of the statutes almost invariably, if it is of earth, has exceedingly steep slopes, poorly compacted soil, an undersized spillway (if there is one), and a poorly constructed outlet works. If the reservoir has water in it seepage is very often visible on the downstream face of the embankment. The effort to place a structure of this type in jurisdiction with the adequate remedial work necessary to bring it into a safe condition, or to have the structure breached, is usually more time consuming than if the owner had followed the procedures defined in the Statutes. Very often these structures pose a great potential hazard and therefore, demand immediate attention.

PROGRAM TRANSFER

From 1929 to 1971 the program was the responsibility of the Highway Department under the immediate direction of the State Bridge Engineer. From the start funding for the program was completely dependent on revenue derived from fees. Even in good years the funds available were inadequate to carry out a program of the scope defined in the statutes.

From the beginning Highway Department Engineers administering this program believed that it should be in a water oriented State Agency. After several unsuccessful attempts legislation was introduced in the 30th Legislature combining the State's program for Supervision of Dams and several other water oriented programs into the newly created Arizona Water Commission. This legislation, House Bill 3, was passed and signed by Governor Jack Williams on April 13, 1971.

The Bill provided for the transfer of the Supervision of Dams Program in its entirety and specified that all non-Federal dams should be under the jurisdiction of the State Water Engineer. It is important to note that after forty years the State officially relinquished jurisdiction over Federal dams and an amendment so stating was included in the revisions to the statutes. At the same time, to provide program

stability, responsibility for financing the program
totally by fee revenue were transferred to the general
fund. The Legislature then appropriated $85,000 in
the first year to the Arizona Water Commission, to
provide for a staff of three full-time engineers and
a secretary.

FIRST YEAR OF OPERATION WITH WATER COMMISSION

Of immediate concern to the new staff were projects
that were already in some phase of either design review or construction. There were under construction
a large concrete arch dam and under design review,
or application, a diversion dam and two flood retarding structures. The staff, relying heavily on a
combined experience of over fifty (50) years in the
water resource field--particularly design, construction, and operation of dams and appurtenances--took
over existing work plus approving applications on
thirteen (13) dams and inspecting five (5) construction projects during their first year.

According to data received from the Highway Department, there were approximately 250 dams that were
under State jurisdiction. This number was immediately
reduced by the number of Federally owned dams as no
longer subject to jurisdiction.

Upon examination of the files, it became apparent
that one of the major tasks was to reexamine the existing dams within the State. For many of the smaller
more remotely located dams there had been no owner
contact, nor inspection, since 1929 or 1930. During
their first year the staff made inspections of 140
operational and jurisdictional dams. Where possible,
owners were notified in advance by letter or telephone
and invited to be present during the inspection. Even
though it had, in many cases, been many years since
the last inspection, most owners were located. Their
cooperation and attitude was good.

From the original Highway Department list there
were approximately 70 structures eliminated from

jurisdiction. In addition to 28 Federal dams this
group included those dams used exclusively for stock
watering, several that were too small to be in jurisdiction, some that were classed as off-stream storage
and eliminated by an Attorney General's opinion,
several that were never built, and a few for other
miscellaneous reasons. The Esperanza Tailings Dam
located in Pima County was one of those eliminated
from jurisdiction because of an earlier Attorney
General's opinion.

EVALUATION OF PROGRAM

The statutes have remained virtually unchanged
since their original enactment in 1929, creating in
some sections ambiguity and confusion for an expanded
operation under a new agency. The basic concept remains sound but need for clarification exists
particularly in the fee structure, authority to act
against violators and jurisdiction of off-stream dams
and reservoirs, stock tanks and tailing dams.

Even though now funded independently of fee
revenue, a fee schedule for this type of regulatory
program is a necessity. The construction of a dam
creates a potential hazard that wasn't there before.
It is encumbent upon the dam owner to contribute part
of the program cost of providing protection to the
general public. The fee serves another very important
practical consideration. It insures the validity of
the application through elimination of frivolous
applications or providing free consulting engineering
to those considering construction of a dam. There
has been some resistance to payment of fees, primarily
by local quasi-government agencies. Clarification
needs to be added to the statutes to remove any doubt
that fees apply equally to all owners and, incidently,
that the fee is based upon the entire project cost
from the first preliminary work to the final construction inspection.

The procedures to act against infractions of the
statutes are spelled out clearly but unfortunately a

method for financing such action was never included. There is such a case before us now in which the State called for remedial action on a dam. Upon failure of the owner to comply, the State was unable to implement the action because funds were not available to pay for the required work. As a result a potentially dangerous dam continued to be operated for a number of years. Some source of emergency funding should be available to carry out action where public safety is jeopardized.

In the cases of tailing dams, offstream storage reservoirs, and stock tanks, exceptions to the Statutes have been made, apparently without thought to the real reason for a safety program. Such a program is to protect the public from the inherent hazard created by construction of a barrier which holds back water. It is not the use of water but rather the fact that it is impounded that creates the need for safety. When a dam meets the height and capacity criteria established by law, those factors which influence its hazard potential should be carefully and realistically evaluated. A low risk structure should be recognized and treated accordingly. Conversely, we would expect to apply highly conservative analysis to any high risk structure.

As a final note in our program evaluation it has been the experience of many in this field in applying Statutes for Safety of Dams that the safety of each project has to be evaluated on the basis of sound engineering and construction principles. Technical codes of standard requirements for design, construction, or surveillance cannot be applied uniformly to the widely varying conditions encountered at different dams, reservoirs and sites. Attempts toward uniform application might impede the art and science of dam design and construction. The Arizona staff adopts this philosophy but does believe that general guidelines and procedures are necessary and should be available for owners and engineers. Such information is now being developed.

TAILINGS DAMS-SAFETY

Tailings Dams present a potential safety problem.

There has been no consistent policy at the State level
and, to our knowledge no Federal regulations dealing
specifically with safety of tailing dams. As the
state agency responsible for a dam safety program,
we are investigating the whole subject and welcome
the opportunity that this international symposium
provides us to gain additional valuable insight.

From the standpoint of dams, we would categorize
these structures into three (3) classes. The first
is the dam that has been built across a natural watercourse with a definable contributing drainage area.
This structure is a dam that is quite capable of
storing a significant volume of water. Without an
adequate spillway it is conceivable that such a
structure could be overtopped with a consequent rapid
erosion and failure of the embankment.

The second type structure and probably more common
is the tailing dam constructed by enclosing an area
of sloping ground with an embankment to contain the
tailings. Here we have only the natural runoff from
the area directly upstream from the perimeter of the
dam. However, for some of the large ponds which
exist this drainage area can encompass several square
miles.

Finally, there is the structure that is entirely
enclosed by an encircling dam. Here we have a
situation where the only natural runoff would be that
within the perimeter of the dike.

Because runoff from precipitation may be extremely
large during the lifetime of a tailing pond, impoundment or diversion of this runoff becomes a major safety
consideration. To cite an example of modern engineering practice in design of dams, a flood retarding dam
on a drainage area of slightly greater than one (1)
square mile has been designed for a peak flood inflow
of 11,000 cubic feet per second. A synthetic flood of
this magnitude is justified for a major project where
hazard is very high.

We do not believe that the typical tailing dam here in Arizona would warrant design of the severity mentioned above. But design for a tailing dam should take into consideration the inflow from a storm of a magnitude commensurate with the hazard created by the dam. By providing for interception and diversion of natural runoff this problem can be minimized as a consideration for the safety of the tailing dam. The remaining water to be considered, a controlled inflow and some precipitation that can fall on the disposal surface, then becomes a basic design problem with known parameters.

From our safety standpoint, the other major consideration, along with hydrology, is an interest in a stable structure. There has been enough attention drawn to tailing dams in recent years to make the mining industry generally, quite aware of this facet of mine tailings. We understand that many of the copper firms involved with tailing dams in Arizona have already made comprehensive engineering studies that consider the structural stability of the dams. Likewise, the U. S. Bureau of Mines in their information circular #8410[2] have produced a thorough treatise on design of tailing dams.

The structural design of an earth embankment, subject to saturation or constructed to retain a saturated material as in the case of a tailing dam will follow the same principles as any other earth dam. The objective is to assure slope stability under all conditions of loading that could reasonably be expected during the lifetime of the project. This would include seismic loading as appropriate for the area in question.

Although Arizona has not been regarded as a seismically active area, in examining the seismic risk map of the United States from the Uniform Building Code,[3] the State is considered a location where moderate damage could be expected. Based on the physical characteristics of the mill tailings, the method of construction, and the saturatation condition of the embankment, there is a strong possibility that

many tailing dams would be vulnerable to a moderate
earthquake.

LOCATION OF TAILING DAMS

According to our best estimates, there are
approximately 19 mills or concentrators located in
seven of the fourteen counties in Arizona. Where
there is a mill there is usually a tailing dam so
we should have approximately 19 tailing dams operating
throughout the State. These are located as follows:

Cochise County at Bisbee

Gila County at Miami, Hayden and Christmas

Greenlee County at Morenci

Mohave County at Chloride

Pima County at Twin Buttes, Sierrita-Esperanza,
Pima, Mission, New Cornelia and Silver Bell

Pinal County at San Manuel and Superior

Yavapai County at Zonia and Bagdad

In addition there will be a new mill and tailing dam
in the vicinity of Sacaton in Pinal County.

SUMMARY

From the standpoint of public safety all dams which
are able to impound water present varying degrees of
risk. Consideration of size, capacity, location, type
of construction, condition of structure, and downstream
development are used to evaluate hazard. Arizona's
tailing dams are characterized by the following hazard
related items:

(1.) They store only a limited quantity of
water.

(2.) Most dams are located in low density
population areas.

(3.)   Surface runoff can be eliminated or by-
       passed with proper design.

(4.)   The structures have a definite operational
       life span.

(5.)   The seismic stability of the typical
       embankment is questionable.

(6.)   There is presently no regulatory control
       specifically oriented toward public safety.

Within the parameters stated above we believe that
tailing dams present a potential hazard. In our
evaluation we intend to include an on-site investigation of each structure. If there appears to be a
valid basis for inclusion of tailing dams within the
State's program for Safety of Dams, we will propose
to modify the statutes to specifically include such
structures.

As a final point which we believe may affect
tailing dams, on August 9, 1972, President Nixon
signed into law H. R. 15951 which authorized a
National Program for Inspection of Dams. This
program defines dams by height and capacity somewhat
greater than Arizona but makes no exceptions for use,
location, shape, or any other factors. The dam
merely has to impound or divert water. Because this
bill was precipitated by the failure of two dams,
one of which had been constructed on mine waste, it
appears quite probable that any mine related structure that resembles a dam will come under Federal
scrutiny. To date, we have no indication of
Federal action in this area.

REFERENCES

1. ARIZONA REVISED STATUTES, TITLE 45, Waters
Chapter 3, Dams & Reservoirs, Articles 1, 2 & 3.
Amended 1971.

2. Kealy, C. D. and Soderberg, R. L., "Design of

Dams for Mill Tailings" U. S. Bureau of Mines,
Information Circular 8410, 1969.

3. Uniform Building Code, International Conference
of Building Officials, "Seismic Risk Map," (Inside
back cover), 1970.

DISCUSSION

E. D'APPOLONIA (E. D'Appolonia Consulting
Engineers Inc.): You indicated that in the
regulations relating to tailings you are going to
follow the format and design procedures laid down
for water impoundment. I'd like to ask, is this
really the route to go again? I think this is very
important to the mining industry. In these tailing
impoundments, the material is laid in layers,
consolidation has occurred, there is desiccation;
it is quite a different problem than building a
water dam. I think someone alluded to this today
and said that we should stop calling these tailings
dams. They should be given a different name,
tailing impoundment, or something else. But I
think we have to be extremely careful in saying that
it is going to sustain material that is hydrostatic
in nature. This is not necessarily so, and has an
important bearing on the design parameters and both
the design and the construction of such facilities.
This is exceedingly important in the development of
any regulation.

BENSON SCOTT (Arizona State Water Commission)
speaking for the paper's author, WESLEY STEINER:
I think probably the best way to answer this
question is in reference to my remark about not
trying to apply hard-and-fast criteria. We're after
only one thing, and it's public safety. We do not
propose to go in to apply some criteria that
obviously would not fit. Frankly, we have not yet
advanced far enough in this subject to really have
a good grip on it. In fact, my attendance at this

Symposium has given me a tremendously greater
knowledge than I had when I first stepped in the
door. But there is no reason to apply something
if it is not going to be appropriate. Also, I made
mention of the fact that these structures do have
a finite lifespan. When you get a tailing dam that
is approaching the end of its useful life, your
water storage ponds -- that is those that I have
seen -- are far removed from the face of the
embankment, and you approach a point somewhere near
California's Division of Safety of Dams in dealing
with land development subdivisions. In some places
they would impound water with a massive fill that
was so long that it finally became ridiculous to
refer to it as a dam; this would be a similar
example for tailings dams. I do not intend to
follow a policy where we just blindly call these
things water barriers like a regular dam.

D. W. McDONOUGH (New York Trap Rock
Corporation): The owner of a prospective dam
engages a professional engineer to design the dam
and he does so. Then that professional engineer is
responsible. His plans are then reviewed by your
department and perhaps changes are suggested. In
this case, does the responsibility of the owner's
engineer transfer to the state?

BENSON SCOTT: The owner of the dam is always
responsible. He can't get away from that. The
state's function is to see that the owner maintains
his responsibility. An engineer working for an
owner is responsible to that owner, so he still
retains responsibility, I would say. It is the
owner's job to prepare designs and plans and
specifications and then submit them to the state.
It is our job to review these and apply a critique.
Occasionally, we find ourselves in a position where
we reach an out-and-out impasse and say, "Well, this
is the only way you can do it." But we'd prefer not
to, because it is not our job to design somebody's
project for him. There is usually more than one
way of doing a design. Does that answer your question?

831

W. A. WAHLER (W. A. Wahler & Associates): The mining industry, as it looks at this problem, sees two independent problems. One is the dump and the the other, the impoundment. There will necessarily be definitional differences here, because construction may be by fluid methods, and it may not be an impoundment. So you need some definitions here.

TECHNOLOGY, REALITY, AND AVAILABILITY

John B. Rigg

Deputy Assistant Secretary
Mineral Resources
U. S. Department of the Interior
Washington, D. C.

INTRODUCTION

In the corridors of the many government buildings in Washington, D.C., there is a phrase one
hears applied with increasing frequency to the expectations held for The United States at the end of
this century. That phrase is "The Second America,"
and its rationale is based on the fact that between
now and Year 2000 we shall have to provide as much
in the way of goods and services, homes and schools,
food and transportation, as has so far been done in
the entire history of the Nation. We shall in this
sense, have built America all over again--a Second
America. There is also implicit in this concept
the notion that we shall have learned something from
our experience in building the First America, and
that the new model will reflect a regard for our
patrimony of nature that was sadly deficient in the
old one.

But if we are going to build America all over
again, and do it with a regard for the world of
nature that we never before exhibited, we are going
to have to begin with a regard for mineral science
and technology that we never before exhibited, either.

It is hard to realize just how vast our mineral
requirements are going to be in another 20 to 30 years.
But it is worth stopping for a moment to remember that
the magical date at which we begin the third millennium
of the Christian Era is now closer to us than the Day
of Infamy when Japanese planes projected us into the
Second World War. Between now and then, we are going
to need 250,000,000,000 barrels of oil; 1,000,000,000,000
cubic feet of natural gas; 100,000,000,000 tons of
stone, sand and gravel; 25,000,000,000 tons of coal;
and 3,500,000,000 tons of iron. By the year 2000,
we can expect demand for aluminum to be eight times
what it is today; demand for copper will nearly quad-
ruple; chromium use will rise 2-1/2 times; demand for
phosphorus may triple; and demand for uranium can be
expected to expand 15 times. Indeed, one of our
major long-range energy problems is to perfect the
breeder reactor before our supplies of low-cost uranium
are exhausted.

These are little more than educated guesses--which
is about all that any projection extending more than
10 years amounts to. Looked at from 1970 consumption
levels they appear to be fantastically large. But
the experience we have had with most forecasts strongly
indicates that such long-range projections are customaril
conservative--almost to the point of timidity. With
all the experience we have had with compound interest
formulas, we still have difficulty in believing that
they are going to continue to operate on such indices
as population, labor force, production and material
requirements. But they will for at least as long as
anyone here is likely to be around. Obviously, we
are going to have to come to a zero population
growth rate at some point in the future, with all its
implications for economic expansion as well. But even

though the birth rate is now at that magic rate of
2.11 children per couple, we will not reach a stable
population for another 70 years or so. Meanwhile,
the course is onward and upward for both population
and the demands it will make upon the economy and
its resource base.

But domestic supply is not keeping up with current
demand, let alone the large increases we have projected. So the gap between consumption and domestic
production is widening every year, and at a disturbing
rate. In 1950, imports of iron ore represented one-
eighth of our supply. Today they account for one-third.
The share of oil imports in total supply rose from one-
eighth to one-quarter in the same period; that of
potash from one-eighth to one-half; aluminum from two-
thirds to seven-eights. Consumption of minerals out-
strips domestic production by $4,000,000,000 a year.
Less than 60 percent of our metals, by value, now come
from domestic mines.

As we turn abroad to satisfy our increasing mineral
needs, however, we are finding that the demands of
other nations are increasing even faster than our
own. The cyclical swings of mineral prices may serve
to mask the onset of a long-term shift in trading
advantage from buyer to seller in the world market
for minerals, but this is precisely what is occurring,
year by year, commodity by commodity. Our bruising
encounters with the Organization of Petroleum Exporting
Countries (OPEC) over the past two years have established
this fact very conclusively for oil. And it will in time
apply to other minerals as well. This is not to say that
the world market for minerals is going to disappear or
become unavailable to us. We must continue to supply
substantial portions of our needs from abroad. But increasingly, we shall have less and less to say about
the terms under which those supplies are made available to us. We have long taken the world market for
granted. It would be foolish to do so in the future.

So we are bound to look homeward for the satis-
faction of the bulk of our expanding mineral needs

for building the Second America, and our problems
are going to be framed by the need to supply these
expanding requirements with domestic mineral deposits
of diminishing quality under more stringent environmental safeguards than the industry is used to ob-
serving. This introduces problems of rising costs;
greater expenditure of energy per unit of minerals
produced; larger areas of land subject to disturbance
which must be rehabilitated; and larger volumes of
waste to dispose of. At the beginning of this century
we were producing copper at the rate of about 300,000
tons per year, most of it from underground mines, from
deposits whose grade averaged higher than 4.0 percent.
In 1970 we produced 1,700,000 tons of copper metal
from ore that averaged 0.65 percent, mostly from open
pit mining. So our waste disposal problem is compounded by the fact that we are producing steadily
increasing volumes of metal from progressively lower
grade ores: some 260,000,000 tons of rock had to be
excavated, moved, processed, and disposed of in 1970
to supply the 1,700,000 tons of metallic copper we
produced that year. And this experience is being repeated in varying degree in every mineral we produce
by mining.

There is, accordingly, a pressing need for a
well-designed and balanced program for the long-term
control of the mine waste problem. This means a long-
range plan of control for all embankment and tailing
systems, both currently in operation and new construction, and a program of research and development to
establish a clearly defined technology for mine waste
disposal and storage. The term "long-range" is of
course subject to qualifications. While the plan has
to be long-range in nature, it must also be sufficiently
flexible to take advantage of the results from research and development work that must be pursued
with a view toward improving methods and techniques
of disposal. Obviously, technology development,
especially for such a complex problem, requires proper
planning and the combining of government, industry,
and educational talent in research and engineering.

In the meantime, there is a requirement for organization and proper operating procedures. Existing impoundments will have to be investigated according to standard guidelines and criteria to evaluate their suitability in terms of stability and environmental requirements, to recommend corrective measures where needed, to review and approve plans and specifications for their improvement, to inspect the improvements and continued enlargements, and to survey the systems after abandonment. For new systems, plans and specifications developed by the operating companies or their consultants will have to be evaluated, construction operations will have to be inspected, and continued surveillance over the systems will have to be maintained after abandonment.

For example, under current law, the U.S. Bureau of Mines has no authority to protect the public from waste embankment failures. The authority is limited to protecting the miners on the job. Neither does it extend to any environmental considerations.

On August 9, 1972, President Nixon signed into law a bill making the Secretary of the Army, through the Corps of Engineers, responsible for safety inspection of dams throughout the United States. This would include all mine waste impoundments and Congress has asked that the assistance of the Departments of Interior and Agriculture be utilized in the inspection process. Although this new law is only an interim expedient, it does provide additional resources for inspecting dams and will serve to further reduce any potential for failures. The national program to be recommended under this law before July, 1974, may also provide a basic approach and direction that could be adopted for dealing with the long-term problem.

However, the need to develop sound engineering and control systems for mine waste disposal is urgent, one that must be faced immediately. The Administration's Mined Area Protection Act, which died in the last Congress, would have provided an important vehicle to achieve this objective. It, or something very much like it, will be proposed to the next Congress.

Even in the absence of such a statute, however, the mining industry as a whole and individual operators in particular have an overriding responsibility to make sure that their coal refuse embankments and mill tailings ponds do not constitute a serious threat to life or the environment.

In this particular example of waste disposal, however, I have only touched upon the basic problem that the mineral industries face.

If we are to meet the challenge of providing minerals for the Second America, we must begin, I am convinced, a massive revitalization and rededication of mineral science and technology. If new resources are to be discovered--as they must--we shall need something better than yesterday's techniques. And yesterday's methods of mining and processing will have to be examined critically in order to develop new technologies that will permit more effective exploitation of the mineral resources now being mined. Moreover, all these things must be done with due regard to health and safety, environmental protection and land use. Downstream, our technology with respect to reuse of mineral commodities--their recycling into productive channels--must be improved and the application of new methods accelerated.

I have prescribed massive doses of improved technology as the remedy for the ills that beset the mineral industries in the full knowledge that technology and technologists are being blamed for just about every malfunction of our society that cannot be charged up to big business or the military. The Nation unfortunately is in the midst of one of its periodic seizures when it pays attention to its starry-eyed utopians, and the result has been a general disregard of rational remedies. The truth of the matter is that without continued intensive application of technolog and the ardent pursuit of new knowledge as the basis for new technology, we have no hopes for advancing in any direction at all. The Second America will never be built, and the First America will disintergrate

because it will no longer be able to meet the
legitimate aspirations of its people for a better
quality of life - including specifically, the restoration and protection of the environment. Without
technological advancement, there can be no economic
growth, save that identified with manpower increases;
without economic growth there can be no surplus of
goods and services to devote to the worthy purposes
to which we all subscribe: the rescue of the environment; the rehabilitation of the poor; the rebuilding
of the cities; the enhancement of cultural values;
the broadening of opportunities for enriching the
life of the individual; the promise to the ordinary
American that five years from now he is going to be
better off materially than he is today. These things
are the legacy of growth; the delivered promise of
technology.

This essential connection between technology and
the quality of life enjoyed by the citizen was recognized by President Nixon in his address on New
Technology Initiatives in 1972. "The impact of new
technology can do much to enrich the quality of our
lives," he said. "The forces which threaten that
quality will be growing at a dramatic pace in the
years ahead. One of the great questions of our time
is whether our capacity to deal with those forces
will grow at a similar rate. The answer to that question
lies in our scientific and technological progress."

We are thus brought back to the focal point of
mining technology: the mineral science college. It
is upon this sparse and tenuous network of technical
institutes that the entire extractive industry depends
for the deposit of existing knowledge, the development
and propagation of new knowledge, and the training
of professional mineral scientists and engineers. And
how frail indeed it is! There are at present only
15 mining schools in the United States which in 1972
graduated 194 mining engineers. While this is a highly
gratifying improvement over the 114 graduated in 1970,
it falls far short of the 500 mining engineers that are
graduated annually by the technical institutes of Poland.

A typical mine in Poland may employ between 100 and 130 mining engineers.

Mining schools throughout the country have suffered from years of neglect both by the mining industry and by the governments of mining states. As a result many have been forced to close--some with long and distinguished records. Others have been required to cut back drastically on faculty and course offerings. Research in mining technology has been foreshortened and even terminated.

Great damage has been done, and much remedial action must be taken. Both educational and research capacity in mineral science and technology must be expanded to accommodate the demand for new knowledge and new talent--a demand accelerated not only by soaring requirements for minerals, but for winning those minerals with minimum harm to the environment and to people.

We must get mining technology and engineering moving forward again, and we must do it with specific regard for the needs of environmental protection and improved health and safety practices.

This renaissance of mineral science and technology of which I have spoken is of critical importance to every American. Like a great inverted pyramid, our trillion-dollar-economy rests upon a narrow base of raw minerals valued at no more than three percent of the total gross national product. But we need to remember that dollars are the language of accountants, not engineers, and that the relevant counting units are not dollars but tons - billions of tons, of stone, sand, gravel, iron ore, coal, copper, zinc, lead, molybdenum, sulphur, potash. The truth is that our entire material existence, and all our hopes for enhancing it rest upon our mineral wealth, and upon those whose efforts form the first step in its conversion to our beneficial use. It is time to give them a hand.

TAILING DISPOSAL TODAY

APPENDICES

TAILING VEGETATION AND STABILIZATION TOUR

NATURAL VEGETATION OF THE SANTA CRUZ AND SAN PEDRO VALLEYS, ARIZONA*

Ervin M. Schmutz
Associate Professor of Range Management
University of Arizona, Tucson

Both the San Manuel and Sahuarita mining areas are located in the Upper Sonoran Desert. Other names by which it is known are Arizona Upland Desert, Sahuaro Desert, and Succulent Desert. In Arizona the Upper Sonoran Desert is located largely on the plains, bajadas, and foothills of the upper Gila River drainage. The vegetation is widely diversified. Trees and shrubs predominate but perennial and ephemeral forbs and grasses are seasonally abundant. The ephemerals in particular are seasonal—the cool-season species growing in the late winter and spring and the warm-season species growing during the summer "monsoon" season. At the higher elevations the Sonoran Desert intergrades into the Desert Grassland where shrubs become scattered and grasses predominate.

The most characteristic species and often the most abundant tree on the bajadas and rocky hills of the Upper Sonoran Desert is the foothill or little-leaf paloverde *(Cercidium microphyllum)* which, when it flowers in the spring, coats the landscape with its brillant yellow blooms. Associated with it in the stream channels is the taller blue paloverde *(Cercidium floridum)*. The dominant species on the lower plains and stream bottoms is velvet mesquite *(Prosopis juliflora* var. *velutina)* where it often forms impenetrable thickets or "bosques." The most picturesque species is the giant saguaro or sahuaro cactus *(Carnegiea gigantea)*, which welcomes the visitor with open arms. Other characteristic species include the ubiquitous creosotebush *(Larrea tridentata)*, desert ironwood *(Olneya tesota)*, catclaw *(Acacia greggii)*, wait-a-minute bush *(Mimosa* sp.)*, whitehorn *(Acacia constricta)*, brittlebush *(Encelia farinosa)*, ocotillo *(Fouquieria splendens)*, jojoba, coffeeberry or goatnut *(Simmondsia chinensis)*, desert broom *(Baccharis)*, triangleleaf bursage *(Ambrosia deltoidea)*, burroweed *(Haplopappus tenuisectus)*, snakeweed *(Gutierrezia)*, soaptree yucca or palm illa *(Yucca elata)*, and numerous cacti.

The other cacti besides saguaro include the tree-like jumping cholla *(Opuntia fulgida)*, the shorter teddybear cholla *(Opuntia biglelovii)*, the staghorn and buckhorn chollas *(Opuntia acanthocarpa, O. spinosior* and *O. versicolor)*, pencil cholla *(Opuntia arbuscula)*, the flat-stemmed prickly pear

(Opuntia engelmannii), night-blooming cereus *(Opuntia greggii)*, the low-growing fishhook or pincushion cacti *(Mammillaria* sp.*)*, and barrel cactus or bisnaga *(Ferocactus wislezeni)*.

Grasses of greater or lesser importance include bush muhly *(Muhlenbergia porteri)*, tobosa *(Hilaria mutica)*, curlymesquite *(Hilaria belangeri)*, Arizona cottontop *(Trichachne californica)*, slim tridens *(Tridens muticus)*, bristlegrass *(Setaria macrostachya)*, fluffgrass *(Tridens pulchella)*, rothrock grama *(Bouteloua rothrockii)*, slender grama *(Bouteloua filiformis)*, black grama *(Bouteloua eripoda)*, sideoats grama *(Bouteloua curtipendula)*, the dropseeds *(Sporobolus* sp.*)*, and various three-awns *(Aristida* sp.*)*. The most abundant forb is the exotic annual filaree *(Erodium cicutarium)*.

*Originally prepared for the conference on "Mining and Ecology in Arid Environment" sponsored by the Department of Mining and Geological Engineering, College of Mines, University of Arizona, Tucscon, 1970.

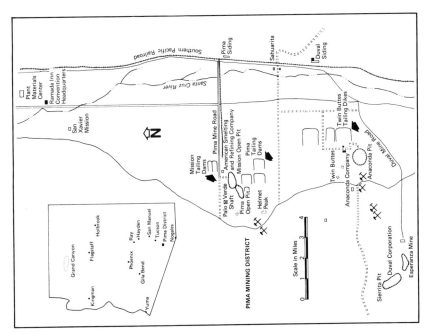

Route of tailing vegetation and stabilization tour.

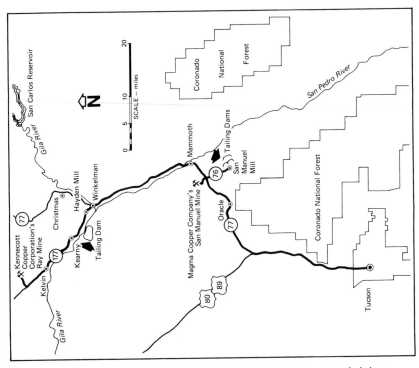

Map of area covered to inspect dam construction by cyclones and siphon reclamation of water.

Decant system at San Manuel's No. 10 tailing dam is inspected by delegates, above. Buried decant line's position is indicated by the line of four wooden cribs protecting overflow inlets (center of picture). The tailing dam is visible

beyond pond (left center). Below left, delegates inspect clarity of pond at Anaconda's Twin Buttes; they take notes, below, at the U.S. Soil Conservation Service Plant Materials Center in Tucson.

Spigotted dam at Mission mine of American Smelting and Refining Company, above. This picture was taken at corner of No. 2 dam. No. 1 dam (on left) is drying out while No. 2 is actively receiving tailing (23,000 tons per day of

tailing flow from mill thickeners). Below left, tour buses stop while delegates inspect vegatation along pipeline. Desert plants at Pima are studied with interest below.

Vegetation is well established in this area.

Delegate inspects a section of pipe and spigot valve during the tour.

REFERENCES TO OTHER PUBLISHED MATERIAL ON TAILINGS

Compiled by the *WORLD MINING* Editorial Staff

Allen, P. F. Tailing Disposal at the Morenci Concentrator. *Transactions AIME. Mining Engineering,* July 1956.

Bacani, Jose M. Pollution Control: P10-M Philex Tailings Dam Project. *Philippine Mining & Engineering Journal,* March 1971.

Bacani, Jose M. Pollution Control: Preliminary feasibility study on the proposed design of tailings pipeline disposal system (common sewer) of various companies of Baguio Mining District to avoid pollution of the Agno and Bued River Systems. *Philippine Mining & Engineering Journal,* August 1971.

Bailey, R. P. Case for Reclamation of Mineral Processing Water. *Canadian Mining Journal,* June 1970.

Bates, Robert C., and Wayment, William R. Laboratory Study of Factors Influencing Water Flow in Mine Backfill. *U.S. Bureau of Mines, RI 7034,* October 1967.

Berg, W. A. Vegetative Stabilization of Mine Wastes. Project cooperators include the Colorado State University Experiment Station, Colorado State Forest Service, Colorado Mining Industrial Development Board, American Metal Climax, and mine and mill operators throughout the state.

Beverly, R. G. Unique Disposal Methods Are Required for Uranium Mill Waste. *Mining Engineering,* June 1968.

Bishop, A. W. The Use of the Slip Circle in the Stability Analysis of Slopes. *Geotechnique,* Vol. 5, 1955.

Bishop, A. W., and Morgenstern, N. Stability Coefficients for Earth Dams. *Geotechnique,* December 1960.

Blinov, S. N. Tendencies in Tailing Reservoir Dam Design. *Tsvet. Metally. Mosk.,* 33, No. 5, 1960. Russian text; English translation.

Bridgstock, Guy. Flash Smelting — Recent Operating Data. Presented at Arizona Section AIME, Tucson, Arizona, December 1971.

Burke, H. H. Design and Construction of Dams for Retention of Solid Wastes, ASCE National Meeting on Water Resources Engineering, New Orleans, Louisiana, February 1969.

Burrill, Scott L., and Bossard, G. W. Tailing Dam Practice at ASARCO's Mission Plant. Paper No. EQC 42, *preprint* prepared for Environmental Quality Conference for the Extractive Industries of the AIME, Washington, D.C., June 1971.

Campbell, David B., and Brawner, C. O. The Tailings Dam, An Engineered Structure. *Western Miner,* April 1971.

Campbell, Dr. Ivor. Sulphur Oxide Control

at the Copper Smelter. Presented at Arizona Section AIME, December 1971.

Canadian Advisory Committee on Rock Mechanics: Report of the Sub-committee on Stability of Waste Embankments. September 1969.

Casagrande, Leo. Characteristics of Cohesionless Soils Affecting the Stability of Slopes and Earth Fills. *Journal of Boston Society of Civil Engineers,* January 1936.

Casagrande, Leo, and MacIver, Bruce N. Design and Construction of Tailings Dams. Presented at the symposium on Stability for Open Pit Mining, Vancouver, B.C., November 1970.

Cedergreen, H. R. Seepage, Drainage and Flow Nets. New York: John Wiley & Sons, 1967.

Chenik, D. The Promotion of a Vegetative Cover on Mine Slimes, Dumps and Sand Dunes. *Journal of the South African Institute of Mining and Metallurgy,* Vol. 60 No. 10, 1960.

Clough, R. W., and Chopra, A. K. Earthquake Stress Analysis in Earth Dams. *Proceedings ASCE,* Vol. 92 EM 2, April 1966.

Corp, E. L., and Bates, Robert C. Flexible Liners for Underground Support. *U.S. Bureau of Mines, RI 6893,* 1967.

Corson, D. R. Stabilization of Hydraulic Backfill with Portland Cement. *U.S. Bureau of Mines, RI 7327,* 1970.

Cumming, Donald A. Drifting at San Manuel. Presented at Arizona Section AIME, December 1971.

Cyanamid Shoots for Instant Reclamation of Mined Land. *Engineering and Mining Journal,* January 1970.

Dahlstrom, D. A. Processing and Disposal of Coal Flotation Tailings. *Mining Congress Journal,* March 1962.

Day, Frank H. Disposal of Metallurgical Wastes. *Mining Congress Journal,* November 1971.

Dean, Karl C., and Havens, Richard. Vegetative Stabilization of Mill Tailings Using Municipal and Mineral Wastes. U.S. Bureau of Mines. Presented at the Environmental Quality Conference for the Extractive Industries, AIME, Washington, D.C., June 1971.

Dean, Karl C., and Havens, Richard. Reclamation of Mineral Milling Wastes. Presented at the AIME Annual Meeting, San Francisco, California, February 1972.

Dean, Karl C., Havens, Richard, and Harper, Kimball T. Chemical and Vegetative Stabilization of a Nevada Copper Porphyry Mill Tailing. *U.S. Bureau of Mines, RI 7261,* May 1969.

Dean, Karl C., Havens, Richard, and Valdez, Espiridion G. Utilization and Stabilization of Solid Mineral Wastes. Presented at the 16th Ontario Industrial Waste Conference, Niagara Falls, Ontario, Canada, June 1969.

Dean, Karl C., Havens, Richard, and Valdez, Espiridion G. Progress in Using and Stabilizing Mineral Wastes. Presented at the AIME Fall Meeting, St. Louis, Missouri, October 1970.

Dean, Karl C., Havens, Richard, and Valdez, Espiridion G. USBM Finds Routes to Stabilizing Mineral Wastes. *Mining Engineering,* December 1971.

Debry, R., and Alvarez, L. Seismic Failures of Chilean Tailings Dams. *Journal of the Soil Mechanics and Foundations Division, Proceedings of ASCE,* Vol. 93, No. SM6, November 1967.

Department of Energy, Mines and Resources. Design Guide for Mine Waste in Canada, 1971.

De Vasto, P. J. Cost Factors for SO_2 Abatement in Copper Smelters. Presented at Arizona Section AIME, Tucson, Arizona, December 1971.

Disposal of Phosphatic Clays. *AIME reprint 70-H-308.*

Djingheuzian, L. E. Tailing Disposal Problems of Alberta Tar-Sands. *Canadian Mining Journal,* May 1953.

Donaldson, G. W. Practical Observations and the Results of Research on the Stability of Slimes Dams for the Gold Mining Industry. *Journal of the South African Institute of Mining and Metallurgy,* October 1969.

Douglass, D. P. Utilization of Waste by Canadian Mines. *Municipal Utilities Magazine,* Vol. 92 No. 6, 1954.

Doyle, D. S., Dahlke, W. L., Oss, D. G., Hull, R. J., and Beling, J. Transportation and Storage of Tailings. Panel discussion at the Minnesota AIME and Mining Symposium, Duluth, Minnesota, January 1972.

Duggan, E. J. Transportation and Deposition of Mill Tailings. *Mining Congress Journal,* April 1963.

Durand, R. Basic Relationships of the Transportation of Solids in Pipes — Experimental Research. *Proceedings of IAHR,* University of Minnesota, September 1953.

Electrolytic Zinc Company of Australia, West Coast Staff. Design and Construction of No. 2 Residue Dam at Roseberry. *Australian Inst. of Mining and Metallurgy Transaction No. 186,* June 1958.

Ellis, Derek V., and Littlepage, Jack L. Marine Discharge of Mine Wastes: Ecosystem Effects and Monitoring Programs. Presented at the CIM Annual Meeting, Vancouver, B.C., October 1971. *Canadian Mining and Metallurgical Bulletin,* April 1972. *CIM Transactions,* Vol. 75, 1972.

Experience with Georgia's Mined Land Reclamation Law. *AIME reprint 70-J-304.*

Finn, A. A. T. Tailing Dam Construction at Mufulira Copper Mines, Ltd., Zambia. *Proceedings, Institution of Mining and Metallurgy* (London), September 1965. (Discussion November 1965.)

Given, E. V. Designing for Tailing Disposal in the Southwest. *Mining Engineering,* July 1959.

Goldick, M. R. Some Developments in Tailing Disposal at Roan Antelope Copper Mines, Northern Rhodesia. *Transactions, Institution of Mining and Metallurgy* (London), Vol. 65, Part 11, No. 597, 1955-56.

Gordon, I. M. Mill Tailing Disposal at Hollinger Mine, Timmins, Ontario. Ontario Industrial Waste Conference, *13th Proceedings,* 1966.

Grubb, H. F. The feasibility of vegetating mine tailings at Climax, Colorado. M. S. thesis, Colorado State University, 1965.

Havens, Richard, and Dean, Karl C. Chemical Stabilization of the Uranium Tailings at Tuba City, Arizona. *U.S. Bureau of Mines, RI 7288,* August 1969.

Hazen, A. Hydraulic Fill Dams. *Transactions, American Society of Civil Engineers,* Vol. 83, 1920.

Hoare, Bert, and Hill, H. M. The Hydraulic Construction of Mine Tailings Dams. *Canadian Mining Journal,* June 1970.

Holiday, B. J., and Wilks, Raymond. Mobile Cyclones Building Tailing Dams. *Engineering and Mining Journal,* October 1959.

How to Build a Good Tailings Dam. *Engineering and Mining Journal,* May 1951.

Interim Report, Mufulira Disaster. *Mining Magazine,* April 1971.

Ito, I., and Terada, M. Some Physical Properties of Mine Slime. *Journal of Suiyokai, Japan,* April 1958.

James, A. L. Stabilization of Surfaces of Mine Tailings Dumps. *The South African Mining and Engineering Journal,* 1964.

James, A. L. Stabilizing mine dumps with vegetation. *Endeavour* (London), Vol. 25, 1966.

Jerabek, F. A., and Hartman, H. L. Investigation of Segregation and Compressibility in Discharged Fill Slurry. *Transactions, Society of Mining Engineers,* Vol. 232, No. 1, March 1965.

Jigens, R. W. Tailings Disposal at Braden Copper Company (Chile), *Mining Engineering,* October 9, 1957.

Jigens, R. W. Tailings Dam Construction at Mufulira Copper (Chile). *Mining Engineering,* October 9, 1967.

Jones, G. K. Waste Disposal and Pollution Control. *Industrial Minerals,* June 1972.

Kantey, B. A. The Application of the Classical Theories of Consolidation of Slimes Dams, S.A. Council for Scientific and Industrial Research, October 1952.

Kealy, Charles Daniel. Seepage Patterns in Mill Tailings Dams as Determined by Finite-Element Models. M.S. thesis, College of Mines, University of Idaho, May 1970.

Kealy, Charles Daniel. Structural-Environmental Analysis of the Slime Zone of a Tailings Pond. Ph.D. Dissertation, Department of Mining Engineering and Metallurgy, College of Mines, University of Idaho, Moscow, Idaho, 1972.

Kealy, Charles Daniel, and Busch, Richard A. Determining Seepage Characteristics of Mill Tailings Dams by the Finite-Element Method. *U.S. Bureau of Mines, RI 7477,* January 1971.

Kealy, Charles Daniel, and Soderberg, R. L. Design of Dams for Mill Tailings. *U.S. Bureau of Mines, IC 8410,* 1969.

Kealy, Charles Daniel, and Williams, Roy

E. Flow Through a Tailings Pond Embankment. *Water Resources Research,* February 1971.

Kealy, Charles Daniel, and Williams, Roy E. Mathematical Models of Groundwater Flow as an Aid for Predicting Slope Stability in Tailings Pond Embankments. *Proceedings* 8th Annual Symposium, Soils Engineering, Pocatello, Idaho. Idaho Department of Highways, Boise, April 1971.

Klohn, Earle J. Evaluation of Tailings Disposal Schemes in the Southwestern United States. Internal Report, 1968.

Klohn, Earle J. Tailings Dams in British Columbia. Presented at the 2nd Symposium on Stability for Open Pit Mining, Vancouver, B.C., November 1971.

Klohn, Earle J. Design and Construction of Tailings Dams. *The Canadian Mining and Metallurgical (CIM) Bulletin,* April 1972. *CIM Transactions,* Vol. 75, 1972.

Klohn, Earle J., and McManus, Kerry J. Control of Pollution from Mine Wastes. *Australian Mining,* November 1971.

Kuralt, R. M. Tailing Disposal. *Mining Engineering,* December 1952.

Lee, K. L., and Seed, H. B. Cyclic Stress Conditions Causing Liquefaction of Sand. *Journal of the Soil Mechanics and Foundations Division,* ASCE, Vol. 93, SM1, 1967.

Lenhart, Walter B. Construction of Tailing Ponds. *Rock Products,* December 1949.

Lenhart, W. B. Control of Tailings from Washing Plants. *Rock Products,* Vol. 53, Nos. 7, 9, & 10, 1950; Vol. 54, Nos. 2, 5, 9 & 10, 1951.

MacIver, Bruce N. How the Soils Engineer Can Help the Mill Man in the Construction of Proper Tailings Dams. *Engineering and Mining Journal,* May 1961.

McArthur, George M. Engineering and Chemical Considerations for Quality Control of Metallurgical Wastes. Presented at the AIME Annual Meeting, San Francisco, California, February 1972.

McKay, L. H. Tailing Disposal at the Allenby Concentrator. *Transactions,* Vol. 53, 1950, reprinted from *The Canadian Mining and Metallurgical (CIM) Bulletin,* January 1950.

Marcopper Story. *Mining Magazine,* June 1971.

Matthews, Dan, and Diaz, Larry. Evaluations of Automating a Ball Mill. Presented at Arizona Section AIME, Tucson, Arizona, December 1971.

May, M., Lang, R., and others. Reclamation of Strip Mine Spoil Banks in Wyoming. Res. J. 51 Wyoming Agricultural Experiment Station. University of Wyoming, 1971.

Mead, William E., and Newbill, Robert A. Design of Embankments for Tailings Ponds and Waste Dumps. Presented at the SME Fall Meeting — Rocky Mountain Minerals Conference, AIME, Las Vegas, Nevada, September 1967.

Mickle, David G. and Hartman, Howard L. Permeability and Compressibility Tests Aid in Selecting Suitable Hydraulic Fill Materials. *Mining Engineering,* November 1961.

Mill Staff. Mill Tailing Disposal at Hollinger. Hollinger Consolidated Gold Mines, Ltd. *Transactions,* Vol. 54, 1951, Annual General Meeting, Quebec City, Quebec, April 1951, *Canadian Institute of Mining and Metallurgy (CIM) Bulletin,* June 1951.

Mink, Leland L., Williams, Roy E., and Wallace, Alfred T. Effect of Industrial and Domestic Effluents on the Water Quality of the Coeur d'Alene River Basin. Pamphlet 149, Idaho Bureau of Mines and Geology, Moscow, Idaho, 1971.

Mitchell, Jack, and Beach, Robert. Unique IMC Tailing Line Solves Freezing Problem. *Engineering and Mining Journal,* August 1964.

National Coal Board. Spoil Heaps and Lagoons. London, 1970.

Neumann, G. W. Tailings Disposal at Brunswick Mining and Smelting. *Canadian Mining Journal,* Vol. 90 No. 6, 1969.

Nicholson, David E., and Busch, Richard A. Earth Pressure at Rest and One-Dimensional Compression in Mine Hydraulic Backfills. *U.S. Bureau of Mines, RI 7198,* October 1968.

Nicholson, David E., and Wayment, William R. Properties of Hydraulic Backfills and Preliminary Vibratory Compaction Tests. *U.S. Bureau of Mines, RI 6477,* 1964.

Nicholson, David E., and Wayment, William R. Vibratory Compaction of Mine

Hydraulic Backfill. *U.S. Bureau of Mines, RI 6922,* 1967.

O'Brien, M. P., and Folsom, R. G. The Transportation of Sand in Pipelines. University of California, published in *Engineering,* Vol. 3 No. 7, 1937.

Ontario Water Resources Commission, Division of Industrial Wastes. Guidelines for Embankment Retention Systems for Waste Slurries, 1967.

Pettibone, Howard C., and Kealy, C. Daniel. The Engineering Properties of Mine Tailings. Presented at the ASCE National Water Resources Engineering Meeting at Phoenix, Arizona, January 1971. Civil Engineering Abstract, Spokane Mining Research Laboratory, U.S. Bureau of Mines, Spokane, Washington.

Phukan, Dr. A. Design and Construction of Tailings Dams. *Western Miner,* December 1971.

Pigott, P. G., Valdez, Espiridion G., and Dean, Karl C. Dry-pressed Building Bricks from Copper Mill Tailings. *U.S. Bureau of Mines, RI 7537,* July 1971.

Report by CSIR to the Chamber of Mines. A Summary of Slimes Dam Practice in the United States of America and Canada, 1956.

Rivett, L. S. and Oko, U.M. Tailings Disposal, Generation of Acidity from Pyrrhotite and Limestone Neutralization of Waste Water at Falconbridge's Onaping Mines. *Deco Trefoil,* Winter Issue, 1971-1972, Denver Equipment Division, Joy Manufacturing Company.

Rubinchik, Y. A. Stability of Reservoirs for Fine-Grained Tailings, *Tsvet. Metally. Mosk.,* 33, No. 4, 1960. Russian text; English translation.

Rumble, R. V., Coughlin, P. M., and Harris, D. P. Slimes Dams for C.A.S.T. Ltd., Diamond Mine, Ghana. *Institution of Mining and Metallurgy Transcription* (Section A, Mining Industry) 75, No. 2, April 1966.

Salter, R. Extract from Tailings Disposal at Silver Bell. American Smelting and Refining Company, Silver Bell Unit, Silver Bell, Arizona. Circa 1956.

Seed, H. B. A Method for Earthquake Resistant Design of Earth Dams. *Journal of the Soil Mechanics and Foundations Division,* ASCE, Vol. 92, No. SM 1, 1966.

Seed, H. B. Landslides During Earthquakes Due to Soil Liquefaction, *Journal of the Soil Mechanics and Foundations Division,* ASCE, Vol. 94, SM 5, 1968.

Seed, H. B., and Idriss, I. M. Analysis of Soil Liquefaction: Niigata Earthquake. *Journal of the Soil Mechanics and Foundations Division,* ASCE, Vol. 93, SM 3, 1967.

Seed, H. B., and Lee, K. L. Liquefaction of Saturated Sands During Cyclic Loading. *Journal of the Soil Mechanics and Foundations Division,* ASCE, Vol. 92, SM 6, 1966.

Seed, H. B., and Wilson, S. D. The Turnagain Heights Landslide, Anchorage, Alaska. *Journal of the Soil Mechanics and Foundations Division,* ASCE, Vol. 93, SM 4, 1966.

Shetron, S. G., and Duffek, R. Establishing Vegetation on Iron Mine Tailings. *Journal of Soil and Water Conservation,* Vol. 25, 1970.

Shikaze, K. Mine Tailings Dam Construction in Ontario. *Canadian Mining Journal,* June 1970; *Proceedings* of the second annual meeting of the Canadian Mineral Processors Association, held at the Mines Branch, Department of Energy, Mines, and Resources, Ottawa, January 1970, "Mineral Processing."

Shriver, William W. Design Considerations for the Henderson Project Tailing and Mill Process Water System. Presented at the SME Fall Meeting and Exhibit. AIME, St. Louis, Missouri, October 1970.

Smith, Edwin S. Tailings Disposal and Liquefaction. *Transactions Society of Mining Engineers, AIME,* June 1969.

Smith, R. W. Flow of Limestone and Clay Slurries in Suspensions. Rep. No. 59-6, Colorado School of Mines Res. Fdn. Inc., February 1959.

Source of Sulphuric Acid in the Lake Water. Falconbridge Nickel Mines Limited. *The Canadian Mining and Metallurgical (CIM) Bulletin,* August 1971.

Sowers, G. F. Earth and Rockfill Dam Engineering. New York: Asia Publishing, 1962.

Stabilization and Beautification of Mine Tailings and Dumps. Part 1: ReRemer, Dr. E. Dale. Drip Irrigation. Part 2: Bach, Dan A. Native Desert Vegetation. Presented at Arizona Section

AIME, Tucson, Arizona, December 1971.

Steinbrugge, Karl V., Schader, Eugene E., Bigglestone, Harry C., and Weers, Carl A. San Fernando Earthquake, February 9, 1971. Pacific Fire Rating Bureau, San Francisco, California.

Tailings Disposal Consolidated Mining and Smelting. *Canadian Mining Journal,* May 1954.

Tailings-Pond Studies. *Mining Magazine,* June 1971.

Tetu, H., and Pells, F. Design, Construction and Initial Operation of the Tailings System at Brenda Mines Ltd. *Canadian Institute of Mining & Metallurgy (CIM) Bulletin,* August 1971.

Thomas, J. E., and Osterloh, E. A. The Construction and Maintenance of Slimes Dams. *Journal of Chemical & Metallurgical & Mining Society of South Africa,* July 1916 and June 1917.

Toland, George C. A Case History: Design of a Gypsum Tailing Pond. *Mining Engineering,* December 1971. Taken from SME preprint 71-1-300.

Truck-Mounted Cyclones Build Tailings Pond. *Engineering and Mining Journal,* June 1954.

U.S. Atomic Energy Commission, Grand Junction Office. A Report of the Monticello Mill Tailing Erosion Control Project, Monticello, Utah. *R.M.O. 3005,* 1963.

U.S. Atomic Energy Commission, Grand Junction Office. Supplement to the Report of the Monticello Mill Tailing Erosion Control Project, Monticello, Utah, *Supplement to R.M.O. 3005,* 1966.

U.S. Atomic Energy Commission, A.E.C. Licensing Guide: Information and Criteria Pertinent to Evaluation of Embankment Retention Systems. Source and Special Nuclear Materials Branch, Division of Materials Licensing, Washington, D.C.

U.S. Bureau of Reclamation, Design of Small Dams. United States Government Printing Office. Washington, D.C., 1965.

U.S. Department of the Interior. Surface Mining and Our Environment, 1967.

U.S. Forest Service and Cooperators. Surface Mine Rehabilitation: Report of Cooperative Administrative Study to Rehabilitate Phosphate Strip-mined Sites. Caribou National Forest, Pocatello, Idaho, 1971.

Volpe, Richard L., and Wahler, William A. Strength of Anisotropically Consolidated Mine Tailing Materials Under Dynamic Loading Conditions. *Proceedings* of the Specialty Session on Soil Dynamics of the 7th International Conference on Soil Mechanics and Foundation Engineering, Mexico City, 1969.

Volpe, R. L., and Wahler, W. A. The Use of Critical Density Concept for Interpreting Dynamic Shear Strength. Discussion on Question No. 36: Recent Developments in the Design and Construction of Earth and Rockfill Dams. 10th Congress of International Commission on Large Dams, Montreal, 1970.

Webb, Steven L., and Smith, Edwin S. Tailing Dam Sealed by Slimes Slurry. *Mining Engineering,* December 1971. Taken from *SME preprint 71-AG-322.*

Western Mines Limited. A Mine in a Park.

Westwood, R. J. Notes on Slime Residue and Tailing Dams. *Journal of Chemical & Metallurgical & Mining Society of S.A.,* 1947.

Wild, Prof. H., and Wiltshire, Dr. G. H. The Problem of Vegetating Rhodesian Mine Dumps Examined. *Chamber of Mines Journal,* November 1971. II. Suggestions for Future Research and Practical Trials. *Chamber of Mines Journal,* December 1971.

Williams, Roy E., Wallace, Alfred T., and Mink, Leland L. Impact of a Well-Managed Tailings Pond System on a Stream. *Mining Congress Journal,* October 1971.

Wilson, Robert M., and Hawson, H. H. Tailings Storage, Giant Mascot Mines Ltd. *Western Miner,* September 1971.

Windolph, Frank. Tailings Pond Design. *Mining Engineering,* November 1961.

Young, C. A. The Use of Vegetation to Stabilize Mine Tailings Areas at Copper Cliff. *Canadian Mining Journal,* June 1969.

INDEX